Great Short Stories

Edited by

WILBUR SCHRAMM DEAN, DIVISION
OF COMMUNICATIONS, UNIVERSITY OF ILLINOIS

HARCOURT BRACE JOVANOVICH, INC.
New York Chicago San Francisco Atlanta Dallas

PRINTED IN THE UNITED STATES OF AMERICA

ISBN 0-15-347157-3

To Louise M. Schramm

who, in the immemorial fashion of mothers,
told me some of the first stories I heard
and many of the best

Acknowledgments

THE EDITOR wishes to thank the following teachers for their help in selecting the short stories to be included in this collection.

Miss Olga Achtenhagen, Head of the English Department, Senior High School, Plainfield, New Jersey; Miss Virginia Alwin, Chairman of the English Department, Rochester High School, Rochester, Minnesota; Mrs. Ruth M. Barns, Head of the English Department, Cooley High School, Detroit, Michigan; Mr. William F. Bauer, Head of the English Department, Senior High School, East Orange, New Jersey; Mr. Joseph C. Blumenthal, Head of the English Department, Mackenzie High School, Detroit, Michigan; Miss Mary Helen Boley, J. Sterling Morton High School, Cicero, Illinois; Miss Martha Brann, Senior High School, Modesto, California; Mr. Philip E. Burnham, St. Paul's School, Concord, New Hampshire; Miss Nanon L. Carr, Manual High and Vocational School, Kansas City, Missouri; Mr. Thomas Cauley, Head of the English Department, Denby High School, Detroit, Michigan; Mr. Richard K. Corbin, Head of the English Department, Senior High School, Peekskill, New York; Mr. Clarence S. Dike, Head of the English Department, Senior High School, Atlantic City, New Jersey; Miss Louise Fike, Senior High School, Decatur, Illinois; Mr. Hardy R. Finch, Head of the English Department, Senior High School, Greenwich, Connecticut; Mr. Francis Griffith, Principal, and members of the English Department, New Utrecht High School, Brooklyn, New York; Mr. George M. Hackman, Head of the English Department, Southeastern High School, Detroit, Michigan; Mrs. Evelyn Hanshaw, Senior High School, Modesto, California; Mrs. Sanford J. Hanson, Sturgeon Bay, Wisconsin; Miss Hortense L. Harris, Head of the English Department, Senior High School, Gloucester, Massachusetts; Miss Frances L. Hueston, Deering High School, Portland, Maine; Mr. J. Edward Hughes, Head of the English Department, Senior High School, Stamford, Connecticut; Mr. Thomas H. Johnson, Lawrenceville School, Lawrenceville, New Jersey; Miss Ethel A. Jones, Redford High School, Detroit, Michigan; Miss Sara E. Jones, Head of the English Department, Senior High

School, Hastings-on-Hudson, New York; Miss Isabel Kincheloe, Division of Curriculum Development, Chicago, Illinois; Dr. A. Barnett Langdale, Chairman of the English Department, Erasmus Hall High School, Brooklyn, New York; Mr. Paul Lovchuk, Redford High School, Detroit, Michigan; Miss Agnes McCarthy, Chairman of the English Department, Faribault High School, Faribault, Minnesota; Mr. Joseph Mersand, Chairman of the English Department, Long Island City High School, Long Island City, New York; Dr. M. M. Nagelberg, Principal, The Lew Wallace Junior High School, Brooklyn, New York; Miss E. Louise Noyes, Senior High School, Santa Barbara, California; Mr. Merrill P. Paine, Director of English, Board of Education, Elizabeth, New Jersey; Miss Margaret Painter, Senior High School, Modesto, California; Mr. Henry B. Priest, Senior High School, Montclair, New Jersey; Miss Alice C. Pulsifer, Head of the English Department, Senior High School, Bristol, Connecticut; Mr. Francis D. Reardon, Head of the English Department, Senior High School, Lowell, Massachusetts; Mr. Richmond L. Scott, Head of the English Department, Peekskill Military Academy, Peekskill, New York; Mr. Frederick Scribner, Senior High School, Greenwich, Connecticut; Mrs. Pauline Stellberger, Redford High School, Detroit, Michigan; Miss Edna L. Sterling, Director of Language Arts, Seattle Public Schools, Seattle, Washington; Miss Catherine J. Sullivan, Benjamin Franklin High School, Rochester, New York; Miss Mildred L. Vorce, Head of the English Department, East Commerce High School, Detroit, Michigan; Miss Virginia Wildi, Head of the English Department, East Rockford High School, Rockford, Illinois; Miss Katharine Stewart Worthington, The Masters School, Dobbs Ferry, New York; Miss Dorothy Wright, Senior High School, Modesto, California; Miss Alice M. Wyman, Head of the English Department, Redford High School, Detroit, Michigan.

Contents

To the Readers of This Book

WHAT IS A SHORT STORY?

YOU KNOW what a short story is, of course. But can you define it?

W. Somerset Maugham, one of the great storytellers of our time, said that a short story is "a piece of fiction that has a unity of impression and that can be read at a single sitting."

Let's be sure we understand that definition. A short story is a piece of *fiction*. That means it is a narrative; unlike articles or essays, it tells about an event or a series of events that happen to people. Furthermore, it is a made-up narrative – unlike history and reportage which are narrative but not fictional. And finally it is prose. There are stories in verse. We call them epics or narrative poems. But when we talk about short stories we mean stories in prose.

Mr. Maugham says also that a short story can be read at *a single sitting*. This is what makes a short story different from the long stories we call novels. A novel may be as long as a million words (like *Gone with the Wind*) or as short as 40,000 words (like *Ethan Frome*). It would be very tiresome to read even a 40,000-word story at one sitting. In modern magazines, short stories average about 5,000 words. Some stories may be as short as 1,000 words (like Daudet's "The Death of the Dauphin"). Others, like Conrad's "The Secret Sharer," may run to 20,000 words. Both these stories are in this book, and you will see that even the longer one can easily be read at one sitting.

Mr. Maugham says furthermore that a short story has a *unity of impression*. He means that every scene, every character, every bit of atmosphere and setting are so chosen as to contribute to one impression in the reader. This is one of the qualities that make a short story a work of art. You can see that it would be easier to create a single impression with a short story than with a novel. The novel is too big and has too many different kinds of materials; it is not usually designed in an attempt to create a single impression. The difference between a short story and a novel is something like the difference between a rifle and a cannon. The cannon hits harder, but the rifle can be aimed more sharply. Or we might say that the difference is like that between a house and a city. The novel, like the city, contains many different kinds of persons doing many different kinds of thing; the story, like the house, is for one small close-knit group of persons, and for one purpose only.

We might mention one or two other things about a short story. You probably know that more short stories are bought and read today than any other form of literature. In fact, when historians write about the twentieth century they may well decide that the short story is the typical and representative literary form of this age, just as the drama has been the great literary form in some periods and the poem in others.

The short story is a particularly American form of art. Of course, men have told stories since the first primitive tribes huddled around campfires, but few stories were printed until high-speed printing presses were developed and large-circulation magazines became possible. That was early in the nineteenth century. It was in American magazines especially that short stories began to appear. Men like Irving, Poe, and Hawthorne established the form of the short story; and Poe was the first great critic, as well as one of the first great writers, of the short story. Now short stories are written in every country of the world, but more stories are still published in the United States than in any other country.

The very popularity of the short story makes a problem for us. With so many stories available, how do we tell a good story from a bad one? And what should we look for when we read a story? What should we look for if we want to get the full pleasure and meaning out of the story?

Let's take up those questions now.

HOW A SHORT STORY IS WRITTEN

We don't have to know, in order to understand or enjoy a short story, exactly what the author wanted us to get out of the story.

Authors don't usually tell us what they intended, and anyway the important thing is what *we* find in the story, not what the author wanted to put there. But let's look once behind the scenes and see a story from an author's viewpoint, in the hope that it may help us to understand stories better and become better readers.

Before going any farther, let's get rid of the idea that there is anything magic or extraordinary about stories or story writers. Everyone tells stories. Some are better than others. Some are told by amateurs to small groups of friends. Others are told by professionals to large audiences. It has been this way since the beginning of civilization. In every age there have been favorite storytellers. In very early times they told their stories at tribal gatherings. Later they were minstrels at the courts of kings. Now they usually appear in magazines or books.

"Windwagon Smith," the story I am going to tell you about, appeared in *The Atlantic Monthly* and later as the title story in a collection of my writing. It is not a great story. It is only a light story. But it has pleased many people, has been many times reprinted, and has won one of the national fiction prizes. I am somewhat embarrassed by using one of my own stories in this collection, but obviously the only stories whose writing I can describe to you from firsthand experience are those I have written. Therefore, immodest or not, I am going to tell you, as nearly as I can remember, how I wrote "Windwagon Smith"; and I suggest that you now read it before I tell you about it.

Windwagon Smith

WINDWAGON SMITH had a face like any other man, and two legs to walk on, but the morning he rode into Westport the quietest mule in town jumped sixteen feet. And some men would have flown like bald eagles that day, if they could.

That was when Westport was the great city of the prairie. Now it is only a far corner of Kansas City and smells like gasoline and coal smoke, but in those days it smelled of prairie grass and clean wind, and was on every road west. No matter where you were going beyond the Missouri, you started at Westport. You followed a rutted trail twenty miles from town to a meadow where Jake Shafer's Negro boy had nailed a box top to a runt cottonwood and painted on it, "Rode to Oregon." There the families for Oregon turned north, and the wagons for Santa Fe and the Spanish cities southwest. West of the crossing, two hundred miles of grass rolled away to the sky, waist-high, blowing black and green and yellow. Your shoes got slick as lard in that grass. Then you came out into the sagebrush, and the grit chewed off your soles and left you barefoot. And about that time the Comanches would come yelling out of the sand hills. All the way across a thousand miles of empty prairie you would wish you were back in Westport, sitting in Punch Dunkelberger's Star of the West saloon, listening to Jake Shafer tell how Davy Crockett could grin the bark off a tree.

Westport could have been the greatest city in the United States. It could have been Boston and New York and Detroit pressed into one and set down in the middle of the prairie, if it hadn't made one mistake. That was about Windwagon Smith.

The morning Windwagon came, Punch Dunkelberger's hound dog woke up bristling like a hairbrush. That dog always slept until noon under his master's hat peg in the Star of the West; he had slept through a cyclone and seven street fights. But that morning he woke up about ten o'clock, waved his nose in the air, howled a long quaver, and slunk into a closet. Two Pawnees in the Star looked at the dog and blew away like smoke. Jake Shafer changed his seat and drew a bead on the door. The door opened slowly. But only Shelby Foster glided in, with his apologetic way, giving a little bow before speaking, because he was from the East and knew manners. When he tried to talk he was so excited he couldn't squeeze the words out, and stood there with his mouth mostly open, his eyes big as soap kettles, and a silly polite look on his face, waving his hands toward the street as though he were batting gnats.

"I never hoped to see the Missouri flow juleps," said Jake Shafer, "or a gopher running a coyote, or Foster without anything to say."

Foster looked behind him and croaked and skipped aside, and there was a crash, and the head and shoulders of Jake's mule Martha appeared in the doorway. The doors slammed back and caught the mule's neck in a pincers, and there she stood like a moose head on the wall, rolling her eyes.

"I can stand bugs in the beer," bellowed Jake in his big barrel voice, "but when the draft animals come in I go out."

When they went out, there was Windwagon Smith.

All they saw at first was a Conestoga wagon coming down the street between the log houses. It was like any other Conestoga wagon, sway-backed, with a horseshoe canvas top. Except for one thing: there was nothing in front of it.

No oxen, no mules, no horses. Nothing. The wagon was just coming down the street.

The Pawnees were peeking from behind trees, eyes bulging like hard-boiled eggs. The dogs were barking, and the ponies that hadn't run away were pulling at their hackamores.

"He's got a sail," said Punch suddenly.

A pole stuck up out of the wagon like a ship's mast, and on it a square of canvas turned half sideways to catch the quartering wind.

A little man in blue denim was riding on the wagon seat. He furled the sail in quick movements, locked the wagon wheel, and came to a stop exactly where Jake's mule had been. When he hopped down from the wagon he walked with a sailor's roll and sway. The dogs quit barking and balanced on their hind legs, ready to go either way. It was so quiet you could hear the stranger's feet crunch in the dust and sand.

"Ahoy!" he said out of the silence. "Think I'll drop anchor and come ashore for a bit of refreshment."

His voice was deep and rolling, with something about it that prolonged the *r*'s and clipped the consonants like axbites in an oak tree.

"My name's Smith," he explained. "I'm the master, the crew, and most of the cargo of this ship, and I aim to do a lot of sailing on the prairie." There was never so much *r* in prairie until he said it.

It was Painted Dog, a Pawnee, who really named him Painted Dog had been behind the nearest tree when Jake's mule jumped into the saloon. "Mule be there," he explained later, "door there. Windwagon blow down street. Whoosh! Mule: here, there!" So they called the stranger Windwagon, for he was the kind of person who had to have a shinier name than Smith.

The whole town followed the stranger to the Star. They made a circle around his table, then circles around that circle, like winding up a ball of yarn, until the room was full. Those who were near passed word over their shoulders to those who were not, so that bulletins would slide outward like waves when you throw a stone in a pond: "He's sitting down"—"sitting down"—and finally, at farthest remove, the Pawnees would hear the news and pass it on: "Sittum down"—"sittum."

The stranger savored his drink like a man who had been long away from the good things. He was one of those old youngsters, anywhere between thirty and fifty. His face was burned and lined, his sandy hair had been tumbled and tousled by many a wind, and his eyes had the perpetual squint that a sailor gets from peeking all day at horizons. People looked mostly at his eyes: they burned like a tent preacher's. When he began to talk, he wasn't bashful or brash, just quiet and sure, and convincing, his big burry voice rolling like the tide. He told how the prairies were going to look tomorrow, speckled with mansions and factories and towns, wealthier than India. But he said people needed one great thing before they could have any of those things. They needed a way to move fast, a way to carry goods from town to town; to build this new prairie of tomorrow they had to have the speed of the wind! Then he talked about his wagon, how it would sail any place on the prairie ten times as fast as a draft animal, yet, without animals to buy or feed, it didn't need to follow crooked trails along rivers, and it would always have free power because the wind never stops on the prairie.

Jake Shafer nodded his head at that, and the circle behind him nodded, and two minutes later the Pawnees were nodding their heads, too; they knew that prairie wind. Then the stranger looked Jake straight in the eye and said he wanted the men of Westport to ante in some money and build a fleet of big sail wagons, like his little one, for the Santa Fe trade. For a minute everybody stared at him. Then somebody snickered, and somebody laughed, and everybody around began to laugh, and the room shook, and mirth rippled outward until the farthest Pawnee was holding his belly and gurgling *ug-ug-ug* in his throat.

When the room was quiet again, the stranger said he had thought they might feel that way. He would be back in a few days; they should think it over. Then he climbed back into his wagon, unfurled the sail, and rumbled away in a great arc toward the west.

II

For the next few days they talked of nothing except Windwagon Smith. Jake Shafer said that he didn't hand over any chips until he saw the cards on the table, and everybody agreed that was sage. Shelby Foster, who had just graduated from a New England college, said that the kind of mathematics they taught in New England colleges proved that such a big wagon couldn't run, and only a fool would invest money in it. Foster had come out to write a book like Francis Parkman's about the Oregon Trail, and went around looking at people and writing in his notebook. And as soon as Foster came out against windwagons people began to look at them more favorably. Jake's daughter Rosalie, who was as sweet as clover honey, said that maybe this was one of the things you just have to believe in — like boats, the first time you see one. Someone suggested that maybe Smith had gone to St. Joe, Westport's rival town, and St. Joe would build windwagons and take over the whole trade; and everybody spent a bad day imagining St. Joe full of millionaires. But a rider from St. Joe said Smith hadn't been up there. And when he hadn't come back in four days, Westport gave him up and thought of other things.

When Windwagon Smith had been gone six days, a trapper came to Westport with a strange story. He had been riding about ten miles from town when he saw a white streak on the prairie. The streak turned out to be an old cow, sticking its head between its legs and uncoiling with ten-foot jumps, stringing its tail out behind like a fence rail. Before he could think what to do about the cow, it sailed past him and disappeared in a funnel of dust. He pondered whether he should catch the cow and race it against all comers, but he didn't know that he *could* catch it; it was the fastest cow he ever saw.

That same day a caravan that had just started west passed back through Westport, headed *east*. The men of the caravan held tight to their guns and kept their mouths shut. One woman who was a little hysterical said they weren't afraid of the Sioux or the Mormons, but they weren't going out on the prairie among the *spirits*. They were going back to Ohio where bodies stayed in their graves!

Punch Dunkelberger and Jake Shafer talked of these events in the Star, Doctor Jackson told his patients about them while he prescribed calomel and mustard plasters, Shelby Foster discussed them with Rosalie Shafer while they looked at the moon. But the meaning was not fully comprehended until the next morning, when the dogs waved their noses in the air again and slunk away, all the ponies that could jump leaped the corrals and started east, and the Indians began to glide around, looking for wide trees. And soon Windwagon sailed down the street, waving to everyone.

"Ahoy!" he said. "I'd have been back yesterday, but came on a caravan and maybe scared them, so I took a long swing off the trail and waited until I was sure they were out of the way."

The town followed him into the Star again, and he showed a stone that was as good as an affidavit for where he had been. It was jagged and black, and still warm from lying in a little gully beyond Council Grove where all the wind blows straight up, hot as Mexican pepper. That gully is one of the side doors to hell, people think. The Doctor worked long division on a table top, and calculated that the windwagon had made nearly seventy miles a day. An ox team was lucky to make fifteen. When Windwagon said he thought he might go to St. Joe, Jake looked at the faces around him and then jumped up and banged the table and said, "By Gum, we'll form a company *here!*" A great whoop went up behind him, and undulated outward, and in a little while the Pawnees were screaming and dancing in the street, the dogs snapping at their heels.

That is how the Westport Prairie Clipper Company was formed. You can see it in the company's minute book. Jake Shafer was elected president; Punch Dunkelberger, vice president; the Doctor, secretary and treasurer. Windwagon could have had any office he wanted, but he wanted only to be Navigator — Navigator of the Prairies, he said with a faraway look in his eyes. He said you had to believe in the future. Columbus had to believe; Dan Boone had to believe in Kentucky before he cut the Wilderness Road; Fulton had to believe that a little engine could push a big boat. Every time progress is made it's because people believe enough in something to take a chance. He said that pretty soon the prairie would be white with sails. The clippers would cruise past the oxen like coyotes past snails. Every day a clipper would dock in Westport with its hold full of gold and spices and blankets, and every day in the Spanish cities (ports, he called them) they would shout, " Make way for the Westport Prairie Clipper! "

Punch Dunkelberger was so near to tears he made the mistake of setting up the whole crowd.

They were slow in starting to build the clippers, because Windwagon was particular. He wanted white oak and hickory for the bed, so it could be curved just right to hold the cargo on slopes; and long-seasoned ash for the spokes and the tillers and all the moving parts that weren't iron. The iron had to be beaten just enough. When Jake saw what a job it was going to be, he said they would build one clipper and try it out before building the others. Windwagon looked a little hurt, but he put the measurements on paper and sent riders to St. Joe and Independence to see what materials they could collect. Some things had to be ordered from St. Louis and Pittsburgh.

While the clipper was building, Windwagon had plenty of time to talk. He was ever one to talk grandly—not boastfully, just grandly. As soon as he got a dozen wagons promised, he began to talk of a hundred-wagon fleet. And one evening he said, " It'll never do any good to have ships unless we have sailors. We've got to build crews at the same time we build clippers. If you are going to be the first captains in the Santa Fe voyage, you've got to learn to pilot."

So Jake climbed into Smith's little wagon one day, with his jaw set firm and his hands holding tight, and Windwagon sat beside him and explained how the sail worked. He let Jake try to steer, and they staggered over the prairie for a while. When they came back, Jake climbed out quickly with the sweat running down his face and said he'd rather drive a runaway bull team than handle a 6 x 6 sail. One by one the other members of the Company began to go out for sailing lessons. They would swell out their muscles and hold on to the tiller as though they were driving a twelve-mule span, and tug at the tiny sail like wrestling a steer. Windwagon would shake his head in despair and take the tiller from them, and make the wagon glide this way and that. When Windwagon steered it was as though the man, the wagon, and the wind were all one will. But when Jake, or Punch, or the Doctor steered, the wagon would stagger and hesitate and groan in its joints. And when the lesson was over, the pupil would climb out as quickly as possible and go into the Star for a long drink.

Windwagon explained that a captain must also know how to navigate. Foster snorted at that; he said that to navigate you need to know the kind of elevated mathematics that is taught only in New England colleges, but Windwagon said that for a man of sense it wasn't necessary to go to college, and he began to teach Westport the common rules about the stars and directions and estimating distances.

Jake Shafer ordered a sextant from Baltimore, and Windwagon nearly cried when he saw it. It reminded him of the sea, and he spent a whole afternoon telling how it feels to skid before a salt breeze, and how the mountains come to the bay at Naples, and how in a few weeks the first clipper would be sailing into Santa Fe.

One day Punch Dunkelberger appeared wearing a captain's cap he had ordered from St. Louis. It was bright blue with silver braid, and Punch looked like baked ham with birthday candles. But in a few weeks everyone had a blue cap. Each new one seemed to have more trimming than the one before, until Punch got ashamed of his and talked of putting a red turkey feather on it. The town was no longer interested in the things it had been. A caravan could hardly buy a mule or an ox in the village. The blacksmith was working on the clipper and had no time to shoe animals or repair wheels. Most of the businessmen closed up shop, hid their leathery faces under blue caps, sighted through the sextant, and tried to walk and talk like Windwagon. It was wonderful to hear them go on about tacking and hauling, port and starb'd.

Sometimes a man would look at himself in his wife's mirror or calculate how much money the experiment was costing him. Then he would go to Windwagon, clear his throat and furrow his brow, and try to say his worries. Always Windwagon would soothe him and tell him about Tomorrow and send him away figuring how much money could be made on one trip to Santa Fe. You couldn't doubt a man who believed as hard as Windwagon.

Shelby Foster was the only man in Westport that Windwagon couldn't convince. Foster stood around and wrote in his notebook and groused. He said he had learned in college how another damned fool once wanted to make a machine that would fly on the wind —

somebody named Darius Green, he said. That led to Foster's quarrel with Rosalie Shafer. When Foster had come to Missouri he had tried once to ride a pony and taken one look at Rosalie, and decided to write his book in Westport rather than on the Trail. Before that, Rosalie hadn't had any beau except on Sunday nights when Punch would come over and sit beside her and talk about the mule business with Jake. She said Punch lacked imagination. Foster would kiss her hand and tell her she was a flower. They would sit close together and he would read poetry to her, the kind they learn in the New England colleges, about skylarks. But sometimes they talked about Windwagon Smith, and Foster said sensible men would lock Windwagon up, and Rosalie called Foster a coward and said he too lacked imagination, and they would sit at opposite ends of the bench and look at the moon individually.

Windwagon had imagination, Rosalie said. And finally she teased him into giving her a sailing lesson, and after that he went out often with her late in the afternoon, when the sun would glint like a Sioux bonfire on Rosalie's hair, and Foster would sit in front of the Star, looking as though he were chewing pickled nails. Rosalie might become a good sailor, Windwagon said; she had sea sense. But that's all he said about her. Foster still went to see her six nights a week, and Punch on Sunday nights, but Punch said she didn't act so interested in the mule business any more.

III

When two caravans wanted to buy windwagons, the men of Westport began to see what kind of business they were in.

"There's no end to it," Windwagon said. "When we build our fleet of a hundred we can squeeze almost everybody else off the trail. When we build a thousand we can take over the whole trade. Then we can build a thousand more and spread out into Iowa and Illinois and maybe start a water-level route beside the Lakes as far east as New York State. Then we'll build a million little wagons and sell them to the Oregon settlers. We'll keep the Santa Fe route to ourselves. We'll have our shipyards over there in the bottom by the creek, and start branches in St. Joe and Independence. We'll train other captains, and become admirals and have fleets under us."

The Doctor calculated they could make two hundred thousand dollars the first year and six million the second. They got so tangled figuring what the income might be the fourth year that Windwagon forgot Rosalie's sailing lesson, and Foster sneaked over and read Milton to her.

One day half a dozen businessmen came up on the boat from St. Louis, looked at the wagon, and offered a thousand dollars cash for it; said they didn't know whether Windwagon was crazy or a genius, but they liked to gamble. Jake laughed at them. They talked to Windwagon a while and offered ten thousand, but Jake told them to go home and dig up some real money.

Foster said Westport contained seven kinds of fools, all bad.

A company of soldiers marched down from Leavenworth one day. They had heard that cannons were being mounted in the wagons to conquer an empire in the Southwest, like Aaron Burr's. There weren't any cannons. Some people thought Windwagon looked a little crestfallen; it was the only thing he hadn't thought of. The soldiers poked around and talked impressively about military possibilities.

Jim Bridger himself came in one day and spent a long time studying the wagon. He looked sad, as though he saw the old West changing. And Kit Carson came up, with his Indian wife, and talked a long time to Windwagon like a brother, and said he wished he were thirty years younger.

Westport was becoming a tourist town. The store stopped carrying powder and stocked little windwagons carved from soft wood. The print shop at St. Joe put out a souvenir booklet all about Windwagon Smith, saying that he had once been an admiral in the Scotch navy, had captured the Sandwich Isles from the cannibals, and had twice sailed around the world. Foster sneered that if the truth were known he'd bet Windwagon had a past a lot different from that. Rosalie said Foster had less imagination than Punch. Windwagon just laughed.

When the windwagon was done, it seemed that the whole population of the western territories came into Westport to see it. You could hardly shuffle your feet without stepping on a dog or baby. The windwagon was ten times as large as a Conestoga wagon, and built with two decks. Passengers could shoot buffalo from the upper deck when regular service started, Windwagon said. When the windwagon service was extended to Africa, they could shoot lions. It had a mainsail as big as a house, and the wheels were a foot wide and tired with iron. Yet, big as it was, it was so beautifully fitted and greased that it moved with hardly a push of the hand. Some were in favor of painting it red, white, and blue, like most of the wagons, but Windwagon said this must have dignity; this wasn't a wagon, it was a clipper ship. They made it blue with silver trimmings, and red spokes in the wheels.

The day before the first trip, the manager of an Eastern railroad said that he didn't think the ship would run but was willing to offer twenty-five thousand for complete rights. Jake was pretty uncertain for a while, and then talked to Windwagon, and came back and laughed and said they wouldn't take a million dollars for the clipper. He talked almost as convincingly as Windwagon.

The Westport Prairie Clipper Company invited the President of the United States to dedicate the new ship, but he regretted. However, two top-hatted men walked into the Star, and when Punch went up to them and said in the new grand manner, "I am Captain Dunkelberger. I don't believe I have the pleasure of your acquaintance," they looked at him oddly and one said he was the Secretary of the Navy and the other the Secretary of War. Then they borrowed ten dollars from him.

The prairie clipper was rolled out to the edge of town, and Rosalie Shafer broke a bottle of corn whisky right prettily over one front wheel. Everybody yelled for a speech from Windwagon, everybody except Shelby Foster. Windwagon climbed up on the upper deck, blew his nose, hawked his throat, and began to talk with that faraway shine in his eyes.

"Ladies and gents," he said, "and them of you as has come a long way to see us today. I want to welcome you to the port of the prairie. And I thank you for coming to see our little ship, the first clipper ever built for trans-prairie shipping in America. And I wish I could tell you what this is going to mean to you. I wish I could paint a picture the way this prairie is going to look in five years. This ship you see here today is only a pack rat compared to the ships you are going to see tied up in this port. There'll be passenger ships and freighters big enough to carry this one on the poop deck, big enough to carry a whole caravan or a whole army. And there'll be little windwagons. Where there's big ones, there's usually little ones, you know. (*Long laughter.*) We'll make so many they won't cost much. And every one of you'll have a little windwagon in your barn, and you can get in it and go anywhere you want on the prairie just as easy as you put a chicken in a pot. This clipper shows that all you have to do is believe in these things and they'll come true. This is just like the sunrise on a new day, only you and me are helping to pull up the sun! "

It was the best speech Windwagon ever made, but he never made a bad speech.

IV

The maiden voyage, Windwagon called it, and said that only the real charter members of the company should go – and the Secretary of War and the Secretary of the Navy, if they were sober. The President could have gone, too, if he had come. But nobody else. Not even Rosalie, who almost bawled in front of everybody when Jake told her no. The passengers boarded the ship and waved their caps. Punch had a red feather in his. Then Windwagon climbed up to the seat he called the bridge, grabbed the tiller, and yelled, " Cast off! " Jake's Negro boy took a block from under one of the wheels, and the clipper began to move.

There wasn't much jerk when they started, for Windwagon payed out the sail slowly, but in a minute Westport was a quarter mile away and the grass under wheel like a green rug. Punch said so later. In two minutes they could hardly see the ponies and the crowd, and Shelby Foster out in front in his red shirt, looking as though he were balancing the family tree on his nose.

They all said they had never felt anything like that ride. It was airy, like flying. That is the way a hawk feels, they guessed. This is the way it feels to scud in a three-master before the trade winds. The clipper swished past an ox team as though it were standing still. A Pawnee on a painted pony tried to race, but was left so far behind he got off his horse and gave the sacred salute of one thumb and four fingers.

Under full sail, the clipper rushed across the prairie. Occasionally it struck a gully or a dry creek bed, and then the body bounced on the springs, and the passengers bounced in their seats. Sometimes it swayed sharply as it hurried down a prairie swell. But the swaying and bouncing were mostly in the body. The great wheels rolled true and straight where the tiller pointed them.

"It runs like a flagship," shouted Windwagon over the whine of the wind. "It'll run to Santa Fe in a week."

He had to give his attention immediately to steering over an acre of badlands. That was when Punch Dunkelberger bounced into the lap of the Secretary of War. Punch weighed three hundred pounds.

"I say," said the Secretary, "don't you think we are going rather fast? For a maiden voyage?" he added.

The Secretary of the Navy looked at the grass swirling past, then looked hastily away from it.

"Go up and talk to him," the Doctor said to Jake.

Jake crawled to the front.

"Don't you think we are going a bit fast?" he said in Windwagon's ear. "Confidentially, some of the passengers who aren't so used to this as we are seem to be getting a little frightened."

Windwagon laughed. He threw back his head and laughed from his toes up, as free as the wind, happy as a child.

"This is just crawling," he said. "Tomorrow we'll be going over this prairie so fast we'll hardly need to touch the ground."

Jake crawled back to his seat and closed his eyes.

"The man is mad," said the Doctor.

"Knock him over the head," said Punch.

"Then who'll steer and stop this thing?" asked Jake.

"True," said the Doctor.

Windwagon looked back over his shoulder. "Would you gentlemen from Washington like to ask any questions?" he called.

"Us? No," grunted the Secretary of War weakly.

The sail thumped like a drum in the wind, and the stench of hot axle grease rose inside the wagon.

"What if we hit something at this speed?" said Jake.

"Or turn over?" said the Secretary of War.

"Don't worry," said Windwagon.

"Can you pull the brake?" asked the Doctor.

"I think I'd better," said Jake. He crawled forward until he could reach the lever.

When the brake caught, the wagon skidded, groaned, began to turn almost at a right angle. It leaned dangerously on its springs. The sail strained and the hickory mast trembled. The wagon came around, grandly, thrillingly. But it didn't stop, and it didn't come out of the turn. It shuddered, hesitated, then swung around so that it was running backwards, slowly at first, then faster and faster.

They said Windwagon gave one slow look at Jake. He didn't say anything. One slow look, more sad than angry, but Jake shriveled under it. And then Windwagon laughed again, that same free laugh from his toes to his mouth, but more rueful. He laughed and turned back and worked with the sail.

Later they knew what had happened. A brake on one wheel will stop a wagon going slow, but not a prairie clipper at full speed. The brake held just long enough to throw the clipper into a sharp turn and lock the steering gear. The sail turned on the mast and twisted its rope beyond chance of furling.

Far back, the crowd watched admiringly as the wagon bore down stern-first upon them, cutting a wide arc over the waves of prairie grass. Not until it was two hundred yards away did they stop cheering. When it was a hundred yards away, they scattered like a buffalo stampede. The prairie streamed pintos.

There were three little gullies in the path of the circle. Every twenty seconds the wagon hit a gully and the passengers bounced around like popcorn. About the tenth gully, the Secretary of War bounced out. He lit on a ball and rolled like a tumbleweed. Then he got up and ran like a jack rabbit away from the path of the wagon. "Stop the ship!" shouted Jake. "Stop the ship at once! We've lost His Honor!"

"You stop it," Punch suggested.

"Excuse me," said the Secretary of the Navy, and jumped. He yelled and sprang up and began to pick things out of his pants.

"Dwarf cactus," observed Punch.

"Gentlemen," said the Doctor, "I know the consequences of broken bones. I do not advise jumping."

Two more passengers jumped, and then another, and finally the Doctor himself. That left Windwagon and Jake and Punch.

"Father," said a sweet voice in the wagon.

Jake covered his eyes with his hands. " Did you ever hear of the voices of your beloved speaking to you just before death? " he asked Punch. Punch held tight and groaned. " Speaking to me, too," he moaned.

" Father," said someone again.

Jake looked toward the back of the wagon.

" Rosalie! " he bellowed.

Rosalie was just climbing out of the compartment Windwagon had designed to hold liquids and pottery on the Santa Fe run.

" Rosalie! " said Punch Dunkelberger, between bounces.

" Miss Shafer! " said Windwagon, looking around quickly.

" What are you doing here? " Jake thundered.

" You know this is a very great thing," yelled Windwagon above the roar of wind and wagon. " Miss Shafer is the first stowaway in the history of prairie clippers." He went back to working with the sail. They said he was just as calm as though this were a box social in the schoolhouse.

Jake said some short ugly words.

" You'd better jump," Punch advised her.

" Don't you dare jump," said Windwagon over his shoulder. " You might get killed."

" I'll take care of you," offered Punch.

" You need a spanking," said Jake.

" I don't need taking care of," Rosalie said to Punch. She looked Jake in the eye.

" You pulled the brake, didn't you? " she said, low and hard.

Jake stared at her.

" You couldn't believe in Windwagon. You couldn't put your chips down and take a chance. You got scared. You pulled the brake."

Jake made gurgling noises.

" I'm going up and sit with Windwagon," Rosalie said. Once she looked back at her father and Punch, who was staring at the nearest exit.

" Don't give up the ship, Captain Dunkelberger," she said sweetly.

The wagon whirled in its circle, the wind shrieking.

" There went Jake! " yelled Punch. Then Punch went.

He said he hit the ground unanimously, every square inch of him.

He pulled himself out of the track and watched the windwagon. There was something beautiful about it even going backwards, something shiplike, birdlike, not wagonlike, with the wind filling out the sail blue-white against the blue-green grass. But he could see something from the ground he couldn't from the clipper: every circle was carrying it farther west. Already at its most distant point it was out of sight behind the swell of the prairie.

" Catch it! Catch it! " yelled Jake, limping along.

" Stop them! " yelled Shelby Foster, bouncing along on a borrowed pony, holding tight to the saddle horn.

The windwagon changed its circles into ovals, its ovals into a pattern that couldn't be made out because it was so far away. The last time anybody saw it, it was scudding backwards into the west, with Shelby Foster after it, far behind, occasionally taking one hand off the saddle horn to shake his fist. Rosalie and Windwagon were sitting close. Whenever they hit a gully they held to each other.

V

The Secretary of the Navy had to walk all the way back to town because he couldn't sit. The others rode back on borrowed ponies, each jog showing up a fresh bruise. In Westport it was like a picnic breaking up after everyone had got indigestion and poison ivy. Shelby Foster came into the Star and said politely, "Good evening, Captain Dunkelberger," and Punch chased him halfway into Independence. Punch had a bandage around his head and was pale as whitewash, but full of fight. It took the Doctor two hours to pick all the cactus spines out of the Secretary of the Navy. Then the secretaries stole two horses and gave a sort of generalized scowl at all of Westport before they rode away.

The town went back into the mule, powder, and bacon business, trying not to hear a tide of scornful laughter that rose in St. Joe and spread and bounced back and forth between the Rockies and the Appalachians. But history seemed to be moving past Westport. The wagons began to go farther north, and when the railroads came in they chose other towns. Westport shrank and Kansas City grew, and after a while Kansas City swallowed Westport and put its street railway through the place where the Star had stood and built its municipal airport on the very land where the windwagon had begun its maiden voyage.

They never saw the windwagon again, although they searched the prairie as far as Council Grove. Of course, there were stories. Every once in a while a bullwhacker would be picked up barefoot and half-dead from thirst, and tell how his draft animals had suddenly reared up at a dust cloud and run away like antelope; and the worst drinker in Independence swore off and became an elder in the Lutheran church because he saw the ghost of a Conestoga wagon floating on the wind near the Pueblo. But that man was always seeing things.

Many a man saw Windwagon Smith after he left Westport, though. He was in the pilothouse, he and a beautiful red-haired woman, when the first steamboat came up the Yellowstone, and they swear that nobody but Windwagon Smith held the golden spike when the two railroads came together at Promontory Point. And not long ago when the first transcontinental airplane roared out of Kansas City a little sandy-haired man closed the plane's door and waved the pilot on. The little man walked like a sailor, they said. His eyes seemed to burn, and he had the perpetual squint that comes from looking always at horizons.

✣ ✣ ✣

HOW A STORY BEGINS

It is very hard for an author to tell exactly at what point in his experience a story starts. Many times, when an author begins to write a story, he finds that he has carried the story in his mind for years, and most of the work has been done before any words are set down on paper. The roots of a story are deeply submerged. They go back as far as an author can remember. When he writes about childhood, some of his own childhood memories go into what he puts down on paper. If he tries to analyze what he has written, he realizes that he has drawn on experiences he has had, persons he has known, conversation he has heard, scenery he has observed, often many years and many miles apart. The characters in a story are likely to reflect all the author has ever learned about people. The ideas in the story are ideas the author has been forming all his life. Literally whatever a man writes seriously and thoughtfully is a product of his whole experience.

But there comes a time when all this experience begins to focus on something which suggests a story. Sometimes the author becomes aware of a character he would like to write about; Willa Cather's story " Neighbor Rosicky " probably started with a character. Sometimes the author becomes aware of a problem or a tangled situation which teases him to work it out. Sometimes the author wants to present an idea or a theme to his readers; the Galsworthy and Wells stories in this volume probably started that way. Sometimes an author is lucky enough to hear the plot of a story, or to see a story happen. Stephen Crane actually went through a shipwreck like the one in " The Open Boat." Both Hawthorne and Longfellow heard of the journey of Evangeline, the Acadian girl, in search of her sweetheart. Hawthorne thought it would make a fine story in prose; Longfellow thought it would make a fine story in verse. Hawthorne deferred to Longfellow, and the result was the narrative poem we know as " Evangeline."

" Windwagon Smith " started with a story which I heard one night in Wyoming, in camp not far from the place where the Mormon leader Brigham Young once met the mountain guide Jim Bridger. As a result of what the guide told him, Young decided to settle the Mormon people around Salt Lake. That story of Brigham Young was told around the campfire that evening, but I was more interested in another story. An old Wyoming settler told me about a queer fellow named Windwagon Thompson who had the idea of putting sails on covered wagons and cruising over the prairie before the wind. " What happened? " I asked. " It didn't work. Broke down," the storyteller said, and spat into the fire.

You can read that legend (of Windwagon *Thomas*) beautifully told in Stanley Vestal's nonfiction book, *Mountain Men*, and it might be interesting for you to read it and see how differently a story writer handles the same material. But at that time I had not read *Mountain Men;* in fact, I doubt that it was published yet, and the story I heard was crude in comparison to Mr. Vestal's version. Yet I could not get the story out of my head. All the next day, while I tried to entice a few trout from the cold Wyoming streams, I kept remembering it. The thing I remembered chiefly was a picture; a prairie schooner with mast and sails billowing out before the wind, sailing over the prairie grass. The grass was high as a man's shoulders then. It looked much like the sea, and even blew in waves when the wind was strong. I had always been impressed by the similarity of the unsettled prairie to the ocean – both of them wide and arched over by great skies, both of them swept by great storms, both of them potentially rich and potentially dangerous, both of them mighty and elemental, both of them making a man in their midst seem small and lonely. When I thought of the sail wagon on that prairie, I began to imagine the wagon looking almost like a clipper ship. That was the picture I stored away when I packed my rod and reel and left Wyoming.

THE PICTURE BECOMES A STORY

It was several years before that picture grew into a story. As I recall it, I began to think about this Windwagon Thompson. What kind of a man could he have been? He was imaginative; that was clear. He was adventurous, or he would not have been out on the great American Desert in the first place. I visualized him as coming from the sea. He was probably a sailor, maybe a captain. He had caught that vision of the prairie as a kind of land-ocean, and had applied his art of sailing to the problems of getting over the land. I thought of him as neither too old to be daring, nor too young to be inexperienced in the arts of the sea. I rather judged he would be the type whose age is hard to guess. He would have the seaman's eye and the seaman's pink and wrinkled skin, I imagined. He would have " long, long thoughts." He would not be talkative, but when he did speak of his plans for prairie sailing, his eyes would shine and his words would roll out better than he knew they could. I began to think I knew Windwagon Thompson pretty well.

What happened when he went to that farthest frontier town and told the hard-bitten frontiersmen of his scheme? Did they scoff at him? Did they think he was crazy? Did anyone want to lock him up? Did he make any converts? Did anyone put money into his scheme? Did he have to build his windwagon with his own hands? When he built it, did any of the skeptics change their minds? Did any of them go with him on that trial ride when the wagon broke down and failed?

I had my own theories. I guessed that he would meet a solid wall of skepticism at first, but that he would make converts and that most of the town would ultimately get back of his scheme. After all, frontiersmen were themselves imaginative and daring. They were used to high-stake and long-chance games. They would be quick to see the promise of fast transportation across the American Desert. But it would take something to convince them—some dramatic event, or some mighty fine oratory.

Other questions came to me. Was Windwagon friendly or moody? Was he sociable or shy? Did he mix with the other men, or sit apart and dream? Did he have a girl? How well educated was he? What would he talk about besides his windwagon?

I had one advantage over some persons who might have set out to write the story of Windwagon Thompson. I had ridden the Oregon Trail one summer and therefore knew the country. I had brought back many pictures and had read diaries and accounts of life in Westport and on the Trail. It was not hard for me, therefore, to imagine the setting in which these events must have occurred.

ELEMENTS OF A STORY

I began to think of all this as a story. Now the practical job of constructing a story is the combining and fusing of a number of elements:

1. The *people* in the story
2. The *plot* of the story
3. The *setting*
4. The *style*, *point of view*, *tone*, *mood*, *atmosphere*, and other factors in the *telling* of the story
5. The *meaning*, the symbolic quality of the story.

Most serious writers feel that the people are the most important part of fiction. Even when a story is about animals, it is usually their human quality that makes them interesting. Sometimes the people are emphasized to such an extent that we call the story a *character* story. Sometimes the focus of interest seems to be the action, and we call it a *plot* story. But no matter where the emphasis falls, still all these elements must be well developed and well integrated if a story is to be completely successful.

My first thinking about this story material had been about the people in the story, and chiefly about Windwagon Thompson. But I had thought of him as a person. When I began to think of Windwagon as the central character in a story, I began to think hard about what would happen in the story.

That meant I had to make an almost infinite number of choices. In one sense, we might describe writing as a series of choices. Some are small (though important) choices between words. Some are big choices — what characters, or what scenes, or what meanings to put into the story. Early in planning the events of a story you have to make one of these big choices; you have to decide, in a general way, where the story is going. Where is the action aiming? What will be the climax? There isn't enough room in a story to let the characters wander around. They must be led in a straight line to the big scene of the story. In this case, I knew at once what the big scene of the story would be. It would have to be the scene where the windwagon gets its trial.

WHO SHOULD TELL THE STORY?

But there were many more choices. For example, who should tell the story? Should I let Windwagon tell it in his own words, or let a spectator tell it, or tell it myself? There were arguments for each of these. Windwagon would be the only person who could tell us what he was really thinking. A spectator could give us a very realistic kind of picture — he was there! On the other hand, I thought we might make Windwagon a more interesting legendary character if we looked *at* him, so to speak, rather than really getting inside his mind; some of the legendary quality might evaporate if we knew too much about him. Furthermore, this story happened a long time ago. Anyone who saw it happen would probably have died by this time. Therefore, if the story were told by a spectator he would have to be telling it some years ago; the narrative wouldn't be contemporary. I decided that I would have greater freedom if I told the story in the author's third person viewpoint.

How should I tell the story? Should I make it tragic or funny?

Should it be an adventure story or a psychological story? I decided that the story should have a Western quality to it. It should have some of the humor and exaggeration of a tall tale. It should also have a legendary quality. I had heard it as a kind of realistic story, but I couldn't think of it in that way. Windwagon was a legendary figure. He was a symbol of something important in the whole story of the West, and his story should have some of the freedom and wildness and imaginative quality that went into the settling of the West. I decided that if I really caught the spirit of Windwagon, I should have to combine the spirit of a tall tale (like the stories of Paul Bunyan and Davy Crockett) with the spirit of an American legend (like the story of the Great Stone Face). That's what I set out to do.

THE CHARACTERS

Very early in my thinking about the story I renamed Windwagon Thompson. I renamed him Smith, for two specific reasons. In the first place, I wanted a very common last name in order to throw into bold relief his exceedingly uncommon nickname—Windwagon. In the second place, I felt that this man stood for something that is almost the spirit of America, and I wanted to underline that quality by using the commonest American name.

The other characters began to fit into the story around Windwagon Smith. Windwagon, of course, is the only clearly defined character; the others are chiefly to show off aspects of him and of the time. I decided there would have to be a girl. I named her Rosalie, and gave her red hair because at that time I happened to be very fond of red hair. Many decisions about stories are made for no more reason than that, but the important decisions are usually made for very good reason. I thought there ought to be a leading citizen, so I created one and gave him Rosalie for a daughter. I gave considerable thought to the question of what characters would represent the conflict in the story. Every story is built around some kind of conflict, some kind of tension. Sometimes the conflict is between two characters, sometimes between man and nature, sometimes wholly within a man's mind. Windwagon's story would be full of tension. Would he get his windwagon built? Would he get his girl? Would the wagon work after it was built? But the more I thought about it, the more convinced I was that the real conflict in the story was between Windwagon's kind of spirit and the opposite kind of spirit: between the people who look ahead and those who look back; the people who stand for change and those who don't have the courage or hardihood or imagination to want change. To symbolize the people who stood on the opposite side from Windwagon, I invented Shelby Foster. I made him come from New England not as a nasty crack at that part of the country, which I love, but merely to contrast the old and the new Americas. I made him read the English poet Milton to Rosalie not as a crack at Milton, whom I also read, but in order to contrast his attempt to interest Rosalie in the past with Windwagon's attempt to interest her in the future. Finally, I made him a college boy not as a crack against college education, which I represent, but in order to contrast the life of books and study with the life of action represented by Windwagon.

The other characters fell into place. Most of them were comic foils — the "Secretary of War" and "Secretary of the Navy," for instance. With another comic character, the barkeeper Punch Dunkelberger, I had an amusing mischance. When the story was all written and accepted, I realized suddenly where I had got that name. A retired and respected tavern owner in my old town was named Punch Dunkel. Somehow the name had come out of my memory, and I had used it without recognizing its connection. My first impulse was to change the name at once. Then I decided to go see Mr. Dunkel, tell him what I had done, and offer to change the character's name in proof if he wished. I went with some misgivings. But Mr. Dunkel was not only gracious, he was pleased. He was rather secretly proud to have his name, or one so like it, in print. He told me on no condition to change the name, and when the story was published he distributed copies to his friends.

Now remember that most of the planning I have described was done before I had written a word on paper. Don't get the idea that I sat for days with chin in hand like The Thinker. Some of this mental work I was hardly aware of doing. The rest of it was so scattered through two years that there was no one long period which I devoted to planning the story. What I really did was to put the idea in my head and let other ideas gather around it. Mark Twain used to write stories that way. Halfway through Tom Sawyer, he stopped – so he said – "to let the tank fill up." I let my tank fill up, and when it was full to overflowing I sat down to write.

WRITING THE STORY

I rewrote this story three times from beginning to end. Some parts of it I rewrote more than three times. After each complete rewriting I put the manuscript in my drawer for several months, so that when I saw it again I would be fresh and better able to criticize and revise it. Writing is hard work; most authors will echo me in that statement. Writing is the hardest work I have ever done, and the loneliest – and the most rewarding.

Some readers asked me whether I had planned details before starting to write. For example, did I know I was going to have all the frontiersmen order sea-captain's caps, or that I was going to describe the dogs balancing on their hind legs so as to be ready to go either way. I did not. Those touches, and many others, came to me while I was writing. The tone was clear in my head before starting to write, but not many of the details. I knew who the characters were going to be, but not much of what they were going to say. I knew where the action was going to lead, but not all the details of it. I knew in general what I wanted the story to mean, but not exactly how to put the meaning into the story.

Traditionally, the hardest parts of a story to write are the beginning and the end. I wrote the beginning of this story at least a dozen times. The way a story starts is important especially because a short piece of fiction must catch the reader, if at all, in the first few paragraphs; otherwise he will discard it and read something else. I knew my story would have to start fast, not only for that reason but also because there was a lot of material to put in. I felt that the action, therefore, had to start at once, and also that there must be some setting very early because many readers would not have a clear picture of old Westport where the action took place. It was a lot of trouble to design the opening paragraphs so that they would introduce the setting, the action, and the main character all together. You will be interested to notice how I finally worked out the problem. Up until the final rewriting, I began the story, "Now Westport is only a far corner of Kansas City and smells like gasoline and coal smoke, but in the old days . . ." On the last version I put in the first paragraph as it now stands. I tried to introduce Windwagon, to suggest that some excitement was to come, and then to pause a moment to set the stage.

The ending, too, came gradually. It was in the ending that I had most trouble trying to combine the inner story with the outer story. The outer story was essentially a Western tall tale. It was full of action, full of humor and racy similes and slapstick and exaggeration. But the inner story was in the spirit of a legend, rather than a tall tale. It had a serious meaning. Windwagon Smith symbolized not only all the transportation on the prairie — railroads, automobiles, and airplanes, all crossing that thousand miles of emptiness — not only that, but also the whole spirit of the settling of the West. Even beyond that, he stood for the daring and inventive and imaginative spirit we like to think of as the American spirit. I hoped readers would get that out of the story, but I didn't want to say it too clearly; I wanted them to have the pleasure of seeing it for themselves.

The problem appeared in a small way in the question of what should happen to the windwagon. Historically, of course, the windwagon was not a success. As far as the tall tale went, the windwagon could be smashed and forgotten. But if the windwagon was going to symbolize the settlement of the West and the streamliners and planes that were to come later, then it could not be destroyed and forgotten.

You will see how I worked out the problem. I tried to make the legendary spirit, the feeling that Windwagon Smith represented something important in the history of America, emerge more and more from the tall tale as the story moved on. That is why I wrote Windwagon's speech as I did. That is why I departed from the story and didn't show the windwagon failing to work or smashing up. I tried to write a leisurely, talkative ending, as in a legend told around a campfire, with the fanciful suggestion that Windwagon might have been in the first steamboat on the Yellowstone, at Promontory Point when the first transcontinental railroad was joined, and at Kansas City when the transcontinental airlines started. My daughter asked me whether I really meant that Windwagon Smith was at all those places. I told her that his spirit was there. "His ghost, you mean, Daddy?" she asked in seven-year-old seriousness. I said that I hoped Windwagon Smith would never die and be a ghost; we needed people like him today. When she looked even more puzzled I drained my coffee cup and hurried off to work. Sometimes it is better not to explain your stories.

But I have bothered you with a long explanation of this story, in the hope that a frank account of how one author writes may help you understand and appreciate stories, and also perhaps help you in your own attempts to write. I want you to get at least one thing from this long description. I want you to realize that stories aren't written as a spring flows water. They don't just flow. They are the products of a great deal of conscious planning and hard work. Authors write them, as best they can, so that you will enjoy reading them. But they also write into them a great deal more than the obvious things: who wins the girl, how the plot comes out, who committed the crime, and the like. To get below the surface, to find the real gold of the story, is your job as a good reader.

And I want to tell you something else which you will have to take on faith until you write a lot of fiction yourself. There are many points of likeness between the way a writer looks at a story and the way a good reader looks at it. In fact, it is almost impossible to become a good writer without first becoming a good reader, and a little experience in writing often hurries the process of becoming a good reader. The two go together, because both require you to look at a story with discrimination and insight.

HOW TO READ A SHORT STORY

You go through three stages in learning to be a good reader of short stories.

First, you read a great many stories.

Second, as you read, you begin to understand better how stories are made and what they mean.

Third, comparing one story with another, you begin to see differences in what they do and how they do it, and how rich in meaning they are, and how they affect you. You become aware that some stories do certain things better than others, and some accomplish more than others. And thus you build up standards for telling a good story from a poor one, and a great story from a good one.

The first stage is no particular problem, because almost everyone likes stories, and they are readily available.

The second stage is more difficult, but you can get a lot of help on it.

The third stage is one in which you are mostly on your own. You can get some help, but for the most part you have to develop your own insights and your own set of standards in your own way.

Therefore, let's assume that you can coast through stage one but that you might need some help on stages two and three. And the best way to master stage two is to learn to understand how a story is built.

THE PEOPLE IN THE STORY

The people in a story are called *characters*. The author's way of telling you what kind of people they are is called *characterization*.

In a long novel, like John Galsworthy's *Forsyte Saga*, you will come to know three generations of a family, and, altogether, perhaps forty or fifty people. In a short story like Galsworthy's " Timber " in this volume, you meet only a few people and really get to know only one. In " Windwagon Smith " there is only one well-defined character. In a short story like Katherine Mansfield's " The Dill Pickle " in this volume, we get a very good impression of two people. That is about par for the short story. In a well-written short story you have the right to expect that you will get to know one or two characters very well.

You will notice that a skillful writer has many ways of telling you what kinds of people his characters are. Most of these ways are not direct. We speak of *direct* characterization when the author tells you straight out. For example, Kipling in " The Incarnation of Krishna Mulvaney " tells you that Mulvaney was " the father in the craft, who had served in many regiments from Bermuda to Halifax, old in war, scarred, reckless, resourceful, and in his pious hours an unequalled soldier." We speak of *indirect* characterization when the author lets you draw your own conclusions about the character on the basis of information he gives you — what other characters think of the person, details of his appearance or action, how he talks, what he thinks, or how he behaves. You have probably noticed that in "Windwagon Smith" almost all the characterization is indirect. This is true of many stories being written today. Here are some of the indirect ways of characterization:

1. *What other characters think of a character.* For example, you may remember that Rosalie said Windwagon Smith had imagination.

2. *Details of a character's appearance or action.* For example, there was this passage about Windwagon: "His face was burned and lined, his sandy hair had been tumbled and tousled by many a wind, and his eyes had the perpetual squint that a sailor gets from peeking all day at horizons. People looked mostly at his eyes: they burned like a tent preacher's. When he began to talk, . . . his big burry voice rolled like the tide." Without ever characterizing him directly, that passage lets you know quite a lot about Windwagon, doesn't it?

3. *What the character himself says.* Much of the characterization in "Windwagon Smith" is this kind. For example, remember this passage about Windwagon's talking: "Windwagon could have had any office he wanted, but he wanted only to be Navigator — Navigator of the Prairies, he said with a faraway look in his eyes. He said you had to believe in the future. Columbus had to believe; Dan Boone had to believe in Kentucky before he cut the Wilderness Road; Fulton had to believe that a little engine could push a big boat. Every time progress is made it's because people believe enough in something to take a chance. He said that pretty soon the prairie would be white with sails. The clippers would cruise past the oxen like coyotes past snails. Every day a clipper would dock in Westport with its hold full of gold and spices and blankets, and every day in the Spanish cities (ports, he called them) they would shout, 'Make way for the Westport Prairie Clipper!'" For an example of a story in which conversation carries almost all the characterization, you can look at Saki's "The Storyteller" in this volume.

4. *What the character thinks.* In "Windwagon Smith" you are never told exactly what Windwagon is thinking. You have to imagine what his thoughts are yourself. Many modern stories, however, are mostly about what is going on in a character's mind. There are two excellent examples in this volume: Hemingway's "Now I Lay

Me," and Katherine Anne Porter's "The Jilting of Granny Weatherall."

5. *How the character behaves in a revealing situation.* This is the most common way of characterizing. After all, it is the way you chiefly find out in everyday life what kind of people your acquaintances are – you watch what they do. And so in a story like "Windwagon Smith" you learn a lot about Windwagon by the time he reacts to Shelby Foster's competition, by the way he convinces the Westport men whenever they lose heart, by the way he reacts when investors want to pay a large sum for the windwagon before it is tried, and finally by the way he reacts on the maiden voyage of the windwagon.

In a story of some length, an author usually has to use most or all of these methods. For instance, take Willa Cather's "Neighbor Rosicky," which you will read in this book. Rosicky is characterized directly – Miss Cather calls him "industrious . . . generous and warm-hearted and affectionate." He is also characterized by description of appearance – his warm hand, his "kind, reassuring grip," his "funny bright eyes," his "brown face creased but not wrinkled" – you will find dozens of such details built up into a very good picture of a lovable old man. You also hear him talk in his homely idiom, a farmer's slow talk, with a touch of his native Bohemia. You see how he behaves in revealing situations. You see how he takes a death sentence from his doctor, how he tries to hold his son's family together, how he reacts when his corn crop burns, how he gives up his car and his leisure for the good of other people, and how he dies. You know what the other characters think of him. You know some of the things he is thinking. You know him very well, because Miss Cather is a master of this kind of character portrait.

When you finish reading one of the stories in this book, think back over it, and ask yourself how many characters in that story you know really well. Then take the one you know best, and ask yourself what kind of person he is. Next, ask yourself how you know what kind of person he is. What characterizing details have stuck in your mind? Do you remember direct or indirect characterizations? Did you learn about the character from what other characters said about him, or what he said, or what he thought, or how he looked, or how he acted? You might want to look back over the story to refresh your memory and to see whether you have missed anything important that would help you to characterize the person.

PLOT

It must be obvious to you that the incidents in a story are not there by chance. The author has chosen them carefully from thousands of possible incidents and events, and put them together in a certain order. In almost every story the order of events fits a definite pattern which you will recognize if you remember one simple fact: *The action of a story moves from a problem to a solution.*

Perhaps we can make that fact easier to use by expanding it somewhat and putting it into a diagram, thus:

Character(s) → *Problem* → *Complications* → *Climax* → *Solution*

A character or characters are introduced. They meet a problem. The situation becomes more complicated, and finally reaches a climactic point of tension. Then the decision is made, the problem is solved, and the story is brought to a close. That is what we mean by the plot of a traditional short story. In some untraditional short stories this plot structure is not clear or important. A few stories (Frank R. Stockton's "The Lady or the Tiger?" is a famous example) end at the climax, and the reader has to solve the problem in his own way. But the overwhelming majority of stories move from problem to solution in the path just described.

Let's look at the steps along that path.

Character(s). We have already spoken about characters and how the author tells you what kind of persons they are. Most stories introduce the characters first. Thus in "Windwagon Smith" you learn something about Windwagon and the people he is dealing with before you are asked to get interested in the problem of the story.

Problem. By problem we mean the conflict, the source of tension in the story. The conflict may be between the *hero* and another character, whom we then call the *antagonist.* Both want something which only one can have. Or each one wants to win superiority over the other. Or one threatens the life of the other. The conflict grows harder until it reaches a climax where the opponents are face to face and one has to win. When one does win, the problem is solved and the tension is relaxed. Thus, both Windwagon and Shelby Foster want Rosalie, and only one can have her.

But in a larger sense "Windwagon Smith" illustrates another kind of conflict. Windwagon's hardest battle isn't with Shelby Foster, but rather with what Foster represents: the forces in society which oppose newness and change. Foster, and the skeptics who had to be convinced and reconvinced, and the passengers who got scared and pulled the brake, represent those forces. And so in many stories you will find a conflict between the hero and society, or between the hero and the forces of nature, or between the hero and fate When you come to Stephen Crane's story "The Open Boat" in this book, you will have a chance to decide whether the conflict in that story is between man and nature, or man and fate.

There is still another kind of problem — a conflict between man and his own personality. This may be a very real and difficult conflict. A man may be fighting an impulse to commit a crime, or a tendency to be cowardly, or a fear that something is going to happen to him. The conflict in De Maupassant's "The Inn" is between a young man marooned in the mountains, and the loneliness and fear which are slowly driving him insane.

In some stories there seems to be no real problem as we have described it. For the most part, these stories emphasize character or idea. Willa Cather's story "Neighbor Rosicky," which is a character story, seems not to fit exactly into the description of a problem we have just given. That is, there seem to be no forces in opposition, and no climax in which the forces are locked in a death struggle. But there is tension in the story; there is tension in every story which really interests us. I don't want to spoil your fun by telling you too much about "Neighbor Rosicky" now before you read it. But as you read it you will have a chance to see what kind of conflict is the source of that tension, and how Miss Cather interests her readers in what is going to happen, without seeming to use the kind of problem most stories use.

Almost every story, however, is built on some kind of conflict, some kind of opposition. Two forces meet. There is a fight to be won, or a mystery to be solved, or a danger that threatens. There is a good chance of the hero failing. Thus tension is created. Interest is aroused. We want to know how the conflict is going to work out. And we read on into the story.

Complications. The author can't leave the tension at the same level if he wants to maintain our interest. He has to keep raising it until he gets to the climax. Therefore, he introduces complications. The mystery (in a detective story) may look easy at first, but the author leads us up a few blind alleys to show us that a solution won't be easy to reach. The hero may have seemed to have a straight road to his goal, but the author introduces some roadblocks and detours. Thus Windwagon's problem seems at first merely to persuade the men of Westport to finance and support the building of the prairie clipper. But then the situation grows more complicated. The question arises whether Windwagon or Foster will win Rosalie, whether the backers will stay convinced, whether the windwagon will work after it is built.

Here you might find it useful to learn another term or two commonly used in talking about fiction. One such term is *suspense.* Suspense is simply the quality of tense anticipation that we feel while we read a story, wondering what is going to happen, sometimes waiting uneasily or fearfully for it to happen. We wonder whether the hero will come through all right. We see dangers looming in his path. We often see those dangers more clearly than he seems to. And thus we hurry on to the climax to find how things come out.

There isn't much suspense in " Windwagon Smith " because it is a light story. You will find much greater suspense in mystery and adventure stories in this book, such as Conrad's " The Secret Sharer," Jack London's " All Gold Cañon," and Sir Arthur Conan Doyle's " The Red-Headed League."

Another useful term is *foreshadowing.* This refers to the suggestions or hints the author gives his readers as to what is going to happen, and how the conflict is going to end. Thus in " Windwagon Smith " I tried to suggest that the real danger to the windwagon might be human trouble rather than mechanical trouble. In detective stories, like " The Red-Headed League," you will find that the author places hints throughout the story; if you are clever enough at that sort of reading, you can pick out those hints and solve the mystery before the author solves it for you. In tragic stories or stories of high tension like "The Inn" you will find many instances where trouble is foreshadowed, and thereby suspense and interest are built up. In all stories, foreshadowing contributes to the credibility of the story.

Climax. The climax is simply the point of highest tension in the story. In "Windwagon Smith" it is the trial of the windwagon. You will notice that this is the point where all the questions of the story have to be answered: will the windwagon work? will Smith win Rosalie? will the Westport men stay loyal to the project? The climax is the point where the hero and his antagonist are at last face to face, and one has to win. When you read "All Gold Cañon" you will find that the climax comes in a fight. In "The Death of the Dauphin" the climax comes entirely in the mind of a little boy; he has been fighting an idea, and finally he has to accept it. But all the action in a well-built story points toward the climax, and all the questions can be answered in terms of what happens at that climactic point.

Solution. One side has to win. The mystery has to be solved. The questions have to be answered. That is the reason for the climax. After the climax, the story usually ends very quickly. The tension is relaxed, and the author has only to pick up the loose ends and tie them neatly. Thus in "Windwagon Smith" I tried to suggest what might have happened to the windwagon after it disappeared, and what happened to Westport, and I tried to point up the meaning of the story and to give it the legendary quality I wanted it to have—all in the few paragraphs after the climax.

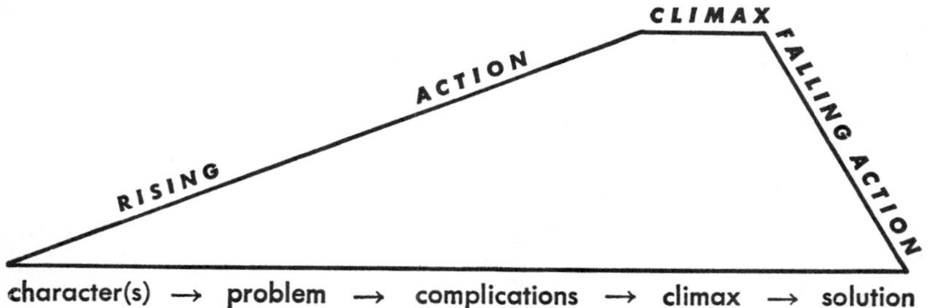

The part of the story before the climax is called the *rising action* of the story, because the tension is rising. The part of the story after the climax is called *falling action.* Most of the story, as you have seen, comes before the climax. When the climax has occurred and the tension is relaxed, then the story hurries to an end.

The preceding diagram, drawn in terms of rising and falling action, may help you to remember the nature of a story plot.

SETTING

The story happens somewhere. It happens in a certain time, in a certain season of the year, amidst certain scenery, and amidst people of a certain kind. In some stories, time and place are important; in others, not. In "Windwagon Smith" they are quite important. Every effort is made to tell the reader early in the story that the action takes place a hundred years ago, at a time before automobiles and airplanes, and almost before railroads; and that it takes place in a frontier outpost on the Oregon Trail, amidst a gay and vigorous frontier society. It would be a very different story without that setting. On the other hand, you will find that setting means little to a story like Chekov's "The Beggar," which could happen anywhere without much changing the point of the story.

If one is writing a novel, he has several hundred pages in which to establish a setting. A short story is, perhaps, twenty typewritten pages; in that short space it is much harder to give a clear sense of setting. There isn't space for long descriptions. You will find that in most stories the author gives you a detail here and a detail there. He tries to *suggest* the setting – make your imagination work, so that you can build the whole picture from a few details.

POINT OF VIEW

Who tells the story? The author has several choices:

The story can be told by the *main character* (as it is, for example, in Poe's "The Tell-Tale Heart").

The story can be told by a *minor character* (as Watson tells of his adventures with Holmes in Conan Doyle's "The Red-Headed League").

The story can be told by *an observer who does not himself enter the story*. This observer may tell us what happens, but not what is going on in the minds of the characters. "Windwagon Smith" is an example of this point of view. Or the observer may tell the story as though he knew exactly what the main characters are thinking. This is called the *omniscient* (all-knowing) *observer* viewpoint. Most of the third person stories in this book are in that form.

Here is a table which will show you the various points of view.

If	*then the story can be told in the*	*by*
The main character's thoughts are to be revealed in the story	First person	The main character
	Third person	An omniscient observer
The main character's thoughts are not to be revealed in the story	First person	A minor character
	Third person	An observer

How does the author choose among these different points of view? He chooses the one which he thinks will best fit his material and bring out the meaning. He has to decide whether it is important for the reader to know what the main character is thinking. If that is important, then he can let the main character tell the story or tell it as an omniscient observer. He has to decide whether the action will seem more real if the story is told by one of the characters. But a character in the story can tell only what he sees happen; therefore, if the author wants to have more freedom in describing the action — if he wants to tell more than any of the characters would know — then he tells the story as an observer.

This is the place to say something about one special way of telling a story which is not quite like any of the points of view just named — the *stream-of-consciousness* method. You will see a variety of this method in Katherine Anne Porter's story, "The Jilting of Granny Weatherall," in this volume. This kind of story actually takes place in the mind of a character, and the story itself is the stream of thoughts and images which pass through the character's mind. These may seem chaotic and disorganized, as thoughts often are, but they give us deep insights into character. You will notice that the plot in this kind of story is not action as we have described story action; it is rather the effect of action on the central character.

TONE, MOOD, ATMOSPHERE

These three terms represent the emotional quality of a story; and are often used interchangeably. More precisely, *tone* is the author's attitude toward what he is presenting — the characters or the whole situation. His attitude may be humorous, for example, or ironic, or sarcastic, or loving. He may be sympathetic toward his characters, or scornful of them. His attitude shows up in the way he writes about the events, and in the events and setting he chooses. *Mood* is the attitude of the characters toward what is happening. It may be sadness, or fear, or happiness, or one of many others. You might say that Windwagon Smith's prevailing mood was a kind of courageous optimism. In some fiction, the mood may change from hope to despair, courage to fear, or vice versa. *Atmosphere* is the general emotional effect of a story or of a scene from a story. It includes the effect of mood, and is controlled by the author's tone. Thus a story may have an atmosphere of gloom or horror or jollity or bewilderment, to give a few examples out of many.

These technical distinctions may not be very important to you now, but they represent facts which are important to you while you are trying to become a better reader. For one thing, unless you notice the author's attitude toward his material, you are likely to miss some of the meaning. He may be writing ironically — *irony* means a contrast between the apparent and the real situation; it is saying one thing but meaning another — and if you do not recognize the irony you will accept the meaning at its surface value. In the second place, when you read Conrad's "The Secret Sharer" in this book you will notice how much the moods of the characters and the atmosphere of the sea contribute to the story. And imagine what one of Poe's horror stories would be like without the spine-tingling atmosphere that Poe makes every reader feel.

THE STORY'S MEANING

Your problem, in becoming a good reader, is to develop insight and understanding so that you can penetrate below the surface happenings of a story to the meaning and symbolic qualities of those happenings. Symbolic means *standing for*. Your problem is to learn to recognize what the surface events of a story stand for. You will find, as you become a better reader, that much of the reward of a story lies below the surface.

But I don't mean to make this sound difficult and mysterious. Let's take "Windwagon Smith" for an example.

Briefly, here is what happens in the story. A man with the look of a sea captain comes to a frontier town and convinces the frontiersmen that they ought to build a prairie schooner that would sail before the wind, rather than being pulled by oxen. After considerable complication, the windwagon is built. Meanwhile, the visitor had been competing with a college boy for the favor of the town beauty. When the windwagon is to be tried out, this girl stows away on board. The trial voyage is successful in that the windwagon sails impressively; but the visitor drives so fast that the passengers become frightened and, one by one, jump out. The two principal backers think the visitor has gone mad. Before they jump out they pull the brake to stop the wagon. The brake twists the sail and throws the wagon out of control. The spectators narrowly escape from the wagon's path, and the wagon disappears on the prairie, carrying the visitor and the beautiful stowaway.

Now, what do these happenings mean? On a fairly obvious level, they stand for situations common and familiar to us. One suitor wins over another by using more imagination, more exciting methods. A community is stirred up over an opportunity to get ahead of other communities. When things look hopeful, there is a great rush to join the parade; but when the going gets rough, there is an equally great rush to get out of the parade.

The Deeper Meanings

But let's get below that level. Let's ask what was the secret of Smith's influence over the shrewd and practical frontiersmen of Westport. He was adventurous, brave, willing to take a chance. But so were they. He was inventive and skillful at using common tools to do uncommon things. So were they. What did he have that they so respected? I think it must have been his quality of imagination. They could be as courageous as he, they were as willing as he to play for high stakes, but they couldn't match his quality of dreams. In a sense Windwagon therefore symbolizes the whole spirit of the frontier — always looking ahead, always restless, always moving into areas of new experience, always dreaming of gold at the end of the trail. The frontiersmen must have recognized that he had in a very pure and concentrated form what they themselves represented.

And it is obvious that these events represent a time of special importance on the American frontier. It is the time when men were becoming impatient with the old pattern of transportation, looking forward to something new. They weren't satisfied with the slow parade of the hunter, the trader, the settler, and the tradesman over the wagon trails and the deer paths. They wanted to hurry the parade. They wanted to shrink distance. They wanted fast transportation because that would mean business and wealth and cities and factories. In a sense the little frontier town of Westport wanted to commit suicide. It wasn't satisfied to be the great city of the wilderness. It wanted to replace shops with factories and the open wilderness with farms; and it did not realize that when that was done the gay and delightful and individualistic life of the frontier would be ended. The story therefore represents the passing of the frontier, and the windwagon symbolizes the trains and automobiles and planes that defeated distance and destroyed the frontier and made a country out of a continent.

There is a still more general meaning. Why did Shafer and Dunkelberger pull the brake on the windwagon? The obvious answer is that they thought Windwagon had gone crazy and were trying to save him, themselves, and the wagon. But there is meaning beyond that. In the contest over Rosalie, Windwagon represents the new; Foster, the old. Foster courts the girl with Milton; Windwagon, with dreams of the new era for Westport. Foster sits on her porch and talks about the noble past of Harvard; Windwagon teaches her to pilot the sail wagon. Windwagon represents newness. In a broader sense, he represents social change. He stands for a new way of life replacing the old. He is a little early; civilization isn't quite ready for his kind of change. But somebody has to *begin* change, and that pioneer is usually called crazy and dangerous. Change never takes place without opposition. Religious pioneers, social pioneers, the first industrialists, the first labor leaders, the men who first advocated independence for this country, the men who first advocated public universities for the boys and girls whose parents were not wealthy – all these had to work under difficulties and against opposition from well-meaning citizens. It was ironic that the brake should be pulled by the solid men of Westport, the men who stood to profit most if the enterprise were successful; and yet they acted for what they thought was the public good, as the opponents of social change always do. Perhaps Windwagon could have avoided some of the trouble if he hadn't let the wagon go so fast. But he wasn't going fast, by later standards. The first automobiles seemed dangerously fast. The first airplanes seemed desperately fast. Windwagon's speed seemed fast only by ox-team standards. And though the first attempts at social change may seem dangerous, and may fail as Windwagon's experiment did, still social change comes. In the end, Windwagon was triumphant and Westport was trampled under advancing civilization. Windwagon won the girl, and people thought they saw him at Promontory Point and on the first Far Western steamboats and at the dedication of the Western airlines, just as the spirit of social pioneers always hovers over later history. Thus the story of Windwagon symbolizes all social change.

"Windwagon Smith" is not a particularly symbolic story. Some stories, like Hawthorne's "Rappaccini's Daughter" which you will read in this book, have most of their interest in their symbolism. Other equally good stories, like Stephen Crane's "The Open Boat," have most of their interest in the realistic story they are telling. You will notice that Hawthorne's story pays little attention to realistic detail, whereas Crane's is very careful to make every detail sharp and real. "Windwagon Smith" is somewhere between those two. It is not as concerned as Crane's story with realistic detail, nor as much with symbolism as Hawthorne's. Yet it has a certain amount of realistic detail, and, as you have seen, it has certain symbolic meanings. Most stories, you will find, fall somewhere in this middle ground.

Some Notes about Meaning

By now, you have probably noticed several things about a story's meaning. For one thing, you have seen that when we talked about meaning we moved from particular facts to generalized meanings. On the surface of a story we have only particulars – facts, details, names. The process of extracting meaning is a process of finding the generalized significance of those surface facts. You are *told* the facts; you have to *derive* the meanings.

In the second place, you have undoubtedly noticed that no paraphrase can express the whole meaning of a story. We have just given a fairly long paraphrase of the meaning of "Windwagon Smith," but that has come nowhere near saying all that the story means to its readers. The briefest paraphrase of a story is called the *theme*, but the whole meaning is always more than the theme, just as a college is more than its motto, or an organization more than its slogan. Many of the stories in this volume have easily stated themes. For example, the theme of Stephen Crane's story "The Open Boat" has been stated as "Fate is inscrutable." The theme of Alphonse Daudet's "The Death of the Dauphin" might be stated as "Human power is no avail against death." As you read those stories, however, notice how much of the richness and meaning of the stories is lost when they are reduced to one thematic sentence.

Finally, I hope you have noticed that you miss much of the richness of a good story if you stop with the surface facts — who wins the girl? how does the hero beat out the villain? who committed the murder? If the story is really good there will be layers of meaning beneath those outer facts. Therein lies the real gold of the story, and it doesn't take very hard digging.

WHAT IS A GOOD STORY?

You may have to remind yourself occasionally, while you are studying short stories and preoccupied with analyzing them, that a story is written primarily to be enjoyed.

I have known students even to believe that a really good story can't be enjoyable; and conversely, that if a story is not enjoyable, there is a good chance it may be a masterpiece. Nothing could be farther from the truth. The greatest stories are those which, throughout the years, have given the deepest pleasure to their readers. If you find you do not enjoy a particular story, first make sure that you are getting everything out of it. Then if you are convinced there is nothing wrong with your reading, you may be sure there is something wrong with the story.

Actually, a good story can give you much more pleasure than

can a poor one, because it is richer and because you can enjoy it on so many levels. Richness is the quality which, more than all others, distinguishes a good story from a poor one. I am going to suggest a simple test of richness which you can use in picking out the good stories from the others.

A GOOD STORY IS RICH IN WORKMANSHIP

What do we mean by good workmanship?

To critics and writers, a fine short story often seems like a small miracle because it accomplishes so much in so little space. Think how much a story has to do. First of all, it must interest a reader and make him want to read on. Then it must introduce several characters and give enough material about them so that the reader will feel he knows them well. It must sketch a setting in which the actions of the characters will seem appropriate. It must narrate the action, leading up to a climax that is both exciting and convincing. And all the characterization and action must be planned with such insight that the story will have meaning beyond the obvious surface meaning. All this in 3,000 to 6,000 words!

Unity of Impression

A short story is therefore like an automobile with just enough gasoline to get to its destination. It can't afford waste motion, or detours, or wrong turns, or side trips. This requirement was recognized by the first distinguished critic of the short story, Edgar Allan Poe, when he developed his theory of "single impression" or, as sometimes called, "unity of impression" or "single effect." In one of the most famous critiques of the short story ever written, Poe said that a writer first selects "a certain unique or single effect to be brought out." Then he invents incidents and "combines such effects as may best aid him in establishing the preconceived effect. If his very first sentence tends not to the outbringing of this effect, then he has failed in his first step. In the whole composition there should be no word written, of which the tendency, direct or indirect, is not to the pre-established design."

Every writer of short stories knows how true this statement is. At some point or other in the process of composing a story, the writer has to stop and ask himself, "Where do I want this story to go? What am I trying to do with it? How can I make it hit one big blow rather than a number of scattering blows? " When he answers that question, he knows what to cut and what to add, and he can pilot his story straight to the goal.

You can see that the logic here works both ways: A good story must aim at a single impression because it is short; and a good story must be short if it is to maintain a single impression.

A well-made story, then, will have a unity of impression. It will be all one piece. It will have no waste parts. You will feel that it fits together, that everything in the story belongs there, and that you do not especially feel the need of anything else.

Credibility of Action

The action in a well-made story will develop smoothly and credibly. Except for the unity of impression, this is the characteristic which is most likely to help you identify a well-made story. Therefore, you should apply some very important questions to the plot of every story: Do the people act as real people would in their situations? Does one scene follow another so reasonably that you are convinced this is how it really would have happened?

In one sense, life is much stranger than fiction. We readily accept coincidence in everyday life. We call it luck or chance or fate. But in fiction we can't accept luck or coincidence. We demand that the solution to the problem must grow out of the characterization and the situation. We demand that the author work out his problem logically. Coincidence is an evasion. It's the easy way out. It's playing a trick on the reader. Therefore, we demand that good fiction have *credibility*, which means that the action must be believable; it must move in a logical and convincing manner without any help from coincidence or luck or chance.

Another way to say this is that we don't want the author to meddle. That is why *surprise endings* don't often appear in the best stories. A surprise ending is simply a surprising turn in the action at the end of a story. O. Henry was the great writer of surprise endings, and his story in this volume, "The Furnished Room," is an example of one. There is nothing wrong with surprise endings if they are credible. Many detective stories are skillfully written so that the ending surprises us because we often miss the little clues which the author had placed throughout the story to show how it is going to work out. But if an author reaches into the story and deliberately turns aside the action simply to startle us — if the ending " just happens " and doesn't convince us that it would have happened in real life — then the story is not well-made. Surprise endings had a great vogue fifty years ago, but have mostly gone out of style now because it is extremely hard to write a surprise ending that will be credible as well as surprising. Readers — as the writers of surprise endings have found — soon tire of tricks.

A well-made story, then, gives you a sense of logicalness and inevitability: with these characters and this situation, it could not have turned out differently. But a poorly designed story is not convincing. It makes you feel that what happens is not true to the characters or to life. The author has meddled. He has not played fair with you.

Other Qualities

A well-made story, as we have said, will have a unity of impression and its action will be credible. It will have other qualities, too, which you will begin to recognize as you read more stories. The very style will be a pleasure to read. The words will fit well together, the turns of phrase will be interesting, the word pictures will be sharp. The incidents will seem sharp and colorful. The setting will be clear and interesting, and will furnish the right background for the events and the people. The whole story, as it unrolls, will give you a sense of good fit and quality and richness.

A GOOD STORY IS RICH IN CHARACTER

If you don't know much about a person, you can describe him with a name or with a few words at most. You can say he is a teacher or a policeman, or a friend of Bobby's, or some girl from New York. But if you know a person well, and want to share your knowledge with someone else, you can't describe the person so briefly. You try to tell what kind of person he is, what he does and what he likes, what his strong and weak points are, and how he got that way.

The difference between thin characterization and rich characterization is the difference between these two ways of describing someone you know. If you finish a story and find that you know about the main character only that he is a detective, or a good man, or a villain, or a handsome young man, then the characterization in that story is not very rich. Let us admit that because a story is so short it is difficult to characterize many persons in detail. But in a rich story, one or two or three characters will be so sharp and real they will seem almost ready to step out of the printed page and speak to you. You will remember them long after you have read the story, and you will ponder why they did certain things, and what must have been going on in their minds at a particular time in the story, and what would have happened if they had faced a different situation. In other words, you will find yourself thinking about these characters as though they were living people you know.

That is a wonderful quality of literature – to be able to create characters who live in our minds. For uncounted generations Aeneas, Helen of Troy, Dido, Antony and Cleopatra, Aladdin, Lancelot, Galahad, Hamlet have been like real people to us. Whole books have been written on many of Shakespeare's characters, because they are characterized so richly that we discuss and analyze them like living persons. You won't be likely to find a Hamlet or a Falstaff or a Lady Macbeth in a short story, but you will find characters like Neighbor Rosicky in Willa Cather's story by that name, and Henry Reifsneider in Theodore Dreiser's "The Lost Phoebe," and the young sea captain in Conrad's "The Secret Sharer," and the boy and his grandfather in Steinbeck's "The Leader of the People." I think you will remember those characters a long time, and you will feel that you have come to know them very well and penetrated far below the surface facts about them. And if so, you will understand what we mean by richness of characterization.

A GOOD STORY IS RICH IN MEANING

A rich story opens windows on life. Let me try to explain this statement.

Some stories give you a kind of intellectual enjoyment, the same sort of pleasure you get from solving a crossword puzzle or working out anagrams. This is the chief kind of pleasure you get, for example, from most detective stories.

Other stories give you an emotional pleasure. You read a love story or an adventure story and imagine yourself going through some of the adventures. Or you read a thriller and feel some of the excitement without having to get into danger yourself. It's exciting and fun while you do it, but it doesn't especially help you to understand the life around you. The story takes you away from your life for a while, but doesn't stay with you.

Then there is the kind of pleasure that comes from richness of meaning. This is the kind of pleasure that stays with you. A story that you enjoy because of its meaning may give you both an intellectual and an emotional pleasure, but it does more than that. It gives you an insight or an understanding that you can carry with you and apply to other life situations. In other words, it is in the deepest sense *true*.

Let's get rid of the idea that a story is necessarily untrue merely because it is a story. Perhaps you have been accustomed to think of stories in terms of the difference between fiction and fact—a news item is true, a piece of fiction is untrue. That distinction is too easy, and it is simply not the case. When you understand why it is not, you will be a long way toward more profitable and pleasant reading.

A news item is a reporter's attempt to write the truth about some specific event. A story is an attempt to write distilled and generalized truth about some problem or situation or kind of person. The less common the event, the better news item it will make. The more common and universal the story situation, the more meaningful it will be. The news reporter tries to record the facts surrounding the event he is recording. The story writer draws on the experience of his entire lifetime in an attempt to get at the real truth about the problem he is dealing with. Thus he is trying, no less than the news reporter, to write the truth, but he is trying to write it on a broader scale and at a greater depth. For whereas the news reporter feels that his job is to record the surface facts and let them speak for themselves, the story writer feels that he must give us enough information so that we can look below the surface and see reasons and causes.

The real test of fiction, then, is whether it opens a window for us and lets us see some part of life more clearly and truly.

Stop a minute and think what that means. Suppose the only way we could learn anything from life were from watching things happen to ourselves and to people around us. That is, suppose all reporters and storytellers (whether through books, magazines, papers, radio, voice, or pictures) were eliminated. Our experience, then, would be no broader than the reach of our senses. Print, radio, voice, pictures have the ability to extend our senses – to lengthen our sight and our hearing to the ends of the earth and through all past time. Furthermore, literature has the even more wonderful quality of letting us share the experience of people who have seen more than we have and in many cases have thought about it more than we have. Many of the greatest men of all time have left us written records of their experience and their thoughts. By means of literature, then, we can look at the world through the windows opened by all these writers – windows we probably could never have opened for ourselves.

This is what makes the richness of a story's meaning. We have talked round about it because it is something you feel rather than measure. But you will feel this richness, and you will recognize it at once. A good story or poem, someone said, is like an artichoke which you peel and peel before getting down to the best part. If a story is rich, you can dig down through layers and layers of meaning. You can study each character, in terms of why he does what he does, what he must be thinking, the system of values by which he acts, his effect on other characters, and the effect of others on him. You can study the reasons why the action goes as it does, why the problem of the story is resolved as it is, and you can judge it in terms of truth and credibility.

You can do that with a good story. You can't do it with a cheap story, because the richness isn't there. When you have labeled the characters as good or bad, pretty or ugly, you have nearly exhausted the story's resources for characterization. When you have sampled the surface glitter and sentimentality you have about exhausted the story's insight on life. That is all you usually find in pulp stories and confession stories and thin stories generally. But really good stories like those in this volume have an entirely different reward for you. Whether you get all that reward is partly up to you. You have to learn to become a good reader in order to get all the richness out of a story. That richness is not only the chief reward of a story; it is also the chief touchstone for distinguishing a good story from a poor one.

Good reading to you!

GLOSSARY OF TERMS

used in talking about the short story

Atmosphere — the general emotional effect of a story or a scene from a story.

Characterization — the author's description and explanation of the people in the story.

Climax — the point of highest tension in the action of the story; the moment when the conflict or problem of the story is about to be resolved.

Conflict — the clash of persons, forces, or ideas which is the basis for the plot of the story.

Falling action — the part of the action of the story that follows the climax.

Fantasy — a story which is realistic except for one important detail, which is so handled as to give the story an imaginative and whimsical tone (for example, "By the Waters of Babylon" which is realistic except for the fact that it is supposed to take place in the future after present civilization has been destroyed).

Foreshadowing — hints inserted by the author to indicate to a careful reader how the action is going to develop, and thus to contribute to the credibility of the plot.

Irony — a striking contrast between the apparent and the real situation.

Meaning — what the story says about life.

Mood — the attitude of the characters in a story toward what is happening. Mood is sometimes used synonymously with atmosphere and tone.

Plot — the plan of action of the story; the movement from problem to solution.

Point of view — the relation of the storyteller to the story.

Problem — the conflict or need or desire which is the source of tension for the plot of the story.

Realistic — writing which gives the impression of sticking close to facts and to the details of everyday life; writing which tries to present life as it seems to be.

Rising action — the part of the action which precedes the climax.

Sentimentality — emotion out of proportion to the situation and not justified by it.

Setting — the place and environment in which the action of the story happens.

Short story — a piece of fiction designed to give a single impression and short enough to be read at one sitting.

Single effect, Single impression (also Unity of impression) — the unity of structure and impact in a well-planned story.

Stream-of-consciousness story — a story which is told by recording the current of thought passing through the mind of a character.

Style — the selection and arrangement of words and sentences.

Surprise ending — an unexpected turn at the end of a plot.

Suspense — the tense anticipation aroused in reading a story.

Symbol, Symbolic — a symbolic story emphasizes meaning on another level; a symbol is a person, object, or action in a story which stands for something else, usually some abstract meaning.

Tension — excitement or anxiety resulting from the conflict in the story.

Theme — a brief statement of the meaning of the story.

Tone — the author's attitude toward what he is presenting, as that attitude is reflected in the story.

The Short Story in America

EDGAR ALLAN POE

The Tell-Tale Heart

If anyone is entitled to be called " father of the short story," Poe deserves that honor. He was the first writer, in the years of printing, to produce a body of short stories admired and imitated throughout the world. He was the first man to state well the critical theory of the story. He developed the detective story and prepared the way for Conan Doyle and the " whodunit " writers of our own day. He developed the mood story, and few since his time have written it as well as he. Still today, a century after his death, he is one of the American authors most widely read abroad.

His life was a strange contradiction. A brilliant thinker, he could never quite organize his own life. Indisputably a genius in literature, he could never quite find the way to personal happiness. Widely respected and admired by persons who read his writing, still he could never quite win respect as a citizen and a neighbor.

He was always being cheated of happiness, and usually because of some fault of his own. Left an orphan at the age of three, he was adopted by a Richmond, Virginia family who cared enough for him to send him to school in England and then to the University of Virginia. It looked like an extraordinary stroke of good fortune for him. But he quarreled with his foster father, and was removed from the University of Virginia after less than a year of study because of his drinking and gambling. Poe joined the coast guard, did well, was appointed to West Point, and seemed on the way to a successful military career. But after eight months he withdrew from the Point, and was disowned by his foster father. He proved a brilliant editor, but was always drinking himself out of a job. He married one of his cousins when she was thirteen. Once again, happiness seemed possible, but he lost his best editorial job, and the couple had to live in stark poverty. His wife died of tuberculosis. He began to struggle up again after that blow. He became engaged to a wealthy widow, who had been his sweetheart in his youth. Once again, it seemed he had a chance to reclaim his personal life. But on the way South to be married, he celebrated too hard, was found unconscious on the street, and died a few days later. His death in 1849 was a tragic waste of talent. He was only forty years old.

As you read this story, remember what Poe said about " single effect "; we reprinted some of his words on that subject in the Introduction. Try to decide what single effect Poe tried to achieve in this story and whether he has met his own standard — that is, whether there is indeed " no word written, of which the tendency, direct or indirect, is not to the pre-established design." In the second place, remember that Poe was a poet and was always concerned with the *sound* of literature. You might like to read this story aloud. Lionel Barrymore and other actors have loved to read it in public because the sound so well fits the effect. In the third place, this is a famous example of a story of atmosphere (see the Introduction for an explanation of this term). Poe tries to create an atmosphere of horror. Notice how he does it.

TRUE! — nervous — very, very dreadfully nervous I had been and am! but why will you say that I am mad? The disease had sharpened my senses — not destroyed — not dulled them. Above all was the sense of hearing acute. I heard all things in the heaven and in the earth. I heard many things in hell. How, then, am I mad? Hearken! and observe how healthily — how calmly I can tell you the whole story.

It is impossible to tell how first the idea entered my brain; but once conceived, it haunted me day and night. Object there was none. Passion there was none. I loved the old man. He had never wronged me. He had never given me insult. For his gold I had no desire. I think it was his eye! Yes, it was this! One of his eyes resembled that of a vulture — a pale blue eye, with a film over it. Whenever it fell upon me, my blood ran cold; and so by degrees — very gradually — I made up my mind to take the life of the old man, and thus rid myself of the eye forever.

Now this is the point. You fancy me mad. Madmen know nothing.

But you should have seen *me*. You should have seen how wisely I proceeded — with what caution — with what foresight — with what dissimulation I went to work!

I was never kinder to the old man than during the whole week before I killed him. And every night, about midnight, I turned the latch of his door and opened it — oh, so gently! And then, when I had made an opening sufficient for my head, I put in a dark-lantern,[1] all closed, closed, so that no light shone out, and then I thrust in my head. Oh, you would have laughed to see how cunningly I thrust it in! I moved it slowly — very, very slowly, so that I might not disturb the old man's sleep. It took me an hour to place my whole head within the opening so far that I could see him as he lay upon his bed. Ha! — would a madman have been so wise as this? And then, when my head was well in the room, I undid the lantern cautiously — oh, so cautiously — cautiously (for the hinges creaked) — I undid it just so much that a single thin ray fell upon the vulture eye. And this I did for seven long nights — every night just at midnight — but I found the eye always closed; and so it was impossible to do the work; for it was not the old man who vexed me, but his Evil Eye. And every morning, when the day broke, I went boldly into the chamber, and spoke courageously to him, calling him by name in a hearty tone, and inquiring how he had passed the night. So you see he would have been a very profound old man, indeed, to suspect that every night, just at twelve, I looked in upon him while he slept.

Upon the eighth night I was more than usually cautious in opening the door. A watch's minute hand moves more quickly than did mine. Never before that night had I *felt* the extent of my own powers — of my sagacity. I could scarcely contain my feelings of triumph. To think that there I was, opening the door, little by little, and he not even to dream of my secret deeds or thoughts. I fairly chuckled at the idea; and perhaps he heard me; for he moved on the bed suddenly, as if startled. Now you may think that I drew back — but no. His room was as black as pitch with the thick darkness (for the shutters were close fastened, through fear of robbers), and so I knew that he could not see the opening of the door, and I kept pushing it on steadily, steadily.

I had my head in, and was about to open the lantern, when my

[1] **dark-lantern:** a lantern with a cover which can be closed to hide the light.

thumb slipped upon the tin fastening, and the old man sprang up in bed, crying out: "Who's there?"

I kept quite still and said nothing. For a whole hour I did not move a muscle, and in the meantime I did not hear him lie down. He was still sitting up in the bed listening;—just as I have done, night after night, hearkening to the death watches in the wall.

Presently I heard a slight groan, and I knew it was the groan of mortal terror. It was not a groan of pain or grief—oh no!—it was the low stifled sound that arises from the bottom of the soul when overcharged with awe. I knew the sound well. Many a night, just at midnight, when all the world slept, it has welled up from my own bosom, deepening, with its dreadful echo, the terrors that distracted me. I say I knew it well. I knew what the old man felt, and pitied him, although I chuckled at heart. I knew that he had been lying awake ever since the first slight noise, when he had turned in the bed. His fears had been ever since growing upon him. He had been trying to fancy them causeless, but could not. He had been saying to himself, "It is nothing but the wind in the chimney—it is only a mouse crossing the floor," or "it is merely a cricket which has made a single chirp." Yes, he had been trying to comfort himself with these suppositions; but he had found all in vain. *All in vain;* because Death, in approaching him, had stalked with his black shadow before him, and enveloped the victim. And it was the mournful influence of the unperceived shadow that caused him to feel—although he neither saw nor heard—to *feel* the presence of my head within the room.

When I had waited a long time, very patiently, without hearing him lie down, I resolved to open a little—a very, very little crevice in the lantern. So I opened it—you cannot imagine how stealthily, stealthily—until, at length, a single dim ray, like the thread of the spider, shot from out the crevice and fell upon the vulture eye.

It was open—wide, wide open—and I grew furious as I gazed upon it. I saw it with perfect distinctness—all a dull blue, with a hideous veil over it that chilled the very marrow in my bones; but I could see nothing else of the old man's face or person: for I had directed the ray, as if by instinct, precisely upon the cursed spot.

And now—have I not told you that what you mistake for madness is but over-acuteness of the senses?—now, I say, there came to my ears a low, dull, quick sound, such as a watch makes when enveloped in cotton. I knew *that* sound well, too. It was the beating of the old man's heart. It increased my fury, as the beating of a drum stimulates the soldier into courage.

But even yet I refrained and kept still. I scarcely breathed. I held the lantern motionless. I tried how steadily I could maintain the ray upon the eye. Meantime the hellish tattoo of the heart increased. It grew quicker and quicker, and louder and louder every instant. The old man's terror *must* have been extreme! It grew louder, I say, louder every moment! — do you mark me well? I have told you that I am nervous: so I am. And now at the dead hour of night, amid the dreadful silence of that old house, so strange a noise as this excited me to uncontrollable terror. Yet, for some minutes longer I refrained and stood still. But the beating grew louder, louder! I thought the heart must burst. And now a new anxiety seized me — the sound would be heard by a neighbor! The old man's hour had come! With a loud yell, I threw open the lantern and leaped into the room. He shrieked once — only once. In an instant I dragged him to the floor, and pulled the heavy bed over him. I then smiled gaily, to find the deed so far done. But, for many minutes, the heart beat on with a muffled sound. This, however, did not vex me; it would not be heard through the wall. At length it ceased. The old man was dead. I removed the bed and examined the corpse. Yes, he was stone, stone dead. I placed my hand upon the heart and held it there many minutes. There was no pulsation. He was stone dead. His eye would trouble me no more.

If still you think me mad, you will think so no longer when I describe the wise precautions I took for the concealment of the body. The night waned, and I worked hastily, but in silence. First of all I dismembered the corpse. I cut off the head and the arms and the legs.

I then took up three planks from the flooring of the chamber, and deposited all between the scantlings. I then replaced the boards so cleverly, so cunningly, that no human eye — not even *his* — could have detected anything wrong. There was nothing to wash out — no stain of any kind — no blood spot whatever. I had been too wary for that. A tub had caught all — ha! ha!

When I had made an end of these labors, it was four o'clock —

still dark as midnight. As the bell sounded the hour, there came a knocking at the street door. I went down to open it with a light heart—for what had I *now* to fear? There entered three men, who introduced themselves, with perfect suavity, as officers of the police. A shriek had been heard by a neighbor during the night: suspicion of foul play had been aroused; information had been lodged at the police office, and they (the officers) had been deputed to search the premises.

I smiled—for *what* had I to fear? I bade the gentlemen welcome. The shriek, I said, was my own in a dream. The old man, I mentioned, was absent in the country. I took my visitors all over the house. I bade them search—search *well*. I led them, at length, to *his* chamber. I showed them his treasures, secure, undisturbed. In the enthusiasm of my confidence, I brought chairs into the room, and desired them *here* to rest from their fatigues, while I myself, in the wild audacity of my perfect triumph, placed my own seat upon the very spot beneath which reposed the corpse of the victim.

The officers were satisfied. My *manner* had convinced them. I was singularly at ease. They sat, and while I answered cheerily, they chatted familiar things. But, ere long, I felt myself getting pale and wished them gone. My head ached, and I fancied a ringing in my ears: but still they sat and still chatted. The ringing became more distinct:—it continued and became more distinct: I talked more freely to get rid of the feeling: but it continued and gained definitiveness—until, at length, I found that the noise was *not* within my ears.

No doubt I now grew *very* pale;—but I talked more fluently, and with a heightened voice. Yet the sound increased—and what could I do? It was a *low, dull, quick sound—much such a sound as a watch makes when enveloped in cotton.* I gasped for breath—and yet the officers heard it not. I talked more quickly—more vehemently; but the noise steadily increased. Why *would* they not be gone? I paced the floor to and fro with heavy strides, as if excited to fury by the observation of the men—but the noise steadily increased. Oh, what *could* I do? I foamed—I raved—I swore! I swung the chair upon which I had been sitting, and grated it upon the boards, but the noise arose over all and continually increased. It grew louder—louder—*louder!* And still the men chatted pleasantly, and smiled. Was it possible they heard not? Ah! — no, no! They heard! — they suspected! — they *knew!* — they were making a *mockery* of my horror! — this I thought, and this I think. But anything was better than this agony! Anything was more tolerable than this derision! I could bear those hypocritical smiles no longer! I felt that I must scream or die! — and now — again! — hark! louder! louder! louder! *louder!* ——

"Villains!" I shrieked, "dissemble no more! I admit the deed! — tear up the planks! — here, here! — it is the beating of his hideous heart!"

READING WITH INSIGHT

1. Just what is happening in this story? Is a man confessing to the police or a judge? Is he trying to explain to someone whose opinion he cares about? Is he trying to "get it off his chest"? Is he half boasting? Is he trying to defend himself? Is he on trial for insanity and trying to prove himself sane? Is he writing or talking?

2. Is the man insane? He tries, of course, to convince us that he is not mad. But can you find any evidence that the author wants us to think the man *is* mad? What does he do that a sane man would not do?

3. The ending of this story depends entirely on the beating of the tell-tale heart. What evidence can you find that the man merely *imagined* he heard the sound? Would you judge it possible that a man could imagine such a sound, especially if he were guilty of a crime and trying to cover it up? Is the beating of the tell-tale heart credible to you?

4. Recalling what Poe said about "single effect" (see Introduction, p. 43), try to name in a few words the effect he sought to achieve in this story. He also said, "If his very initial sentence tends not to the outbringing of this effect, then he has failed in his first step." How does the first sentence in this story fit into the apparent purpose? Why does he talk about madness and hearing in the first paragraph? Can you find any parts of the story that are not necessary, or has Poe lived up to his own doctrine that there should be no waste parts?

5. The mood in this story is a kind of terror born of madness. Can you find some examples of how Poe wrote that mood into the story? For example, recall the horrible scene when the murderer goes at midnight every night for seven nights just to look at his sleeping and intended victim.

6. Throughout this story, there is a rising current of fear and tension. Notice how Poe builds that up. For example, the murderer does not kill his victim at once; he waits until the eighth night to do it. The murderer sits on the very part of the floor under which he had buried the victim. What other instances can you recall in which Poe has thus built up suspense?

7. From among the choices he had, Poe chose to tell this story in the first person, and to let the main character do the talking. Why do you suppose he did this? How would it have been a different kind of story if told in the third person?

8. Why did the policemen stay so long? Did they suspect anything?

9. We talked in the Introduction about the whole meaning of a story. We should be leaving out a great deal of the meaning of this story if we should say that the meaning is "Crime doesn't pay." What would we be leaving out?

10. What is the problem or the conflict in this story? Or are there several? Would you say, for example, that the narrator's own internal tension which he resolves by confessing is one problem? What is the conflict that interests you most as a reader? Where does the climax occur? Does the tension rise up to the point of climax?

11. There are a number of examples of sharp, clear pictures in this story. For example, the narrator says that his hand moved more slowly than the minute hand of a watch. What others can you find?

12. A device much used by authors who write of dramatic events is called *understatement.* One example of this is the way Poe describes the actual dismemberment of the body. He merely says, matter-of-factly, that "I dismembered the corpse. I cut off the head and the arms and the legs." Why does he write it that way, instead of putting in the gory details?

If you like this story, you will be interested in

Poe. *The Fall of the House of Usher.*
The Pit and the Pendulum.
W. W. Jacobs. *The Monkey's Paw.*
Wilbur Daniel Steele. *Footfalls.*
Ambrose Pierce. *The Man and the Snake.*

NATHANIEL HAWTHORNE

Rappaccini's Daughter

BESIDE THE picture of Poe, doomed to be unhappy, put the picture of his contemporary, Hawthorne, doomed to be lonely.

Hawthorne was too much the New England Puritan ever to get into Poe's troubles with liquor and gambling. But if Poe was sometimes too free and easy, Hawthorne was sometimes too much in bondage to conscience. If Poe was sometimes too gregarious, Hawthorne was too much a recluse. When he was a boy in Salem, Massachusetts, he used to say that not twenty people in town were aware of his existence. He went away to college at Bowdoin (where Longfellow was one of his classmates), then came back again to the family home in Salem, and for all practical purposes spent the next twelve years in his room. He seldom saw his own family, even at meals, and almost never left the house except for an occasional walk early in the morning or late at night. He became a recluse for two reasons. One was his shyness. The other was his determination to become a writer. In the mornings he studied, in the afternoons he wrote, in the evenings he read, and after most people were in bed he stole out of the house for a brief walk.

Later in life he became less a recluse. He married, lived a while in Concord, held several government jobs, and finally served for four years as consul to Liverpool. He lived twenty years longer than Poe (1804–1864) and that made a great difference because it gave him a chance to write some of the long books to which authors often turn as they grow older. Poe, you will remember, died at 40; Hawthorne wrote his greatest novel, *The Scarlet Letter*, when he was 52.

As Poe was interested in mood and effect, so Hawthorne was interested in character. The thing that concerned him was how people thought, how they solved their problems, especially the problems of sin and conscience. *The Scarlet Letter* is about sin and conscience. The story that follows is about a man who tried to change the laws of nature, and how that experiment worked out in the lives of two characters. As you read it, notice how differently Hawthorne treated the story from the way Poe would have written it.

When Hawthorne first published this story, he pretended it was a translation from an unknown French writer. This he probably did for several reasons. For one thing, it was stylish then to play that sort of trick. In the second place, it gave an excuse for the European setting, for the somewhat European style, and for the legendary plot. In the third place, it gave him a chance to enjoy the little joke of ponderously introducing his own story. Mark Twain used to do that same thing in lectures; he would introduce Mark Twain, leave the stage, then come back on and give his lecture. The audience loved it.

A YOUNG man, named Giovanni Guasconti,[1] came, very long ago, from the more southern region of Italy, to pursue his studies at the University of Padua.[2] Giovanni, who had but a scanty supply of gold ducats[3] in his pocket, took lodgings in a high and gloomy chamber of an old edifice which looked not unworthy to have been the palace of a Paduan noble, and which, in fact, exhibited over its entrance the armorial bearings of a family long since extinct. The young stranger, who was not unstudied in the great poem of his country, recollected that one of the ancestors of this family, and perhaps an occupant of this very mansion, had been pictured by Dante as a partaker of the immortal agonies of his Inferno.[4] These reminiscences and associations, together with the tendency to heartbreak natural to a young man for the first time out of his native sphere, caused Giovanni to sigh heavily as he looked around the desolate and ill-furnished apartment.

"Holy Virgin, signor!" cried old Dame Lisabetta, who, won by the youth's remarkable beauty of person, was kindly endeavoring to give the chamber a habitable air, "what a sigh was that to come out of a young man's heart! Do you find this old mansion gloomy? For the love of Heaven, then, put your head out of the window, and you will see as bright sunshine as you have left in Naples."

Guasconti mechanically did as the old woman advised, but could not quite agree with her that the Paduan sunshine was as cheerful

1 **Giovanni Guasconti** (jō-vän'nē qwäs-kōn'tē).

2 **Padua:** city in northern Italy, not far from Venice.

3 **ducats:** coins worth a little over two dollars.

4 **Inferno:** Dante's epic poem, "The Divine Comedy," begins with a description of the Infernal regions where sinners are punished.

Look up

as that of southern Italy. Such as it was, however, it fell upon a garden beneath the window and expended its fostering influences on a variety of plants, which seemed to have been cultivated with exceeding care.

"Does this garden belong to the house?" asked Giovanni.

"Heaven forbid, signor, unless it were fruitful of better pot herbs than any that grow there now," answered old Lisabetta. "No; that garden is cultivated by the own hands of Signor Giacomo Rappaccini,[1] the famous doctor, who, I warrant him, has been heard of as far as Naples. It is said that he distils these plants into medicines that are as potent as a charm. Oftentimes you may see the signor doctor at work, and perchance the signora, his daughter, too, gathering the strange flowers that grow in the garden."

The old woman had now done what she could for the aspect of the chamber; and, commending the young man to the protection of the saints, took her departure.

Giovanni still found no better occupation than to look down into the garden beneath his window. From its appearance, he judged it to be one of those botanic gardens which were of earlier date in Padua than elsewhere in Italy or in the world. Or, not improbably, it might once have been the pleasure-place of an opulent family; for there was the ruin of a marble fountain in the center sculptured with rare art, but so woefully shattered that it was impossible to trace the original design from the chaos of remaining fragments. The water, however, continued to gush and sparkle into the sunbeams as cheerfully as ever. A little gurgling sound ascended to the young man's window, and made him feel as if the fountain were an immortal spirit that sung its song unceasingly and without heeding the vicissitudes around it, while one century embodied it in marble and another scattered the perishable garniture on the soil. All about the pool into which the water subsided grew various plants, that seemed to require a plentiful supply of moisture for the nourishment of gigantic leaves, and, in some instances, flowers gorgeously magnificent. There was one shrub in particular, set in a marble vase in the midst of the pool, that bore a profusion of purple blossoms, each of which had the luster and richness of a gem; and the whole together made a

[1] **Giacomo Rappaccini** (jä′kō-mō răp-ȧ-chē′nē).

show so resplendent that it seemed enough to illuminate the garden, even had there been no sunshine. Every portion of the soil was peopled with plants and herbs, which, if less beautiful, still bore tokens of assiduous care, as if all had their individual virtues, known to the scientific mind that fostered them. Some were placed in urns, rich with old carving, and others in common garden pots; some crept serpentlike along the ground or climbed on high, using whatever means of ascent was offered them. One plant had wreathed itself round a statue of Vertumnus,[1] which was thus quite veiled and shrouded in a drapery of hanging foliage, so happily arranged that it might have served a sculptor for a study.

While Giovanni stood at the window he heard a rustling behind a screen of leaves, and became aware that a person was at work in the garden. His figure soon emerged into view, and showed itself to be that of no common laborer, but a tall, emaciated, sallow, and sickly-looking man, dressed in a scholar's garb of black. He was beyond the middle term of life, with gray hair, a thin, gray beard, and a face singularly marked with intellect and cultivation, but which could never, even in his more youthful days, have expressed much warmth of heart.

Nothing could exceed the intentness with which this scientific gardener examined every shrub which grew in his path: it seemed as if he was looking into their inmost nature, making observations in regard to their creative essence, and discovering why one leaf grew in this shape and another in that, and wherefore such and such flowers differed among themselves in hue and perfume. Nevertheless, in spite of this deep intelligence on his part, there was no approach to intimacy between himself and these vegetable existences. On the contrary, he avoided their actual touch or the direct inhaling of their odors with a caution that impressed Giovanni most disagreeably; for the man's demeanor was that of one walking among malignant influences, such as savage beasts, or deadly snakes, or evil spirits, which, should he allow them one moment of license, would wreak upon him some terribly fatality. It was strangely frightful to the young man's imagination to see this air of insecurity in a person cultivating a garden, that most simple and innocent of human toils, and

[1] **Vertumnus: Roman god of changing season and growing vegetation.**

which had been alike the joy and labor of the unfallen parents of the race. Was this garden, then, the Eden of the present world? And this man, with such perception of harm in what his own hands caused to grow, — was he the Adam?

The distrustful gardener, while plucking away the dead leaves or pruning the too luxuriant growth of the shrubs, defended his hands with a pair of thick gloves. Nor were these his only armor. When, in his walk through the garden, he came to the magnificent plant that hung its purple gems beside the marble fountain, he placed a kind of mask over his mouth and nostrils, as if all this beauty did but conceal a deadlier malice; but, finding his task still too dangerous, he drew back, removed the mask, and called loudly, but in the infirm voice of a person affected with inward disease.

"Beatrice! Beatrice!"

"Here am I, my father. What would you?" cried a rich and youthful voice from the window of the opposite house — a voice as rich as a tropical sunset, and which made Giovanni, though he knew not why, think of deep hues of purple or crimson and of perfumes heavily delectable. "Are you in the garden?"

"Yes, Beatrice," answered the gardener, "and I need your help."

Soon there emerged from under a sculptured portal the figure of a young girl, arrayed with as much richness of taste as the most splendid of the flowers, beautiful as the day, and with a bloom so deep and vivid that one shade more would have been too much. She looked redundant with life, health, and energy; all of which attributes were bound down and compressed, as it were, and girdled tensely, in their luxuriance. Yet Giovanni's fancy must have grown morbid while he looked down into the garden; for the impression which the fair stranger made upon him was as if here were another flower, the human sister of those vegetable ones, as beautiful as they, more beautiful than the richest of them, but still to be touched only with a glove, nor to be approached without a mask. As Beatrice came down the garden path, it was observable that she handled and inhaled the odor of several of the plants which her father had most sedulously avoided.

"Here, Beatrice," said the latter, "see how many needful offices require to be done to our chief treasure. Yet, shattered as I am, my life might pay the penalty of approaching it so closely as circumstances demand. Henceforth, I fear, this plant must be consigned to your sole charge."

"And gladly will I undertake it," cried again the rich tones of the young lady, as she bent toward the magnificent plant and opened her arms as if to embrace it. "Yes, my sister, my splendor, it shall be Beatrice's task to nurse and serve thee; and thou shalt reward her with thy kisses and perfumed breath, which to her is as the breath of life."

Then, with all the tenderness in her manner that was so strikingly expressed in her words, she busied herself with such attentions as the plant seemed to require; and Giovanni, at his lofty window, rubbed his eyes and almost doubted whether it were a girl tending her favorite flower, or one sister performing the duties of affection to another. The scene soon terminated. Whether Dr. Rappaccini had finished his labors in the garden, or that his watchful eye had caught the stranger's face, he now took his daughter's arm and retired. Night was already closing in; oppressive exhalations seemed to proceed from the plants and steal upward past the open window; and Giovanni, closing the lattice, went to his couch and dreamed of a rich flower and beautiful girl. Flower and maiden were different, and yet the same, and fraught with some strange peril in either shape.

But there is an influence in the light of morning that tends to rectify whatever errors of fancy, or even of judgment, we may have incurred during the sun's decline, or among the shadows of the night, or in the less wholesome glow of moonshine. Giovanni's first movement, on starting from sleep, was to throw open the window and gaze down into the garden which his dreams had made so fertile of mysteries. He was surprised and a little ashamed to find how real and matter-of-fact an affair it proved to be, in the first rays of the sun which gilded the dewdrops that hung upon leaf and blossom, and, while giving a brighter beauty to each rare flower, brought everything within the limits of ordinary experience. The young man rejoiced that, in the heart of the barren city, he had the privilege of overlooking this spot of lovely and luxuriant vegetation. It would serve, he said to himself, as a symbolic language to keep him in communion with Nature. Neither the sickly and thoughtworn Dr. Giacomo Rappaccini, it is true, nor his brilliant daughter, were now visible; so that Giovanni could not determine how much of the singularity which he attributed to both was due to their own qualities and how much to his wonder-working fancy; but he was inclined to take a most rational view of the whole matter.

In the course of the day he paid his respects to Signor Pietro Baglioni,[1] professor of medicine in the university, a physician of eminent repute, to whom Giovanni had brought a letter of introduction. The professor was an elderly personage, apparently of genial nature, and habits that might almost be called jovial. He kept the young man to dinner, and made himself very agreeable by the freedom and liveliness of his conversation, especially when warmed by a flask or two of Tuscan wine.[2] Giovanni, conceiving that men of science, inhabitants of the same city, must needs be on familiar terms with one another, took an opportunity to mention the name of Dr. Rappaccini. But the professor did not respond with so much cordiality as he had anticipated.

"Ill would it become a teacher of the divine art of medicine," said Professor Pietro Baglioni, in answer to a question of Giovanni, "to withhold due and well-considered praise of a physician so eminently skilled as Rappaccini; but, on the other hand, I should answer it but scantily to my conscience were I to permit a worthy youth like yourself, Signor Giovanni, the son of an ancient friend, to imbibe erroneous ideas respecting a man who might hereafter chance to hold your life and death in his hands. The truth is, our worshipful Dr. Rappaccini has as much science as any member of the faculty – with perhaps one single exception – in Padua, or all Italy; but there are certain grave objections to his professional character."

"And what are they?" asked the young man.

"Has my friend Giovanni any disease of body or heart, that he is so inquisitive about physicians?" said the professor, with a smile. "But as for Rappaccini, it is said of him – and I, who know the man well, can answer for its truth – that he cares infinitely more for science than for mankind. His patients are interesting to him only as subjects for some new experiment. He would sacrifice human life, his own among the rest, or whatever else was dearest to him, for the sake of adding so much as a grain of mustard seed to the great heap of his accumulated knowledge."

[1] **Pietro Baglioni** (pyâ′trō̆ bä-lyō̄′nē̆).

[2] **Tuscan wine:** Tuscany is a famous wine-producing province of Italy.

"Methinks he is an awful man indeed," remarked Guasconti, mentally recalling the cold and purely intellectual aspect of Rappaccini. "And yet, worshipful professor, is it not a noble spirit? Are there many men capable of so spiritual a love of science?"

"God forbid," answered the professor, somewhat testily; "at least, unless they take sounder views of the healing art than those adopted by Rappaccini. It is his theory that all medicinal virtues are comprised within those substances which we term vegetable poisons. These he cultivates with his own hands, and is said even to have produced new varieties of poison, more horribly deleterious than Nature, without the assistance of this learned person, would ever have plagued the world withal. That the signor doctor does less mischief than might be expected with such dangerous substances is undeniable. Now and then, it must be owned, he has effected, or seemed to effect, a marvellous cure; but, to tell you my private mind, Signor Giovanni, he should receive little credit for such instances of success, — they being probably the work of chance, — but should be held strictly accountable for his failures, which may justly be considered his own work."

The youth might have taken Baglioni's opinions with many grains of allowance had he known that there was a professional warfare of long continuance between him and Dr. Rappaccini, in which the latter was generally thought to have gained the advantage. If the reader be inclined to judge for himself, we refer him to certain black-letter [1] tracts on both sides, preserved in the medical department of the University of Padua.

"I know not, most learned professor," returned Giovanni, after musing on what had been said of Rappaccini's exclusive zeal for science, — "I know not how dearly this physician may love his art; but surely there is one object more dear to him. He has a daughter."

"Aha!" cried the professor, with a laugh. "So now our friend Giovanni's secret is out. You have heard of this daughter, whom all the young men in Padua are wild about, though not half a dozen have ever had the good hap to see her face. I know little of the Signora Beatrice save that Rappaccini is said to have instructed her deeply in his science, and that, young and beautiful as fame reports her, she is already qualified to fill a professor's chair. Perchance her

[1] **black-letter: the kind of writing done by medieval scribes; hence, ancient tracts.**

father destines her for mine! Other absurd rumors there be, not worth talking about or listening to. So now, Signor Giovanni, drink off your glass of lachryma."[1]

Guasconti returned to his lodgings somewhat heated with the wine he had quaffed, and which caused his brain to swim with strange fantasies in reference to Dr. Rappaccini and the beautiful Beatrice. On his way, happening to pass by a florist's he bought a fresh bouquet of flowers.

Ascending to his chamber, he seated himself near the window, but within the shadow thrown by the depth of the wall, so that he could look down into the garden with little risk of being discovered. All beneath his eye was a solitude. The strange plants were basking in the sunshine, and now and then nodding gently to one another, as if in acknowledgment of sympathy and kindred. In the midst, by the shattered fountain, grew the magnificent shrub, with its purple gems clustering all over it; they glowed in the air, and gleamed back again out of the depths of the pool, which thus seemed to overflow with colored radiance from the rich reflection that was steeped in it. At first, as we have said, the garden was a solitude. Soon, however, — as Giovanni had half hoped, half feared, would be the case, — a figure appeared beneath the antique sculptured portal, and came down between the rows of plants, inhaling their various perfumes as if she were one of those beings of old classic fable that lived upon sweet odors. On again beholding Beatrice, the young man was even startled to perceive how much her beauty exceeded his recollection of it; so brilliant, so vivid, was its character, that she glowed amid the sunlight, and, as Giovanni whispered to himself, positively illuminated the more shadowy intervals of the garden path. Her face being now more revealed than on the former occasion, he was struck by its expression of simplicity and sweetness, — qualities that had not entered into his idea of her character, and which made him ask anew what manner of mortal she might be. Nor did he fail again to observe, or imagine, an analogy between the beautiful girl and the gorgeous shrub that hung its gemlike flowers over the fountain, — a resemblance which Beatrice seemed to have indulged a fantastic humor in heightening, both by the arrangement of her dress and the selection of its hues.

[1] **lachryma:** an Italian wine.

Approaching the shrub, she threw open her arms, as with a passionate ardor, and drew its branches into an intimate embrace — so intimate that her features were hidden in its leafy bosom and her glistening ringlets all intermingled with the flowers.

"Give me thy breath, my sister," exclaimed Beatrice; "for I am faint with common air. And give me this flower of thine, which I separate with gentlest fingers from the stem and place it close beside my heart."

With these words the beautiful daughter of Rappaccini plucked one of the richest blossoms of the shrub, and was about to fasten it in her bosom. But now, unless Giovanni's draughts of wine had bewildered his senses, a singular incident occurred. A small orange-colored reptile, of the lizard or chameleon species, chanced to be creeping along the path, just at the feet of Beatrice. It appeared to Giovanni, — but, at the distance from which he gazed, he could scarcely have seen anything so minute, — it appeared to him, however, that a drop or two of moisture from the broken stem of the flower descended upon the lizard's head. For an instant the reptile contorted itself violently, and then lay motionless in the sunshine. Beatrice observed this remarkable phenomenon, and crossed herself, sadly, but without surprise; nor did she therefore hesitate to arrange the fatal flower in her bosom. There it blushed, and almost glimmered with the dazzling effect of a precious stone, adding to her dress and aspect the one appropriate charm which nothing else in the world could have supplied. But Giovanni, out of the shadow of his window, bent forward and shrank back, and murmured and trembled.

"Am I awake? Have I my senses?" said he to himself. "What is this being? Beautiful shall I call her, or inexpressibly terrible?"

Beatrice now strayed carelessly through the garden, approaching closer beneath Giovanni's window, so that he was compelled to thrust his head quite out of its concealment in order to gratify the intense and painful curiosity which she excited. At this moment there came a beautiful insect over the garden wall; it had, perhaps, wandered through the city, and found no flowers or verdure among those antique haunts of men until the heavy perfumes of Dr. Rappaccini's shrubs had lured it from afar. Without alighting on the flowers, this winged brightness seemed to be attracted by Beatrice, and lingered in the air and fluttered about her head. Now, here it could not be but that Giovanni Guasconti's eyes deceived him. Be that as it might, he fancied that, while Beatrice was gazing at the insect with childish delight, it grew faint and fell at her feet; its bright wings shivered; it was dead — from no cause that he could discern, unless it were the atmosphere of her breath. Again Beatrice crossed herself and sighed heavily as she bent over the dead insect.

An impulsive movement of Giovanni drew her eyes to the window. There she beheld the beautiful head of the young man — rather a Grecian than an Italian head, with fair, regular features, and a glistening of gold among his ringlets — gazing down upon her like a being that hovered in mid-air. Scarcely knowing what he did, Giovanni threw down the bouquet which he had hitherto held in his hand.

"Signora," said he, "there are pure and healthful flowers. Wear them for the sake of Giovanni Guasconti."

"Thanks, signor," replied Beatrice, with her rich voice, that came forth as it were like a gush of music, and with a mirthful expression half childish and half womanlike. "I accept your gift, and would fain recompense it with this precious purple flower; but if I toss it into the air it will not reach you. So Signor Guasconti must even content himself with my thanks."

She lifted the bouquet from the ground, and then, as if inwardly ashamed at having stepped aside from her maidenly reserve to respond to a stranger's greeting, passed swiftly homeward through the garden. But few as the moments were, it seemed to Giovanni, when she was on the point of vanishing beneath the sculptured portal, that his beautiful bouquet was already beginning to wither in her grasp. It was an idle thought; there could be no possibility of distinguishing a faded flower from a fresh one at so great a distance.

For many days after this incident the young man avoided the window that looked into Dr. Rappaccini's garden, as if something ugly and monstrous would have blasted his eyesight had he been betrayed into a glance. He felt conscious of having put himself, to a certain extent, within the influence of an unintelligible power by the communication which he had opened with Beatrice. The wisest course would have been, if his heart were in any real danger, to quit his lodgings and Padua itself at once; the next wiser, to have accustomed himself, as far as possible, to the familiar and daylight view of Beatrice—thus bringing her rigidly and systematically within the limits of ordinary experience. Least of all, while avoiding her sight, ought Giovanni to have remained so near this extraordinary being that the proximity and possibility even of intercourse should give a kind of substance and reality to the wild vagaries which his imagination ran riot continually in producing. Guasconti had not a deep heart—or, at all events, its depths were not sounded now; but he had a quick fancy, and an ardent southern temperament, which rose every instant to a higher fever pitch. Whether or no Beatrice possessed those terrible attributes, that fatal breath, the affinity with those so beautiful and deadly flowers which were indicated by what Giovanni had witnessed, she had at least instilled a fierce and subtle poison into his system. It was not love, although her rich beauty was a madness to him; nor horror, even while he fancied her spirit to be imbued with the same baneful essence that seemed to pervade her physical frame; but a wild offspring of both love and horror that had each parent in it, and burned like one and shivered like the other. Giovanni knew not what to dread; still less did he know what to hope; yet hope and dread kept a continual warfare in his breast, alternately vanquishing one another and starting up afresh to renew the contest. Blessed are all simple emotions, be they dark or bright! It is the lurid intermixture of the two that produces the illuminating blaze of the infernal regions.

Sometimes he endeavored to assuage the fever of his spirit by a rapid walk through the streets of Padua or beyond its gates: his footsteps kept time with the throbbings of his brain, so that the walk was apt to accelerate itself to a race. One day he found himself arrested; his arm was seized by a portly personage, who had turned back on recognizing the young man and expended much breath in overtaking him.

"Signor Giovanni! Stay, my young friend!" cried he. "Have you forgotten me? That might well be the case if I were as much altered as yourself."

It was Baglioni, whom Giovanni had avoided ever since their first meeting, from a doubt that the professor's sagacity would look too deeply into his secrets. Endeavoring to recover himself, he stared forth wildly from his inner world into the outer one and spoke like a man in a dream.

"Yes; I am Giovanni Guasconti. You are Professor Pietro Baglioni. Now let me pass!"

"Not yet, not yet, Signor Giovanni Guasconti," said the professor, smiling, but at the same time scrutinizing the youth with an earnest glance. "What! did I grow up side by side with your father? and shall his son pass me like a stranger in these old streets of Padua? Stand still, Signor Giovanni; for we must have a word or two before we part."

"Speedily, then, most worshipful professor, speedily," said Giovanni, with feverish impatience. "Does not your worship see that I am in haste?"

Now, while he was speaking there came a man in black along the street, stooping and moving feebly like a person in inferior health. His face was all overspread with a most sickly and sallow hue, but yet so pervaded with an expression of piercing and active intellect that an observer might easily have overlooked the merely physical attributes and have seen only this wonderful energy. As he passed, this person exchanged a cold and distant salutation with Baglioni, but fixed his eyes upon Giovanni with an intentness that seemed to bring out whatever was within him worthy of notice. Nevertheless, there was a peculiar quietness in the look, as if taking merely a speculative, not a human, interest in the young man.

"It is Dr. Rappaccini!" whispered the professor when the stranger had passed. "Has he ever seen your face before?"

"Not that I know," answered Giovanni, starting at the name.

"He *has* seen you! he must have seen you!" said Baglioni hastily. "For some purpose or other, this man of science is making a study of you. I know that look of his! It is the same that coldly illuminates his face as he bends over a bird, a mouse, or a butterfly, which, in pursuance of some experiment, he has killed by the perfume of a flower; a look as deep as Nature itself, but without Nature's warmth of love. Signor Giovanni, I will stake my life upon it, you are the subject of one of Rappaccini's experiments!"

"Will you make a fool of me?" cried Giovanni passionately. "*That*, signor professor, were an untoward experiment."

"Patience! patience!" replied the imperturbable professor. "I tell thee, my poor Giovanni, that Rappaccini has a scientific interest in thee. Thou hast fallen into fearful hands! And the Signora Beatrice, — what part does she act in this mystery? "

But Guasconti, finding Baglioni's pertinacity intolerable, here broke away, and was gone before the professor could again seize his arm. He looked after the young man intently and shook his head.

" This must not be," said Baglioni to himself. " The youth is the son of my old friend, and shall not come to any harm from which the arcana [1] of medical science can preserve him. Besides, it is too insufferable an impertinence in Rappaccini, thus to snatch the lad out of my own hands, as I may say, and make use of him for his infernal experiments. This daughter of his! It shall be looked to. Perchance, most learned Rappaccini, I may foil you where you little dream of it! "

Meanwhile Giovanni had pursued a circuitous route, and at length found himself at the door of his lodgings. As he crossed the threshold he was met by old Lisabetta, who smirked and smiled, and was evidently desirous to attract his attention; vainly, however, as the ebullition of his feelings had momentarily subsided into a cold and dull vacuity. He turned his eyes full upon the withered face that was puckering itself into a smile, but seemed to behold it not. The old dame, therefore, laid her grasp upon his cloak.

" Signor! signor! " whispered she, still with a smile over the whole breadth of her visage, so that it looked not unlike a grotesque carving in wood, darkened by centuries. " Listen, signor! There is a private entrance into the garden! "

" What do you say? " exclaimed Giovanni, turning quickly about, as if an inanimate thing should start into feverish life. " A private entrance into Dr. Rappaccini's garden? "

" Hush! hush! not so loud! " whispered Lisabetta, putting her hand over his mouth. " Yes; into the worshipful doctor's garden, where you may see all his fine shrubbery. Many a young man in Padua would give gold to be admitted among those flowers."

Giovanni put a piece of gold into her hand.

" Show me the way," said he.

A surmise, probably excited by his conversation with Baglioni, crossed his mind, that this interposition of old Lisabetta might per-

[1] arcana: secrets.

chance be connected with the intrigue, whatever were its nature, in which the professor seemed to suppose that Dr. Rappaccini was involving him. But such a suspicion, though it disturbed Giovanni, was inadequate to restrain him. The instant that he was aware of the possibility of approaching Beatrice, it seemed an absolute necessity of his existence to do so. It mattered not whether she were angel or demon; he was irrevocably within her sphere, and must obey the law that whirled him onward, in ever-lessening circles, toward a result which he did not attempt to foreshadow; and yet, strange to say, there came across him a sudden doubt whether this intense interest on his part were not delusory; whether it were really of so deep and positive a nature as to justify him in now thrusting himself into an incalculable position; whether it were not merely the fantasy of a young man's brain, only slightly or not at all connected with his heart.

He paused, hesitated, turned half about, but again went on. His withered guide led him along several obscure passages, and finally undid a door, through which, as it was opened, there came the sight and sound of rustling leaves, with the broken sunshine glimmering among them. Giovanni stepped forth, and, forcing himself through the entanglement of a shrub that wreathed its tendrils over the hidden entrance, stood beneath his own window in the open area of Dr. Rappaccini's garden.

How often is it the case that, when impossibilities have come to pass and dreams have condensed their misty substance into tangible realities, we find ourselves calm, and even coldly self-possessed, amid circumstances which it would have been a delirium of joy or agony to anticipate; Fate delights to thwart us thus. Passion will choose his own time to rush upon the scene, and lingers sluggishly behind when an appropriate adjustment of events would seem to summon his appearance. So was it now with Giovanni. Day after day his pulses had throbbed with feverish blood at the improbable idea of an interview with Beatrice, and of standing with her, face to face, in this very garden, basking in the Oriental sunshine of her beauty, and snatching from her full gaze the mystery which he deemed the riddle of his own existence. But now there was a singular and untimely equanimity within his breast. He threw a glance around the garden to discover if Beatrice or her father were present, and, perceiving that he was alone, began a critical observation of the plants.

The aspect of one and all of them dissatisfied him; their gorgeousness seemed fierce, passionate, and even unnatural. There was hardly an individual shrub which a wanderer, straying by himself through a forest, would not have been startled to find growing wild, as if an unearthly face had glared at him out of the thicket. Several also would have shocked a delicate instinct by an appearance of artificialness indicating that there had been such commixture, and, as it were, adultery, of various vegetable species, that the production was no longer of God's making, but the monstrous offspring of man's depraved fancy, glowing with only an evil mockery of beauty. They were probably the result of experiment, which in one or two cases had succeeded in mingling plants individually lovely into a compound possessing the questionable and ominous character that distinguished the whole growth of the garden. In fine, Giovanni recognized but two or three plants in the collection, and those of a kind that he well knew to be poisonous. While busy with these contemplations he heard the rustling of a silken garment, and, turning, beheld Beatrice emerging from beneath the sculptured portal.

Giovanni had not considered with himself what should be his deportment; whether he should apologize for his intrusion into the garden, or assume that he was there with the privity at least, if not by the desire, of Dr. Rappaccini or his daughter; but Beatrice's manner placed him at his ease, although leaving him still in doubt by what agency he had gained admittance. She came lightly along the path and met him near the broken fountain. There was surprise in her face, but brightened by a simple and kind expression of pleasure.

"You are a connoisseur in flowers, signor," said Beatrice, with a smile, alluding to the bouquet which he had flung her from the window. "It is no marvel, therefore, if the sight of my father's rare collection has tempted you to take a nearer view. If he were here, he could tell you many strange and interesting facts as to the nature and habits of these shrubs; for he has spent a lifetime in such studies, and this garden is his world."

"And yourself, lady," observed Giovanni, "if fame says true, — you likewise are deeply skilled in the virtues indicated by these rich blossoms and these spicy perfumes. Would you deign to be my instructress, I should prove an apter scholar than if taught by Signor Rappaccini himself."

"Are there such idle rumors?" asked Beatrice, with the music of a pleasant laugh. "Do people say that I am skilled in my father's science of plants? What a jest is there! No; though I have grown up among these flowers, I know no more of them than their hues and perfume; and sometimes methinks I would fain rid myself of even that small knowledge. There are many flowers here, and those not the least brilliant, that shock and offend me when they meet my eye. But pray, signor, do not believe these stories about my science. Believe nothing of me save what you see with your own eyes."

"And must I believe all that I have seen with my own eyes?" asked Giovanni, pointedly, while the recollection of former scenes made him shrink. "No, signora; you demand too little of me. Bid me believe nothing save what comes from your own lips."

It would appear that Beatrice understood him. There came a deep flush to her cheek; but she looked full into Giovanni's eyes, and responded to his gaze of uneasy suspicion with a queenlike haughtiness.

"I do so bid you, signor," she replied. "Forget whatever you may have fancied in regard to me. If true to the outward senses, still it may be false in its essence; but the words of Beatrice Rappaccini's lips are true from the depths of the heart outward. Those you may believe."

A fervor glowed in her whole aspect and beamed upon Giovanni's consciousness like the light of truth itself; but while she spoke there was a fragrance in the atmosphere around her, rich and delightful, though evanescent, yet which the young man, from an indefinable reluctance, scarcely dared to draw into his lungs. It might be the odor of the flowers. Could it be Beatrice's breath which thus embalmed her words with a strange richness, as if by steeping them in her heart? A faintness passed like a shadow over Giovanni and flitted away; he seemed to gaze through the beautiful girl's eyes into her transparent soul, and felt no more doubt or fear.

The tinge of passion that had colored Beatrice's manner vanished; she became gay, and appeared to derive a pure delight from her communion with the youth not unlike what the maiden of a lonely island might have felt conversing with a voyager from the civilized world. Evidently her experience of life had been confined within the limits of that garden. She talked now about matters as simple as the daylight or summer clouds, and now asked questions in reference to the city, or Giovanni's distant home, his friends, his mother, and his sisters — questions indicating such seclusion, and such lack of familiarity with modes and forms, that Giovanni responded as if to an infant. Her spirit gushed out before him like a fresh rill that was just catching its first glimpse of the sunlight and wondering at the reflections of earth and sky which were flung into its bosom. There came thoughts, too, from a deep source, and fantasies of a gemlike brilliancy, as if diamonds and rubies sparkled upward among the bubbles of the fountain. Ever and anon there gleamed across the young man's mind a sense of wonder that he should be walking side by side with the being who had so wrought upon his imagination, whom he had idealized in such hues of terror, in whom he had positively witnessed such manifestations of dreadful attributes, — that he should be conversing with Beatrice like a brother, and should find her so human and so maidenlike. But such reflections were only momentary; the effect of her character was too real not to make itself familiar at once.

In this free intercourse they had strayed through the garden, and now, after many turns among its avenues, were come to the shattered fountain, beside which grew the magnificent shrub, with its treasury of glowing blossoms. A fragrance was diffused from it which Giovanni recognized as identical with that which he had attributed to Beatrice's breath, but incomparably more powerful. As her eyes fell upon it, Giovanni beheld her press her hand to her bosom as if her heart were throbbing suddenly and painfully.

"For the first time in my life," murmured she, addressing the shrub, "I had forgotten thee."

"I remember, signora," said Giovanni, "that you once promised to reward me with one of these living gems for the bouquet which I had the happy boldness to fling to your feet. Permit me now to pluck it as a memorial of this interview."

He made a step toward the shrub with extended hand; but Beatrice darted forward, uttering a shriek that went through his heart like a dagger. She caught his hand and drew it back with the whole force of her slender figure. Giovanni felt her touch thrilling through his fibers.

"Touch it not!" exclaimed she, in a voice of agony. "Not for thy life! It is fatal!"

Then, hiding her face, she fled from him and vanished beneath the sculptured portal. As Giovanni followed her with his eyes, he beheld the emaciated figure and pale intelligence of Dr. Rappaccini, who had been watching the scene, he knew not how long, within the shadow of the entrance.

No sooner was Guasconti alone in his chamber than the image of Beatrice came back to his passionate musings, invested with all the witchery that had been gathering around it ever since his first glimpse of her, and now likewise imbued with a tender warmth of girlish womanhood. She was human; her nature was endowed with all gentle and feminine qualities; she was worthiest to be worshiped; she was capable, surely, on her part, of the height and heroism of love. Those tokens which he had hitherto considered as proofs of a frightful peculiarity in her physical and moral system were now either forgotten, or, by the subtle sophistry of passion transmitted into a golden crown of enchantment, rendering Beatrice the more admirable by so much as she was the more unique. Whatever had looked ugly was now beautiful; or, if incapable of such a change, it stole away and hid itself among those shapeless half ideas which throng the dim region beyond the daylight of our perfect consciousness. Thus did he spend the night, nor fell asleep until the dawn had begun to awake the slumbering flowers in Dr. Rappaccini's garden, whither Giovanni's dreams doubtless led him. Up rose the sun in his due season, and, flinging his beams upon the young man's eyelids, awoke him to a sense of pain. When thoroughly aroused, he became sensible of a burning and tingling agony in his hand — in his right hand — the very hand which Beatrice had grasped in her own when he was on the point of plucking one of the gemlike flowers. On the back of that hand there was now a purple print like that of four small fingers, and the likeness of a slender thumb upon his wrist.

Oh, how stubbornly does love, — or even that cunning semblance of love which flourishes in the imagination, but strikes no depth of root into the heart, — how stubbornly does it hold its faith until the moment comes when it is doomed to vanish into thin mist! Giovanni wrapped a handkerchief about his hand and wondered what evil thing had stung him, and soon forgot his pain in a reverie of Beatrice.

After the first interview, a second was in the inevitable course of what we call fate. A third; a fourth; and a meeting with Beatrice in the garden was no longer an incident in Giovanni's daily life, but the whole space in which he might be said to live; for the anticipation and memory of that ecstatic hour made up the remainder. Nor was it otherwise with the daughter of Rappaccini. She watched for the youth's appearance, and flew to his side with confidence as unreserved as if they had been playmates from early infancy — as if they were such playmates still. If, by any unwonted chance, he failed to come at the appointed moment, she stood beneath the window and sent up the rich sweetness of her tones to float around him in his chamber and echo and reverberate throughout his heart: " Giovanni! Giovanni! Why tarriest thou? Come down! " And down he hastened into that Eden of poisonous flowers.

But, with all this intimate familiarity, there was still a reserve in Beatrice's demeanor, so rigidly and invariably sustained that the idea of infringing it scarcely occurred to his imagination. By all appreciable signs, they loved; they had looked love with eyes that conveyed the holy secret from the depths of one soul into the depths of the other, as if it were too sacred to be whispered by the way; they had even spoken love in those gushes of passion when their spirits darted forth in articulated breath like tongues of long-hidden flame; and yet there had been no seal of lips, no clasp of hands, nor any slightest caress such as love claims and hallows. He had never touched one of the gleaming ringlets of her hair; her garment — so marked was the physical barrier between them — had never been waved against him by a breeze. On the few occasions when Giovanni had seemed tempted to overstep the limit, Beatrice grew so sad, so stern, and withal wore such a look of desolate separation, shuddering at itself, that not a spoken word was requisite to repel him. At such times he was startled at the horrible suspicions that rose, monster-like, out of the caverns of his heart and stared him in the face; his love grew thin and faint as the morning mist; his doubts alone had substance. But, when Beatrice's face brightened again after the momentary shadow, she was transformed at once from the mysterious, questionable being whom he had watched with so much awe and horror; she was now the beautiful and unsophisticated girl whom he felt that his spirit knew with a certainty beyond all other knowledge.

A considerable time had now passed since Giovanni's last meeting with Baglioni. One morning, however, he was disagreeably surprised by a visit from the professor, whom he had scarcely thought of for whole weeks, and would willingly have forgotten still longer. Given up as he had long been to a pervading excitement, he could tolerate no companions except upon condition of their perfect sympathy with his present state of feeling. Such sympathy was not to be expected from Professor Baglioni.

The visitor chatted carelessly for a few moments about the gossip of the city and the university, and then took up another topic.

"I have been reading an old classic author lately," said he, "and met with a story that strangely interested me. Possibly you may remember it. It is of an Indian prince, who sent a beautiful woman as a present to Alexander the Great. She was as lovely as the dawn and gorgeous as the sunset; but what especially distinguished her was a certain rich perfume in her breath — richer than a garden of Persian roses. Alexander, as was natural to a youthful conqueror, fell in love at first sight with this magnificent stranger; but a certain sage physician, happening to be present, discovered a terrible secret in regard to her."

"And what was that?" asked Giovanni, turning his eyes downward to avoid those of the professor.

"That this lovely woman," continued Baglioni, with emphasis, "had been nourished with poisons from her birth upward, until her whole nature was so imbued with them that she herself had become the deadliest poison in existence. Poison was her element of life. With that rich perfume of her breath she blasted the very air. Her love would have been poison — her embrace death. Is not this a marvelous tale?"

"A childish fable," answered Giovanni, nervously starting from his chair. "I marvel how your worship finds time to read such nonsense among your graver studies."

"By the by," said the professor, looking uneasily about him, "what singular fragrance is this in your apartment? Is it the perfume of your gloves? It is faint, but delicious; and yet, after all, by no means agreeable. Were I to breathe it long, methinks it would make me ill. It is like the breath of a flower; but I see no flowers in the chamber."

"Nor are there any," replied Giovanni, who had turned pale as the professor spoke; "nor, I think, is there any fragrance except in your worship's imagination. Odors, being a sort of element combined of the sensual and the spiritual, are apt to deceive us in this manner. The recollection of a perfume, the bare idea of it, may easily be mistaken for a present reality."

"Ay; but my sober imagination does not often play such tricks," said Baglioni; "and, were I to fancy any kind of odor, it would be that of some vile apothecary drug, wherewith my fingers are likely enough to be imbued. Our worshipful friend Rappaccini, as I have heard, tinctures his medicaments with odors richer than those of Araby.[1] Doubtless, likewise, the fair and learned Signora Beatrice would minister to her patients with draughts as sweet as a maiden's breath; but woe to him that sips them!"

Giovanni's face evinced many contending emotions. The tone in which the professor alluded to the pure and lovely daughter of Rappaccini was a torture to his soul; and yet the intimation of a view of her character, opposite to his own, gave instantaneous distinctness to a thousand dim suspicions, which now grinned at him like so many demons. But he strove hard to quell them and to respond to Baglioni with a true lover's perfect faith.

"Signor professor," said he, "you were my father's friend; perchance, too, it is your purpose to act a friendly part toward his son. I would fain feel nothing toward you save respect and deference; but I pray you to observe, signor, that there is one subject on which we must not speak. You know not the Signora Beatrice. You cannot, therefore, estimate the wrong – the blasphemy, I may even say – that is offered to her character by a light or injurious word."

"Giovanni! my poor Giovanni!" answered the professor, with a calm expression of pity, "I know this wretched girl far better than yourself. You shall hear the truth in respect to the poisoner Rappaccini and his poisonous daughter; yes, poisonous as she is beautiful. Listen; for, even should you do violence to my gray hairs, it shall

[1] **Araby:** Arabia. Many spices came from the Middle East.

not silence me. That old fable of the Indian woman has become a truth by the deep and deadly science of Rappaccini and in the person of the lovely Beatrice."

Giovanni groaned and hid his face.

"Her father," continued Baglioni, "was not restrained by natural affection from offering up his child in this horrible manner as the victim of his insane zeal for science; for, let us do him justice, he is as true a man of science as ever distilled his own heart in an alembic.[1] What, then, will be your fate? Beyond a doubt you are selected as the material of some new experiment. Perhaps the result is to be death; perhaps a fate more awful still. Rappaccini, with what he calls the interest of science before his eyes, will hesitate at nothing."

"It is a dream," muttered Giovanni to himself; "surely it is a dream."

"But," resumed the professor, "be of good cheer, son of my friend. It is not yet too late for the rescue. Possibly we may even succeed in bringing back this miserable child within the limits of ordinary nature, from which her father's madness has estranged her. Behold this little silver vase! It was wrought by the hands of the renowned Benvenuto Cellini,[2] and is well worthy to be a love gift to the fairest dame in Italy. But its contents are invaluable. One little sip of this antidote would have rendered the most virulent poisons of the Borgias[3] innocuous. Doubt not that it will be as efficacious against those of Rappaccini. Bestow the vase, and the precious liquid within it, on your Beatrice, and hopefully await the result."

Baglioni laid a small, exquisitely wrought silver vial on the table and withdrew, leaving what he had said to produce its effect upon the young man's mind.

"We will thwart Rappaccini yet," thought he, chuckling to himself, as he descended the stairs; "but, let us confess the truth of him, he is a wonderful man — a wonderful man indeed; a vile empiric,[4] however, in his practice, and therefore not to be tolerated by those who respect the good old rules of the medical profession."

[1] **alembic**: apparatus for distilling. This is a figurative way of saying that Rappaccini's heart was in his work.

[2] **Benvenuto Cellini** (bān-vā-nōō'tō chäl-lē'nē).

[3] **Borgias**: Italian family supposed to have poisoned some of their enemies.

[4] **empiric**: a quack or faker.

Throughout Giovanni's whole acquaintance with Beatrice, he had occasionally, as we have said, been haunted by dark surmises as to her character; yet so thoroughly had she made herself felt by him as a simple, natural, most affectionate, and guileless creature, that the image now held up by Professor Baglioni looked as strange and incredible as if it were not in accordance with his own original conception. True, there were ugly recollections connected with his first glimpses of the beautiful girl; he could not quite forget the bouquet that withered in her grasp, and the insect that perished amid the sunny air, by no ostensible agency save the fragrance of her breath. These incidents, however, dissolving in the pure light of her character, had no longer the efficacy of facts, but were acknowledged as mistaken fantasies, by whatever testimony of the senses they might appear to be substantiated. There is something truer and more real than what we can see with the eyes and touch with the finger. On such better evidence had Giovanni founded his confidence in Beatrice, though rather by the necessary force of her high attributes than by any deep and generous faith on his part. But now his spirit was incapable of sustaining itself at the height to which the early enthusiasm of passion had exalted it; he fell down, groveling among earthly doubts, and defiled therewith the pure whiteness of Beatrice's image. Not that he gave her up; he did but distrust. He resolved to institute some decisive test that should satisfy him, once for all, whether they were those dreadful peculiarities in her physical nature which could not be supposed to exist without some corresponding monstrosity of soul. His eyes, gazing down afar, might have deceived him as to the lizard, the insect, and the flowers; but if he could witness, at the distance of a few paces, the sudden blight of one fresh and healthful flower in Beatrice's hand, there would be room for no further question. With this idea he hastened to the florist's and purchased a bouquet that was still gemmed with the morning dewdrops.

It was now the customary hour of his daily interview with Beatrice. Before descending into the garden, Giovanni failed not to look at his figure in the mirror, — a vanity to be expected in a beautiful young man, yet, as displaying itself at that troubled and feverish moment, the token of a certain shallowness of feeling and insincerity of character. He did gaze, however, and said to himself that his features had never before possessed so rich a grace, nor his eyes such vivacity, nor his cheeks so warm a hue of superabundant life.

"At least," thought he, "her poison has not yet insinuated itself into my system. I am no flower to perish in her grasp."

With that thought he turned his eyes on the bouquet, which he had never once laid aside from his hand. A thrill of indefinable horror shot through his frame on perceiving that those dewy flowers were already beginning to droop; they wore the aspect of things that had been fresh and lovely yesterday. Giovanni grew white as marble, and stood motionless before the mirror, staring at his own reflection there as at the likeness of something frightful. He remembered Baglioni's remark about the fragrance that seemed to pervade the chamber. It must have been the poison in his breath! Then he shuddered — shuddered at himself. Recovering from his stupor, he began to watch with curious eye a spider that was busily at work hanging its web from the antique cornice of the apartment, crossing and recrossing the artful system of interwoven lines — as vigorous and active a spider as ever dangled from an old ceiling. Giovanni bent toward the insect, and emitted a deep, long breath. The spider suddenly ceased its toil; the web vibrated with a tremor originating in the body of the small artisan. Again Giovanni sent forth a breath, deeper, longer, and imbued with a venomous feeling out of his heart: he knew not whether he were wicked, or only desperate. The spider made a convulsive gripe with his limbs and hung dead across the window.

"Accursed! accursed!" muttered Giovanni, addressing himself. "Hast thou grown so poisonous that this deadly insect perishes by thy breath?"

At that moment a rich, sweet voice came floating up from the garden.

"Giovanni! Giovanni! It is past the hour! Why tarriest thou? Come down!"

"Yes," muttered Giovanni again. "She is the only being whom my breath may not slay! Would that it might!"

He rushed down, and in an instant was standing before the bright and loving eyes of Beatrice. A moment ago his wrath and despair had been so fierce that he could have desired nothing so much as to wither her by a glance; but with her actual presence there came influences which had too real an existence to be at once shaken off: recollections of the delicate and benign power of her feminine nature, which had so often enveloped him in a religious calm; recollections of many a holy and passionate outgush of her heart, when the pure fountain had been unsealed from its depths and made visible in its transparency to his mental eye; recollections which, had Giovanni known how to estimate them, would have assured him that all this ugly mystery was but an earthly illusion, and that, whatever mist of evil might seem to have gathered over her, the real Beatrice was a heavenly angel. Incapable as he was of such high faith, still her presence had not utterly lost its magic. Giovanni's rage was quelled into an aspect of sullen insensibility. Beatrice, with a quick spiritual sense, immediately felt that there was a gulf of blackness between them which neither he nor she could pass. They walked on together, sad and silent, and came thus to the marble fountain and to its pool of water on the ground, in the midst of which grew the shrub that bore gemlike blossoms. Giovanni was affrighted at the eager enjoyment — the appetite, as it were — with which he found himself inhaling the fragrance of the flowers.

"Beatrice," asked he, abruptly, "whence came this shrub?"

"My father created it," answered she, with simplicity.

"Created it! created it!" repeated Giovanni. "What mean you, Beatrice?"

"He is a man fearfully acquainted with the secrets of Nature," replied Beatrice; "and, at the hour when I first drew breath, this plant sprang from the soil, the offspring of his science, of his intellect, while I was but his earthly child. Approach it not!" continued she, observing with terror that Giovanni was drawing nearer to the shrub. "It has qualities that you little dream of. But I, dearest Giovanni, — I grew up and blossomed with the plant and was nourished with its breath. It was my sister, and I loved it with a human affection; for, alas! — hast thou not suspected it? — there was an awful doom."

Here Giovanni frowned so darkly upon her that Beatrice paused and trembled. But her faith in his tenderness reassured her, and made her blush that she had doubted for an instant.

"There was an awful doom," she continued, "the effect of my father's fatal love of science, which estranged me from all society of my kind. Until Heaven sent thee, dearest Giovanni, oh, how lonely was thy poor Beatrice! "

" Was it a hard doom? " asked Giovanni, fixing his eyes upon her.

" Only of late have I known how hard it was," answered she, tenderly. " Oh, yes; but my heart was torpid,[1] and therefore quiet."

Giovanni's rage broke forth from his sullen gloom like a lightning flash out of a dark cloud.

" Accursed one! " cried he, with venomous scorn and anger. " And, finding thy solitude wearisome, thou hast severed me likewise from all the warmth of life and enticed me into thy region of unspeakable horror! "

" Giovanni! " exclaimed Beatrice, turning her large bright eyes upon his face. The force of his words had not found its way into her mind; she was merely thunderstruck.

" Yes, poisonous thing! " repeated Giovanni, beside himself with passion. " Thou hast done it! Thou hast blasted me! Thou hast filled my veins with poison! Thou hast made me as hateful, as ugly, as loathsome and deadly a creature as thyself — a world's wonder of hideous monstrosity! Now, if our breath be happily as fatal to ourselves as to all others, let us join our lips in one kiss of unutterable hatred, and so die! "

" What has befallen me? " murmured Beatrice, with a low moan out of her heart. " Holy Virgin, pity me, a poor heartbroken child! "

" Thou, — dost thou pray? " cried Giovanni, still with the same fiendish scorn. " Thy very prayers, as they come from thy lips, taint the atmosphere with death. Yes, yes; let us pray! Let us to church and dip our fingers in the holy water at the portal! They that come after us will perish as by a pestilence! Let us sign crosses[2] in the air! It will be scattering curses abroad in the likeness of holy symbols! "

" Giovanni," said Beatrice, calmly, for her grief was beyond passion, " why dost thou join thyself with me thus in those terrible words? I, it is true, am the horrible thing thou namest me. But thou, — what hast thou to do, save with one other shudder at my hideous

[1] **torpid:** dormant, sleeping.

[2] **sign crosses:** make the sign of the cross. He means they will pollute the very air, even by making religious signs.

misery to go forth out of the garden and mingle with thy race, and forget that there ever crawled on earth such a monster as poor Beatrice? "

" Dost thou pretend ignorance? " asked Giovanni, scowling upon her. " Behold! this power have I gained from the pure daughter of Rappaccini."

There was a swarm of summer insects flitting through the air in search of the food promised by the flower odors of the fatal garden. They circled round Giovanni's head, and were evidently attracted toward him by the same influence which had drawn them for an instant within the sphere of several of the shrubs. He sent forth a breath among them, and smiled bitterly at Beatrice as at least a score of the insects fell dead upon the ground.

" I see it! I see it! " shrieked Beatrice. " It is my father's fatal science! No, no, Giovanni; it was not I! Never! never! I dreamed only to love thee and be with thee a little time, and so to let thee pass away, leaving but thine image in mine heart; for, Giovanni, believe it, though my body be nourished with poison, my spirit is God's creature, and craves love as its daily food. But my father, – he has united us in this fearful sympathy. Yes; spurn me, tread upon me, kill me! Oh, what is death after such words as thine? But it was not I. Not for a world of bliss would I have done it."

Giovanni's passion had exhausted itself in its outburst from his lips. There now came across him a sense, mournful, and not without tenderness, of the intimate and peculiar relationship between Beatrice and himself. They stood, as it were, in an utter solitude, which would be made none the less solitary by the densest throng of human life. Ought not, then, the desert of humanity around them to press this insulated pair closer together? If they should be cruel to one another, who was there to be kind to them? Besides, thought Giovanni, might there not still be a hope of his returning within the limits of ordinary nature, and leading Beatrice, the redeemed Beatrice, by the hand? O, weak, and selfish, and unworthy spirit, that could dream of an earthly union and earthly happiness as possible, after such deep love had been so bitterly wronged as was Beatrice's love by Giovanni's blighting words! No, no; there could be no such hope. She must pass heavily, with that broken heart, across the borders of Time — she must bathe her hurts in some fount of paradise, and forget her grief in the light of immortality, and *there* be well.

But Giovanni did not know it.

"Dear Beatrice," said he, approaching her, while she shrank away as always at his approach, but now with a different impulse, "dearest Beatrice, our fate is not yet so desperate. Behold! there is a medicine, potent, as a wise physician has assured me, and almost divine in its efficacy. It is composed of ingredients the most opposite to those by which thy awful father has brought this calamity upon thee and me. It is distilled of blessed herbs. Shall we not quaff it together, and thus be purified from evil?"

"Give it me!" said Beatrice, extending her hand to receive the little silver vial which Giovanni took from his bosom. She added, with a peculiar emphasis, "I will drink; but do thou await the result."

She put Baglioni's antidote to her lips; and, at the same moment, the figure of Rappaccini emerged from the portal and came slowly toward the marble fountain. As he drew near, the pale man of science seemed to gaze with a triumphant expression at the beautiful youth and maiden, as might an artist who should spend his life in achieving a picture or a group of statuary and finally be satisfied with his success. He paused; his bent form grew erect with conscious power; he spread out his hands over them in the attitude of a father imploring a blessing upon his children; but those were the same hands that had thrown poison into the stream of their lives. Giovanni trembled. Beatrice shuddered nervously, and pressed her hand upon her heart.

"My daughter," said Rappaccini, "thou art no longer lonely in the world. Pluck one of those precious gems from thy sister shrub and bid thy bridegroom wear it in his bosom. It will not harm him now. My science and the sympathy between thee and him have so wrought within his system that he now stands apart from common men, as thou dost, daughter of my pride and triumph, from ordinary women. Pass on, then, through the world, most dear to one another and dreadful to all besides!"

"My father," said Beatrice, feebly, — and still as she spoke she kept her hand upon her heart, — "wherefore didst thou inflict this miserable doom upon thy child?"

"Miserable!" exclaimed Rappaccini. "What mean you, foolish girl? Dost thou deem it misery to be endowed with marvelous gifts against which no power nor strength could avail an enemy — misery, to be able to quell the mightiest with a breath — misery, to be as terrible as thou art beautiful? Wouldst thou, then, have preferred the condition of a weak woman, exposed to all evil and capable of none?"

"I would fain have been loved, not feared," murmured Beatrice, sinking down upon the ground. "But now it matters not. I am going, father, where the evil which thou hast striven to mingle with my being will pass away like a dream — like the fragrance of these poisonous flowers, which will no longer taint my breath among the flowers of Eden. Farewell, Giovanni! Thy words of hatred are like lead within my heart; but they, too, will fall away as I ascend. Oh, was there not, from the first, more poison in thy nature than in mine?"

To Beatrice, — so radically had her earthly part been wrought upon by Rappaccini's skill, — as poison had been life, so the powerful antidote was death; and thus the poor victim of man's ingenuity and of thwarted nature, and of the fatality that attends all such efforts of perverted wisdom, perished there, at the feet of her father and Giovanni. Just at that moment Professor Pietro Baglioni looked forth from the window, and called loudly, in a tone of triumph mixed with horror, to the thunderstricken man of science.

"Rappaccini! Rappaccini! and is *this* the upshot of your experiment!"

READING WITH INSIGHT

1. A good way to begin thinking about this story is to think about its meaning. It must be apparent to you that this is no mere adventure story, nor is it, like "The Tell-Tale Heart," a relatively simple story of mood and atmosphere. It is a story by an exceedingly thoughtful man, and it is rich with meaning. In fact, you probably have already guessed that what happens on the surface of the story is less important than the meaning below the surface. Some persons might state the theme of this story by the proverb, "One man's

meat is another man's poison." What is there in the story that this statement misses?

2. This story is an allegory. That is, the surface events stand for other events. The events in this story refer to the story of the Garden of Eden. See how many parallels you can find. Remember that there are several mentions of Eden in the story. Rappaccini's garden is referred to in that way, and you will recall how Beatrice talked about the beautiful shrub which she would not let Giovanni touch—"Touch it not!" she said. "Not for thy life! It is fatal!" If you will think back to the story of the Garden of Eden, you will recall the fatal fruit of the forbidden tree and remember that it was the Tree of Knowledge. Then recall that the forbidden shrub was also a tree of knowledge: Rappaccini was making a scientific experiment, and was willing to sacrifice anything in his search for knowledge. In what other details is "Rappaccini's Daughter" like the Eden story? Compare the outcomes of the two stories.

3. If you can see the parallel between this story and the Eden story, you are ready to say something about the deeper meaning of the Hawthorne story. Hawthorne is writing about sin. What sin in this story compares to Eve's sin in the Bible story? And how is the punishment for this sin like the punishment for Eve's sin? Is Hawthorne saying that death is the only way to atone for sin?

4. Someone has said that Rappaccini's fault was meddling with what is exclusively God's business, and that he had no right to use his science for such a purpose. What limits if any do you think can be put on the search for knowledge? For example, how would you apply this question to what scientists did in creating the atomic bomb?

5. Why do you think Rappaccini performed this experiment? For the good of his daughter? To see if it could be done? To establish scientific laws? To prove what a great scientist he was? What evidence can you find in the story to support your answer?

6. As Beatrice dies, she says to Giovanni, "Oh, was there not, from the first, more poison in thy nature than in mine?" What does she mean by that statement?

7. What might have happened if Baglioni had kept out of the events of the story?

8. Turning now to the form of the story, you have probably no-

ticed that the problem is more complex than that of "The Tell-Tale Heart." That was a relatively simple plot involving only one person, and one major decision. This problem, however, is made up from a number of tensions. Can you name them all? There is the effort of Rappaccini, the scientist, to alter nature, to create a new kind of human being and a new kind of world. There is the struggle between Rappaccini and Baglioni. There is the love of Beatrice and Giovanni. There is the struggle of Giovanni with the poisonous world of Rappaccini. Are there others? The climax of the action, you will probably agree, is the point where Beatrice drinks Baglioni's antidote which is poison to her. But where is the climactic moment in the love story? Where is the climax in the story of Rappaccini's experiment? Where is it in the rivalry of the two doctors? It takes great skill to weave several threads of plot together like this in a short story.

9. Hawthorne does not tell us directly until late in the story that the flowers in the mysterious garden are poisonous, and that Beatrice herself has become poisonous. However, he foreshadows this knowledge, so that we suspect it and then realize gradually that it is true. Can you pick out the instances of this foreshadowing? For example, Giovanni sees the peculiar way in which Rappaccini tends his garden, and a little later watches Beatrice in the same garden and gets the impression that she is "another flower, the human sister of the vegetable ones."

10. This story is told in the third person. Which characters' thoughts are revealed in the story? Why do you suppose Hawthorne chose to tell this story in the third person rather than to have Giovanni tell it in his own voice?

11. Does Beatrice realize, when she drinks Baglioni's antidote, that it will kill her? How do you know?

12. Would it be just as effective to write this kind of story in a modern setting, or is the ancient and foreign setting necessary? Can you think of a way in which this plot and meaning might be applied to a modern situation?

If you like this story, you will be interested in

Hawthorne. *The Birthmark.*
Ethan Brand.
The Great Stone Face.
The Scarlet Letter (novel).
Thomas Hardy. *Three Strangers.*
Dorothy Canfield Fisher. *Portrait of a Philosopher.*
The Thread without a Knot.

BRET HARTE

The Outcasts of Poker Flat

The best thing that ever happened to Bret Harte happened in 1853 when he was 19. In that year his widowed mother took him to live in California. The great gold strike had occurred only four years before they came to California. They found a country of mining camps and frontier hamlets. But Bret Harte discovered gold of a different kind. He found enough literary material to last him all his life.

Harte stayed only 18 years in the West. He never felt especially at home there and never adapted himself to Western ways. As soon as he had built a literary reputation he hurried east to write for *The Atlantic Monthly*. His last 20 years he spent in Europe, and he died in London.

But his best writing was done in California, and all his best writing was about the West. California was good to him. It gave him newspaper training. It appointed him secretary of the California Mint so that he would have plenty of time for writing. It made him editor of an ambitious new magazine, *The Overland Monthly*. In its second number he published "The Luck of Roaring Camp." The next year he published "The Outcasts of Poker Flat" and "Tennessee's Partner." Those stories made him such a sensation that *The Atlantic Monthly* offered him $10,000 a year to write Western stories for them, and he hurried back to New York. But he never wrote anything else as good as those three stories from his California years.

Harte was a part of a movement in American writing that has been called the local color movement. Local color writers were interested in the quaintness and differentness of various parts of the country. They wrote about the scenery, the customs, and the language, but from a different viewpoint than the realists of our own day. Local color writers were impressed by how romantic, how quaint, how unusual all these places and people were. They were collectors, and they went around exclaiming at the quaintness of the specimens. That is not to say that they were not very good writers, as you will see from the story that follows. As you read it, notice how Harte uses the local color of frontier California.

AS Mr. John Oakhurst, gambler, stepped into the main street of Poker Flat on the morning of the twenty-third of November, 1850, he was conscious of a change in its moral atmosphere since the preceding night. Two or three men, conversing earnestly together, ceased as he approached, and exchanged significant glances. There was a Sabbath lull in the air, which, in a settlement unused to Sabbath influences, looked ominous.

Mr. Oakhurst's calm, handsome face betrayed small concern in these indications. Whether he was conscious of any predisposing cause was another question. "I reckon they're after somebody," he reflected; "likely it's me." He returned to his pocket the handkerchief with which he had been whipping away the red dust of Poker Flat from his neat boots, and quietly discharged his mind of further conjecture.

In point of fact, Poker Flat was "after somebody." It had lately suffered the loss of several thousand dollars, two valuable horses, and a prominent citizen. It was experiencing a spasm of virtuous reaction, quite as lawless and ungovernable as any of the acts that had provoked it. A secret committee had determined to rid the town of all improper persons. This was done permanently in regard of two men who were then hanging from the boughs of a sycamore in the gulch, and temporarily in the banishment of certain other objectionable characters. I regret to say that some of these were ladies.

Mr. Oakhurst was right in supposing that he was included in this category. A few of the committee had urged hanging him as a possible example and a sure method of reimbursing themselves from his pockets of the sums he had won from them. "It's agin justice," said Jim Wheeler, "to let this yer young man from Roaring Camp — an entire stranger — carry away our money." But a crude sentiment of equity residing in the breasts of those who had been fortunate enough to win from Mr. Oakhurst overruled this narrower local prejudice.

Mr. Oakhurst received his sentence with philosophic calmness, none the less coolly that he was aware of the hesitation of his judges. He was too much of a gambler not to accept fate. With him life was at best an uncertain game, and he recognized the usual percentage in favor of the dealer.

A body of armed men accompanied the deported wickedness of

Poker Flat to the outskirts of the settlement. Besides Mr. Oakhurst, who was known to be a coolly desperate man, and for whose intimidation the armed escort was intended, the expatriated party consisted of a young woman familiarly known as "The Duchess"; another who had won the title of "Mother Shipton"; and "Uncle Billy," a suspected sluice-robber and confirmed drunkard. The cavalcade provoked no comments from the spectators, nor was any word uttered by the escort. Only when the gulch which marked the uttermost limit of Poker Flat was reached, the leader spoke briefly and to the point. The exiles were forbidden to return at the peril of their lives.

As the escort disappeared, their pent-up feelings found vent in a few hysterical tears from the Duchess, some bad language from Mother Shipton, and a Parthian volley of expletives from Uncle Billy. The philosophic Oakhurst alone remained silent. He listened calmly to Mother Shipton's desire to cut somebody's heart out, to the repeated statements of the Duchess that she would die in the road, and to the alarming oaths that seemed to be bumped out of Uncle Billy as he rode forward. With the easy good humor characteristic of his class, he insisted upon exchanging his own riding horse, "Five-Spot," for the sorry mule which the Duchess rode. But even this act did not draw the party into any closer sympathy. The young woman readjusted her somewhat draggled plumes with a feeble, faded coquetry; Mother Shipton eyed the possessor of "Five-Spot" with malevolence, and Uncle Billy included the whole party in one sweeping anathema.

The road to Sandy Bar — a camp that, not having as yet experienced the regenerating influences of Poker Flat, consequently seemed to offer some invitation to the emigrants — lay over a steep mountain range. It was distant a day's severe travel. In that advanced season the party soon passed out of the moist, temperate regions of the foothills into the dry, cold, bracing air of the Sierras. The trail was narrow and difficult. At noon the Duchess, rolling out of her saddle upon the ground, declared her intention of going no farther, and the party halted.

The spot was singularly wild and impressive. A wooded amphitheater, surrounded on three sides by precipitous cliffs of naked granite, sloped gently toward the crest of another precipice that overlooked the valley. It was, undoubtedly, the most suitable spot for a camp, had camping been advisable. But Mr. Oakhurst knew that scarcely half the journey to Sandy Bar was accomplished, and the party were not equipped or provisioned for delay. This fact he pointed out to his companions curtly, with a philosophic commentary on the folly of "throwing up their hand before the game was played out." But they were furnished with liquor, which in this emergency stood them in place of food, fuel, rest, and prescience. In spite of his remonstrances, it was not long before they were more or less under its influence. Uncle Billy passed rapidly from a bellicose state into one of stupor, the Duchess became maudlin, and Mother Shipton snored. Mr. Oakhurst alone remained erect, leaning against a rock, calmly surveying them.

Mr. Oakhurst did not drink. It interfered with a profession which required coolness, impassiveness, and presence of mind, and, in his own language, he "couldn't afford it." As he gazed at his recumbent fellow exiles, the loneliness begotten of his pariah trade, his habits of life, his very vices, for the first time seriously oppressed him. He bestirred himself in dusting his black clothes, washing his hands and face, and other acts characteristic of his studiously neat habits, and for a moment forgot his annoyance. The thought of deserting his weaker and more pitiable companions never perhaps occurred to him. Yet he could not help feeling the want of that excitement which, singularly enough, was most conducive to that calm equanimity for which he was notorious. He looked at the gloomy walls that rose a thousand feet sheer above the circling pines around him; at the sky, ominously clouded, at the valley below, already deepening into shadow; and, doing so, suddenly he heard his own name called.

A horseman slowly ascended the trail. In the fresh, open face of the newcomer Mr. Oakhurst recognized Tom Simson, otherwise known as "The Innocent," of Sandy Bar. He had met him some months before over a "little game," and had, with perfect equanimity, won the entire fortune – amounting to some forty dollars – of that guileless youth. After the game was finished, Mr. Oakhurst drew the youthful speculator behind the door and thus addressed him: "Tommy, you're a good little man, but you can't gamble worth a cent. Don't try it over again." He then handed him his money back, pushed him gently from the room, and so made a devoted slave of Tom Simson.

There was a remembrance of this in his boyish and enthusiastic greeting of Mr. Oakhurst. He had started, he said, to go to Poker Flat to seek his fortune. " Alone? " No, not exactly alone; in fact (a giggle), he had run away with Piney Woods. Didn't Mr. Oakhurst remember Piney? She that used to wait on the table at the Temperance House? They had been engaged a long time, but old Jake Woods had objected, and so they had run away, and were going to Poker Flat to be married, and here they were. And they were tired out, and how lucky it was they had found a place to camp, and company. All this the Innocent delivered rapidly, while Piney, a stout, comely damsel of fifteen, emerged from behind the pine tree, where she had been blushing unseen, and rode to the side of her lover.

Mr. Oakhurst seldom troubled himself with sentiment, still less with propriety; but he had a vague idea that the situation was not fortunate. He retained, however, his presence of mind sufficiently to kick Uncle Billy, who was about to say something, and Uncle Billy was sober enough to recognize in Mr. Oakhurst's kick a superior power that would not bear trifling. He then endeavored to dissuade Tom Simson from delaying further, but in vain. He even pointed out the fact that there was no provision, nor means of making a camp. But, unluckily, the Innocent met this objection by assuring the party that he was provided with an extra mule loaded with provisions, and by the discovery of a rude attempt at a log house near the trail. " Piney can stay with Mrs. Oakhurst," said the Innocent, pointing to the Duchess, " and I can shift for myself."

Nothing but Mr. Oakhurst's admonishing foot saved Uncle Billy from bursting into a roar of laughter. As it was, he felt compelled to retire up the cañon until he could recover his gravity. There he confided the joke to the tall pine trees, with many slaps of his leg, contortions of his face, and the usual profanity. But when he returned to the party, he found them seated by a fire — for the air had grown strangely chill and the sky overcast — in apparently amicable conversation. Piney was actually talking in an impulsive girlish fashion to the Duchess, who was listening with an interest and animation she had not shown for many days. The Innocent was holding forth, apparently with equal effect, to Mr. Oakhurst, and Mother Shipton, who was actually relaxing into amiability. "Is this yer a d——d picnic?" said Uncle Billy, with inward scorn, as he surveyed the sylvan group, the glancing firelight, and the tethered animals in the foreground. Suddenly an idea mingled with the alcoholic fumes that disturbed his brain. It was apparently of a jocular nature, for he felt impelled to slap his leg again and cram his fist into his mouth.

As the shadows crept slowly up the mountain, a slight breeze rocked the tops of the pine trees and moaned through their long and gloomy aisles. The ruined cabin, patched and covered with pine boughs, was set apart for the ladies. As the lovers parted, they unaffectedly exchanged a kiss, so honest and sincere that it might have been heard above the swaying pines. The frail Duchess and the malevolent Mother Shipton were probably too stunned to remark upon this last evidence of simplicity, and so turned without a word to the hut. The fire was replenished, the men lay down before the door, and in a few minutes were asleep.

Mr. Oakhurst was a light sleeper. Toward morning he awoke benumbed and cold. As he stirred the dying fire, the wind, which was now blowing strongly, brought to his cheek that which caused the blood to leave it — snow!

He started to his feet with the intention of awakening the sleepers, for there was no time to lose. But turning to where Uncle Billy had been lying, he found him gone. A suspicion leaped to his brain, and a curse to his lips. He ran to the spot where the mules had been tethered — they were no longer there. The tracks were already rapidly disappearing in the snow.

The momentary excitement brought Mr. Oakhurst back to the fire with his usual calm. He did not waken the sleepers. The Innocent slumbered peacefully, with a smile on his good-humored, freckled face; Piney slept beside her frailer sisters as sweetly as though attended by celestial guardians; and Mr. Oakhurst, drawing his blanket over his shoulders, stroked his mustaches and waited for the dawn. It came slowly in a whirling mist of snowflakes that dazzled and confused the eye. What could be seen of the landscape appeared magically changed. He looked over the valley, and summed up the present and future in two words, "Snowed in!"

A careful inventory of the provisions, which, fortunately for the party, had been stored within the hut, and so escaped the felonious fingers of Uncle Billy, disclosed the fact that with care and prudence they might last ten days longer. "That is," said Mr. Oakhurst, *sotto voce*[1] to the Innocent, "if you're willing to board us. If you ain't — and perhaps you'd better not — you can wait till Uncle Billy gets back with provisions." For some occult reason, Mr. Oakhurst could not bring himself to disclose Uncle Billy's rascality, and so offered the hypothesis that he had wandered from the camp and had accidentally stampeded the animals. He dropped a warning to the Duchess and Mother Shipton, who of course knew the facts of their associate's defection. "They'll find out the truth about us *all* when they find out anything," he added significantly, "and there's no good frightening them now."

Tom Simson not only put all his worldly store at the disposal of Mr. Oakhurst, but seemed to enjoy the prospect of their enforced seclusion. "We'll have a good camp for a week, and then the snow'll melt, and we'll all go back together." The cheerful gaiety of the young man and Mr. Oakhurst's calm infected the others. The Innocent, with the aid of pine boughs, extemporized a thatch for the roofless cabin, and the Duchess directed Piney in the rearrangement of the interior with a taste and tact that opened the blue eyes of that provincial maiden to their fullest extent. "I reckon now you're used to fine things at Poker Flat," said Piney. The Duchess turned away sharply to conceal something that reddened her cheeks through their professional tint, and Mother Shipton requested Piney not to "chatter." But when Mr. Oakhurst returned from a weary search for the trail, he heard the sound of happy laughter echoed from the rocks. He stopped in some alarm, and his thoughts first naturally reverted to the whisky, which he had prudently cached. "And yet it don't somehow sound like whisky," said the gambler. It was not until he caught sight of the blazing fire through the still blinding storm, and the group around it, that he settled to the conviction that it was "square fun."

Whether Mr. Oakhurst had cached his cards with the whisky as something debarred the free access of the community, I cannot say. It was certain that, in Mother Shipton's words, he "didn't say 'cards' once" during that evening. Haply the time was beguiled by

[1] sotto voce (sōt′tō vō′chā): in an undertone. (Italian.)

an accordion, produced somewhat ostentatiously by Tom Simson from his pack. Notwithstanding some difficulties attending the manipulation of this instrument, Piney Woods managed to pluck several reluctant melodies from its keys, to an accompaniment by the Innocent on a pair of bone castanets. But the crowning festivity of the evening was reached in a rude camp-meeting hymn, which the lovers, joining hands, sang with great earnestness and vociferation. I fear that a certain defiant tone and Covenanter's swing to its chorus, rather than any devotional quality, caused it speedily to infect the others, who at last joined in the refrain:

"I'm proud to live in the service of the Lord,
And I'm bound to die in His army."

The pines rocked, the storm eddied and whirled above the miserable group, and the flames of their altar leaped heavenward, as if in token of the vow.

At midnight the storm abated, the rolling clouds parted, and the stars glittered keenly above the sleeping camp. Mr. Oakhurst, whose professional habits had enabled him to live on the smallest possible amount of sleep, in dividing the watch with Tom Simson, somehow managed to take upon himself the greater part of that duty. He excused himself to the Innocent by saying that he had "often been a week without sleep." "Doing what?" asked Tom. "Poker!" replied Oakhurst sententiously. "When a man gets a streak of luck — real luck — he don't get tired. The luck gives in first. Luck," continued the gambler reflectively, "is a mighty queer thing. All you know about it for certain is that it's bound to change. And it's finding out when it's going to change that makes you. We've had a streak of bad luck since we left Poker Flat — you come along, and slap you get into it, too. If you can hold your cards right along you're all right. For," added the gambler, with cheerful irrelevance —

"I'm proud to live in the service of the Lord,
And I'm bound to die in His army."

The third day came, and the sun, looking through the white-curtained valley, saw the outcasts divide their slowly decreasing store of provisions for the morning meal. It was one of the peculiarities of that mountain climate that its rays diffused a kindly warmth over the wintry landscape, as if in regretful commiseration of the past. But it revealed drift on drift of snow piled high around the hut — a hopeless, uncharted, trackless sea of white lying below the rocky shores to which the castaways still clung. Through the marvelously clear air the smoke of the pastoral village of Poker Flat rose miles away. Mother Shipton saw it, and from a remote pinnacle of her rocky fastness hurled in that direction a final malediction. It was her last vituperative attempt, and perhaps for that reason was invested with a certain degree of sublimity. It did her good, she privately informed the Duchess. "Just you go out there and cuss, and see." She then set herself to the task of amusing "the child," as she and the Duchess were pleased to call Piney. Piney was no chicken, but it was a soothing and original theory of the pair thus to account for the fact that she didn't swear and wasn't improper.

When night crept up again through the gorges, the reedy notes of the accordion rose and fell in fitful spasms and long-drawn gasps by the flickering campfire. But music failed to fill entirely the aching void left by insufficient food, and a new diversion was proposed by Piney — storytelling. Neither Mr. Oakhurst nor his female companions caring to relate their personal experiences, this plan would have failed too, but for the Innocent. Some months before he had chanced upon a stray copy of Mr. Pope's ingenious translation of the Iliad. He now proposed to narrate the principal incidents of that poem — having thoroughly mastered the argument and fairly forgotten the words — in the current vernacular of Sandy Bar. And so for the rest of that night the Homeric demigods again walked the earth. Trojan bully and wily Greek wrestled in the winds, and the great pines in the cañon seemed to bow to the wrath of the son of Peleus.[1] Mr. Oakhurst listened with quiet satisfaction. Most especially was he interested in the fate of "Ashheels," as the Innocent persisted in denominating the "swift-footed Achilles."

So, with small food and much of Homer and the accordion, a week passed over the heads of the outcasts. The sun again forsook them, and again from leaden skies the snowflakes were sifted over the land. Day by day closer around them drew the snowy circle, until at last they looked from their prison over drifted walls of dazzling

[1] **son of Peleus:** Achilles, the greatest of the Greek warriors in the siege of Troy. His anger was one of the turning points of that battle.

white, that towered twenty feet above their heads. It became more and more difficult to replenish their fires, even from the fallen trees beside them, now half hidden in the drifts. And yet no one complained. The lovers turned from the dreary prospect and looked into each other's eyes, and were happy. Mr. Oakhurst settled himself coolly to the losing game before him. The Duchess, more cheerful than she had been, assumed the care of Piney. Only Mother Shipton — once the strongest of the party — seemed to sicken and fade. At midnight on the tenth day she called Oakhurst to her side. "I'm going," she said, in a voice of querulous weakness, "but don't say anything about it. Don't waken the kids. Take the bundle from under my head, and open it." Mr. Oakhurst did so. It contained Mother Shipton's rations for the last week, untouched. "Give 'em to the child," she said, pointing to the sleeping Piney. "You've starved yourself," said the gambler. "That's what they call it," said the woman querulously, as she lay down again, and, turning her face to the wall, passed quietly away.

The accordion and the bones were put aside that day, and Homer was forgotten. When the body of Mother Shipton had been committed to the snow, Mr. Oakhurst took the Innocent aside, and showed him a pair of snowshoes, which he had fashioned from the old packsaddle. "There's one chance in a hundred to save her yet," he said, pointing to Piney; "but it's there," he added, pointing toward Poker Flat. "If you can reach there in two days she's safe." "And you?" asked Tom Simson. "I'll stay here," was the curt reply.

The lovers parted with a long embrace. "You are not going, too?" said the Duchess, as she saw Mr. Oakhurst apparently waiting to accompany him. "As far as the cañon," he replied. He turned suddenly and kissed the Duchess, leaving her pallid face aflame, and her trembling limbs rigid with amazement.

Night came, but not Mr. Oakhurst. It brought the storm again and the whirling snow. Then the Duchess, feeding the fire, found that someone had quietly piled beside the hut enough fuel to last a few days longer. The tears rose to her eyes, but she hid them from Piney.

The women slept but little. In the morning, looking into each other's faces, they read their fate. Neither spoke, but Piney, accepting the position of the stronger, drew near and placed her arm around the Duchess's waist. They kept this attitude for the rest of the day. That night the storm reached its greatest fury, and, rending asunder the protecting pines, invaded the very hut.

Toward morning they found themselves unable to feed the fire, which gradually died away. As the embers slowly blackened, the Duchess crept closer to Piney, and broke the silence of many hours: " Piney, can you pray? " " No, dear," said Piney simply. The Duchess, without knowing exactly why, felt relieved, and, putting her head upon Piney's shoulder, spoke no more. And so reclining, the younger and purer pillowing the head of her soiled sister upon her virgin breast, they fell asleep.

The wind lulled as if it feared to waken them. Feathery drifts of snow, shaken from the long pine boughs, flew like white-winged birds, and settled about them as they slept. The moon through the rifted clouds looked down upon what had been the camp. But all human stain, all trace of earthly travail, was hidden beneath the spotless mantle mercifully flung from above.

They slept all day that day and the next, nor did they waken when voices and footsteps broke the silence of the camp. And when pitying fingers brushed the snow from their wan faces, you could scarcely have told from the equal peace that dwelt upon them which was she that had sinned. Even the law of Poker Flat recognized this, and turned away, leaving them still locked in each other's arms.

But at the head of the gulch, on one of the largest pine trees, they found the deuce of clubs pinned to the bark with a bowie knife. It bore the following, written in pencil in a firm hand:

†

BENEATH THIS TREE

LIES THE BODY

OF

JOHN OAKHURST,

WHO STRUCK A STREAK OF BAD LUCK

ON THE 23RD OF NOVEMBER 1850,

AND

HANDED IN HIS CHECKS

ON THE 7TH DECEMBER, 1850.

†

And pulseless and cold, with a Derringer[1] by his side and a bullet in his heart, though still calm as in life, beneath the snow lay he who was at once the strongest and yet the weakest of the outcasts of Poker Flat.

READING WITH INSIGHT

1. Since this is a local color story, you might begin by noticing the kind of " color " Harte puts into this story. What can you remember about the scenery? About the customs? About the unusual types of people? About names and expressions which are put in quotation marks to indicate their unusualness?

2. Which of these two things is Harte saying in this story: a) " These are unique and picturesque people " or b) " These are real people just like the rest of us. This is the way people really are." Quote passages from the story to support your point of view.

3. Somebody has said that the theme of this story is, " Scratch the ugliest rock and you may reveal a gold nugget." Do you agree with this statement of the theme, and if so, how would you say Harte makes the point? If you do not agree with this statement of the theme, how would you state it?

4. You might call this a story of contrasts. There is, for example, the contrast between the innocence of Tom Simson and his bride and the somewhat soiled worldliness of the other characters. What is the contrast between Uncle Billy and John Oakhurst? What is the contrast within Oakhurst's character? In what way was he weak? In what way strong? What other contrasts can you name?

5. The plot of this story is especially interesting for you to study, for one reason, because of the speed with which the problem is complicated. Look at the first part of the story and notice how speedily the " Sabbath lull " gives way to real tensions and problems. Oakhurst realizes something is wrong. Then the vigilance committee appears. Soon the problems and difficulties of all the characters are interwined. List the obstacles that pile up to keep the outcasts from reaching their destination.

6. The plot of the story might be described as a steady progress

[1] **Derringer: a short pistol of large caliber.**

downward toward inevitable failure — as Oakhurst explained it, "a streak of bad luck," unbroken or unchanged. But is there also an upward movement in the story? Recall what kind of people started out from Poker Flat. What change takes place in those people during the story?

7. A question to which you should give particular attention is are the characters real? Do they react as real people would? For example, why did Uncle Billy take *all* the horses? Was that in his character, or was it merely a device of the author to get the travelers stuck in the mountains? Appy this test to the Duchess, to Mother Shipton, and to Oakhurst. What is your conclusion about the characters in this story?

8. Harte told this story from a third person viewpoint. What difficulties would he have had if he had tried to tell it in the first person?

9. Notice the first sentence. In what way does it follow Poe's theory that the very first sentence should tend to bring out the desired effect of the story?

10. Some critics point out what they think are artificialities in Harte's writing. Artificialities are parts of a story which are unnecessary ornaments; they are not bone and sinew of the story. Did you notice any artificialities in this story? For example, do you like Harte's use of the hymn, or does that seem artificial to you? Does the conversation strike you as real or stagy? Does any of the writing seem artificial and stilted? These questions are not intended to prejudice you against the story; they are merely questions you are entitled to ask about any story.

11. What is the author's attitude toward his characters? Is he sympathetic to them? Is he amused by them? Does he seem to feel superior to them? If you are a very good reader, you will find examples of how the author's way of writing about his characters shows his attitude toward them.

12. How does the theme of the story square with your own experience? Can you give examples of people who are all bad or all good? Do you know of people supposedly good, who cracked under pressure; or people supposedly bad, who proved better than their reputation?

If you like this story, you will be interested in

Harte. *The Luck of Roaring Camp.*
The Postmistress of Laurel Run.
Tennessee's Partner.
Jack London. *All-Gold Cañon.*
To Build a Fire.
George W. Cable. *Posson Jone.*

STEPHEN CRANE

The Open Boat

POE LIVED only to the age of 40. But Stephen Crane lived only to be 28 – from 1871 to 1900. In those few years of his adult life he wrote one of the best novels and some of the best stories and poems of his time. Thinking of men like Crane, one always wonders what would have happened if they had lived longer. What would Crane have written? Would he have produced new novels that might have made his fine *The Red Badge of Courage* seem like child's play? His free verse poems were already widely imitated; would he have come to be a leading poet? Carl Van Doren has said that modern American literature began with Crane; if he had lived out his three score and ten, would he have been one of the leading lights of our literature? It is tempting to imagine how his great talent might have developed.

Crane got a great deal of his training in writing for newspapers. He was born in Newark, New Jersey and started to work on New Jersey papers before he went to college. In his brief time at Lafayette and Syracuse, he continued to be a newspaper correspondent. He left college at 19, and went to work on the New York *Herald* and *Tribune*. He borrowed $700 to pay for the publishing of his first novel (under a pseudonym), then began to write *The Red Badge of Courage*. Crane wrote in this novel one of the most vivid and realistic war stories of all time, although he had never seen a battle. Ambrose Bierce said of the book, "He knows nothing of war, yet he is drenched in blood. Most beginners who deal with this subject spatter themselves only with ink." When the New York papers found how well he could write about wars, they made him a war correspondent, sent him to Cuba and Greece, then to cover the Spanish-American War. On his way to a small war in Cuba he was shipwrecked off the coast of Florida. From that experience came the material for the story "The Open Boat" which you are about to read, a story which H. G. Wells called "the finest short story in the English language."

Crane's health had suffered from the privations and hardships of covering the war in Greece. The exposure in the open boat weakened him further. He was unable to resist an infection that had been gathering in his lungs, and he died of tuberculosis.

"The Open Boat" is worth studying from many points of view, but you will find it an especially good example of the theme story.

I

NONE of them knew the color of the sky. Their eyes glanced level, and were fastened upon the waves that swept toward them. These waves were of the hue of slate, save for the tops, which were of foaming white, and all of the men knew the colors of the sea. The horizon narrowed and widened, and dipped and rose, and at all times its edge was jagged with waves that seemed thrust up in points like rocks.

Many a man ought to have a bathtub larger than the boat which here rode upon the sea. These waves were most wrongfully and barbarously abrupt and tall, and each froth-top was a problem in small-boat navigation.

The cook squatted in the bottom, and looked with both eyes at the six inches of gunwale which separated him from the ocean. His sleeves were rolled over his fat forearms, and the two flaps of his unbuttoned vest dangled as he bent to bail out the boat. Often he said, "That was a narrow clip." As he remarked it he invariably gazed eastward over the broken sea.

The oiler, steering with one of the two oars in the boat, sometimes raised himself suddenly to keep clear of water that swirled in over the stern. It was a thin little oar and it seemed often ready to snap.

The correspondent, pulling at the other oar, watched the waves and wondered why he was there.

The injured captain, lying in the bow, was at this time buried in that profound dejection and indifference which comes, temporarily at least, to even the bravest and most enduring when, willy-nilly, the firm fails, the army loses, the ship goes down. The mind of the master of a vessel is rooted deep in the timbers of her, though he has commanded for a day or a decade, and this captain had on him the stern impression of a scene in the grays of dawn of seven turned faces, and later a stump of a top-mast with a white ball on it that slashed to and fro at the waves, went low and lower, and down. Thereafter there was something strange in his voice. Although steady, it was deep with mourning, and of a quality beyond oration or tears.

"Keep 'er a little more south, Billie," said he.

"'A little more south,' sir," said the oiler in the stern.

A seat in this boat was not unlike a seat upon a bucking bronco, and by the same token, a bronco is not much smaller. The craft pranced and reared and plunged like an animal. As each wave came, and she rose for it, she seemed like a horse making at a fence outrageously high. The manner of her scramble over these walls of water is a mystic thing, and, moreover, at the top of them were ordinarily these problems in white water, the foam racing down from the summit of each wave, requiring a new leap, and a leap from the air. Then, after scornfully bumping a crest, she would slide and race and splash down a long incline, and arrive bobbing and nodding in front of the next menace.

A singular disadvantage of the sea lies in the fact that, after successfully surmounting one wave, you discover that there is another behind it, just as important and just as nervously anxious to do something effective in the way of swamping boats. In a ten-foot dinghy[1] one can get an idea of the resources of the sea in the line of waves that is not probable to the average experience, which is never at sea in a dinghy. As each slaty wall of water approached, it shut all else from the view of the men in the boat, and it was not difficult to imagine that this particular wave was the final outburst of the ocean, the last effort of the grim water. There was a terrible grace in the move of the waves, and they came in silence, save for the snarling of the crests.

In the wan light the faces of the men must have been gray. Their eyes must have glinted in strange ways as they gazed steadily astern. Viewed from a balcony, the whole thing would, doubtless, have been weirdly picturesque. But the men in the boat had no time to see it, and if they had had leisure, there were other things to occupy their minds. The sun swung steadily up the sky, and they knew it was broad day because the color of the sea changed from slate to

[1] **dinghy:** a small rowboat, often carried on the deck of a ship.

emerald-green streaked with amber lights, and the foam was like tumbling snow. The process of the breaking day was unknown to them. They were aware only of this effect upon the color of the waves that rolled toward them.

In disjointed sentences the cook and the correspondent argued as to the difference between a lifesaving station and a house of refuge. The cook had said: "There's a house of refuge just north of the Mosquito Inlet Light,[1] and as soon as they see us they'll come off in their boat and pick us up."

"As soon as who see us?" said the correspondent.

"The crew," said the cook.

"Houses of refuge don't have crews," said the correspondent. "As I understand them, they are only places where clothes and grub are stored for the benefit of shipwrecked people. They don't carry crews."

"Oh, yes, they do," said the cook.

"No, they don't," said the correspondent.

"Well, we're not there yet, anyhow," said the oiler in the stern.

"Well," said the cook, "perhaps it's not a house of refuge that I'm thinking of as being near Mosquito Inlet Light; perhaps it's a life-saving station."

"We're not there yet," said the oiler in the stern.

II

As the boat bounced from the top of each wave, the wind tore through the hair of the hatless men, and as the craft plopped her stern down again the spray splashed past them. The crest of each of these waves was a hill, from the top of which the men surveyed, for a moment, a broad tumultuous expanse, shining and wind-riven. It was probably splendid. It was probably glorious, this play of the free sea, wild with lights of emerald and white and amber.

"Bully good thing it's an onshore wind," said the cook. "If not, where would we be? Wouldn't have a show."

"That's right," said the correspondent.

[1] **Mosquito Inlet Light**: you will find the places mentioned in this story on the east coast of Florida, about 29 north latitude.

The busy oiler nodded his assent.

Then the captain, in the bow, chuckled in a way that expressed humor, contempt, tragedy, all in one. " Do you think we've got much of a show now, boys? " said he.

Whereupon the three were silent, save for a trifle of hemming and hawing. To express any particular optimism at this time they felt to be childish and stupid, but they all doubtless possessed this sense of the situation in their mind. A young man thinks doggedly at such times. On the other hand, the ethics of their condition was decidedly against any open suggestion of hopelessness. So they were silent.

" Oh, well," said the captain, soothing his children, " we'll get ashore all right."

But there was that in his tone which made them think, so the oiler quoth: " Yes! If this wind holds! "

The cook was bailing: " Yes! If we don't catch hell in the surf."

Canton flannel gulls flew near and far. Sometimes they sat down on the sea, near patches of brown seaweed that rolled on the waves with a movement like carpets on a line in a gale. The birds sat comfortably in groups, and they were envied by some in the dinghy, for the wrath of the sea was no more to them than it was to a covey of prairie chickens a thousand miles inland. Often they came very close and stared at the men with black beadlike eyes. At these times they were uncanny and sinister in their unblinking scrutiny, and the men hooted angrily at them, telling them to be gone. One came, and evidently decided to alight on the top of the captain's head. The bird flew parallel to the boat and did not circle, but made short sidelong jumps in the air in chicken-fashion. His black eyes were wistfully fixed upon the captain's head. " Ugly brute," said the oiler to the bird. " You look as if you were made with a jackknife." The cook and the correspondent swore darkly at the creature. The captain naturally wished to knock it away with the end of the heavy painter [1]; but he did not dare do it, because anything resembling an emphatic gesture would have capsized this freighted boat, and so with his open hand, the captain gently and carefully waved the gull away. After it had been discouraged from the pursuit the captain breathed

[1] **painter:** rope with which boat is tied to dock.

easier on account of his hair, and others breathed easier because the bird struck their minds at this time as being somehow gruesome and ominous.

In the meantime the oiler and the correspondent rowed; and also they rowed. They sat together in the same seat, and each rowed an oar. Then the oiler took both oars; then the correspondent took both oars; then the oiler; then the correspondent. They rowed and they rowed. The very ticklish part of the business was when the time came for the reclining one in the stern to take his turn at the oars. By the very last star of truth, it is easier to steal eggs from under a hen than it was to change seats in the dinghy. First the man in the stern slid his hand along the thwart and moved with care, as if he were of Sèvres.[1] Then the man in the rowing seat slid his hand along the other thwart. It was all done with the most extraordinary care. As the two sidled past each other, the whole party kept watchful eyes on the coming wave, and the captain cried: "Look out, now! Steady, there!"

The brown mats of seaweed that appeared from time to time were like islands, bits of earth. They were traveling, apparently, neither one way nor the other. They were, to all intents, stationary. They informed the men in the boat that it was making progress slowly toward the land.

The captain, rearing cautiously in the bow after the dinghy soared on a great swell, said that he had seen the lighthouse at Mosquito Inlet. Presently the cook remarked that he had seen it. The correspondent was at the oars then, and for some reason he too wished to look at the lighthouse; but his back was toward the far shore, and the waves were important, and for some time he could not seize an opportunity to turn his head. But at last there came a wave more gentle than the others, and when at the crest of it he swiftly scoured the western horizon.

"See it?" said the captain.

"No," said the correspondent, slowly; "I didn't see anything."

"Look again," said the captain. He pointed. "It's exactly in that direction."

At the top of another wave the correspondent did as he was bid, and this time his eyes chanced on a small, still thing on the edge of

[1] **Sèvres:** delicate porcelain, easily breakable.

the swaying horizon. It was precisely like the point of a pin. It took an anxious eye to find a lighthouse so tiny.

"Think we'll make it, Captain?"

"If this wind holds and the boat don't swamp, we can't do much else," said the captain.

The little boat, lifted by each towering sea and splashed viciously by the crests, made progress that in the absence of seaweed was not apparent to those in her. She seemed just a wee thing wallowing miraculously, top up, at the mercy of five oceans. Occasionally a great spread of water, like white flames, swarmed into her.

"Bail her, cook," said the captain, serenely.

"All right, Captain," said the cheerful cook.

III

It would be difficult to describe the subtle brotherhood of men that was here established on the seas. No one said that it was so. No one mentioned it. But it dwelt in the boat, and each man felt it warm him. They were a captain, an oiler, a cook, and a correspondent, and they were friends, friends in a more curiously ironbound degree than may be common. The hurt captain, lying against the water jar in the bow, spoke always in a low voice and calmly, but he could never command a more ready and swiftly obedient crew than the motley three of the dinghy. It was more than a mere recognition of what was best for the common safety. There was surely in it a quality that was personal and heartfelt. And after this devotion to the commander of the boat there was this comradeship that the correspondent, for instance, who had been taught to be cynical of men, knew even at the time was the best experience of his life. But no one said that it was so. No one mentioned it.

"I wish we had a sail," remarked the captain. "We might try my overcoat on the end of an oar and give you two boys a chance to rest." So the cook and the correspondent held the mast and spread wide the overcoat. The oiler steered, and the little boat made good way with her new rig. Sometimes the oiler had to scull sharply to keep a sea from breaking into the boat, but otherwise sailing was a success.

Meanwhile the lighthouse had been growing slowly larger. It had now almost assumed color, and appeared like a little gray shadow on the sky. The man at the oars could not be prevented from turning his head rather often to try for a glimpse of this little gray shadow.

At last, from the top of each wave the men in the tossing boat could see land. Even as the lighthouse was an upright shadow on the sky, this land seemed but a long black shadow on the sea. It certainly was thinner than paper. "We must be about opposite New Smyrna," said the cook, who had coasted this shore often in schooners. "Captain, by the way, I believe they abandoned that lifesaving station there about a year ago."

"Did they?" said the captain.

The wind slowly died away. The cook and the correspondent were not now obliged to slave in order to hold high the oar. But the waves continued their old impetuous swooping at the dinghy, and the little craft, no longer under way, struggled woundily over them. The oiler or the correspondent took the oars again.

Shipwrecks are *à propos* [1] of nothing. If men could only train for them and have them occur when the men had reached pink condition, there would be less drowning at sea. Of the four in the dinghy none had slept any time worth mentioning for two days and two nights previous to embarking in the dinghy, and in the excitement of clambering about the deck of a foundering ship they had also forgotten to eat heartily.

For these reasons, and for others, neither the oiler nor the correspondent was fond of rowing at this time. The correspondent wondered ingenuously how in the name of all that was sane could there be people who thought it amusing to row a boat. It was not an amusement; it was a diabolical punishment, and even a genius of mental aberrations could never conclude that it was anything but a horror to the muscles and a crime against the back. He mentioned to the boat in general how the amusement of rowing struck him, and the weary-faced oiler smiled in full sympathy. Previously to the foundering, by the way, the oiler had worked double-watch in the engine room of the ship.

"Take her easy, now, boys," said the captain. "Don't spend yourselves. If we have to run a surf you'll need all your strength, because we'll sure have to swim for it. Take your time."

[1] **à propos: pertinent.**

Slowly the land arose from the sea. From a black line it became a line of black and a line of white, trees and sand. Finally, the captain said that he could make out a house on the shore. " That's the house of refuge, sure," said the cook. " They'll see us before long, and come out after us."

The distant lighthouse reared high. " The keeper ought to be able to make us out now, if he's looking through a glass," said the captain. " He'll notify the lifesaving people."

" None of those other boats could have got ashore to give word of the wreck," said the oiler, in a low voice. " Else the lifeboat would be out hunting us."

Slowly and beautifully the land loomed out of the sea. The wind came again. It had veered from the northeast to the southeast. Finally, a new sound struck the ears of the men in the boat. It was the low thunder of the surf on the shore. " We'll never be able to make the lighthouse now," said the captain. " Swing her head a little more north, Billie," said he.

" ' A little more north,' sir," said the oiler.

Whereupon the little boat turned her nose once more down the wind, and all but the oarsman watched the shore grow. Under the influence of this expansion doubt and direful apprehension was leaving the minds of the men. The management of the boat was still most absorbing, but it could not prevent a quiet cheerfulness. In an hour, perhaps, they would be ashore.

Their backbones had become thoroughly used to balancing in the boat, and they now rode this wild colt of a dinghy like circus men. The correspondent thought that he had been drenched to the skin, but happening to feel in the top pocket of his coat, he found therein eight cigars. Four of them were soaked with sea water; four were perfectly scatheless. After a search, somebody produced three dry matches, and thereupon the four waifs rode impudently in their little boat, and with an assurance of an impending rescue shining in their eyes, puffed at the big cigars and judged well and ill of all men. Everybody took a drink of water.

IV

"Cook," remarked the captain, "there don't seem to be any signs of life about your house of refuge."

"No," replied the cook. "Funny they don't see us!"

A broad stretch of lowly coast lay before the eyes of the men. It was of dunes topped with dark vegetation. The roar of the surf was plain, and sometimes they could see the white lip of a wave as it spun up the beach. A tiny house was blocked out black upon the sky. Southward, the slim lighthouse lifted its little gray length.

Tide, wind, and waves were swinging the dinghy northward. "Funny they don't see us," said the men.

The surf's roar was here dulled, but its tone was nevertheless thunderous and mighty. As the boat swam over the great rollers, the men sat listening to this roar. "We'll swamp sure," said everybody.

It is fair to say here that there was not a lifesaving station within twenty miles in either direction; but the men did not know this fact, and in consequence they made dark and opprobrious remarks concerning the eyesight of the nation's lifesavers. Four scowling men sat in the dinghy, and surpassed records in the invention of epithets.

"Funny they don't see us."

The lightheartedness of a former time had completely faded. To their sharpened minds it was easy to conjure pictures of all kinds of incompetency and blindness and, indeed, cowardice. There was the shore of the populous land, and it was bitter and bitter to them that from it came no sign.

"Well," said the captain, ultimately, "I suppose we'll have to make a try for ourselves. If we stay out here too long, we'll none of us have strength left to swim after the boat swamps."

And so the oiler, who was at the oars, turned the boat straight for the shore. There was a sudden tightening of muscles. There was some thinking.

"If we don't all get ashore," said the captain, – "if we don't all get ashore, I suppose you fellows know where to send news of my finish?"

They then briefly exchanged some addresses and admonitions. As for the reflections of the men, there was a great deal of rage in them. Perchance they might be formulated thus: "If I am going to be drowned — if I am going to be drowned — if I am going to be drowned, why, in the name of the seven mad gods who rule the sea, was I allowed to come thus far and contemplate sand and trees? Was I brought here merely to have my nose dragged away as I was about to nibble the sacred cheese of life? It is preposterous! If this old ninny-woman, Fate, cannot do better than this, she should be deprived of the management of men's fortunes. She is an old hen who knows not her intention. If she has decided to drown me, why did she not do it in the beginning, and save me all this trouble? The whole affair is absurd. . . . But no; she cannot mean to drown me. She dare not drown me. She cannot drown me. Not after all this work! " Afterward the man might have had an impulse to shake his fist at the clouds. " Just you drown me, now, and then hear what I call you! "

The billows that came at this time were more formidable. They seemed always just about to break and roll over the little boat in a turmoil of foam. There was a preparatory and long growl in the speech of them. No mind unused to the sea would have concluded that the dinghy could ascend these sheer heights in time. The shore was still afar. The oiler was a wily surfman. " Boys," he said swiftly, " she won't live three minutes more, and we're too far out to swim. Shall I take her to sea again, Captain? "

" Yes; go ahead! " said the captain.

This oiler, by a series of quick miracles and fast and steady oarsmanship, turned the boat in the middle of the surf and took her safely to sea again.

There was a considerable silence as the boat bumped over the furrowed sea to deeper water. Then somebody in gloom spoke: " Well, anyhow, they must have seen us from the shore by now."

The gulls went in slanting flight up the wind toward the gray, desolate east. A squall, marked by dingy clouds, and clouds brick-red, like smoke from a burning building, appeared from the south-east.

" What do you think of those lifesaving people? Ain't they peaches? "

" Funny they haven't seen us."

" Maybe they think we're out here for sport! Maybe they think we're fishin'. Maybe they think we're damned fools."

It was a long afternoon. A changed tide tried to force them southward, but wind and wave said northward. Far ahead, where coast line, sea, and sky formed their mighty angle, there were little dots which seemed to indicate a city on the shore.

"St. Augustine?"

The captain shook his head. "Too near Mosquito Inlet."

And the oiler rowed, and then the correspondent rowed; then the oiler rowed. It was a weary business. The human back can become the seat of more aches and pains than are registered in books for the composite anatomy of a regiment. It is a limited area, but it can become the theater of innumerable muscular conflicts, tangles, wrenches, knots, and other comforts.

"Did you ever like to row, Billie?" asked the correspondent.

"No," said the oiler; "hang it!"

When one exchanged the rowing seat for a place in the bottom of the boat, he suffered a bodily depression that caused him to be careless of everything save an obligation to wiggle one finger. There was cold sea water swashing to and fro in the boat, and he lay in it. His head, pillowed on a thwart, was within an inch of the swirl of a wave-crest, and sometimes a particularly obstreperous sea came inboard and drenched him once more. But these matters did not annoy him. It is almost certain that if the boat capsized he would have tumbled comfortably out upon the ocean as if he felt sure that it was a great, soft mattress.

"Look! There's a man on the shore!"

"Where?"

"There! See 'im? See 'im?"

"Yes, sure! He's walking along."

"Now he's stopped. Look! He's facing us!"

"He's waving at us!"

"So he is! By thunder!"

"Ah, now we're all right! Now we're all right! There'll be a boat out here for us in half an hour."

"He's going on. He's running. He's going up to that house there."

The remote beach seemed lower than the sea, and it required a searching glance to discern the little black figure. The captain saw a floating stick and they rowed to it. A bath towel was by some weird chance in the boat, and tying this on the stick, the captain waved it. The oarsman did not dare turn his head, so he was obliged to ask questions.

"What's he doing now?"

"He's standing still again. He's looking, I think. . . . There he goes again. Toward the house. . . . Now he's stopped again."

"Is he waving at us?"

"No, not now! He was, though."

"Look! There comes another man!"

"He's running."

"Look at him go, would you!"

"Why, he's on a bicycle. Now he's met the other man. They're both waving at us. Look!"

"There comes something up the beach."

"What the devil is that thing?"

"Why, it looks like a boat."

"Why, certainly it's a boat."

"No, it's on wheels."

"Yes, so it is. Well, that must be the lifeboat. They drag them along shore on a wagon."

"That's the lifeboat, sure."

"No, by ——, it's – it's an omnibus."

"I tell you it's a lifeboat."

"It is not! It's an omnibus. I can see it plain. See? One of these big hotel omnibuses."

"By thunder, you're right. It's an omnibus, sure as fate. What do you suppose they are doing with an omnibus? Maybe they are going around collecting the life crew, hey?"

"That's it, likely. Look! There's a fellow waving a little black flag. He's standing on the steps of the omnibus. There come those other two fellows. Now they're all talking together. Look at the fellow with the flag. Maybe he ain't waving it!"

"That ain't a flag, is it? That's his coat. Why, certainly, that's his coat."

"So it is. It's his coat. He's taken it off and is waving it around his head. But would you look at him swing it!"

"Oh, say, there isn't any lifesaving station there. That's just a winter resort hotel omnibus that has brought over some of the boarders to see us drown."

"What's that idiot with the coat mean? What's he signaling, anyhow?"

"It looks as if he were trying to tell us to go north. There must be a lifesaving station up there."

"No! He thinks we're fishing. Just giving us a merry hand. See? Ah, there, Willie!"

"Well, I wish I could make something out of those signals. What do you suppose he means?"

"He don't mean anything. He's just playing."

"Well, if he'd just signal us to try the surf again, or to go to sea and wait, or go north, or go south, or go to the devil – there would be some reason in it. But look at him. He just stands there and keeps his coat revolving like a wheel. The ass!"

"There come more people."

"Now there's quite a mob. Look! Isn't that a boat?"

"Where? Oh, I see where you mean. No, that's no boat."

"That fellow is still waving his coat."

"He must think we like to see him do that. Why don't he quit it? It don't mean anything."

"I don't know. I think he is trying to make us go north. It must be that there's a lifesaving station there somewhere."

"Say, he ain't tired yet. Look at 'im wave!"

"Wonder how long he can keep that up. He's been revolving his coat ever since he caught sight of us. He's an idiot. Why aren't they getting men to bring a boat out? A fishing boat – one of those big yawls – could come out here all right. Why don't he do something?"

"Oh, it's all right now."

"They'll have a boat out here for us in less than no time, now that they've seen us."

A faint yellow tone came into the sky over the low land. The shadows on the sea slowly deepened. The wind bore coldness with it, and the men began to shiver.

"Holy smoke!" said one, allowing his voice to express his impious mood, "if we keep on monkeying out here! If we've got to flounder out here all night!"

"Oh, we'll never have to stay here all night! Don't you worry.

They've seen us now, and it won't be long before they'll come chasing out after us."

The shore grew dusky. The man waving a coat blended gradually into this gloom, and it swallowed in the same manner the omnibus and the group of people. The spray, when it dashed uproariously over the side, made the voyagers shrink and swear like men who were being branded.

"I'd like to catch the chump who waved the coat. I feel like soaking him one, just for luck."

"Why? What did he do?"

"Oh, nothing, but then he seemed so damned cheerful."

In the meantime the oiler rowed, and then the correspondent rowed, and then the oiler rowed. Gray-faced and bowed forward, they mechanically, turn by turn, plied the leaden oars. The form of the lighthouse had vanished from the southern horizon, but finally a pale star appeared, just lifting from the sea. The streaked saffron in the west passed before the all-merging darkness, and the sea to the east was black. The land had vanished, and was expressed only by the low and drear thunder of the surf.

"If I am going to be drowned – if I am going to be drowned – if I am going to be drowned, why, in the name of the seven mad gods who rule the sea, was I allowed to come thus far and contemplate sand and trees? Was I brought here merely to have my nose dragged away as I was about to nibble the sacred cheese of life?"

The patient captain, drooped over the water jar, was sometimes obliged to speak to the oarsman.

"Keep her head up! Keep her head up!"

"Keep her head up, sir." The voices were weary and low.

This was surely a quiet evening. All save the oarsman lay heavily and listlessly in the boat's bottom. As for him, his eyes were just capable of noting the tall black waves that swept forward in a most sinister silence, save for an occasional subdued growl of a crest.

The cook's head was on a thwart, and he looked without interest at the water under his nose. He was deep in other scenes. Finally he spoke. "Billie," he murmured, dreamfully, "what kind of pie do you like best?"

V

"Pie," said the oiler and the correspondent, agitatedly. "Don't talk about those things, blast you! "

"Well," said the cook, "I was just thinking about ham sandwiches, and —— "

A night on the sea in an open boat is a long night. As darkness settled finally, the shine of the light, lifting from the sea in the south, changed to full gold. On the northern horizon a new light appeared, a small bluish gleam on the edge of the waters. These two lights were the furniture of the world. Otherwise there was nothing but waves.

Two men huddled in the stern, and distances were so magnificent in the dinghy that the rower was enabled to keep his feet partly warmed by thrusting them under his companions. Their legs indeed extended far under the rowing-seat until they touched the feet of the captain forward. Sometimes, despite the efforts of the tired oarsman, a wave came piling into the boat, an icy wave of the night, and the chilling water soaked them anew. They would twist their bodies for a moment and groan, and sleep the dead sleep once more, while the water in the boat gurgled about them as the craft rocked.

The plan of the oiler and the correspondent was for one to row until he lost the ability, and then arouse the other from his sea-water couch in the bottom of the boat.

The oiler plied the oars until his head dropped forward, and the overpowering sleep blinded him, and he rowed yet afterward. Then he touched a man in the bottom of the boat, and called his name. "Will you spell me for a little while? " he said meekly.

"Sure, Billie," said the correspondent, awakening and dragging himself to a sitting position. They exchanged places carefully, and the oiler, cuddling down in the sea water at the cook's side, seemed to go to sleep instantly.

The particular violence of the sea had ceased. The waves came without snarling. The obligation of the man at the oars was to keep the boat headed so that the tilt of the rollers would not capsize her, and to preserve her from filling when the crests rushed past. The black waves were silent and hard to be seen in the darkness. Often one was almost upon the boat before the oarsman was aware.

In a low voice the correspondent addressed the captain. He was not sure that the captain was awake, although this iron man seemed to be always awake. "Captain, shall I keep her making for that light north, sir?"

The same steady voice answered him. "Yes. Keep it about two points off the port bow."

The cook had tied a life belt around himself in order to get even the warmth which this clumsy cork contrivance could donate, and he seemed almost stovelike when a rower, whose teeth invariably chattered wildly as soon as he ceased his labor, dropped down to sleep.

The correspondent, as he rowed, looked down at the two men sleeping underfoot. The cook's arm was around the oiler's shoulders, and, with their fragmentary clothing and haggard faces, they were the babes of the sea, a grotesque rendering of the old babes in the wood.

Later he must have grown stupid at his work, for suddenly there was a growling of water, and a crest came with a roar and a swash into the boat, and it was a wonder that it did not set the cook afloat in his life belt. The cook continued to sleep, but the oiler sat up, blinking his eyes and shaking with the new cold.

"Oh, I'm awful sorry, Billie," said the correspondent contritely.

"That's all right, old boy," said the oiler, and lay down again and was asleep.

Presently it seemed that even the captain dozed, and the correspondent thought that he was the one man afloat on all the oceans. The wind had a voice as it came over the waves, and it was sadder than the end.

There was a long, loud swishing astern of the boat, and a gleaming trail of phosphorescence, like blue flame, was furrowed on the black waters. It might have been made by a monstrous knife.

Then there came a stillness, while the correspondent breathed with open mouth and looked at the sea.

Suddenly there was another swish and another long flash of bluish light, and this time it was alongside the boat, and might almost have been reached with an oar. The correspondent saw an enormous fin speed like a shadow through the water, hurling the crystalline spray and leaving the long glowing trail.

The correspondent looked over his shoulder at the captain. His face was hidden, and he seemed to be asleep. He looked at the babes of the sea. They certainly were asleep. So, being bereft of sympathy, he leaned a little way to one side and swore softy into the sea.

But the thing did not then leave the vicinity of the boat. Ahead or astern, on one side or the other, at intervals long or short, fled the long sparkling streak, and there was to be heard the whirroo of the dark fin. The speed and power of the thing was greatly to be admired. It cut the water like a gigantic and keen projectile.

The presence of this biding thing did not affect the man with the same horror that it would if he had been a picnicker. He simply looked at the sea dully and swore in an undertone.

Nevertheless, it is true that he did not wish to be alone with the thing. He wished one of his companions to awake by chance and keep him company with it. But the captain hung motionless over the water jar, and the oiler and the cook in the bottom of the boat were plunged in slumber.

VI

"If I am going to be drowned — if I am going to be drowned — if I am going to be drowned, why, in the name of the seven mad gods who rule the sea, was I allowed to come thus far and contemplate sand and trees?"

During this dismal night, it may be remarked that a man would conclude that it was really the intention of the seven mad gods to drown him, despite the abominable injustice of it. For it was certainly an abominable injustice to drown a man who had worked so hard, so hard. The man felt it would be a crime most unnatural. Other people had drowned at sea since galleys swarmed with painted sails, but still ——

When it occurs to a man that nature does not regard him as important, and that she feels she would not maim the universe by disposing of him, he at first wishes to throw bricks at the temple, and he hates deeply the fact that there are no brick and no temples. Any visible expression of nature would surely be pelleted with his jeers.

Then, if there be no tangible thing to hoot he feels, perhaps, the desire to confront a personification and indulge in pleas, bowed to one knee, and with hands supplicant, saying: "Yes, but I love myself."

A high cold star on a winter's night is the word he feels that she says to him. Thereafter he knows the pathos of his situation.

The men in the dinghy had not discussed these matters, but each had, no doubt, reflected upon them in silence and according to his mind. There was seldom any expression upon their faces save the general one of complete weariness. Speech was devoted to the business of the boat.

To chime the notes of his emotion, a verse mysteriously entered the correspondent's head. He had even forgotten that he had forgotten this verse, but it suddenly was in his mind.

"A soldier of the Legion lay dying in Algiers,
There was a lack of woman's nursing, there was dearth of woman's tears;
But a comrade stood beside him, and he took that comrade's hand,
And he said: 'I shall never see my own, my native land.'"

In his childhood, the correspondent had been made acquainted with the fact that a soldier of the Legion lay dying in Algiers, but he had never regarded the fact as important. Myriads of his school-fellows had informed him of the soldier's plight, but the dinning had naturally ended by making him perfectly indifferent. He had never considered it his affair that a soldier of the Legion lay dying in Algiers, nor had it appeared to him as a matter for sorrow. It was less to him than the breaking of a pencil's point.

Now, however, it quaintly came to him as a human, living thing. It was no longer merely a picture of a few throes in the breast of a poet, meanwhile drinking tea and warming his feet at the grate; it was an actuality — stern, mournful, and fine.

The correspondent plainly saw the soldier. He lay on the sand with his feet out straight and still. While his pale left hand was upon his chest in an attempt to thwart the going of his life, the blood came between his fingers. In the far Algerian distance, a city of low square forms was set against a sky that was faint with the last sunset hues. The correspondent, plying the oars and dreaming of the slow and slower movements of the lips of the soldier, was moved by a profound and perfectly impersonal comprehension. He was sorry for the soldier of the Legion who lay dying in Algiers.

The thing which had followed the boat and waited, had evidently grown bored at the delay. There was no longer to be heard the slash of the cut-water, and there was no longer the flame of the long trail. The light in the north still glimmered, but it was apparently no nearer to the boat. Sometimes the boom of the surf rang in the correspondent's ears, and he turned the craft seaward then and rowed harder. Southward, someone had evidently built a watch fire on the beach. It was too low and too far to be seen, but it made a shimmering, roseate reflection upon the bluff back of it, and this could be discerned from the boat. The wind came stronger, and sometimes a wave suddenly raged out like a mountain cat, and there was to be seen the sheen and sparkle of a broken crest.

The captain, in the bow, moved on his water jar and sat erect. "Pretty long night," he observed to the correspondent. He looked at the shore. "Those lifesaving people take their time."

"Did you see that shark playing around?"

"Yes, I saw him. He was a big fellow, all right."

"Wish I had known you were awake."

Later the correspondent spoke into the bottom of the boat.

"Billie!" There was a slow and gradual disentanglement. "Billie, will you spell me?"

"Sure," said the oiler.

As soon as the correspondent touched the cold, comfortable sea water in the bottom of the boat and had huddled close to the cook's life belt, he was deep in sleep, despite the fact that his teeth played all the popular airs. This sleep was so good to him that it was but a moment before he heard a voice call his name in a tone that demonstrated the last stages of exhaustion. "Will you spell me?"

"Sure, Billie."

The light in the north had mysteriously vanished, but the correspondent took his course from the wide-awake captain.

Later in the night they took the boat farther out to sea, and the captain directed the cook to take one oar at the stern and keep the boat facing the seas. He was to call out if he should hear the thunder of the surf. This plan enabled the oiler and the correspondent to get respite together. "We'll give those boys a chance to get into shape again," said the captain. They curled down and, after a few preliminary chatterings and trembles, slept once more the dead sleep. Neither knew they had bequeathed to the cook the company of another shark, or perhaps the same shark.

As the boat caroused on the waves, spray occasionally bumped over the side and gave them a fresh soaking, but this had no power to break their repose. The ominous slash of the wind and the water affected them as it would have affected mummies.

"Boys," said the cook, with the notes of every reluctance in his voice, "she's drifted in pretty close. I guess one of you had better take her to sea again." The correspondent, aroused, heard the crash of the toppled crests.

As he was rowing, the captain gave him some whisky-and-water, and this steadied the chills out of him. "If I ever get ashore and anybody shows me even a photograph of an oar ——"

At last there was a short conversation.

"Billie. . . . Billie, will you spell me?"

"Sure," said the oiler.

VII

When the correspondent again opened his eyes, the sea and the sky were each of the gray hue of the dawning. Later, carmine and gold was painted upon the waters. The morning appeared finally, in its splendor, with a sky of pure blue, and the sunlight flamed on the tips of the waves.

On the distant dunes were set many little black cottages, and a tall white windmill reared above them. No man, nor dog, nor bicycle appeared on the beach. The cottages might have formed a deserted village.

The voyagers scanned the shore. A conference was held in the boat. "Well," said the captain, "if no help is coming, we might better try a run through the surf right away. If we stay out here much longer we will be too weak to do anything for ourselves at all." The others silently acquiesced in this reasoning. The boat was headed for the beach. The correspondent wondered if none ever ascended the tall wind-tower, and if then they never looked seaward. This tower was a giant, standing with its back to the plight of the ants. It represented in a degree, to the correspondent, the serenity of Nature amid the struggles of the individual — Nature in the wind, and Nature in the vision of men. She did not seem cruel to him then, nor beneficent, nor treacherous, nor wise. But she was indifferent, flatly indifferent. It is, perhaps, plausible that a man in this situation, impressed with the unconcern of the universe, should see the innumerable flaws of his life, and have them taste wickedly in his mind, and wish for another chance. A distinction between right and wrong seems absurdly clear to him then, in this new ignorance of the grave-edge, and he understands that if he were given another opportunity he would mend his conduct and his words, and be better and brighter during an introduction or at a tea.

"Now, boys," said the captain, "she is going to swamp, sure. All we can do is to work her in as far as possible, and then, when she swamps, pile out and scramble for the beach. Keep cool now, and don't jump until she swamps sure."

The oiler took the oars. Over his shoulders he scanned the surf. "Captain," he said, "I think I'd better bring her about, and keep her head on to the seas and back her in."

"All right, Billie," said the captain. "Back her in." The oiler swung the boat then and, seated in the stern, the cook and the correspondent were obliged to look over their shoulders to contemplate the lonely and indifferent shore.

The monstrous inshore rollers heaved the boat high until the men were again enabled to see the white sheets of water scudding up the slanted beach. "We won't get in very close," said the captain. Each time a man could wrest his attention from the rollers, he turned his glance toward the shore, and in the expression of the eyes during this contemplation there was a singular quality. The correpondent, observing the others, knew that they were not afraid, but the full meaning of their glances was shrouded.

As for himself, he was too tired to grapple fundamentally with the fact. He tried to coerce his mind into thinking of it, but the mind was dominated at this time by the muscles, and the muscles said they did not care. It merely occurred to him that if he should drown it would be a shame.

There were no hurried words, no pallor, no plain agitation. The men simply looked at the shore. "Now, remember to get well clear of the boat when you jump," said the captain.

Seaward the crest of a roller suddenly fell with a thunderous crash, and the long white comber came roaring down upon the boat.

"Steady now," said the captain. The men were silent. They turned their eyes from the shore to the comber and waited. The boat slid up the incline, leaped at the furious top, bounced over it, and swung down the long back of the wave. Some water had been shipped and the cook bailed it out.

But the next crest crashed also. The tumbling, boiling flood of white water caught the boat and whirled it almost perpendicular. Water swarmed in from all sides. The correspondent had his hands on the gunwale at this time, and when the water entered at that place he swiftly withdrew his fingers, as if he objected to wetting them.

The little boat, drunken with this weight of water, reeled and snuggled deeper into the sea.

"Bail her out, cook! Bail her out," said the captain.

"All right, Captain," said the cook.

"Now, boys, the next one will do for us, sure," said the oiler. "Mind to jump clear of the boat."

The third wave moved forward, huge, furious, implacable. It fairly swallowed the dinghy, and almost simultaneously the men tumbled into the sea. A piece of life belt had lain in the bottom of the boat, and as the correspondent went overboard he held this to his chest with his left hand.

The January water was icy, and he reflected immediately that it was colder than he had expected to find it on the coast of Florida. This appeared to his dazed mind as a fact important enough to be noted at the time. The coldness of the water was sad; it was tragic. This fact was somehow so mixed and confused with his opinion of his own situation that it seemed almost a proper reason for tears. The water was cold.

When he came to the surface he was conscious of little but the noisy water. Afterward he saw his companions in the sea. The oiler was ahead in the race. He was swimming strongly and rapidly. Off to the correspondent's left, the cook's great white and corked back bulged out of the water, and in the rear the captain was hanging with his one good hand to the keel of the overturned dinghy.

There is a certain immovable quality to a shore, and the correspondent wondered at it amid the confusion of the sea.

It seemed also very attractive, but the correspondent knew that it was a long journey, and he paddled leisurely. The piece of life preserver lay under him, and sometimes he whirled down the incline of a wave as if he were on a hand-sled.

But finally he arrived at a place in the sea where travel was beset with difficulty. He did not pause swimming to inquire what manner of current had caught him, but there his progress ceased. The shore was set before him like a bit of scenery on a stage, and he looked at it and understood with his eyes each detail of it.

As the cook passed, much farther to the left, the captain was calling to him, "Turn over on your back, cook! Turn over on your back and use the oar."

"All right, sir." The cook turned on his back, and, paddling with an oar, went ahead as if he were a canoe.

Presently the boat also passed to the left of the correspondent, with the captain clinging with one hand to the keel. He would have appeared like a man raising himself to look over a board fence if it were not for the extraordinary gymnastics of the boat. The correspondent marveled that the captain could still hold to it.

They passed on nearer to shore, — the oiler, the cook, the captain, — and following them went the water jar, bouncing gaily over the seas.

The correspondent remained in the grip of this strange new enemy, a current. The shore, with its white slope of sand and its green bluff, topped with little silent cottages, was spread like a picture before him. It was very near to him then, but he was impressed as one who, in a gallery,[1] looks at a scene from Brittany or Algiers.

He thought: "I am going to drown? Can it be possible? Can it be possible? Can it be possible?" Perhaps an individual must consider his own death to be the final phenomenon of nature.

But later a wave perhaps whirled him out of this small deadly current, for he found suddenly that he could again make progress toward the shore. Later still he was aware that the captain, clinging

[1] **gallery: art gallery.**

with one hand to the keel of the dinghy, had his face turned away from the shore and toward him, and was calling his name. " Come to the boat! Come to the boat! "

In his struggle to reach the captain and the boat, he reflected that when one gets properly wearied drowning must really be a comfortable arrangement — a cessation of hostilities accompanied by a large degree of relief; and he was glad of it, for the main thing in his mind for some moments had been horror of the temporary agony; he did not wish to be hurt.

Presently he saw a man running along the shore. He was undressing with most remarkable speed. Coat, trousers, shirt, everything flew magically off him.

" Come to the boat! " called the captain.

" All right, Captain." As the correspondent paddled, he saw the captain let himself down to bottom and leave the boat. Then the correspondent performed his one little marvel of the voyage. A large wave caught him and flung him with ease and supreme speed completely over the boat and far beyond it. It struck him even then as an event in gymnastics and a true miracle of the sea. An overturned boat in the surf is not a plaything to a swimming man.

The correspondent arrived in water that reached only to his waist, but his condition did not enable him to stand for more than a moment. Each wave knocked him into a heap, and the undertow pulled at him.

Then he saw the man who had been running and undressing, and undressing and running, come bounding into the water. He dragged ashore the cook, and then waded toward the captain; but the captain waved him away and sent him to the correspondent. He was naked — naked as a tree in winter; but a halo was about his head, and he shone like a saint. He gave a strong pull, and a long drag, and a a bully heave at the correspondent's hand. The correspondent, schooled in the minor formulae, said, " Thanks, old man." But suddenly the man cried, " What's that? " He pointed a swift finger. The correspondent said, " Go."

In the shallows, face downward, lay the oiler. His forehead touched sand that was periodically, between each wave, clear of the sea.

The correspondent did not know all that transpired afterward.

When he achieved safe ground he fell, striking the sand with each particular part of his body. It was as if he had dropped from a roof, but the thud was grateful to him.

It seems that instantly the beach was populated with men with blankets, clothes, and flasks, and women with coffeepots and all the remedies sacred to their minds. The welcome of the land to the men from the sea was warm and generous; but a still and dripping shape was carried slowly up the beach, and the land's welcome for it could only be the different and sinister hospitality of the grave.

When it came night, the white waves paced to and fro in the moonlight, and the wind brought the sound of the great sea's voice to the men on shore, and they felt that they could then be interpreters.

READING WITH INSIGHT

1. The first thing you are likely to notice about this story is how real it seems. Before we analyze it any farther, ask yourself how Crane gets that air of reality in the story.

2. This story is notable for the little pictures, the images, the sharp descriptions that are scattered through it. For example, the water foaming into the boat from a whitecap is described as being "like white flames." The horizon was "jagged with waves that seemed thrust up in points like rocks." The gulls are described as "Canton flannel gulls." What especially sharp pictures of this kind can you pick out of the story? What examples of fine use of color?

3. Little pictures like these are often called "sense impressions" because they are the result of using the senses very sharply and well — seeing, hearing, smelling, feeling, tasting, and then describing the experience so that someone else can understand the impression we got. Have you ever tried to look out a window and tell someone what you saw? Have you ever tried sitting with your eyes closed, and writing down what you heard and smelled? Have you ever tried describing the feel of clean clothes, or the taste of cherry pie, or the bark of a dog? Every writer tries things like that. He opens up his senses, and then tries to find the right words to let someone else know what sense impressions he received. Try it; you'll be surprised

how many new sights, sounds, smells, tactile impressions, and tastes you will be able to receive. You are being bombarded all the time by these sense impressions, but you don't perceive many of them. Crane perceived a lot of them.

4. How does Crane use description to set the mood of the story? For example, the changing color of the sea.

5. How does he use description to make the story move? For example, what change do you notice in the way things look when the shipwrecked men are more hopeful and when they become discouraged again?

6. One of the most admired things about this story is the way Crane describes the passage of day into night, and vice versa. How does he do this? See pages 121 and 127, for example.

7. Some critics have thought that this story has a movement like the waves of the sea. The boatmen's hopes go up and down, like the waves. They come in almost to safety, and then are pulled away again. Up and down, all through the story. Cite examples of this movement in the story.

8. How well do you know these characters? Do they seem real? Do they react to this situation as you think real characters would? How would you compare the reality of these characters, for instance, with Bret Harte's characters in "The Outcasts of Poker Flat"?

9. This story shows man looking pretty small beside nature. On what occasions, if ever, have you had this feeling of insignificance and helplessness before nature — for instance, beside the ocean, or mountains, or a storm, or a desert, or some other great natural phenomenon?

10. Where is the climax in this story? Can you list the steps by which the tension rises to the climax?

11. Not much happens until the climax. The men sit in the boat, steer, occasionally row, sleep when they can, bail out the water, watch, and wait. How does Crane keep us interested during all this long time of no action?

12. One statement of the theme in this story might be, "Fate is unpredictable." For example, there is no apparent reason why the oiler, the strong man of the crew, should drown, while the others should be saved. Crane felt this injustice of nature very strongly.

Supposing that this is a good statement of the theme, how does the theme fall short of expressing the whole meaning of the story?

13. Crane used repetitions at a number of places in the story, apparently because he wanted to give us a sense of the heartbreaking monotony of the experience in the boat at the mercy of the sea. Can you pick out some of these repetitions?

14. This story is a good illustration of irony, which is a term much used in discussing modern literature. Irony means a big difference between what is said and what is meant, or between the outcome that is expected and what actually happens. For example, the drowning of the oiler might be called "the irony of fate." When Crane describes how picturesque the little boat doubtless would have looked to an outsider, he was being ironical. What other examples of irony in the story have you noticed?

If you like this story, you will be interested in

Crane. *A Mystery of Heroism.*
The Red Badge of Courage (novel).
Joseph Conrad. *Typhoon.*
The Secret Sharer.
Rudyard Kipling. *In Flood Time.*

JACK LONDON

All-Gold Cañon

JACK LONDON's first story was published in the same California magazine that published Bret Harte's first successful story, *The Overland Monthly*. And both Harte and London wrote about mining camps and outdoor life. But there were few other similarities.

Harte felt always like an exiled Easterner in the West. As soon as he had struck literary gold, he hurried east, and finally landed in London. He wrote about the mining country always with a touch of artifice, a sense of the picture-postcard quality of what he was describing. But London lived and loved the Western life. He was a perfect example of the he-man, red-meat school of writers. He left school at 14, tried one job after another, shipped before the mast to the northern seas and Japan, tramped across the United States and Canada as a hobo. This was for experience. Thirsty for knowledge, he went back to high school and tried the University of California for a few months. Then came the Alaskan gold strike, and he was off to the Klondike. He didn't strike gold, but he struck more experience.

When he finally stayed in one place long enough to write, he wrote of red-blooded outdoor men like those he had seen (and like himself). He wrote of high adventure like that he had seen and participated in. He wrote of miners, prize fighters, sailors, wolves, and dogs. His heroes are good fighters, and they have to fight to survive. London loved a good fight, and loved to write about strong men fighting. He was always sympathetic for an underdog, but his real love was for the strong man who by his own muscle and wit proved the truth of Darwin's doctrine of "survival of the fittest."

London lived from 1876 to 1916. You have probably read his *The Call of the Wild*, a novel which tells about a dog which left civilization and returned to become leader of a pack of wolves. This is his most famous story. You will find it a good study in plot.

It was the green heart of the cañon, where the walls swerved back from the rigid plan and relieved their harshness of line by making a little sheltered nook and filling it to the brim with sweetness and roundness and softness. Here all things rested. Even the narrow stream ceased its turbulent downrush long enough to form a quiet pool. Knee-deep in the water, with drooping head and half-shut eyes, drowsed a red-coated, many-antlered buck.

On one side, beginning at the very lip of the pool, was a tiny meadow, a cool, resilient surface of green that extended to the base of the frowning wall. Beyond the pool a gentle slope of earth ran up and up to meet the opposing wall. Fine grass covered the slope — grass that was spangled with flowers, with here and there patches of color, orange and purple and golden. Below, the cañon was shut in. There was no view. The walls leaned together abruptly and the cañon ended in a chaos of rocks, moss-covered and hidden by a green screen of vines and creepers and boughs of trees. Up the cañon rose far hills and peaks, the big foothills, pine-covered and remote. And far beyond, like clouds upon the border of the sky, towered minarets of white, where the Sierra's eternal snows flashed austerely the blazes of the sun.

There was no dust in the cañon. The leaves and flowers were clean and virginal. The grass was young velvet. Over the pool three cottonwoods sent their snowy fluffs fluttering down the quiet air. On the slope the blossoms of the wine-wooded manzanita filled the air with springtime odors, while the leaves, wise with experience, were already beginning their vertical twist against the coming aridity of summer. In the open spaces on the slope, beyond the farthest shadow reach of the manzanita, poised the mariposa lilies, like so many flights of jeweled moths suddenly arrested and on the verge of trembling into flight again. Here and there that woods harlequin,[1] the madrone, permitting itself to be caught in the act of changing its pea green trunk to madder red, breathed its fragrance into the air from great clusters of waxen bells. Creamy white were these bells, shaped like lilies of the valley, with the sweetness of perfume that is of the springtime.

There was not a sigh of wind. The air was drowsy with its weight of perfume. It was a sweetness that would have been cloying had

[1] **harlequin:** a brightly dressed clown.

the air been heavy and humid. But the air as sharp and thin. It was as starlight transmuted into atmosphere, shot through and warmed by sunshine, and flower-drenched with sweetness.

An occasional butterfly drifted in and out through the patches of light and shade. And from all about rose the low and sleepy hum of mountain bees — feasting Sybarites [1] that jostled one another good-naturedly at the board, nor found time for rough discourtesy. So quietly did the little stream drip and ripple its way through the cañon that it spoke only in faint and occasional gurgles. The voice of the stream was as a drowsy whisper, ever interrupted by dozings and silences, ever lifted again in the awakenings.

The motion of all things was a drifting in the heart of the cañon. Sunshine and butterflies drifted in and out among the trees. The hum of the bees and the whisper of the stream were a drifting of sound. And the drifting sound and drifting color seemed to weave together in the making of a delicate and intangible fabric which was the spirit of the place. It was a spirit of peace that was not of death, but of smooth-pulsing life, of quietude that was not silence, of movement that was not action, of repose that was quick with existence without being violent with struggle and travail. The spirit of the place was the spirit of the peace of the living, somnolent with the easement and content of prosperity, and undisturbed by rumors of far wars.

The red-coated, many-antlered buck acknowledged the lordship of the spirit of the place and dozed knee-deep in the cool, shaded pool. There seemed no flies to vex him, and he was languid with rest. Sometimes his ears moved when the stream awoke and whispered; but they moved lazily, with foreknowledge that it was merely the stream grown garrulous at discovery that it had slept.

But there came a time when the buck's ears lifted and tensed with swift eagerness for sound. His head was turned down the cañon. His sensitive, quivering nostrils scented the air. His eyes could not pierce the green screen through which the stream rippled away, but to his ears came the voice of a man. It was a steady, monotonous, singsong voice. Once the buck heard the harsh clash of metal upon rock. At the sound he snorted with a sudden start that jerked him

[1] **Sybarites: the people of the ancient city of Sybaris, noted for their love of luxury and feasting.**

through the air from water to meadow, and his feet sank into the young velvet, while he pricked his ears and again scented the air. Then he stole across the tiny meadow, pausing once and again to listen, and faded away out of the cañon like a wraith, soft-footed and without sound.

The clash of steel-shod soles against the rocks began to be heard, and the man's voice grew louder. It was raised in a sort of chant and became distinct with nearness, so that the words could be heard:

> "T'n around an' tu'n yo' face
> Untoe them sweet hills of grace
> (D' pow'rs of sin yo' am scornin'!).
> Look about an' look aroun',
> Fling yo' sin-pack on d' groun'
> (Yo' will meet wid d' Lord in d' mornin'!)"

A sound of scrambling accompanied the song, and the spirit of the place fled away on the heels of the red-coated buck. The green screen was burst asunder, and a man peered out at the meadow and the pool and the sloping sidehill. He was a deliberate sort of man. He took in the scene with one embracing glance, then ran his eyes over the details to verify the general impression. Then, and not until then, did he open his mouth in vivid and solemn approval: "Smoke of life an' snakes of purgatory! Will you just look at that! Wood an' water an' grass an' a sidehill! A pocket hunter's delight an' a cayuse's [1] paradise! Cool green for tired eyes! Pink pills for pale people ain't in it. A secret pasture for prospectors and a resting place for tired burros, by damn!"

He was a sandy-complexioned man in whose face geniality and humor seemed the salient characteristics. It was a mobile face, quick-changing to inward mood and thought. Thinking was in him a visible process. Ideas chased across his face like wind-flaws across the surface of a lake. His hair, sparse and unkempt of growth, was as indeterminate and colorless as his complexion. It would seem that all the color of his frame had gone into his eyes, for they were startlingly blue. Also, they were laughing and merry eyes, within them much of the naïveté and wonder of the child; and yet, in an unassertive way, they contained much of calm self-reliance and strength

[1] **cayuse: an Indian pony.**

of purpose founded upon self-experience and experience of the world.

From out the screen of vines and creepers he flung ahead of him a miner's pick and shovel and gold pan. Then he crawled out himself into the open. He was clad in faded overalls and black cotton shirt, with hobnailed brogans on his feet, and on his head a hat whose shapelessness and stains advertised the rough usage of wind and rain in sun and camp smoke. He stood erect, seeing wide-eyed the secrecy of the scene and sensuously inhaling the warm, sweet breath of the cañon garden through nostrils that dilated and quivered with delight. His eyes narrowed to laughing slits of blue, his face wreathed itself in joy, and his mouth curled in a smile as he cried aloud: "Jumping dandelions and happy hollyhocks, but that smells good to me! Talk about your attar o' roses an' cologne factories! They ain't in it!"

He had the habit of soliloquy. His quick-changing facial expressions might tell every thought and mood, but the tongue, perforce, ran hard after, repeating, like a second Boswell.[1]

The man lay down on the lip of the pool and drank long and deep of its water. "Tastes good to me," he murmured, lifting his head and gazing across the pool at the sidehill, while he wiped his mouth with the back of his hand. The sidehill attracted his attention. Still lying on his stomach, he studied the hill formation long and carefully. It was a practiced eye that traveled up the slope to the crumbling cañon wall and back and down again to the edge of the pool. He scrambled to his feet and favored the sidehill with a second survey.

"Looks good to me," he concluded, picking up his pick and shovel and gold pan.

He crossed the stream below the pool, stepping agilely from stone to stone. Where the sidehill touched the water he dug up a shovelful of dirt and put it into the gold pan. He squatted down, holding the pan in his two hands, and partly immersing it in the stream. Then he imparted to the pan a deft circular motion that sent the water sluicing in and out through the dirt and gravel. The larger and the lighter particles worked to the surface, and these, by a skill-

[1] Boswell: James Boswell wrote the life of Samuel Johnson. He gathered his material by painstakingly recording Johnson's conversations.

ful dipping movement of the pan, he spilled out and over the edge. Occasionally, to expedite matters, he rested the pan and with his fingers raked out the large pebbles and pieces of rock.

The contents of the pan diminished rapidly until only fine dirt and the smallest bits of gravel remained. At this stage he began to work very deliberately and carefully. It was fine washing, and he washed fine and finer, with a keen scrutiny and delicate and fastidious touch. At last the pan seemed empty of everything but water; but with a quick semicircular flirt that sent the water flying over the shallow rim into the stream, he disclosed a layer of black sand on the bottom of the pan. So thin was this layer that it was like a streak of paint. He examined it closely. In the midst of it was a tiny golden speck. He dribbled a little water in over the depressed edge of the pan. With a quick flirt he sent the water sluicing across the bottom, turning the grains of black sand over and over. A second tiny golden speck rewarded his effort.

The washing had now become very fine — fine beyond all need of ordinary placer mining. He worked the black sand, a small portion at a time, up the shallow rim of the pan. Each small portion he examined sharply, so that his eyes saw every grain of it before he allowed it to slide over the edge and away. Jealously, bit by bit, he let the black sand slip away. A golden speck, no larger than a pinpoint, appeared on the rim, and by his manipulation of the water it returned to the bottom of the pan. And in such fashion another speck was disclosed, and another. Great was his care of them. Like a shepherd he herded his flock of golden specks so that not one should be lost. At last, of the pan of dirt nothing remained but his golden herd. He counted it, and then, after all his labor, set it flying out of the pan with one final swirl of water.

But his blue eyes were shining with desire as he rose to his feet. "Seven," he muttered aloud, asserting the sum of the specks for which he had toiled so hard and which he had so wantonly thrown away. "Seven," he repeated, with the emphasis of one trying to impress a number on his memory.

He stood still a long while, surveying the hillside. In his eyes was a curiosity, new aroused and burning. There was an exultance about his bearing and a keenness like that of a hunting animal catching the fresh scent of game.

He moved down the stream a few steps and took a second panful of dirt.

Again came the careful washing, the jealous herding of the golden specks, and the wantonness with which he sent them flying into the stream when he had counted their number.

"Five," he muttered, and repeated, "five."

He could not forbear another survey of the hill before filling the pan farther down the stream. His golden herds diminished. "Four, three, two, two, one," were his memory tabulations as he moved down the stream. When but one speck of gold rewarded his washing, he stopped and built a fire of dry twigs. Into this he thrust the gold pan and burned it till it was blue-black. He held up the pan and examined it critically. Then he nodded approbation. Against such a color background he could defy the tiniest yellow speck to elude him.

Still moving down the stream, he panned again. A single speck was his reward. A third pan contained no gold at all. Not satisfied with this, he panned three times again, taking his shovels of dirt within a foot of one another. Each pan proved empty of gold, and the fact, instead of discouraging him, seemed to give him satisfaction. His elation increased with each barren washing, until he arose, exclaiming jubilantly, "If it ain't the real thing, may they knock off my head with sour apples!"

Returning to where he had started operations, he began to pan up the stream. At first his golden herds increased — increased prodigiously. "Fourteen, eighteen, twenty-one, twenty-six," ran his memory tabulations. Just above the pool he struck his richest pan, — thirty-five colors.

"Almost enough to save," he remarked regretfully, as he allowed the water to sweep them away.

The sun climbed to the top of the sky. The man worked on. Pan by pan he went up the stream, the tally of results steadily decreasing.

"It's just booful, the way it peters out," he exulted when a shovelful of dirt contained no more than a single speck of gold.

And when no specks at all were found in several pans, he straightened up and favored the hillside with a confident glance.

"Ah, ha! Mr. Pocket!" he cried out, as though to an auditor hidden somewhere above him beneath the surface of the slope. "Ah, ha! Mr. Pocket! I'm a-comin', I'm a-comin', an' I'm shorely gwine to get yer! You heah me, Mr. Pocket? I'm gwine to get yer as shore as punkins ain't cauliflowers!"

He turned and flung a measuring glance at the sun poised above him in the azure of the cloudless sky. Then he went down the cañon, following the line of shovel holes he had made in filling the pans. He crossed the stream below the pool and disappeared through the green screen. There was little opportunity for the spirit of the place to return with its quietude and repose, for the man's voice, raised in ragtime song, still dominated the cañon with possession.

After a time, with a greater clashing of steel-shod feet on rock, he returned. The green screen was tremendously agitated. It surged back and forth in the throes of a struggle. There was a loud grating and clanging of metal. The man's voice leaped to a higher pitch and was sharp with imperativeness. A large body plunged and panted. There was a snapping and ripping and rending, and amid a shower of falling leaves a horse burst through the screen. On its back was a pack, and from this trailed broken vines and torn creepers. The animal gazed with astonished eyes at the scene into which it had been precipitated, then dropped its head to the grass and began contentedly to graze. A second horse scrambled into view, slipping once on the mossy rocks and regaining equilibrium when its hoofs sank into the yielding surface of the meadow. It was riderless, though on its back was a high-horned Mexican saddle, scarred and discolored by long usage.

The man brought up the rear. He threw off pack and saddle, with an eye to camp location, and gave the animals their freedom to graze. He unpacked his food and got out frying pan and coffeepot. He gathered an armful of dry wood, and with a few stones made a place for his fire.

"My!" he said, "but I've got an appetite. I could scoff[1] iron filings an' horseshoe nails an' thank you kindly, ma'am, for a second helpin'."

He straightened up, and while he reached for matches in the pocket of his overalls his eyes traveled across the pool to the sidehill. His fingers had clutched the matchbox, but they relaxed their

[1] **scoff**: gulp down, scoff at the difficulty of eating.

hold and the hand came out empty. The man wavered perceptibly. He looked at his preparations for cooking and he looked at the hill.

"Guess I'll take another whack at her," he concluded, starting to cross the stream.

"They ain't no sense in it, I know," he mumbled apologetically. "But keepin' grub back an hour ain't goin' to hurt none, I reckon."

A few feet back from his first line of test pans he started a second line. The sun dropped down the western sky, the shadows lengthened, but the man worked on. He began a third line of test pans. He was crosscutting the hillside, line by line, as he ascended. The center of each line produced the richest pans, while the ends came where no colors showed in the pan. And as he ascended the hillside the lines grew perceptibly shorter. The regularity with which their length diminished served to indicate that somewhere up the slope the last line would be so short as to have scarcely length at all, and that beyond could come only a point. The design was growing into an inverted **V**. The converging sides of this **V** marked the boundaries of the gold-bearing dirt.

The apex of the **V** was evidently the man's goal. Often he ran his eye along the converging sides and on up the hill, trying to divine the apex — the point where the gold-bearing dirt must cease. Here resided "Mr. Pocket," for so the man familiarly addressed the imaginary point above him on the slope, crying out: "Come down out o' that, Mr. Pocket! Be right smart an' agreeable, an' come down!"

"All right," he would add later, in a voice resigned to determination.

"All right, Mr. Pocket. It's plain to me I got to come right up an' snatch you out bald-headed. An' I'll do it! I'll do it!" he would threaten still later.

Each pan he carried down to the water to wash, and as he went higher up the hill the pans grew richer, until he began to save the gold in an empty baking-powder can which he carried carelessly in his hip pocket. So engrossed was he in his toil that he did not notice the long twilight of oncoming night. It was not until he tried vainly to see the gold colors in the bottom of the pan that he realized the passage of time. He straightened up abruptly. An expression of whimsical wonderment and awe overspread his face as he drawled, —

"Gosh darn my buttons! if I didn't plumb forget dinner!"

He stumbled across the stream in the darkness and lighted his long delayed fire. Flapjacks and bacon and warmed over beans constituted his supper. Then he smoked a pipe by the smoldering coals, listening to the night noises and watching the moonlight stream through the cañon. After that he unrolled his bed, took off his heavy shoes, and pulled the blankets up to his chin. His face showed white in the moonlight, like the face of a corpse. But it was a corpse that knew its resurrection, for the man rose suddenly on one elbow and gazed across at his hillside.

" Good night, Mr. Pocket," he called sleepily. " Good night."

He slept through the early gray of morning until the direct rays of the sun smote his closed eyelids, when he awoke with a start and looked about him until he had established the continuity of his existence and identified his present self with the days previously lived.

To dress, he had merely to buckle on his shoes. He glanced at his fireplace and at his hillside, wavered, but fought down the temptation and started the fire.

" Keep yer shirt on, Bill; keep yer shirt on," he admonished himself. " What's the good of rushin'? No use in gettin' all het up an' sweaty. Mr. Pocket'll wait for you. He ain't a-runnin' away before you can get yer breakfast. Now, what you want, Bill, is something fresh in yer bill o' fare. So it's up to you to go an' get it."

He cut a short pole at the water's edge and drew from one of his pockets a bit of line and a draggled fly that had once been a royal coachman.

" Mebbe they'll bite in the early morning," he muttered, as he made his first cast into the pool. And a moment later he was gleefully crying: " What'd I tell you, eh? What'd I tell you? "

He had no reel, nor any inclination to waste time, and by main strength, and swiftly, he drew out of the water a flashing ten inch trout. Three more, caught in rapid succession, furnished his breakfast. When he came to the steppingstones on his way to his hillside, he was struck by a sudden thought, and paused.

" I'd just better take a hike downstream a ways," he said. " There's no tellin' what cuss may be snoopin' around."

But he crossed over on the stones, and with a " I really oughter take that hike," the need of the precaution passed out of his mind and he fell to work.

At nightfall he straightened up. The small of his back was stiff from stooping toil, and as he put his hand behind him to soothe the protesting muscles, he said: —

"Now what d'ye think of that? I clean forgot my dinner again! If I don't watch out, I'll sure be degeneratin' into a two-meal-a-day crank."

"Pockets is the worst things I ever see for makin' a man absent-minded," he communed that night, as he crawled into his blankets. Nor did he forget to call up the hillside, "Good night, Mr. Pocket! Good night!"

Rising with the sun, and snatching a hasty breakfast, he was early at work. A fever seemed to be growing in him, nor did the increasing richness of the test pans allay this fever. There was a flush in his cheek other than that made by the heat of the sun, and he was oblivious to fatigue and the passage of time. When he filled a pan with dirt, he ran down the hill to wash it; nor could he forbear running up the hill again, panting and stumbling profanely, to refill the pan.

He was now a hundred yards from the water, and the inverted **V** was assuming definite proportions. The width of the pay dirt steadily decreased, and the man extended in his mind's eye the sides of the **V** to their meeting place far up the hill. This was his goal, the apex of the **V**, and he panned many times to locate it.

"Just about two yards above that manzanita bush an' a yard to the right," he finally concluded.

Then the temptation seized him. "As plain as the nose on your face," he said, as he abandoned his laborious crosscutting and climbed to the indicated apex. He filled a pan and carried it down the hill to wash. It contained no trace of gold. He dug deep, and he dug shallow, filling and washing a dozen pans, and was unrewarded even by the tiniest golden speck. He was enraged at having yielded to the temptation, and cursed himself blasphemously and pridelessly. Then he went down the hill and took up the crosscutting.

"Slow an' certain, Bill; slow an' certain," he crooned. "Short cuts to fortune ain't in your line, an' it's about time you know it. Get wise, Bill; get wise. Slow an' certain 's the only hand you can play; so go to it, an' keep to it, too."

As the crosscuts decreased, showing that the sides of the **V** were converging, the depth of the **V** increased. The gold trace was dipping into the hill. It was only at thirty inches beneath the surface that he could get colors in his pan. The dirt he found at twenty-five inches from the surface, and at thirty-five inches, yielded barren pans. At the base of the V by the water's edge, he had found the gold colors at the grass roots. The higher he went up the hill, the deeper the gold dipped. To dig a hole three feet deep in order to get one test pan was a task of no mean magnitude; while between the man and the apex intervened an untold number of such holes to be dug. "An' there's no tellin' how much deeper it'll pitch," he sighed, in a moment's pause, while his fingers soothed his aching back.

Feverish with desire, with aching back and stiffening muscles, with pick and shovel gouging and mauling the soft brown earth, the man toiled up the hill. Before him was the smooth slope, spangled with flowers and made sweet with their breath. Behind him was devastation. It looked like some terrible eruption breaking out on the smooth skin of the hill. His slow progress was like that of a slug, befouling beauty with a monstrous trail.

Though the dipping gold trace increased the man's work, he found consolation in the increasing richness of the pans. Twenty cents, thirty cents, fifty cents, sixty cents, were the values of the gold found in the pans, and at nightfall he washed his banner pan, which gave him a dollar's worth of gold dust from a shovelful of dirt.

"I'll just bet it's my luck to have some inquisitive cuss come buttin' in here on my pasture," he mumbled sleepily that night as he pulled the blankets up to his chin.

Suddenly he sat upright. "Bill!" he called sharply. "Now, listen to me, Bill; d'ye hear! It's up to you, tomorrow mornin', to mosey round an' see what you can see. Understand? Tomorrow morning, an' don't you forget it!"

He yawned and glanced across at his sidehill. "Good night, Mr. Pocket," he called.

In the morning he stole a march on the sun, for he had finished breakfast when its first rays caught him, and he was climbing the wall of the cañon where it crumbled away and gave footing. From outlook at the top he found himself in the midst of loneliness. As far as he could see, chain after chain of mountains heaved themselves into his vision. To the east his eyes, leaping the miles between range and range and between many ranges, brought up at last against the white-peaked Sierras, — the main crest, where the backbone of the Western world reared itself against the sky. To the north and south he could see more distinctly the cross systems that broke through the main trend of the sea of mountains. To the west the ranges fell away, one behind the other, diminishing and fading into the gentle foothills that, in turn, descended into the great valley which he could not see.

And in all that mighty sweep of earth he saw no sign of man nor of the handiwork of man, save only the torn bosom of the hillside at his feet. The man looked long and carefully. Once, far down his own cañon, he thought he saw in the air a faint hint of smoke. He looked again and decided that it was the purple haze of the hills made dark by a convolution of the cañon wall at its back.

"Hey, you, Mr. Pocket!" he called down into the cañon. "Stand out from under! I'm a-comin', Mr. Pocket! I'm a-comin'!"

The heavy brogans on the man's feet made him appear clumsy-footed, but he swung down from the giddy height as lightly and airily as a mountain goat. A rock, turning under his foot on the edge of the precipice, did not disconcert him. He seemed to know the precise time required for the turn to culminate in disaster, and in the meantime he utilized the false footing itself for the momentary earth contact necessary to carry him on into safety. Where the earth sloped so steeply that it was impossible to stand for a second upright, the man did not hesitate. His foot pressed the impossible surface for but a fraction of the fatal second and gave him the bound that carried him onward. Again, where even the fraction of a second's footing was out of the question, he would swing his body past by a moment's handgrip on a jutting knob of rock, a crevice, or a precariously rooted shrub. At last, with a wild leap and yell, he exchanged the face of the wall for an earth slide and finished the descent in the midst of several tons of sliding earth and gravel.

His first pan of the morning washed out over two dollars in coarse gold. It was from the center of the **V**. To either side the diminution in the values of the pans was swift. His lines of crosscutting holes were growing very short. The converging sides of the inverted **V** were only a few yards apart. Their meeting point was only a few yards above him. But the pay streak was dipping deeper and deeper into the earth. By early afternoon he was sinking the test holes five feet before the pans could show the gold trace.

For that matter, the gold trace had become something more than a trace; it was a placer mine in itself, and the man resolved to come back, after he had found the pocket, and work over the ground. But the increasing richness of the pans began to worry him. By later afternoon the worth of the pans had grown to three and four dollars. The man scratched his head perplexedly and looked a few feet up the hill at the manzanita bush that marked approximately the apex of the **V**. He nodded his head and said oracularly: "It's one o' two things, Bill; one o' two things. Either Mr. Pocket's spilled himself all out an' down the hill, or else Mr. Pocket's that rich you maybe won't be able to carry him all away with you. And that'd be tough, wouldn't it, now?" He chuckled at contemplation of so pleasant a dilemma.

Nightfall found him by the edge of the stream, his eyes wrestling with the gathering darkness over the washing of a five-dollar pan.

"Wisht I had an electric light to go on working," he said.

He found sleep difficult that night. Many times he composed himself and closed his eyes for slumber to overtake him; but his blood pounded with too strong desire, and as many times his eyes opened and he murmured wearily, "Wisht it was sunup."

Sleep came to him in the end, but his eyes were open with the first paling of the stars, and the gray of dawn caught him with breakfast finished and climbing the hillside in the direction of the secret abiding place of Mr. Pocket.

The first crosscut the man made, there was space for only three holes, so narrow had become the pay streak and so close was he to the fountainhead of the golden stream he had been following for four days.

"Be ca'm, Bill; be ca'm," he admonished himself, as he broke ground for the final hole where the sides of the **V** had at last come together in a point.

"I've got the almighty cinch on you, Mr. Pocket, an' you can't lose me," he said many times as he sank the hole deeper and deeper.

Four feet, five feet, six feet, he dug his way down into the earth. The digging grew harder. His pick grated on broken rock. He examined the rock. "Rotten quartz," was his conclusion as, with the shovel, he cleared the bottom of the hole of loose dirt. He attacked the crumbling quartz with the pick, bursting the disintegrating rock asunder with every stroke.

He thrust his shovel into the loose mass. His eye caught a gleam of yellow. He dropped the shovel and squatted suddenly on his heels. As a farmer rubs the clinging earth from fresh dug potatoes, so the man, a piece of rotten quartz held in both hands. rubbed the dirt away.

" Sufferin' Sardanapolis! " he cried. " Lumps an' chunks of it! Lumps an' chunks of it! "

It was only half rock he held in his hand. The other half was virgin gold. He dropped it into his pan and examined another piece. Little yellow was to be seen, but with his strong fingers he crumbled the rotten quartz away till both hands were filled with glowing yellow. He rubbed the dirt away from fragment after fragment, tossing them into the gold pan. It was a treasure hole. So much had the quartz rotted away that there was less of it than there was of gold. Now and again he found a piece to which no rock clung — a piece that was all gold. A chunk, where the pick had laid open the heart of the gold, glittered like a handful of yellow jewels, and he cocked his head at it and slowly turned it around and over to observe the rich play of the light upon it.

" Talk about yer Too Much Gold diggin's! " the man snorted contemptuously. " Why, this diggin' 'd make it look like thirty cents. This diggin' is All Gold. An' right here an' now I name this yere cañon ' All-Gold Cañon,' b' gosh! "

Still squatting on his heels, he continued examining the fragments and tossing them into the pan. Suddenly there came to him a premonition of danger. It seemed a shadow had fallen upon him. But there was no shadow. His heart had given a great jump up into his throat and was choking him. Then his blood slowly chilled and he felt the sweat of his shirt cold against his flesh.

He did not spring up nor look around. He did not move. He was considering the nature of the premonition he had received, trying to locate the source of the mysterious force that had warned him striving to sense the imperative presence of the unseen thing that threatened him. There is an aura of things hostile, made manifest by messengers too refined for the senses to know; and this aura he felt, but knew not how he felt it His was the feeling as when a cloud passes over the sun. It seemed that between him and life had passed something dark and smothering and menacing, a gloom, as it were, that swallowed up life and made for death — his death.

Every force of his being impelled him to spring up and confront the unseen danger, but his soul dominated the panic, and he remained squatting on his heels, in his hands a chunk of gold. He did not dare to look around, but he knew by now that there was something behind him and above him. He made believe to be interested in the gold in his hand. He examined it critically, turned it over and over, and rubbed the dirt from it. And all the time he knew that something behind him was looking at the gold over his shoulder.

Still feigning interest in the chunk of gold in his hand, he listened intently, and he heard the breathing of the thing behind him. His eyes searched the ground in front of him for a weapon, but they saw only the uprooted gold, worthless to him now in his extremity. There was his pick, a handy weapon on occasion; but this was not such an occasion. The man realized his predicament. He was in a narrow hole that was seven feet deep. His head did not come to the surface of the ground. He was in a trap.

He remained squatting on his heels. He was quite cool and collected; but his mind, considering every factor, showed him only his helplessness. He continued rubbing the dirt from the quartz fragments and throwing the gold into the pan. There was nothing else for him to do. Yet he knew that he would have to rise up, sooner or later, and face the danger that breathed at his back. The minutes passed, and with the passage of each minute he knew that by so much he was nearer the time when he must stand up, or else — and his wet shirt went cold against his flesh again at the thought — or else he might receive death as he stooped there over his treasure.

Still he squatted on his heels, rubbing dirt from gold and debating in just what manner he should rise up. He might rise up with a rush and claw his way out of the hole to meet whatever threatened on the even footing above ground; or he might rise up slowly and carelessly, and feign casually to discover the thing that breathed at his back. His instinct and every fighting fiber of his body favored the mad, clawing rush to the surface. His intellect, and the craft thereof, favored the slow and cautious meeting with the thing that menaced and that he could not see. And while he debated, a loud, crashing noise burst on his ear. At the same instant he received a stunning blow on the left side of the back, and from the point of impact felt a rush of flame through his flesh. He sprang up in the air, but halfway to his feet collapsed. His body crumpled in like a leaf withered in sudden heat, and he came down, his chest across his pan of gold, his face in the dirt and rock, his legs tangled and twisted because of the restricted space at the bottom of the hole. His legs twitched convulsively several times. His body was shaken as with a mighty ague. There was a slow expansion of the lungs, accompanied by a deep sigh. Then the air was slowly, very slowly, exhaled, and his body as slowly flattened itself down into inertness.

Above, revolver in hand, a man was peering down over the edge of the hole. He peered for a long time at the prone and motionless body beneath him. After a while the stranger sat down on the edge of the hole so that he could see into it, and rested the revolver on his knee. Reaching his hand into a pocket, he drew out a wisp of brown paper. Into this he dropped a few crumbs of tobacco. The combination became a cigarette, brown and squat, with the ends turned in. Not once did he take his eyes from the body at the bottom of the hole. He lighted the cigarette and drew its smoke into his lungs with a caressing intake of the breath. He smoked slowly. Once the cigarette went out and he relighted it. And all the while he studied the body beneath him.

In the end he tossed the cigarette stub away and rose to his feet. He moved to the edge of the hole. Spanning it, a hand resting on each edge, and with the revolver still in the right hand, he muscled his body down into the hole. While his feet were yet a yard from the bottom he released his hands and dropped down.

At the instant his feet struck bottom he saw the pocket miner's arm leap out, and his own legs knew a swift, jerking grip that overthrew him. In the nature of the jump his revolver hand was above his head. Swiftly as the grip had flashed about his legs, just as swiftly he brought the revolver down. He was still in the air, his fall in process of completion, when he pulled the trigger. The explosion was deafening in the confined space. The smoke filled the hole so that he could see nothing. He struck the bottom on his back, and like a cat's the pocket miner's body was on top of him. Even as the miner's body passed on top the stranger crooked in his right arm to fire; and even in that instant the miner, with a quick thrust of elbow, struck his wrist. The muzzle was thrown up, and the bullet thudded into the dirt of the side of the hole.

The next instant the stranger felt the miner's hand grip his wrist. The struggle was now for the revolver. Each man strove to turn it against the other's body. The smoke in the hole was clearing. The stranger, lying on his back, was beginning to see dimly. But suddenly he was blinded by a handful of dirt deliberately flung into his eyes by his antagonist. In that moment of shock his grip on the revolver was broken. In the next moment he felt a smashing darkness descend upon his brain, and in the midst of the darkness even the darkness ceased.

But the pocket miner fired again and again, until the revolver was empty. Then he tossed it from him and, breathing heavily, sat down on the dead man's legs.

The miner was sobbing and struggling for breath. "Measly skunk!" he panted; "a-campin' on my trail an' lettin' me do the work, an' then shootin' me in the back!"

He was half crying from anger and exhaustion. He peered at the face of the dead man. It was sprinkled with loose dirt and gravel, and it was difficult to distinguish the features.

"Never laid eyes on him before," the miner concluded his scrutiny. "Just a common an' ordinary thief, damn him! An' he shot me in the back! He shot me in the back!"

He opened his shirt and felt himself, front and back, on his left side.

"Went clean through, and no harm done!" he cried jubilantly. "I'll bet he aimed all right, all right; but he drew the gun over when he pulled the trigger — the cuss! But I fixed 'm! Oh, I fixed 'm!"

His fingers were investigating the bullet hole in his side, and a shade of regret passed over his face. "It's goin' to be stiff," he said. "An' it's up to me to get mended an' get out o' here."

He crawled out of the hole and went down the hill to his camp. Half an hour later he returned, leading his pack horse. His open shirt disclosed the rude bandages with which he had dressed his wounds. He was slow and awkward with his left-hand movements, but that did not prevent his using the arm.

The bight of the pack rope under the dead man's shoulders enabled him to heave the body out of the hole. Then he set to work gathering up his gold. He worked steadily for several hours, pausing often to rest his stiffening shoulder and to exclaim: " He shot me in the back, the measly skunk! He shot me in the back! "

When his treasure was quite cleaned up and wrapped securely into a number of blanket-covered parcels, he made an estimate of its value.

" Four hundred pounds, or I'm a Hottentot," he concluded. " Say two hundred in quartz an' dirt; that leaves two hundred pounds of gold. Bill! Wake up! Two hundred pounds of gold! Forty thousand dollars! An' it's yourn — all yourn! "

He scratched his head delightedly and his fingers blundered into an unfamilar groove. They quested along it for several inches. It was a crease through his scalp where the second bullet had plowed.

He walked angrily over to the dead man.

" You would, would you? " he bullied. " You would, eh? Well, I fixed you good an' plenty, an' I'll give you decent burial, too. That's more 'n you'd have done for me."

He dragged the body to the edge of the hole and toppled it in. It struck the bottom with a dull crash, on its side, the face twisted up to the light. The miner peered down at it.

" An' you shot me in the back! " he said accusingly.

With pick and shovel he filled the hole. Then he loaded the gold on his horse. It was too great a load for the animal, and when he had gained his camp he transferred part of it to his saddle horse. Even so, he was compelled to abandon a portion of his outfit, — pick and shovel and gold pan, extra food and cooking utensils, and divers odds and ends.

The sun was at the zenith when the man forced the horses at the screen of vines and creepers. To climb the huge boulders the animals were compelled to uprear and struggle blindly through the tangled mass of vegetation. Once the saddle horse fell heavily, and the man removed the pack to get the animal on his feet. After it started on its way again the man thrust his head out from among the leaves and peered up at the sidehill.

" The measly skunk! " he said, and disappeared.

There was a ripping and tearing of vines and boughs. The trees surged back and rorth, marking the passage of the animals through the midst of them. There was a clashing of steel-shod hoofs on stone, and now and again an oath or a sharp cry of command. Then the voice of the man was raised in song:

"Tu'n around an' tu'n yo' face
Untoe them sweet hills of grace
(D' pow'rs of sin yo' am scornin'!).
Look about an' look aroun',
Fling yo' sin-pack on d' groun'
(Yo' will meet wid d' Lord in d' mornin'!)"

The song grew faint and fainter, and through the silence crept back the spirit of the place. The stream once more drowsed and whispered; the hum of the mountain bees rose sleepily. Down through the perfume-weighted air fluttered the snowy fluffs of the cottonwoods. The butterflies drifted in and out among the trees, and over all blazed the quiet sunshine. Only remained the hoof marks in the meadow and the torn hillside to mark the boisterous trail of the life that had broken the peace of the place and passed on.

READING WITH INSIGHT

1. You will find it interesting to notice how different writers begin their stories. For example, look back and see how Crane begins "The Open Boat." Do you like his beginning or London's beginning in this story better? What, if anything, is gained by starting with the scenery as seen through the characters' eyes (as Crane does) rather than the scenery as seen through the author's eyes (as London does)?

2. Why do you think London begins and ends this story with a passage of nature description? With what in the story does the peace of nature contrast?

3. What would you say is the theme of this story — that is, what is London trying to say about life? Here are some suggestions turned in by other students: "To the victor belongs the spoils." "You've got to fight for what you get out of life." "All life is a

fight, and only the fittest survive." "Nature is peaceful until man disturbs it." "The civilization of man is only a veneer; scrape it and you'll find a beast underneath." Does any of these statements seem adequate? If not, how would you express the meaning?

4. This is a story about the same country as "The Outcasts of Poker Flat." Which of these stories gives you a better picture of the country? Which one tells you more about the way people lived in that country, about a hundred years ago, when these stories were supposed to have taken place? Cite some especially good examples of London's description.

5. The last three stories all have been built around strong men — the oiler in "The Open Boat," Oakhurst in "The Outcasts of Poker Flat," and Bill, the miner, in this story. In what way is each one strong, and in what way is each one weak? Were the two who died any weaker than Bill who won his fight and survived? Did those two die because of weakness or for some other reason? Did Bill win because of his strength or for some other reason?

6. Another way to look at the question we have just asked is to recall that Oakhurst says he fell victim to a run of bad luck. The oiler falls victim to what looks like a trick of fate. What seems to be London's attitude toward luck and fate, as shown in what happens to his chief character in this story?

7. This is a good story with which to study plot. Notice especially that the conflict is very clear in the plot structure. In general, the miner Bill has first to face a conflict with nature, then a conflict with the highjacker. List the steps in this twofold conflict as the tension rises to the climax.

8. The writer in this story had to bring the highjacker in as a surprise, and yet he had to make his readers realize, when they stopped to think about it, that it was a perfectly natural and believable thing for the highjacker to appear. He solved the problem by putting in little hints of what was going to come. We call this *foreshadowing*. What examples of foreshadowing did you notice? What signs did you notice that the miner himself rather expected someone to try to cut in on his claim?

9. How does this story square with your own experience? Would you say that a person does tend to grow careless when he becomes very excited over something he is doing?

If you like this story, you will be interested in

London. *To Build a Fire.*
The Call of the Wild (novel).
Prosper Mérimée. *Mateo Falcone.*
James Oliver Curwood. *Kazan.*

O. HENRY

The Furnished Room

THE STORY writer we know as O. Henry was born William Sidney Porter, in Greensboro, North Carolina, in 1862, and died in 1910. He went to Texas when he was 20, spent two years on a ranch, and then ten years in Austin. He was accused of embezzling funds from a bank where he had been a teller, and ran away to Central and South America. Although he insisted he was innocent, when he came back to face trial in 1898, he was sentenced to five years in the penitentiary in Columbus, Ohio. This might have ruined the career of most men, but it began Porter's career. In jail he had time to write, and he began to send stories to the popular magazines under the pen name O. Henry.

He was released from prison in a little less than four years, and in 1902 moved to New York, the city he had come to love above all others. That was one great influence on his writing. Most of his stories, like "The Furnished Room," are about New York; he tried to catch the spirit of the metropolis and the four million people who lived there. In 1903 the New York *World* gave him a contract to write one story a week for their Sunday edition. That was a second great influence on his writing. The newspaper required him to keep his stories within the length of a page, gave him a varied and demanding audience, and made him compete for this audience with the sensational news and pictures of the day. It was not surprising that, under these newspaper conditions, he developed his liking for the surprise ending.

The story you are about to read is one of the most famous of O. Henry's surprise ending stories. It is quite typical also in its use of New York atmosphere, and in withholding its "punch line" until the very last paragraph. O. Henry went to great lengths to throw his reader off guard, and then – like a skillful boxer – to hit him a knockout blow when he was not expecting it.

RESTLESS, shifting, fugacious as time itself is a certain vast bulk of the population of the red brick district of the lower West Side. Homeless, they have a hundred homes. They flit from furnished room to furnished room, transients forever – transients in abode, transients in heart and mind. They sing " Home, Sweet Home " in ragtime; they carry their *lares et penates* [1] in a bandbox; their vine is entwined about a picture hat; a rubber plant is their fig tree.

Hence the houses of this district, having had a thousand dwellers, should have a thousand tales to tell, mostly dull ones, no doubt; but it would be strange if there could not be found a ghost or two in the wake of all these vagrant guests.

One evening after dark a young man prowled among these crumbling red mansions, ringing their bells. At the twelfth he rested his lean hand baggage upon the step and wiped the dust from his hatband and forehead. The bell sounded faint and far away in some remote, hollow depths.

To the door of this, the twelfth house whose bell he had rung, came a housekeeper who made him think of an unwholesome, surfeited worm that had eaten its nut to a hollow shell and now sought to fill the vacancy with edible lodgers.

He asked if there was a room to let.

" Come in," said the housekeeper. Her voice came from her throat; her throat seemed lined with fur. " I have the third floor, back, vacant since a week back. Should you wish to look at it? "

The young man followed her up the stairs. A faint light from no particular source mitigated the shadows of the halls. They trod noiselessly upon a stair carpet that its own loom would have forsworn. It seemed to have become vegetable; to have degenerated in that rank, sunless air to lush lichen or spreading moss that grew in patches to the staircase and was viscid under the foot like organic matter. At each turn of the stairs were vacant niches in the wall. Perhaps plants had once been set within them. If so, they had died in that foul and tainted air. It may be that statues of the saints had stood there, but it was not difficult to conceive that imps and devils

[1] **lares et penates:** household gods which the Greeks and Romans carried with them wherever they moved. Here the phrase means personal possessions.

had dragged them forth in the darkness and down to the unholy depths of some furnished pit below.

"This is the room," said the housekeeper, from her furry throat. "It's a nice room. It ain't often vacant. I had some most elegant people in it last summer — no trouble at all, and paid in advance to the minute. The water's at the end of the hall. Sprowls and Mooney kept it three months. They done a vaudeville sketch. Miss B'retta Sprowls — you may have heard of her — oh, that was just the stage names — right there over the dresser is where the marriage certificate hung, framed. The gas is here, and you see there is plenty of closet room. It's a room everybody likes. It never stays idle long."

"Do you have many theatrical people rooming here?" asked the young man.

"They comes and goes. A good proportion of my lodgers is connected with the theaters. Yes, sir, this is the theatrical district. Actor people never stays long anywhere. I get my share. Yes, they comes and they goes."

He engaged the room, paying for a week in advance. He was tired, he said, and would take possession at once. He counted out the money. The room had been made ready, she said, even to towels and water. As the housekeeper moved away he put, for the thousandth time, the question that he carried at the end of his tongue.

"A young girl — Miss Vashner — Miss Eloise Vashner — do you remember such a one among your lodgers? She would be singing on the stage, most likely. A fair girl, of medium height and slender, with reddish, gold hair and a dark mole near her left eyebrow."

"No, I don't remember the name. Them stage people has names they change as often as their rooms. They comes and they goes. No, I can't call that one to mind."

No. Always no. Five months of ceaseless interrogation and the inevitable negative. So much time spent by day in questioning managers, agents, schools, and choruses; by night among the audiences of theaters from all-star casts down to music hall so low that he dreaded to find what he most hoped for. He who had loved her best had tried to find her. He was sure that since her disappearance from home this great, water-girt city held her somewhere, but it was like a monstrous quicksand, shifting its particles constantly, with no foundation, its upper granules of today buried tomorrow in ooze and slime.

The furnished room received its latest guest with a first glow of pseudo-hospitality, a hectic, haggard, perfunctory welcome like the specious smile of a demirep. The sophistical comfort came in reflected gleams from the decayed furniture, the ragged brocade upholstery of a couch and two chairs, a foot-wide cheap pier glass between the two windows, from one or two gilt picture frames and a brass bedstead in a corner.

The guest reclined, inert, upon a chair, while the room, confused in speech as though it were an apartment in Babel, tried to discourse to him of its divers tenantry.

A polychromatic [1] rug like some brilliant-flowered rectangular, tropical islet lay surrounded by a billowy sea of soiled matting. Upon the gay-papered wall were those pictures that pursue the homeless one from house to house—The Huguenot Lovers,[2] The First Quarrel, The Wedding Breakfast, Psyche at the Fountain. The mantel's chastely severe outline was ingloriously veiled behind some pert drapery drawn rakishly askew like the sashes of the Amazonian ballet. Upon it was some desolate flotsam cast aside by the room's marooned when a lucky sail had borne them to a fresh port—a trifling vase or two, pictures of actresses, a medicine bottle, some stray cards out of a deck.

One by one, as the characters of a cryptograph [3] become explicit, the little signs left by the furnished room's procession of guests developed a significance. The threadbare space in the rug in front of the dresser told that lovely women had marched in the throng. The tiny fingerprints on the wall spoke of little prisoners trying to feel their way to sun and air. A splattered stain, raying like the shadow of a bursting bomb, witnessed where a hurled glass or bottle had splintered with its contents against the wall. Across the pier glass had been scrawled with a diamond in staggering letters the name

[1] **polychromatic:** many-colored.

[2] **The Huguenot Lovers, etc.:** reproductions of paintings printed and sold cheaply and widely.

[3] **cryptograph:** code to be deciphered.

"Marie." It seemed that the succession of dwellers in the furnished room had turned in fury — perhaps tempted beyond forbearance by its garish coldness — and wreaked upon it their passions. The furniture was chipped and bruised; the couch, distorted by bursting springs, seemed a horrible monster that had been slain during the stress of some grotesque convulsion. Some more potent upheaval had cloven a great slice from the marble mantel. Each plank in the floor owned its particular cant and shriek as from a separate and individual agony. It seemed incredible that all this malice and injury nad been wrought upon the room by those who had called it for a time their home; and yet it may have been the cheated home instinct surviving blindly, the resentful rage at false household gods that had kindled their wrath. A hut that is our own we can sweep and adorn and cherish.

The young tenant in the chair allowed these thoughts to file, softshod, through his mind, while there drifted into the room furnished sounds and furnished scents. He heard in one room a tittering and incontinent, slack laughter; in others the monologue of a scold, the rattling of dice, a lullaby, and one crying dully; above him a banjo tinkled with spirit. Doors banged somewhere; the elevated trains roared intermittently; a cat yowled miserably upon a back fence. And he breathed the breath of the house — a dank savor rather than a smell — a cold, musty effluvium as from underground vaults mingled with the reeking exhalations of linoleum and mildewed and rotten woodwork.

Then, suddenly, as he rested there, the room was filled with the strong, sweet odor of mignonette. It came as upon a single buffet of wind with such sureness and fragrance and emphasis that it almost seemed a living visitant. And the man cried aloud: "What, dear?" as if he had been called, and sprang up and faced about. The rich odor clung to him and wrapped him around. He reached out his arms for it, all his senses for the time confused and commingled. How could one be peremptorily called by an odor? Surely it must have been a sound. But, was it not the sound that had touched, that had caressed him?

"She has been in this room," he cried, and he sprang to wrest from it a token, for he knew he would recognize the smallest thing that had belonged to her or that she had touched. This enveloping scent of mignonette, the odor that she had loved and made her own — whence came it?

The room had been but carelessly set in order. Scattered upon the flimsy dresser scarf were half a dozen hairpins — those discreet, indistinguishable friends of womankind, feminine of gender, infinite of mood and uncommunicative of tense. These he ignored, conscious of their triumphant lack of identity. Ransacking the drawers of the dresser, he came upon a discarded, tiny, ragged handkerchief. He pressed it to his face. It was racy and insolent with heliotrope; he hurled it to the floor. In another drawer he found odd buttons, a theater program, a pawnbroker's card, two lost marshmallows, a book on the divination of dreams. In the last was a woman's black satin hair bow, which halted him, poised between ice and fire. But the black satin hair bow also is femininity's demure, impersonal, common ornament and tells no tales.

And then he traversed the room like a hound on the scent, skimming the walls, considering the corners of the bulging matting on his hands and knees, rummaging mantel and tables, the curtains and hangings, the drunken cabinet in the corner, for a visible sign, unable to perceive that she was there beside, around, against, within, above him, clinging to him, wooing him, calling him so poignantly through the finer senses that even his grosser ones became cognizant of the call. Once again he answered loudly: " Yes, dear! " and turned, wild-eyed, to gaze on vacancy, for he could not yet discern form and color and love and outstretched arms in the odor of mignonette. Whence that odor, and since when have odors had a voice to call? Thus he groped.

He burrowed in crevices and corners, and found corks and cigarettes. These he passed in passive contempt. But once he found in a fold of the matting a half-smoked cigar, and this he ground beneath his heel with a green and trenchant oath. He sifted the room from end to end. He found dreary and ignoble small records of many a peripatetic tenant; but of her whom he sought, and who may have lodged there, and whose spirit seemed to hover there, he found no trace.

And then he thought of the housekeeper.

He ran from the haunted room downstairs and to a door that

showed a crack of light. She came out to his knock. He smothered his excitement as best he could.

"Will you tell me, madam," he besought her, "who occupied the room I have before I came?"

"Yes, sir. I can tell you again. 'Twas Sprowls and Mooney, as I said. Miss B'retta Sprowls it was in the theaters, but Missis Mooney she was. My house is well known for respectability. The marriage certificate hung, framed, on a nail over —"

"What kind of a lady was Miss Sprowls — in looks, I mean?"

"Why, black-haired, sir, short, and stout, with a comical face. They left a week ago Tuesday."

"And before they occupied it?"

"Why, there was a single gentleman connected with the draying business. He left owing me a week. Before him was Missis Crowder and her two children that stayed four months; and back of them was old Mr. Doyle, whose sons paid for him. He kept the room six months. That goes back a year, sir, and further I do not remember."

He thanked her and crept back to his room. The room was dead. The essence that had vivified it was gone. The perfume of mignonette had departed. In its place was the old, stale odor of moldy house furniture, of atmosphere in storage.

The ebbing of his hope drained his faith. He sat staring at the yellow, singing gaslight. Soon he walked to the bed and began to tear the sheets into strips. With the blade of his knife he drove them tightly into every crevice around windows and door. When all was snug and taut, he turned out the light, turned the gas full on again, and laid himself gratefully upon the bed.

* * * *

It was Mrs. McCool's night to go with the can for beer. So she fetched it and sat with Mrs. Purdy in one of those subterranean retreats where housekeepers foregather and the worm dieth seldom.

"I rented out my third floor, back, this evening," said Mrs. Purdy, across a fine circle of foam. "A young man took it. He went up to bed two hours ago."

"Now, did ye, Mrs. Purdy, ma'am?" said Mrs. McCool, with intense admiration. "You do be a wonder for rentin' rooms of that kind. And did ye tell him, then?" she concluded in a husky whisper laden with mystery.

"Rooms," said Mrs. Purdy, in her furriest tones, "are furnished for to rent. I did not tell him, Mrs. McCool."

"'Tis right ye are, ma'am; 'tis by rentin' rooms we kape alive. Ye have the rale sense for business, ma'am. There be many people will rayjict the rentin' of a room if they be tould a suicide has been after dyin' in the bed of it."

"As you say, we has our living to be making," remarked Mrs. Purdy.

"Yis, ma'am; 'tis true. 'Tis just one wake ago this day I helped ye lay out the third floor, back. A pretty slip of a colleen she was to be killin' herself wid the gas — a swate little face she had, Mrs. Purdy, ma'am."

"She'd a-been called handsome, as you say," said Mrs. Purdy, assenting but critical, "but for that mole she had a-growin' by her left eyebrow. Do fill up your glass again, Mrs. McCool."

READING WITH INSIGHT

1. What was the effect on you or the ending? Were you surprised? Did you guess how the story was going to end? Were you moved? Were you shocked?

2. There are really only two characters in this story; the third, who comes in at the end of the story, is merely someone for the housekeeper to talk to so the reader can overhear the story. There is, however, a character who is dead before the story starts — the young woman for whom the young man is searching. We know almost as much about her as about the others. What would you guess is her story? Where did she come from? Why did she come to New York? What was her relation to the young man? Why did she not keep in touch with him? Why did she kill herself? How much information of that kind can you deduce from what O. Henry tells you?

3. The central question is, why did the young man commit suicide? You should answer that question for yourself before making up your mind about the story. Does O. Henry tell you enough about the young man, his background, his character, his relation to the

girl, so that you can judge whether he was really being true to character when he killed himself?

4. The young man's act seems to result more than anything else from his smelling the mignonette. Did he really smell it, or only imagine it? If he does not really smell the mignonette, is the story any more than a coincidence? Why should a story be more than a coincidence? If he does really smell it, through some kind of extrasensory perception as may be suggested in the story, do you think O. Henry is justified in making the story depend on such an unlikely situation? Why?

5. The surprise comes in the last few sentences of the story. Look back and see what hints the author has given you before he tells you the surprise.

6. What does O. Henry mean when he says that the "threadbare space in the rug in front of the dresser told that lovely women had marched in the throng."

7. To set the stage, O. Henry starts this story with a little dissertation on the lower West Side of New York. What else does this beginning add to the story? To answer this question, try to imagine what the story would be without it.

8. What is he trying to say about the big city? In what way is the story of the boy and the girl merely an illustration of the larger meaning of the story? What is the larger meaning?

9. What do you think of this story as a whole? Do you find it satisfying? Do you think the surprise ending is effective or merely tricky? Do you think the characters stand out as real and memorable people? Do you think the author makes his point about the effect of the big city on people? How would you compare this way of writing a story with some you have read — for example, Crane's and London's, both of which were written about the same time as this story?

If you like this story, you will be interested in

O. Henry. *Gift of the Magi.*
A Municipal Report.
Guy de Maupassant. *The Necklace.*
Thomas Bailey Aldrich. *Marjorie Daw.*

THEODORE DREISER

The Lost Phoebe

DREISER was born in Terre Haute, Indiana in 1871, and spent a year at Indiana University, but soon went to Chicago to work. After a while he got into newspaper work, in Chicago, St. Louis, Pittsburgh, and New York. Then he changed to magazine editing and came finally to be editor-in-chief for the Butterick Publications. When he published his first novel, and it was withdrawn almost immediately by the publisher because it was "too frank" and treated sex too casually, readers learned with amazement that the author was the cautious and conservative editor of the eminently respectable magazine for women, *The Delineator!*

Throughout his career (he died in 1945) Dreiser's books were attacked because of their frankness. The publicity from those attacks, of course, made them sell better and gave the author more chance to write. In general, his writing was distinguished by a characteristic which most critics called honesty: he tried desperately hard to set down facts as he saw them, without polishing them, without deodorizing, without moralizing on them. He believed desperately in the importance of details, and felt that every small fact could make some contribution to the truth of the situation being investigated. Therefore, some of his writing seems cluttered with facts, and his best-known tragedy, *An American Tragedy*, takes hundreds of pages to describe one courtroom trial. But he took that space because he was trying to get at the real cause — not the surface cause — of a crime. He was therefore citing all the evidence. And this was his usual procedure. Even though his writing was sometimes rough and his subject matter unpleasant, still he gave the impression always of trying to write honestly about life as he saw it. He seems to be saying, "I'll put down the evidence. You make up your own mind."

"The Lost Phoebe" is not typical of Dreiser's subject matter, but it

THE LOST PHOEBE From *Free and Other Stories*, by Theodore Dreiser, published by Simon and Schuster, Inc. Reprinted by permission of Mrs. Helen Dreiser.

is representative of his honesty and simplicity of writing. It is noteworthy also for its unaffected feeling and for the way the author builds up a lengendary quality about the story of Henry Reifsneider.

THEY lived together in a part of the country which was not so prosperous as it had once been, about three miles from one of those small towns that, instead of increasing in population, is steadily decreasing. The territory was not very thickly settled; perhaps a house every other mile or so, with large areas of corn- and wheat-land and fallow fields that at odd seasons had been sown to timothy and clover. Their particular house was part log and part frame, the log portion being the old original home of Henry's grandfather. The new portion, of now rain-beaten, timeworn slabs, through which the wind squeaked in the chinks at times, and which several overshadowing elms and a butternut tree made picturesque and reminiscently pathetic, but a little damp, was erected by Henry when he was twenty-one and just married.

That was forty-eight years before. The furniture inside, like the house outside, was old and mildewy and reminiscent of an earlier day. You have seen the whatnot of cherry wood, perhaps, with spiral legs and fluted top. It was there. The old-fashioned four-poster bed, with its ball-like protuberances and deep curving incisions, was there also, a sadly alienated descendant of an early Jacobean ancestor. The bureau of cherry was also high and wide and solidly built, but faded-looking, and with a musty odor. The rag carpet that underlay all these sturdy examples of enduring furniture was a weak, faded, lead-and-pink-colored affair woven by Phoebe Ann's own hands, when she was fifteen years younger than she was when she died. The creaky wooden loom on which it had been done now stood like a dusty, bony skeleton, along with a broken rocking chair, a worm-eaten clothespress — Heaven knows how old — a lime-stained bench that had once been used to keep flowers on outside the door, and other decrepit factors of household utility, in an east room that was a lean-to against this so-called main portion. All sorts of other broken-down furniture were about this place; an antiquated clotheshorse, cracked in two of its ribs; a broken mirror in an old cherry frame, which had fallen from a nail and cracked itself three days before their youngest son, Jerry, died; an extension hatrack, which once had had porcelain knobs on the ends of its pegs; and a sewing machine, long since outdone in its clumsy mechanism by rivals of a newer generation.

The orchard to the east of the house was full of gnarled old apple trees, worm-eaten as to trunks and branches, and fully ornamented with green and white lichens, so that it had a sad, greenish-white, silvery effect in moonlight. The low outhouses, which had once housed chickens, a horse or two, a cow, and several pigs, were covered with patches of moss as to their roof, and the sides had been free of paint for so long that they were blackish gray as to color, and a little spongy. The picket fence in front, with its gate squeaky and askew, and the side fences of the stake-and-rider type were in an equally run-down condition. As a matter of fact, they had aged synchronously with the persons who lived here, old Henry Reifsneider and his wife Phoebe Ann.

They had lived here, these two, ever since their marriage, forty-eight years before, and Henry had lived here before that from his childhood up. His father and mother, well along in years when he was a boy, had invited him to bring his wife here when he had first fallen in love and decided to marry; and he had done so. His father and mother were the companions of himself and his wife for ten years after they were married, when both died; and then Henry and Phoebe were left with their five children growing lustily apace. But all sorts of things had happened since then. Of the seven children, all told, that had been born to them, three had died; one girl had gone to Kansas; one boy had gone to Sioux Falls, never even to be heard of after; another boy had gone to Washington; and the last girl lived five counties away in the same State, but was so burdened with cares of her own that she rarely gave them a thought. Time and a commonplace home life that had never been attractive had weaned them thoroughly, so that, wherever they went, they gave little thought as to how it might be with their father and mother.

Old Henry Reifsneider and his wife Phoebe were a loving couple. You perhaps know how it is with simple natures that fasten themselves like lichens on the stones of circumstance and weather their days to a crumbling conclusion. The great world sounds widely, but it has no call for them. They have no soaring intellect. The orchard, the meadow, the cornfield, the pigpen, and the chicken-lot measure the range of their human activities. When the wheat is headed it is reaped and threshed; when the corn is browned and frosted it is cut and shocked; when the timothy is in full head it is cut, and the haycock erected. After that comes winter, with the hauling of grain to market, the sawing and splitting of wood, the simple chores of fire-building, meal-getting, occasional repairing, and visiting. Beyond these and the changes of weather — the snows, the rains, and the fair days — there are no immediate, significant things. All the rest of life is a far-off, clamorous phantasmagoria, flickering like Northern lights in the night, and sounding as faintly as cowbells tinkling in the distance.

Old Henry and his wife Phoebe were as fond of each other as it is possible for two old people to be who have nothing else in this life to be fond of. He was a thin old man, seventy when she died, a queer, crotchety person with coarse gray-black hair and beard, quite straggly and unkempt. He looked at you out of dull, fishy, watery eyes that had deep-brown crow's-feet at the sides. His clothes, like the clothes of many farmers, were aged and angular and baggy, standing out at the pockets, not fitting about the neck, protuberant and worn at elbow and knee. Phoebe Ann was thin and shapeless, a very umbrella of a woman, clad in shabby black, and with a black bonnet for her best wear. As time had passed, and they had only themselves to look after, their movements had become slower and slower, their activities fewer and fewer. The annual keep of pigs had been reduced from five to one grunting porker, and the single horse which Henry now retained was a sleepy animal, not overnourished and not very clean. The chickens, of which formerly there was a large flock, had almost disappeared, owing to ferrets, foxes, and the lack of proper care, which produces disease. The former healthy garden was now a straggling memory of itself, and the vines and flower beds that formerly ornamented the windows and dooryard had now become choking thickets. A will had been made which divided the small tax-eaten property equally among the remaining four, so that it was really of no interest to any of them. Yet these two lived together in peace and sympathy, only that now and then old Henry would become unduly cranky, complain ing almost invariably that something had been neglected or mislaid which was of no importance at all.

"Phoebe, where's my corn knife? You ain't never minded to let my things alone no more."

"Now you hush, Henry," his wife would caution him in a cracked and squeaky voice. "If you don't, I'll leave yuh. I'll git up and walk out of here some day, and then where would y' be? Y' ain't got anybody but me to look after yuh, so yuh just behave yourself. Your corn knife's on the mantel where it's allus been unless you've gone an' put it summers else."

Old Henry, who knew his wife would never leave him in any circumstances, used to speculate at times as to what he would do if she were to die. That was the one leaving that he really feared. As he climbed on the chair at night to wind the old, long-pendulumed, double-weighted clock, or went finally to the front and the back door to see that they were safely shut in, it was a comfort to know that Phoebe was there, properly ensconced on her side of the bed, and that if he stirred restlessly in the night, she would be there to ask what he wanted.

"Now, Henry, do lie still! You're as restless as a chicken."

"Well, I can't sleep, Phoebe."

"Well, yuh needn't roll so, anyhow. Yuh kin let me sleep."

This usually reduced him to a state of somnolent ease. If she wanted a pail of water, it was a grumbling pleasure for him to get it; and if she did rise first to build the fires, he saw that the wood was cut and placed within easy reach. They divided this simple world nicely between them.

As the years had gone on, however, fewer and fewer people had called. They were well-known for a distance of as much as ten square miles as old Mr. and Mrs. Reifsneider, honest, moderately Christian, but too old to be really interesting any longer. The writing of letters had become an almost impossible burden too difficult to continue or even negotiate via others, although an occasional letter still did arrive from the daughter in Pemberton County. Now and then some old friend stopped with a pie or cake or a roasted chicken or duck, or merely to see that they were well; but even these kindly-minded visits were no longer frequent.

One day in the early spring of her sixty-fourth year Mrs. Reifsneider took sick, and from a low fever passed into some indefinable ailment which, because of her age, was no longer curable. Old Henry drove to Swinnerton, the neighboring town, and procured a doctor. Some friends called, and the immediate care of her was taken off his hands. Then one chill spring night she died, and old Henry, in a fog of sorrow and uncertainty, followed her body to the nearest graveyard, an unattractive space with a few pines growing in it. Although he might have gone to the daughter in Pemberton or sent for her, it was really too much trouble and he was too weary and fixed. It was suggested to him at once by one friend and another that he come to stay with them awhile, but he did not see fit. He was so old and so fixed in his notions and so accustomed to the exact surroundings he had known all his days, that he could not think of leaving. He wanted to remain near where they had put his Phoebe; and the fact that he would have to live alone did not trouble him in the least. The living children were notified and the care of him offered if he would leave, but he would not.

"I kin make a shift for myself," he continually announced to old Dr. Morrow, who had attended his wife in this case. "I kin cook a little, and, besides, it don't take much more'n coffee an' bread in the mornin's to satisfy me. I'll get along now well enough. Yuh just let me be." And after many pleadings and proffers of advice, with supplies of coffee and bacon and baked bread duly offered and accepted, he was left to himself. For a while he sat idly outside his door brooding in the spring sun. He tried to revive his interest in farming, and to keep himself busy and free from thought by looking after the fields, which of late had been much neglected. It was a gloomy thing to come in of an evening, however, or in the afternoon and find no shadow of Phoebe where everything suggested her. By degrees he put a few of her things away. At night he sat beside his lamp and read in the papers that were left him occasionally or in a Bible that he had neglected for years, but he could get little solace from these things. Mostly he held his hand over his mouth and looked at the floor as he sat and thought of what had become of her, and how soon he himself would die. He made a great business of making his coffee in the morning and frying himself a little bacon at night; but his appetite was gone. The shell in which he had been housed so long seemed vacant, and its shadows were suggestive of immedicable griefs. So he lived quite dolefully for five long months, and then a change began.

It was one night, after he had looked after the front and the back door, wound the clock, blown out the light, and gone through all the selfsame motions that he had indulged in for years, that he went to bed not so much to sleep as to think. It was a moonlight night. The green-lichen-covered orchard just outside and to be seen from his bed where he now lay was a silvery affair, sweetly spectral. The moon shone through the east windows, throwing the pattern of the panes on the wooden floor, and making the old furniture, to which he was accustomed, stand out dimly in the room. As usual he had been thinking of Phoebe and the years when they had been young together, and of the children who had gone, and the poor shift he was making of his present days. The house was coming to be in a very bad state indeed. The bedclothes were in disorder and not clean, for he made a wretched shift of washing. It was a terror to him. The roof leaked, causing things, some of them, to remain damp for weeks at a time, but he was getting into that brooding state where he would accept anything rather than exert himself. He preferred to pace slowly to and fro or to sit and think.

By twelve o'clock of this particular night he was asleep, however, and by two had waked again. The moon by this time had shifted to a position on the western side of the house, and it now shone in through the windows of the living room and those of the kitchen beyond. A certain combination of furniture—a chair near a table, with his coat on it, the half-open kitchen door casting a shadow, and the position of a lamp near a paper—gave him an exact representation of Phoebe leaning over the table as he had often seen her do in life. It gave him a great start. Could it be she—or her ghost? He had scarcely ever believed in spirits; and still—He looked at her fixedly in the feeble half-light, his old hair tingling oddly at the roots, and then sat up. The figure did not move. He put his thin legs out of the bed and sat looking at her, wondering if this could really be Phoebe. They had talked of ghosts often in their lifetime, of apparitions and omens; but they had never agreed that such things could be. It had never been a part of his wife's creed that she could have a spirit that could return to walk the earth. Her afterworld was quite a different affair, a vague heaven, no less, from which the righteous did not trouble to return. Yet here she was now, bending over the table in her black skirt and gray shawl, her pale profile outlined against the moonlight.

"Phoebe," he called, thrilling from head to toe and putting out one bony hand, "have yuh come back?"

The figure did not stir, and he arose and walked uncertainly to the door, looking at it fixedly the while. As he drew near, however, the apparition resolved itself into its primal content—his old coat over the high-backed chair, the lamp by the paper, the half-open door.

"Well," he said to himself, his mouth open, "I thought shore I saw her." And he ran his hand strangely and vaguely through his hair, the while his nervous tension relaxed. Vanished as it had, it gave him the idea that she might return.

Another night, because of this first illusion, and because his mind was now constantly on her and he was old, he looked out of the window that was nearest his bed and commanded a hencoop and pigpen and a part of the wagon-shed, and there, a faint mist exuding from the damp of the ground, he thought he saw her again. It was one of those little wisps of mist, one of those faint exhalations of the earth that rise in a cool night after a warm day, and flicker like small white cypresses of fog before they disappear. In life it had been a custom of hers to cross this lot from her kitchen door to the pigpen to throw in any scrap that was left from her cooking, and here she was again. He sat up and watched it strangely, doubtfully, because of his previous experience, but inclined, because of the nervous titillation that passed over his body, to believe that spirits really were, and that Phoebe, who would be concerned because of his lonely state, must be thinking about him, and hence returning. What other way would she have? How otherwise could she express herself? It would be within the province of her charity so to do, and like her loving interest in him. He quivered and watched it eagerly; but, a faint breath of air stirring, it wound away toward the fence and disappeared.

A third night, as he was actually dreaming, some ten days later, she came to his bedside and put her hand on his head.

"Poor Henry!" she said. "It's too bad."

He roused out of his sleep, actually to see her, he thought, moving from his bedroom into the one living room, her figure a shadowy mass of black. The weak straining of his eyes caused little points of light to flicker about the outlines of her form. He arose, greatly astonished, walked the floor in the cool room, convinced that Phoebe was coming back to him. If he only thought sufficiently, if he made it perfectly clear by his feeling that he needed her greatly, she would come back, this kindly wife, and tell him what to do. She would perhaps be with him much of the time, in the night, anyhow; and that would make him less lonely, this state more endurable.

In age and with the feeble it is not such a far cry from the subtleties of illusion to actual hallucination, and in due time this transition was made for Henry. Night after night he waited, expecting her return. Once in his weird mood he thought he saw a pale light moving about the room, and another time he thought he saw her walking in the orchard after dark. It was one morning when the details of his lonely state were virtually unendurable that he woke with the thought that she was not dead. How he had arrived at this conclusion it is hard to say. His mind had gone. In its place was a fixed illusion. He and Phoebe had had a senseless quarrel. He had reproached her for not leaving his pipe where he was accustomed to find it, and she had left. It was an aberrated [1] fulfillment of her old jesting threat that if he did not behave himself she would leave him.

"I guess I could find yuh ag'in," he had always said. But her cackling threat had always been:

"Yuh'll not find me if I ever leave yuh. I guess I kin git some place where yuh can't find me."

This morning when he arose he did not think to build the fire in the customary way or to grind his coffee and cut his bread, as was his wont, but solely to meditate as to where he should search for her and how he should induce her to come back. Recently the one horse had been dispensed with because he found it cumbersome and beyond his needs. He took down his soft crush hat after he had dressed himself, a new glint of interest and determination in his eye, and taking his black crook cane from behind the door, where he had always placed it, started out briskly to look for her among the nearest neighbors. His old shoes clumped soundly in the dust as he walked, and his gray-black locks, now grown rather long, straggled

[1] **aberrated: disordered, abnormal.**

out in a dramatic fringe or halo from under his hat. His short coat stirred busily as he walked, and his hands and face were peaked and pale.

"Why, hello, Henry! Where're yuh goin' this mornin'? " inquired Farmer Dodge, who, hauling a load of wheat to market, encountered him on the public road. He had not seen the aged farmer in months, not since his wife's death, and he wondered now, seeing him looking so spry.

"Yuh ain't seen Phoebe, have yuh? " inquired the old man, looking up quizzically.

"Phoebe who? " inquired Farmer Dodge, not for the moment connecting the name with Henry's dead wife.

"Why, my wife Phoebe, o' course. Who do yuh s'pose I mean? " He stared up with a pathetic sharpness of glance from under his shaggy, gray eyebrows.

"Wall, I'll swan, Henry, yuh ain't jokin', are yuh? " said the solid Dodge, a pursy man, with a smooth, hard, red face. "It can't be your wife yuh're talkin' about. She's dead."

"Dead! Shucks! " retorted the demented Reifsneider. "She left me early this mornin', while I was sleepin'. She allus got up to build the fire, but she's gone now. We had a little spat last night, an' I guess that's the reason. But I guess I kin find her. She's gone over to Matilda Race's; that's where she's gone."

He started briskly up the road, leaving the amazed Dodge to stare in wonder after him.

"Well, I'll be switched! " he said aloud to himself. "He's clean out'n his head. That poor old feller's been livin' down there till he's gone out'n his mind. I'll have to notify the authorities." And he flicked his whip with great enthusiasm. "Geddap! " he said, and was off.

Reifsneider met no one else in this poorly populated region until he reached the whitewashed fence of Matilda Race and her husband three miles away. He had passed several other houses en route, but these not being within the range of his illusion were not considered. His wife, who had known Matilda well, must be here. He opened the picket gate which guarded the walk, and stamped briskly up to the door.

"Why, Mr. Reifsneider," exclaimed old Matilda herself, a stout woman, looking out of the door in answer to his knock, "what brings yuh here this mornin'? "

"Is Phoebe here? " he demanded eagerly.

"Phoebe who? What Phoebe? " replied Mrs. Race, curious as to this sudden development of energy on his part.

"Why, my Phoebe, o' course. My wife Phoebe. Who do yuh s'pose? Ain't she here now? "

"Lawsy me! " exclaimed Mrs. Race, opening her mouth. "Yuh pore man! So you're clean out'n your mind now. Yuh come right in and sit down. I'll git yuh a cup o' coffee. O' course your wife ain't here; but yuh come in an' sit down. I'll find her fer yuh after a while. I know where she is."

The old farmer's eyes softened, and he entered. He was so thin and pale a specimen, pantalooned and patriarchal, that he aroused Mrs. Race's extremest sympathy as he took off his hat and laid it on his knees quite softly and mildly.

"We had a quarrel last night, an' she left me," he volunteered.

"Laws! laws! " sighed Mrs. Race, there being no one present with whom to share her astonishment as she went to her kitchen. "The pore man! Now somebody's just got to look after him. He can't be allowed to run around the country this way lookin' for his dead wife. It's turrible."

She boiled him a pot of coffee and brought in some of her new-baked bread and fresh butter. She set out some of her best jam and put a couple of eggs to boil, lying wholeheartedly the while.

"Now yuh stay right there, Uncle Henry, till Jake comes in, an' I'll send him to look for Phoebe. I think it's more'n likely she's over to Swinnerton with some o' her friends. Anyhow, we'll find out. Now yuh just drink this coffee an' eat this bread. Yuh must be tired. Yuh've had a long walk this mornin'." Her idea was to take counsel with Jake, her man, and perhaps have him notify the authorities.

She bustled about, meditating on the uncertainties of life, while old Reifsneider thrummed on the rim of his hat with his pale fingers and later ate abstractedly of what she offered. His mind was on his wife, however, and since she was not here, or did not appear, it wandered vaguely away to a family by the name of Murray, miles away in another direction. He decided after a time that he would not wait for Jake Race to hunt his wife but would seek her for himself. He must be on, and urge her to come back.

"Well, I'll be goin'," he said, getting up and looking strangely about him. "I guess she didn't come here after all. She went over to the Murrays', I guess. I'll not wait any longer, Mis' Race. There's a lot to do over to the house today." And out he marched in the face of her protest, taking to the dusty road again in the warm spring sun, his cane striking the earth as he went.

It was two hours later that this pale figure of a man appeared in the Murrays' doorway, dusty, perspiring, eager. He had tramped all of five miles, and it was noon. An amazed husband and wife of sixty heard his strange query, and realized also that he was mad. They begged him to stay to dinner, intending to notify the authorities later and see what could be done; but though he stayed to partake of a little something, he did not stay long, and was off again to another distant farmhouse, his idea of many things to do and his need of Phoebe impelling him. So it went for that day and the next and the next, the circle of his inquiry ever widening.

The process by which a character assumes the significance of being peculiar, his antics weird, yet harmless, in such a community, is often involute [1] and pathetic. This day, as has been said, saw Reifsneider at other doors, eagerly asking his unnatural question, and leaving a trail of amazement, sympathy, and pity in his wake. Although the authorities were informed — the county sheriff, no less — it was not deemed advisable to take him into custody; for when those who knew old Henry, and had for so long, reflected on the condition of the county insane asylum, a place which, because of the poverty of the district, was of staggering aberration and sickening environment, it was decided to let him remain at large; for, strange to relate, it was found on investigation that at night he returned peaceably enough to his lonesome domicile, there to discover whether his wife had returned, and to brood in loneliness until the morning. Who would lock up a thin, eager, seeking old man with iron-gray hair and an attitude of kindly, innocent inquiry, particularly when he was well known for a past of only kindly servitude and reliability? Those who had known him best rather agreed that he should be allowed to roam at large. He could do no harm. There

[1] **involute:** involved, intricate.

were many who were willing to help him as to food, old clothes, the odds and ends of his daily life — at least at first. His figure after a time became not so much a commonplace as an accepted curiosity, and the replies, "Why, no, Henry; I ain't seen her," or "No, Henry; she ain't been here today," more customary.

For several years thereafter then he was an odd figure in the sun and rain, on dusty roads and muddy ones, encountered occasionally in strange and unexpected places, pursuing his endless search. Undernourishment, after a time, although the neighbors and those who knew his history gladly contributed from their store, affected his body; for he walked much and ate little. The longer he roamed the public highway in this manner, the deeper became his strange hallucination; and finding it harder and harder to return from his more and more distant pilgrimages, he finally began taking a few utensils with him from his home, making a small package of them, in order that he might not be compelled to return. In an old tin coffeepot of large size he placed a small tin cup, a knife, fork, and spoon, some salt and pepper, and to the outside of it, by a string forced through a pierced hole, he fastened a plate, which could be released, and which was his woodland table. It was no trouble for him to secure the little food that he needed, and with a strange, almost religious dignity, he had no hesitation in asking for that much. By degrees his hair became longer and longer, his once black hat became an earthen brown, and his clothes threadbare and dusty.

For all of three years he walked, and none knew how wide were his perambulations, nor how he survived the storms and cold. They could not see him, with homely rural understanding and forethought, sheltering himself in haycocks, or by the sides of cattle, whose warm bodies protected him from the cold, and whose dull understandings were not opposed to his harmless presence. Overhanging rocks and trees kept him at times from the rain, and a friendly hayloft or corncrib was not above his humble consideration.

The involute progression of hallucination is strange. From asking at doors and being constantly rebuffed or denied, he finally came to the conclusion that although his Phoebe might not be in any of the houses at the doors of which he inquired, she might nevertheless be within the sound of his voice. And so, from patient inquiry, he began to call sad, occasional cries, that ever and anon waked the quiet landscapes and ragged hill regions, and set to echoing his thin "O-o-o Phoebe! O-o-o Phoebe!" It had a pathetic, albeit insane, ring, and many a farmer or plowboy came to know it even from afar and say, "There goes old Reifsneider."

Another thing that puzzled him greatly after a time and after many hundreds of inquiries was, when he no longer had any particular dooryard in view and no special inquiry to make, which way to go. These crossroads, which occasionally led in four or even six directions, came after a time to puzzle him. But to solve this knotty problem, which became more and more of a puzzle, there came to his aid another hallucination. Phoebe's spirit or some power of the air or wind or nature would tell him. If he stood at the center of the parting of the ways, closed his eyes, turned thrice about, and called "O-o-o Phoebe!" twice, and then threw his cane straight before him, that would surely indicate which way to go for Phoebe, or one of these mystic powers would surely govern its direction and fall! In whichever direction it went, even though, as was not infrequently the case, it took him back along the path he had already come, or across fields, he was not so far gone in his mind but that he gave himself ample time to search before he called again. Also the hallucination seemed to persist that at some time he would surely find her. There were hours when his feet were sore, and his limbs weary, when he would stop in the heat to wipe his seamed brow, or in the cold to beat his arms. Sometimes, after throwing away his cane, and finding it indicating the direction from which he had just come, he would shake his head wearily and philosophically, as if contemplating the unbelievable or an untoward fate, and then start briskly off. His strange figure came finally to be known in the farthest reaches of three or four counties. Old Reifsneider was a pathetic character. His fame was wide.

Near a little town called Watersville, in Green County, perhaps four miles from that minor center of human activity, there was a place or precipice locally known as the Red Cliff, a sheer wall of red sandstone, perhaps a hundred feet high, which raised its sharp face for half a mile or more above the fruitful cornfields and orchards that lay beneath, and which was surmounted by a thick growth of trees. The slope that slowly led up to it from the opposite side was covered by a rank growth of beech, hickory, and ash, through which threaded a number of wagon-tracks crossing at various angles. In fair weather it had become old Reifsneider's habit, so inured was he by now to the open, to make his bed in some such patch of trees as this, to fry his bacon or boil his eggs at the foot of some tree before laying himself down for the night. Occasionally, so light and inconsequential was his sleep, he would walk at night. More often, the moonlight or some sudden wind stirring in the trees or a reconnoitering animal arousing him, he would sit up and think, or pursue his quest in the moonlight or the dark, a strange, unnatural, half wild, half savage-looking but utterly harmless creature, calling at lonely road crossings, staring at dark and shuttered houses, and wondering where, where Phoebe could really be.

That particular lull that comes in the systole-diastole [1] of this earthly ball at two o'clock in the morning invariably aroused him, and though he might not go any farther he would sit up and contemplate the darkness or the stars, wondering. Sometimes in the strange processes of his mind he would fancy that he saw moving among the trees the figure of his lost wife, and then he would get up to follow, taking his utensils, always on a string, and his cane. If she seemed to evade him too easily he would run, or plead, or, suddenly losing track of the fancied figure, stand awed or disappointed, grieving for the moment over the almost insurmountable difficulties of his search.

It was in the seventh year of these hopeless peregrinations, in the dawn of a similar springtime to that in which his wife had died, that he came at last one night to the vicinity of this selfsame patch that crowned the rise to the Red Cliff. His far-flung cane, used as a divining rod at the last crossroads, had brought him hither. He had walked many, many miles. It was after ten o'clock at night, and he was very weary. Long wandering and little eating had left him but a shadow of his former self. It was a question now not so much of physical strength but of spiritual endurance which kept him up. He had scarcely eaten this day, and now exhausted he set himself down in the dark to rest and possibly to sleep.

[1] **systole-diastole:** these terms refer to the rhythmic beat of the heart which forces the blood through the veins. Here Dreiser is comparing the rhythmic alternation of day and night to the heartbeat.

Curiously on this occasion a strange suggestion of the presence of his wife surrounded him. It would not be long now, he counseled with himself, although the long months had brought him nothing, until he should see her, talk to her. He fell asleep after a time, his head on his knees. At midnight the moon began to rise, and at two in the morning, his wakeful hour, was a large silver disk shining through the trees to the east. He opened his eyes when the radiance became strong, making a silver pattern at his feet and lighting the woods with strange lusters and silvery, shadowy forms. As usual, his old notion that his wife must be near occurred to him on this occasion, and he looked about him with a speculative, anticipatory eye. What was it that moved in the distant shadows along the path by which he had entered — a pale, flickering will-o'-the-wisp that bobbed gracefully among the trees and riveted his expectant gaze? Moonlight and shadows combined to give it a strange form and a strange reality, this fluttering of bog-fire or dancing of wandering fireflies. Was it truly his lost Phoebe? By a circuitous route it passed about him, and in his fevered state he fancied that he could see the very eyes of her, not as she was when he last saw her in the black dress and shawl but now a strangely younger Phoebe, gayer, sweeter, the one whom he had known years before as a girl. Old Reifsneider got up. He had been expecting and dreaming of this hour all these years, and now as he saw the feeble light dancing lightly before him he peered at it questioningly, one thin hand in his gray hair.

Of a sudden there came to him now for the first time in many years the full charm of her girlish figure as he had known it in boyhood, the pleasing, sympathetic smile, the brown hair, the blue sash she had once worn about her waist at a picnic, her gay, graceful movements. He walked around the base of the tree, straining with his eyes, forgetting for once his cane and utensils, and following eagery after. On she moved before him, a will-o'-the-wisp of the spring, a little flame above her head, and it seemed as though among the small saplings of ash and beech and the thick trunks of hickory and elm that she signaled with a young, a lightsome hand.

" O Phoebe! Phoebe! " he called. " Have yuh really come? Have yuh really answered me? " And hurrying faster, he fell once, scrambling lamely to his feet, only to see the light in the distance dancing illusively on. On and on he hurried until he was fairly running, brushing his ragged arms against the trees, striking his hands and face against impeding twigs. His hat was gone, his lungs were breathless, his reason quite astray, when coming to the edge of the cliff he saw her below among a silvery bed of apple trees now blooming in the spring.

"O Phoebe!" he called. "O Phoebe! Oh, no, don't leave me!" And feeling the lure of a world where love was young and Phoebe as this vision presented her, a delightful epitome of their quondam[1] youth, he gave a gay cry of "Oh, wait, Phoebe!" and leaped.

Some farmer-boys, reconnoitering this region of bounty and prospect some few days afterward, found first the tin utensils tied together under the tree where he had left them, and then later at the foot of the cliff, pale, broken, but elate, a molded smile of peace and delight upon his lips, his body. His old hat was discovered lying under some low-growing saplings the twigs of which had held it back. No one of all the simple population knew how eagerly and joyously he had found his lost mate.

READING WITH INSIGHT

1. What does the long description of the Reifsneider farm and house accomplish? Is it merely for background? Does it help you to characterize anyone? What does it tell you about the life Henry and Phoebe had lived?

2. The action in this story begins rather late. Are you interested in the part of the story before the action starts? If so, how does Dreiser get you interested?

3. The plot of this story is built around Henry's search for his lost Phoebe. Describe the source of tension, the steps in the rising action, the climax, and the falling action.

4. This story seems to be simple and artless, but actually it is very carefully put together. Why has the author tried to make it appear artless?

5. In the introduction the author builds a kind of legend around Henry Reifsneider. How does he achieve this legendary quality?

6. In this simple and seemingly artless writing there are still pas-

[1] quondam: former.

sages of beauty. For example, recall the sentences in the fifth paragraph: "You perhaps know how it is with simple natures that fasten themselves like lichens on the stones of circumstance and weather their days to a crumbling conclusion. The great world sounds widely, but it has no call for them." What other effective passages can you point out?

7. Why is this picture of an unkempt, dirty, insane old man, as it appears in this story, not repulsive? How does the author keep it from being repulsive? What is the effect of the story on you? Do you think it is pathetic? Sentimental? Sad? Beautiful? What?

8. You will be interested in comparing this story with Miss Cather's story of simple folk, "Neighbor Rosicky," which follows, and with Sherwood Anderson's seemingly artless small-town story, "Sophistication," which appears later in the book.

9. Phoebe is a symbol as well as a character. What did she mean to Henry? Just his wife or something more? For example, did she come to stand for his lost youth? For security? Home? The ideal? What might the search for the lost Phoebe symbolize in modern life?

10. One critic has described the meaning of this story in terms like this: "Everyone yearns for things he doesn't have, especially for youth and for victory over death. And all of us at one time or another follow will-o'-the-wisps." Does this seem to you to be an adequate description of the meaning of this story? If not, give your idea of the meaning.

If you like this story, you will be interested in

Washington Irving. *The Legend of Sleepy Hollow.*
Oliver LaFarge. *North Is Black.*
Wilbur Schramm. *Boone Over the Pacific.*
Mary E. Wilkins Freeman. *The New England Nun.*

WILLA CATHER

Neighbor Rosicky

Miss Cather lived many years on the Nebraska plains among such families as the one she describes in this fine character story. Born in Virginia, she was taken to Nebraska when she was eight years old. Here she came to know the immigrant farmers, and came to respect both them and the big bare country they were trying to make into rich farms. She went to the University of Nebraska, then to Pittsburgh to work on a newspaper. Later when she found a position teaching English in high school, she began to write stories. Some of them came to the editor of *McClure's Magazine*, who recognized her talent and offered her a part-time job on his editorial staff. After a few years of this work, she resigned and gave all her time to writing novels and stories.

The rest of her life was a quiet one—writing, traveling, spending vacations in the Southwest and on the plains where she had grown up. For much of her best work, she drew her subject matter from this plains country. "Art," she once said, "is remembered youth." Be that as it may, many of her best novels and stories, like the story of Rosicky, are about the farmers who tried to win the farming West, and won strength from battling those dry and empty plains. Miss Cather lived from 1875 to 1947.

I

When Doctor Burleigh told neighbor Rosicky he had a bad heart, Rosicky protested.

"So? No, I guess my heart was always pretty good. I got a little asthma, maybe. Just a awful short breath when I was pitchin' hay last summer, dat's all."

"Well now, Rosicky, if you know more about it than I do, what did you come to me for? It's your heart that makes you short of breath, I tell you. You're sixty-five years old, and you've always worked hard, and your heart's tired. You've got to be careful from now on, and you can't do heavy work any more. You've got five boys at home to do it for you."

The old farmer looked up at the Doctor with a gleam of amusement in his queer triangular-shaped eyes. His eyes were large and lively, but the lids were caught up in the middle in a curious way, so that they formed a triangle. He did not look like a sick man. His brown face was creased but not wrinkled, he had a ruddy color in his smooth-shaven cheeks and in his lips, under his long brown mustache. His hair was thin and ragged around his ears, but very little gray. His forehead, naturally high and crossed by deep parallel lines, now ran all the way up to his pointed crown. Rosicky's face had the habit of looking interested, – suggested a contented disposition and a reflective quality that was gay rather than grave. This gave him a certain detachment, the easy manner of an onlooker and observer.

"Well, I guess you ain't got no pills fur a bad heart, Doctor Ed. I guess the only thing is fur me to git me a new one."

Doctor Burleigh swung round in his desk chair and frowned at the old farmer. "I think if I were you I'd take a little care of the old one, Rosicky."

Rosicky shrugged. "Maybe I don't know how. I expect you mean fur me not to drink my coffee no more."

"I wouldn't, in your place. But you'll do as you choose about that. I've never yet been able to separate a Bohemian from his coffee or his pipe. I've quit trying. But the sure thing is you've got to cut out farm work. You can feed the stock and do chores about the barn, but you can't do anything in the fields that makes you short of breath."

"How about shelling corn?"

"Of course not!"

Rosicky considered with puckered brows.

"I can't make my heart go no longer'n it wants to, can I, Doctor Ed?"

"I think it's good for five or six years yet, maybe more, if you'll take the strain off it. Sit around the house and help Mary. If I had a good wife like yours, I'd want to stay around the house."

His patient chuckled. "It ain't no place fur a man. I don't like no old man hanging round the kitchen too much. An' my wife, she's a awful hard worker her own self."

"That's it; you can help her a little. My Lord, Rosicky, you are one of the few men I know who has a family he can get some comfort out of; happy dispositions, never quarrel among themselves, and they treat you right. I want to see you live a few years and enjoy them."

"Oh, they're good kids, all right," Rosicky assented.

The Doctor wrote him a prescription and asked him how his oldest son, Rudolph, who had married in the spring, was getting on. Rudolph had struck out for himself, on rented land. "And how's Polly? I was afraid Mary mightn't like an American daughter-in-law, but it seems to be working out all right."

"Yes, she's a fine girl. Dat widder woman bring her daughters up very nice. Polly got lots of spunk, an' she got some style, too. Da's nice, for young folks to have some style." Rosicky inclined his head gallantly. His voice and his twinkly smile were an affectionate compliment to his daughter-in-law.

"It looks like a storm, and you'd better be getting home before it comes. In town in the car? " Doctor Burleigh rose.

"No, I'm in de wagon. When you got five boys, you ain't got much chance to ride round in de Ford. I ain't much for cars, noway."

"Well, it's a good road out to your place; but I don't want you bumping around in a wagon much. And never again on a hayrake, remember! "

Rosicky placed the Doctor's fee delicately behind the desk telephone, looking the other way, as if this were an absent-minded gesture. He put on his plush cap and his corduroy jacket with a sheepskin collar, and went out.

The Doctor picked up his stethoscope and frowned at it as if he were seriously annoyed with the instrument. His wished it had been telling tales about some other man's heart, some old man who didn't look the Doctor in the eye so knowingly, or hold out such a warm brown hand when he said good-by. Doctor Burleigh had been a poor boy in the country before he went away to medical school;

he had known Rosicky almost ever since he could remember, and he had a deep affection for Mrs. Rosicky.

Only last winter he had had such a good breakfast at Rosicky's, and that when he needed it. He had been out all night on a long, hard confinement case at Tom Marshall's, — a big rich farm where there was plenty of stock and plenty of feed and a great deal of expensive farm machinery of the newest model, and no comfort whatever. The woman had too many children and too much work, and she was no manager. When the baby was born at last, and handed over to the assisting neighbor woman, and the mother was properly attended to, Burleigh refused any breakfast in that slovenly house, and drove his buggy — the snow was too deep for a car — eight miles to Anton Rosicky's place. He didn't know another farmhouse where a man could get such a warm welcome, and such good strong coffee with rich cream. No wonder the old chap didn't want to give up his coffee!

He had driven in just when the boys had come back from the barn and were washing up for breakfast. The long table, covered with a bright oilcloth, was set out with dishes waiting for them, and the warm kitchen was full of the smell of coffee and hot biscuit and sausage. Five big handsome boys, running from twenty to twelve, all with what Burleigh called natural good manners, — they hadn't a bit of the painful self-consciousness he himself had to struggle with when he was a lad. One ran to put his horse away, another helped him off with his fur coat and hung it up, and Josephine, the youngest child and the only daughter, quickly set another place under her mother's direction.

With Mary, to feed creatures was the natural expression of affection, — her chickens, the calves, her big hungry boys. It was a rare pleasure to feed a young man whom she seldom saw and of whom she was as proud as if he belonged to her. Some country housekeepers would have stopped to spread a white cloth over the oilcloth, to change the thick cups and plates for their best china, and the wooden-handled knives for plated ones. But not Mary.

"You must take us as you find us, Doctor Ed. I'd be glad to put out my good things for you if you was expected, but I'm glad to get you any way at all."

He knew she was glad,—she threw back her head and spoke out as if she were announcing him to the whole prairie. Rosicky hadn't said anything at all; he merely smiled his twinkling smile, put some more coal on the fire, and went into his own room to pour the Doctor a little drink in a medicine glass. When they were all seated, he watched his wife's face from his end of the table and spoke to her in Czech. Then, with the instinct of politeness which seldom failed him, he turned to the Doctor and said slyly; "I was just tellin' her not to ask you no questions about Mrs. Marshall till you eat some breakfast. My wife, she's terrible fur to ask questions."

The boys laughed, and so did Mary. She watched the Doctor devour her biscuit and sausage, too much excited to eat anything herself. She drank her coffee and sat taking in everything about her visitor. She had known him when he was a poor country boy, and was boastfully proud of his success, always saying: "What do people go to Omaha for, to see a doctor, when we got the best one in the state right here?" If Mary liked people at all, she felt physical pleasure in the sight of them, personal exultation in any good fortune that came to them. Burleigh didn't know many women like that, but he knew she was like that.

When his hunger was satisfied, he did, of course, have to tell them about Mrs. Marshall, and he noticed what a friendly interest the boys took in the matter.

Rudolph, the oldest one (he was still living at home then), said: "The last time I was over there, she was lifting them big heavy milk cans, and I knew she ought not to be doing it."

"Yes, Rudolph told me about that when he come home, and I said it wasn't right," Mary put in warmly. "It was all right for me to do them things up to the last, for I was terrible strong, but that woman's weakly. And do you think she'll be able to nurse it, Ed?" She sometimes forgot to give him the title she was so proud of. "And to think of your being up all night and then not able to get a decent breakfast! I don't know what's the matter with such people."

"Why, Mother," said one of the boys, "if Doctor Ed had got breakfast there, we wouldn't have him here. So you ought to be glad."

"He knows I'm glad to have him, John, any time. But I'm sorry for that poor woman, how bad she'll feel the Doctor had to go away in the cold without his breakfast."

"I wish I'd been in practice when these were getting born." The doctor looked down the row of close-clipped heads. "I missed some good breakfasts by not being."

The boys began to laugh at their mother because she flushed so red, but she stood her ground and threw up her head. "I don't care, you wouldn't have got away from this house without breakfast. No doctor ever did. I'd have had something ready fixed that Anton could warm up for you."

The boys laughed harder than ever, and exclaimed at her: "I'll bet you would!" "She would, that!"

"Father, did you get breakfast for the doctor when we were born?"

"Yes, and he used to bring me my breakfast, too, mighty nice. I was always awful hungry!" Mary admitted with a guilty laugh.

While the boys were getting the Doctor's horse, he went to the window to examine the house plants. "What do you do to your geraniums to keep them blooming all winter, Mary? I never pass this house that from the road I don't see your windows full of flowers."

She snapped off a dark red one, and a ruffled new green leaf, and put them in his buttonhole. "There, that looks better. You look too solemn for a young man, Ed. Why don't you git married? I'm worried about you. Settin' at breakfast, I looked at you real hard, and I seen you've got some gray hairs already."

"Oh, yes! They're coming. Maybe they'd come faster if I married."

"Don't talk so. You'll ruin your health eating at the hotel. I could send your wife a nice loaf of nut bread, if you only had one. I don't like to see a young man getting gray. I'll tell you something, Ed; you make some strong black tea and keep it handy in a bowl, and every morning just brush it into your hair, an' it'll keep the gray from showin' much. That's the way I do!"

Sometimes the Doctor heard the gossipers in the drugstore wondering why Rosicky didn't get on faster. He was industrious, and so were his boys, but they were rather free and easy, weren't pushers, and they didn't always show good judgment. They were comfortable, they were out of debt, but they didn't get much ahead. Maybe, Doctor Burleigh reflected, people as generous and warm-hearted and affectionate as the Rosickys never got ahead much; maybe you could not enjoy your life and put it into the bank, too.

II

When Rosicky left Doctor Burleigh's office, he went into the farm-implement store to light his pipe and put on his glasses and read over the list Mary had given him. Then he went into the general merchandise place next door and stood about until the pretty girl with the plucked eyebrows, who always waited on him, was free. Those eyebrows, two thin India-ink strokes, amused him, because he remembered how they used to be. Rosicky always prolonged his shopping by a little joking; the girl knew the old fellow admired her, and she liked to chaff with him.

"Seems to me about every other week you buy ticking, Mr. Rosicky, and always the best quality," she remarked as she measured off the heavy bolt with red stripes.

"You see, my wife is always makin' goosefedder pillows, an' de thin stuff don't hold in dem little down-fedders."

"You must have lots of pillows at your house."

"Sure. She makes quilts of dem, too. We sleeps easy. Now she's makin' a fedder quilt for my son's wife. You know Polly, that married my Rudolph. How much my bill, Miss Pearl? "

"Eight eighty-five."

"Chust make it nine, and put in some candy fur de women."

"As usual. I never did see a man buy so much candy for his wife. First thing you know, she'll be getting too fat."

"I'd like dat. I ain't much fur all dem slim women like what de style is now."

"That's one for me, I suppose, Mr. Bohunk! " Pearl sniffed and elevated her India-ink strokes.

When Rosicky went out to his wagon, it was beginning to snow, — the first snow of the season, and he was glad to see it. He rattled out of town and along the highway through a wonderfully rich stretch of country, the finest farms in the county. He admired this High Prairie, as it was called, and always liked to drive through it.

His own place lay in a rougher territory, where there was some clay in the soil and it was not so productive. When he bought his land, he hadn't the money to buy on High Prairie; so he told his boys, when they grumbled, that if their land hadn't some clay in it, they wouldn't own it at all. All the same, he enjoyed looking at these fine farms, as he enjoyed looking at a prize bull.

After he had gone eight miles, he came to the graveyard, which lay just at the edge of his own hayland. There he stopped his horses and sat still on his wagon seat, looking about at the snowfall. Over yonder on the hill he could see his own house, crouching low, with the clump of orchard behind and the windmill before, and all down the gentle hill-slope the rows of pale gold cornstalks stood out against the white field. The snow was falling over the cornfield and the pasture and the hayland, steadily, with every little wind, — a nice dry snow. The graveyard had only a light wire fence about it and was all overgrown with long red grass. The fine snow, settling into this red grass and upon the few little evergreens and the headstones, looked very pretty.

It was a nice graveyard, Rosicky reflected, sort of snug and home-like, not cramped or mournful, — a big sweep all round it. A man could lie down in the long grass and see the complete arch of the sky over him, hear the wagons go by; in summer the mowing machine rattled right up to the wire fence. And it was so near home. Over there across the cornstalks his own roof and windmill looked so good to him that he promised himself to mind the Doctor and take care of himself. He was awful fond of his place, he admitted. He wasn't anxious to leave it. And it was a comfort to think that he would never have to go farther than the edge of his own hayfield. The snow, falling over his barnyard and the graveyard, seemed to draw things together like. And they were all old neighbors in the graveyard, most of them friends; there was nothing to feel awkward or embarrassed about. Embarrassment was the most disagreeable feeling Rosicky knew. He didn't often have it, — only with certain people whom he didn't understand at all.

Well, it was a nice snowstorm; a fine sight to see the snow falling so quietly and graciously over so much open country. On his cap and shoulders, on the horses' backs and manes, light, delicate, mysterious it fell; and with it a dry cool fragrance was released into the air. It meant rest for vegetation and men and beasts, for the ground itself; a season of long nights for sleep, leisurely breakfasts, peace by the fire. This and much more went through Rosicky's mind, but he merely told himself that winter was coming, clucked to his horses, and drove on.

When he reached home, John, the youngest boy, ran out to put away his team for him, and he met Mary coming up from the outside cellar with her apron full of carrots. They went into the house together. On the table, covered with oilcloth figured with clusters of blue grapes, a place was set, and he smelled hot coffeecake of some kind. Anton never lunched in town; he thought that extravagant, and anyhow he didn't like the food. So Mary always had something ready for him when he got home.

After he was settled in his chair, stirring his coffee in a big cup, Mary took out of the oven a pan of *kolache* [1] stuffed with apricots, examined them anxiously to see whether they had got too dry, put them beside his plate, and then sat down opposite him.

Rosicky asked her in Czech if she wasn't going to have any coffee.

She replied in English, as being somehow the right language for transacting business: "Now what did Doctor Ed say, Anton? You tell me just what."

"He said I was to tell you some compliments, but I forgot 'em." Rosicky's eyes twinkled.

"About you, I mean. What did he say about your asthma?"

"He says I ain't got no asthma." Rosicky took one of the little rolls in his broad brown fingers. The thickened nail of his right thumb told the story of his past.

"Well, what is the matter? And don't try to put me off."

"He don't say nothing much, only I'm a little older, and my heart ain't so good like it used to be."

Mary started and brushed her hair back from her temples with both hands as if she were a little out of her mind. From the way she glared, she might have been in a rage with him.

"He says there's something the matter with your heart? Doctor Ed says so?"

"Now don't yell at me like I was a hog in de garden, Mary. You know I always did like to hear a woman talk soft. He didn't say

[1] **kolache:** Bohemian pastry with fruit center.

anything de matter wid my heart, only it ain't so young like it used to be, an' he tell me not to pitch hay or run de corn-sheller."

Mary wanted to jump up, but she sat still. She admired the way he never under any circumstances raised his voice or spoke roughly. He was city-bred, and she was country-bred; she often said she wanted her boys to have their papa's nice ways.

"You never have no pain there, do you? It's your breathing and your stomach that's been wrong. I wouldn't believe nobody but Doctor Ed about it. I guess I'll go see him myself. Didn't he give you no advice?"

"Chust to take it easy like, an' stay round de house dis winter. I guess you got some carpenter work for me to do. I kin make some new shelves for you, and I want dis long time to build a closet in de boys' room and make dem two little fellars keep dere clo'es hung up."

Rosicky drank his coffee from time to time, while he considered. His mustache was of the soft long variety and came down over his mouth like the teeth of a buggy rake over a bundle of hay. Each time he put down his cup he ran his blue handkerchief over his lips. When he took a drink of water, he managed very neatly with the back of his hand.

Mary sat watching him intently, trying to find any change in his face. It is hard to see anyone who has become like your own body to you. Yes, his hair had got thin, and his high forehead had deep lines running from left to right. But his neck, always clean shaved except in the busiest seasons, was not loose or baggy. It was burned a dark reddish-brown, and there were deep creases in it, but it looked firm and full of blood. His cheeks had a good color. On either side of his mouth there was a half-moon down the length of his cheek, not wrinkles, but two lines that had come there from his habitual expression. He was shorter and broader than when she married him; his back had grown broad and curved, a good deal like the shell of an old turtle, and his arms and legs were short.

He was fifteen years older than Mary, but she had hardly ever thought about it before. He was her man, and the kind of man she liked. She was rough, and he was gentle,—city-bred, as she always said. They had been shipmates on a rough voyage and had stood by each other in trying times. Life had gone well with them because, at bottom, they had the same ideas about life. They agreed, without discussion, as to what was important and what was secondary. They didn't often exchange opinions, even in Czech, — it was as if they had thought the same thought together. A good deal had to be sacrificed and thrown overboard in a hard life like theirs, and they had never disagreed as to the things that could go. It had been a hard life, and a soft life, too. There wasn't anything brutal in the short, broad-backed man with the three-cornered eyes and the forehead that went on to the top of his skull. He was a city man, a gentle man, and though he had married a rough farm girl, he had never touched her without gentleness.

They had been at one accord not to hurry through life, not to be always skimping and saving. They saw their neighbors buy more land and feed more stock than they did, without discontent. Once when the creamery agent came to the Rosickys to persuade them to sell him their cream, he told them how much money the Fasslers, their nearest neighbors, had made on their cream last year.

"Yes," said Mary, "and look at them Fassler children! Pale, pinched little things, they look like skimmed milk. I'd rather put some color into my children's faces than put money into the bank."

The agent shrugged and turned to Anton.

"I guess we'll do like she says," said Rosicky.

III

Mary very soon got into town to see Doctor Ed, and then she had a talk with her boys and set a guard over Rosicky. Even John, the youngest, had his father on his mind. If Rosicky went to throw hay down from the loft, one of the boys ran up the ladder and took the fork from him. He sometimes complained that though he was getting to be an old man, he wasn't an old woman yet.

That winter he stayed in the house in the afternoons and carpentered, or sat in the chair between the window full of plants and the wooden bench where the two pails of drinking water stood. This spot was called "Father's corner," though it was not a corner at all. He had a shelf there, where he kept his Bohemian papers and his pipes and tobacco, and his shears and needles and thread and tailor's thimble. Having been a tailor in his youth, he couldn't bear to see a woman patching at his clothes, or at the boys'. He liked tailoring, and always patched all the overalls and jackets and work shirts. Occasionally he made over a pair of pants one of the older boys had outgrown, for the little fellow.

While he sewed, he let his mind run back over his life. He had a good deal to remember, really; life in three countries. The only part of his youth he didn't like to remember was the two years he had spent in London, in Cheapside,[1] working for a German tailor who was wretchedly poor. Those days, when he was nearly always hungry, when his clothes were dropping off him for dirt, and the sound of a strange language kept him in continual bewilderment, had left a sore spot in his mind that wouldn't bear touching.

He was twenty when he landed at Castle Garden in New York, and he had a protector who got him work in a tailor shop in Vesey Street, down near the Washington Market. He looked upon that part of his life as very happy. He became a good workman, he was industrious, and his wages were increased from time to time. He minded his own business and envied nobody's good fortune. He went to night school and learned to read English. He often did overtime work and was well-paid for it, but somehow he never saved anything. He couldn't refuse a loan to a friend, and he was self-indulgent. He liked a good dinner, and a little went for beer, a little for tobacco; a good deal went to the girls. He often stood through an opera on Saturday nights; he could get standing room for a dollar. Those were the great days of opera in New York. and it gave a fellow something to think about for the rest of the week. Rosicky had a quick ear, and a childish love of all the stage splendor: the scenery, the costumes, the ballet. He usually went with a chum, and after the performance they had beer and maybe some oysters somewhere. It was a fine life; for the first five years or so it satisfied him completely. He was never hungry or cold or dirty, and everything amused him: a fire, a dogfight, a parade, a storm, a ferry ride. He thought New York the finest, richest, friendliest city in the world.

Moreover, he had what he called a happy home life. Very near the tailor shop was a small furniture factory, where an old Austrian, Loeffler, employed a few skilled men and made unusual furniture,

[1] **Cheapside:** a low-rent district in the business part of London.

most of it to order, for the rich German housewives uptown. The top floor of Loeffler's five-story factory was a loft, where he kept his choice lumber and stored the odd pieces of furniture left on his hands. One of the young workmen he employed was a Czech, and he and Rosicky became fast friends. They persuaded Loeffler to let them have a sleeping room in one corner of the loft. They bought good beds and bedding and had their pick of the furniture kept up there. The loft was low-pitched, but light and airy, full of windows, and good-smelling by reason of the fine lumber put up there to season. Old Loeffler used to go down to the docks and buy wood from South America and the East from the sea captains. The young men were as foolish about their house as a bridal pair. Zichec, the young cabinetmaker, devised every sort of convenience, and Rosicky kept their clothes in order. At night and on Sundays, when the quiver of machinery underneath was still, it was the quietest place in the world, and on summer nights all the sea winds blew in. Zichec often practiced on his flute in the evening. They were both fond of music and went to the opera together. Rosicky thought he wanted to live like that for ever.

But as the years passed, all alike, he began to get a little restless. When spring came round, he would begin to feel fretted, and he got to drinking. He was likely to drink too much of a Saturday night. On Sunday he was languid and heavy, getting over his spree. On Monday he plunged into work again. So he never had time to figure out what ailed him, though he knew something did. When the grass turned green in Park Place, and the lilac hedge at the back of Trinity churchyard put out its blossoms, he was tormented by a longing to run away. That was why he drank too much; to get a temporary illusion of freedom and wide horizons.

Rosicky, the old Rosicky, could remember as if it were yesterday the day when the young Rosicky found out what was the matter with him. It was on a Fourth of July afternoon, and he was sitting in Park Place in the sun. The lower part of New York was empty. Wall Street, Liberty Street, Broadway, all empty. So much stone and asphalt with nothing going on, so many empty windows. The emptiness was intense, like the stillness in a great factory when the machinery stops and the belts and bands cease running. It was too great a change, it took all the strength out of one. Those blank buildings, without the stream of life pouring through them, were like empty jails. It struck young Rosicky that this was the trouble with big cities; they built you in from the earth itself, cemented you away from any contact with the ground. You lived in an unnatural world, like the fish in an aquarium, who were probably much more comfortable than they ever were in the sea.

On that very day he began to think seriously about the articles he had read in the Bohemian papers, describing prosperous Czech farming communities in the West. He believed he would like to go out there as a farm hand; it was hardly possible that he could ever have land of his own. His people had always been workmen; his father and grandfather had worked in shops. His mother's parents had lived in the country, but they rented their farm and had a hard time to get along. Nobody in his family had ever owned any land, — that belonged to a different station of life altogether. Anton's mother died when he was little, and he was sent into the country to her parents. He stayed with them until he was twelve, and formed those ties with the earth and the farm animals and growing things which are never made at all unless they are made early. After his grandfather died, he went back to live with his father and stepmother, but she was very hard on him, and his father helped him to get passage to London.

After that Fourth of July day in Park Place, the desire to return to the country never left him. To work on another man's farm would be all he asked; to see the sun rise and set and to plant things and watch them grow. He was a very simple man. He was like a tree that has not many roots, but one taproot that goes down deep. He subscribed for a Bohemian paper printed in Chicago, then for one printed in Omaha. His mind got farther and farther west. He began to save a little money to buy his liberty. When he was thirty-five, there was a great meeting in New York of Bohemian athletic societies, and Rosicky left the tailor shop and went home with the Omaha delegates to try his fortune in another part of the world.

IV

Perhaps the fact that his own youth was well over before he began to have a family was one reason why Rosicky was so fond of his boys. He had almost a grandfather's indulgence for them. He had never had to worry about any of them — except, just now, a little about Rudolph.

On Saturday night the boys always piled into the Ford, took little Josephine, and went to town to the moving-picture show. One Saturday morning they were talking at the breakfast table about starting early that evening, so that they would have an hour or so to see the Christmas things in the stores before the show began. Rosicky looked down the table.

"I hope you boys ain't disappointed, but I want you to let me have de car tonight. Maybe some of you can go in with de neighbors."

Their faces fell. They worked hard all week, and they were still like children. A new jackknife or a box of candy pleased the older ones as much as the little fellow.

"If you and Mother are going to town," Frank said, "maybe you could take a couple of us along with you, anyway."

"No, I want to take de car down to Rudolph's, and let him and Polly go to de show. She don't git into town enough, an' I'm afraid she's gettin' lonesome, and he can't afford no car yet."

That settled it. The boys were a good deal dashed. Their father took another piece of apple cake and went on: "Maybe next Saturday night de two little fellers can go along wid dem."

"Oh, is Rudolph going to have the car every Saturday night?"

Rosicky did not reply at once; then he began to speak seriously: "Listen, boys; Polly ain't lookin' so good. I don't like to see nobody lookin' sad. It comes hard fur a town girl to be a farmer's wife. I don't want no trouble to start in Rudolph's family. When it starts, it ain't so easy to stop. An American girl don't git used to our ways all at once. I like to tell Polly she and Rudolph can have the car every Saturday night till after New Year's, if it's all right with you boys."

"Sure it's all right, Papa," Mary cut in. "And it's good you thought about that. Town girls is used to more than country girls. I lay awake nights, scared she'll make Rudolph discontented with the farm."

The boys put as good a face on it as they could. They surely looked forward to their Saturday nights in town. That evening

Rosicky drove the car the half mile down to Rudolph's new, bare little house.

Polly was in a short-sleeved gingham dress, clearing away the supper dishes. She was a trim, slim little thing, with blue eyes and shingled yellow hair, and her eyebrows were reduced to a mere brush-stroke, like Miss Pearl's.

"Good evening, Mr. Rosicky. Rudolph's at the barn, I guess." She never called him father, or Mary mother. She was sensitive about having married a foreigner. She never in the world would have done it if Rudolph hadn't been such a handsome, persuasive fellow and such a gallant lover. He had graduated in her class in the high school in town, and their friendship began in the ninth grade.

Rosicky went in, though he wasn't exactly asked. "My boys ain't goin' to town tonight, an' I brought de car over fur you two to go in to de picture show."

Polly, carrying dishes to the sink, looked over her shoulder at him. "Thank you. But I'm late with my work tonight, and pretty tired. Maybe Rudolph would like to go in with you."

"Oh, I don't go to de shows! I'm too old-fashioned. You won't feel so tired after you ride in de air a ways. It's a nice clear night, an' it ain't cold. You go an' fix yourself up, Polly, an' I'll wash de dishes an' leave everything nice fur you."

Polly blushed and tossed her bob. "I couldn't let you do that, Mr. Rosicky. I wouldn't think of it."

Rosicky said nothing. He found a bib apron on a nail behind the kitchen door. He slipped it over his head and then took Polly by her two elbows and pushed her gently toward the door of her own room. "I washed up de kitchen many times for my wife, when de babies was sick or somethin'. You go an' make yourself look nice. I like you to look prettier'n any of dem town girls when you go in. De young folks must have some fun, an' I'm goin' to look out fur you, Polly."

That kind, reassuring grip on her elbows, the old man's funny bright eyes, made Polly want to drop her head on his shoulder for a second. She restrained herself, but she lingered in his grasp at the door of her room, murmuring tearfully: "You always lived in the city when you were young, didn't you? Don't you ever get lonesome out here?"

As she turned round to him, her hand fell naturally into his, and he stood holding it and smiling into her face with his peculiar, knowing, indulgent smile without a shadow of reproach in it. "Dem big cities is all right fur de rich, but dey is terrible hard fur de poor."

"I don't know. Sometimes I think I'd like to take a chance. You lived in New York, didn't you?"

"An' London. Da's bigger still. I learned my trade dere. Here's Rudolph comin', you better hurry."

"Will you tell me about London sometime?

"Maybe. Only I ain't no talker, Polly. Run an' dress yourself up."

The bedroom door closed behind her, and Rudolph came in from the outside, looking anxious. He had seen the car and was sorry any of his family should come just then. Supper hadn't been a very pleasant occasion. Halting in the doorway, he saw his father in a kitchen apron, carrying dishes to the sink. He flushed crimson and something flashed in his eye. Rosicky held up a warning finger.

"I brought de car over fur you an' Polly to go to de picture show, an' I made her let me finish here so you won't be late. You go put on a clean shirt, quick!"

"But don't the boys want the car, Father?"

"Not tonight dey don't." Rosicky fumbled under his apron and found his pants pocket. He took out a silver dollar and said in a hurried whisper: "You go an' buy dat girl some ice cream an' candy tonight, like you was courtin'. She's awful good friends wid me."

Rudolph was very short of cash, but he took the money as if it hurt him. There had been a crop failure all over the county. He had more than once been sorry he'd married this year.

In a few minutes the young people came out, looking clean and a little stiff. Rosicky hurried them off, and then he took his own time with the dishes. He scoured the pots and pans and put away the milk and swept the kitchen. He put some coal in the stove and shut off the draughts, so the place would be warm for them when they got home late at night. Then he sat down and had a pipe and listened to the clock tick.

Generally speaking, marrying an American girl was certainly a risk. A Czech should marry a Czech. It was lucky that Polly was the daughter of a poor widow woman; Rudolph was proud, and if she had a prosperous family to throw up at him, they could never make it go. Polly was one of four sisters, and they all worked; one was bookkeeper in the bank, one taught music, and Polly and her younger sister had been clerks, like Miss Pearl. All four of them were musical, had pretty voices, and sang in the Methodist choir, which the eldest sister directed.

Polly missed the sociability of a store position. She missed the choir, and the company of her sisters. She didn't dislike housework, but she disliked so much of it. Rosicky was a little anxious about this pair. He was afraid Polly would grow so discontented that Rudy would quit the farm and take a factory job in Omaha. He had worked for a winter up there, two years ago, to get money to marry on. He had done very well, and they would always take him back at the stockyards. But to Rosicky that meant the end of everything for his son. To be a landless man was to be a wage earner, a slave, all your life; to have nothing, to be nothing.

Rosicky thought he would come over and do a little carpentering for Polly after the New Year. He guessed she needed jollying. Rudolph was a serious sort of chap, serious in love and serious about his work.

Rosicky shook out his pipe and walked home across the fields. Ahead of him the lamplight shone from his kitchen windows. Suppose he were still in a tailor shop on Vesey Street, with a bunch of pale, narrow-chested sons working on machines, all coming home tired and sullen to eat supper in a kitchen that was a parlor also; with another crowded, angry family quarreling just across the dumb-waiter shaft, and squeaking pulleys at the windows where dirty washings hung on dirty lines above a court full of old brooms and mops and ash cans. . . .

He stopped by the windmill to look up at the frosty winter stars and draw a long breath before he went inside. That kitchen with the shining windows was dear to him; but the sleeping fields and bright stars and the noble darkness were dearer still.

V

On the day before Christmas the weather set in very cold; no snow, but a bitter, biting wind that whistled and sang over the flat land and lashed one's face like fine wires. There was baking going on in the Rosicky kitchen all day, and Rosicky sat inside, making over a coat that Albert had outgrown into an overcoat for John. Mary had a big red geranium in bloom for Christmas, and a row of Jerusalem cherry trees, full of berries. It was the first year she had ever grown these; Doctor Ed brought her the seeds from Omaha when he went to some medical convention. They reminded Rosicky of plants he had seen in England; and all afternoon, as he stitched, he sat thinking about those two years in London, which his mind usually shrank from even after all this while.

He was a lad of eighteen when he dropped down into London, with no money and no connections except the address of a cousin who was supposed to be working at a confectioner's. When he went to the pastry shop, however, he found that the cousin had gone to America. Anton tramped the streets for several days, sleeping in doorways and on the Embankment,[1] until he was in utter despair. He knew no English, and the sound of the strange language all about him confused him. By chance he met a poor German tailor who had learned his trade in Vienna, and could speak a little Czech. This tailor, Lifschnitz, kept a repair shop in a Cheapside basement, underneath a cobbler. He didn't much need an apprentice, but he was sorry for the boy and took him in for no wages but his keep and what he could pick up. The pickings were supposed to be coppers given you when you took work home to a customer. But most of the customers called for their clothes themselves, and the coppers that came Anton's way were very few. He had, however, a place to sleep. The tailor's family lived upstairs in three rooms; a kitchen, a bedroom, where Lifschnitz and his wife and five children slept, and a living room. Two corners of this living room were curtained off for lodgers; in one Rosicky slept on an old horsehair sofa, with a feather quilt to wrap himself in. The other corner was rented to a wretched, dirty boy, who was studying the violin. He actually practiced there. Rosicky was dirty, too. There was no way to be any-

[1] **Embankment**: the bank of the Thames River.

thing else. Mrs. Lifschnitz got the water she cooked and washed with from a pump in a brick court, four flights down. There were bugs in the place, and multitudes of fleas, though the poor woman did the best she could. Rosicky knew she often went empty to give another potato or a spoonful of dripping to the two hungry, sad-eyed boys who lodged with her. He used to think he would never get out of there, never get a clean shirt to his back again. What would he do, he wondered, when his clothes actually dropped to pieces and the worn cloth wouldn't hold patches any longer?

It was still early when the old farmer put aside his sewing and his recollections. The sky had been a dark gray all day, with not a gleam of sun, and the light failed at four o'clock. He went to shave and change his shirt while the turkey was roasting. Rudolph and Polly were coming over for supper.

After supper they sat round in the kitchen, and the younger boys were saying how sorry they were it hadn't snowed. Everybody was sorry. They wanted a deep snow that would lie long and keep the wheat warm, and leave the ground soaked when it melted.

"Yes, sir!" Rudolph broke out fiercely; "if we have another dry year like last year, there's going to be hard times in this country."

Rosicky filled his pipe. "You boys don't know what hard times is. You don't owe nobody, you got plenty to eat an' keep warm, an' plenty water to keep clean. When you got them, you can't have it very hard."

Rudolph frowned, opened and shut his big right hand, and dropped it clenched upon his knee. "I've got to have a good deal more than that, Father, or I'll quit this farming gamble. I can always make good wages railroading, or at the packing house, and be sure of my money."

"Maybe so," his father answered dryly.

Mary, who had just come in from the pantry and was wiping her hands on the roller towel, thought Rudy and his father were getting too serious. She brought her darning basket and sat down in the middle of the group.

"I ain't much afraid of hard times, Rudy," she said heartily. "We've had a plenty, but we've always come through. Your father wouldn't never take nothing very hard, not even hard times. I got a mind to tell you a story on him. Maybe you boys can't hardly remember the year we had that terrible hot wind, that burned everything up on the Fourth of July? All the corn an' the gardens. An' that was in the days when we didn't have alfalfa yet, – I guess it wasn't invented.

"Well, that very day your father was out cultivatin' corn, and I was here in the kitchen makin' plum preserves. We had bushels of plums that year. I noticed it was terrible hot, but it's always hot in the kitchen when you're preservin', an' I was too busy with my plums to mind. Anton come in from the field about three o'clock, an' I asked him what was the matter.

"'Nothin',' he says, 'but it's pretty hot, an' I think I won't work no more today.' He stood round for a few minutes an' then he says: 'Ain't you near through? I want you should git up a nice supper for us tonight. It's Fourth of July.'

"I told him to git along, that I was right in the middle of preservin', but the plums would taste good on hot biscuit. 'I'm goin' to have fried chicken, too,' he says, and he went off an' killed a couple. You three oldest boys was little fellers, playin' round outside, real hot an' sweaty, an' your father took you to the horse tank down by the windmill an' took off your clothes an' put you in. Them two box elder trees was little then, but they made shade over the tank. Then he took off all his own clothes, an' got in with you. While he was playin' in the water with you, the Methodist preacher drove into our place to say how all the neighbors was goin' to meet at the schoolhouse that night, to pray for rain. He drove right to the windmill, of course, and there was your father and you three with no clothes on. I was in the kitchen door, an' I had to laugh, for the preacher acted like he ain't never seen a naked man before. He surely was embarrassed, an' your father couldn't git to his clothes; they was all hangin' up on the windmill to let the sweat dry out of 'em. So he laid in the tank where he was, an' put one of you boys on top of him to cover him up a little, an' talked to the preacher.

"When you got through playin' in the water, he put clean clothes on you and a clean shirt on himself, and by that time I'd begun to get supper. He says: 'It's too hot in here to eat comfortable. Let's have a picnic in the orchard. We'll eat our supper behind the mulberry hedge, under them linden trees.'

"So he carried our supper down, an' a bottle of my wild-grape wine, an' everything tasted good, I can tell you. The wind got cooler as the sun was goin' down, and it turned out pleasant, only I noticed how the leaves was curled up on the linden trees. That made me think, an' I asked your father if that hot wind all day hadn't been terrible hard on the gardens an' the corn.

"'Corn,' he says, 'there ain't no corn.'

"'What you talkin' about?' I said. 'Ain't we got forty acres?'

"'We ain't got an ear,' he says, 'nor nobody else ain't got none. All the corn in this country was cooked by three o'clock today, like you'd roasted it in an oven.'

"'You mean you won't get no crop at all?' I asked him. I couldn't believe it, after he'd worked so hard.

"'No crop this year,' he says. 'That's why we're havin' a picnic. We might as well enjoy what we got.'

"An' that's how your father behaved, when all the neighbors was so discouraged they couldn't look you in the face. An' we enjoyed ourselves that year, poor as we was, an' our neighbors wasn't a bit better off for bein' miserable. Some of 'em grieved till they got poor digestions and couldn't relish what they did have."

The younger boys said they thought their father had the best of it. But Rudolph was thinking that, all the same, the neighbors had managed to get ahead more, in the fifteen years since that time. There must be something wrong about his father's way of doing things. He wished he knew what was going on in the back of Polly's mind. He knew she liked his father, but he knew, too, that she was afraid of something. When his mother sent over coffeecake or prune tarts or a loaf of fresh bread, Polly seemed to regard them with a certain suspicion. When she observed to him that his brothers had nice manners, her tone implied that it was remarkable they should have. With his mother she was stiff and on her guard. Mary's hearty frankness and gusts of good humor irritated her. Polly was afraid of being unusual or conspicuous in any way, of being "ordinary," as she said!

When Mary had finished her story, Rosicky laid aside his pipe.

"You boys like me to tell you about some of dem hard times I been through in London?" Warmly encouraged, he sat rubbing his forehead along the deep creases. It was bothersome to tell a long story in English (he nearly always talked to the boys in Czech), but he wanted Polly to hear this one.

"Well, you know about dat tailor shop I worked in in London? I had one Christmas dere I ain't never forgot. Times was awful bad before Christmas; de boss ain't got much work, an' have it awful hard to pay his rent. It ain't so much fun, bein' poor in a big city like London, I'll say! All de windows is full of good t'ings to eat, an' all de pushcarts in de streets is full, an' you smell 'em all de time, an' you ain't got no money, — not a damn bit. I didn't mind de cold so much, though I didn't have no overcoat, chust a short jacket I'd outgrowed so it wouldn't meet on me, an' my hands was chapped raw. But I always had a good appetite, like you all know, an' de sight of dem pork pies in de windows was awful fur me!

"Day before Christmas was terrible foggy dat year, an' dat fog gits into your bones and makes you all damp like. Mrs. Lifschnitz didn't give us nothin' but a little bread an' drippin' for supper, because she was savin' to try for to give us a good dinner on Christmas Day. After supper de boss say I can go an' enjoy myself, so I went into de streets to listen to de Christmas singers. Dey sing old songs an' make very nice music, an' I run after dem a good ways, till I got awful hungry. I t'ink maybe I go home. I can sleep till morning an' forgit my belly.

"I went into my corner real quiet, and roll up in my fedder quilt. But I ain't got my head down, till I smell somet'ing good. Seem like it git stronger an' stronger, an' I can't git to sleep noway. I can't understand dat smell. Dere was a gaslight in a hall across de court, dat always shine in at my window a little. I got up an' look round. I got a little wooden box in my corner fur a stool, 'cause I ain't got no chair. I picks up dat box, and under it dere is a roast goose on a platter! I can't believe my eyes. I carry it to de window where de light comes in, an' touch it and smell it to find out, an' den I taste it to be sure. I say, I will eat chust one little bite of dat goose, so I can go to sleep, and tomorrow I won't eat none at all. But I tell you, boys, when I stop, one half of dat goose was gone!"

The narrator bowed his head, and the boys shouted. But little Josephine slipped behind his chair and kissed him on the neck beneath his ear.

"Poor little Papa, I don't want him to be hungry!"

"Da's long ago, child. I ain't never been hungry since I had your mudder to cook fur me."

"Go on and tell us the rest, please," said Polly.

"Well, when I come to realize what I done, of course, I felt terrible. I felt better in de stomach, but very bad in de heart. I set on my bed wid dat platter on my knees, an' it all come to me; how hard dat poor woman save to buy dat goose, and how she get some neighbor to cook it dat got more fire, an' how she put it in my corner to keep it away from dem hungry children. Dey was a old carpet hung up to shut my corner off, an' de children wasn't allowed to go in dere. An' I know she put it in my corner because she trust me more'n she did de violin boy. I can't stand it to face her after I spoil de Christmas. So I put on my shoes and go out into de city. I tell myself I better throw myself in de river; but I guess I ain't dat kind of a boy.

"It was after twelve o'clock, an' terrible cold, an' I start out to walk about London all night. I walk along de river awhile, but dey was lots of drunks all along; men, and women too. I chust move along to keep away from the police. I git onto de Strand, an' den over to New Oxford Street, where dere was a big German restaurant on de ground floor, wid big windows all fixed up fine, an' I could see de people havin' parties inside. While I was lookin' in, two men and two ladies come out, laughin' and talkin' and feelin' happy about all dey been eatin' an' drinkin', and dey was speakin' Czech, — not like de Austrians, but like de home folks talk it.

"I guess I went crazy, an' I done what I ain't never done before nor since. I went right up to dem gay people an' begun to beg dem: 'Fellow countrymen, for God's sake give me money enough to buy a goose!'

"Dey laugh, of course, but de ladies speak awful kind to me, an' dey take me back into de restaurant and give me hot coffee and cakes, an' make me tell all about how I happened to come to London, an' what I was doin' dere. Dey take my name and where I work down on paper, an' both of dem ladies give me ten shillings.

"De big market at Covent Garden ain't very far away, an' by dat time it was open. I go dere an' buy a big goose an' some pork pies, an' potatoes and onions, an' cakes an' oranges fur de children, — all I could carry! When I git home, everybody is still asleep. I pile all I bought on de kitchen table, an' go in an' lay down on my bed, an' I ain't waken up till I hear dat woman scream when she come out into her kitchen. My goodness, but she was surprise! She laugh an' cry at de same time, an' hug me and waken all de children. She ain't stop fur no breakfast; she git de Christmas dinner ready dat morning, and we all sit down an' eat all we can hold. I ain't never seen dat violin boy have all he can hold before.

"Two three days after dat, de two men come to hunt me up, an' dey ask my boss, and he give me a good report an' tell dem I was a steady boy all right. One of dem Bohemians was very smart an' run a Bohemian newspaper in New York, an' de odder was a rich man, in de importing business, an' dey been traveling togedder. Dey told me how t'ings was easier in New York, an' offered to pay my passage when dey was goin' home soon on a boat. My boss say to me: 'You go. You ain't got no chance here, an' I like to see you git ahead, fur you always been a good boy to my woman, and fur dat fine Christmas dinner you give us all.' An' da's how I got to New York."

That night when Rudolph and Polly, arm in arm, were running home across the fields with the bitter wind at their backs, his heart leaped for joy when she said she thought they might have his family come over for supper on New Year's Eve. "Let's get up a nice supper, and not let your mother help at all; make her be company for once."

"That would be lovely of you, Polly," he said humbly. He was a very simple, modest boy, and he, too, felt vaguely that Polly and her sisters were more experienced and worldly than his people.

VI

The winter turned out badly for farmers. It was bitterly cold, and after the first light snows before Christmas there was no snow at all, — and no rain. March was as bitter as February. On those days when the wind fairly punished the country, Rosicky sat by his window. In the fall he and the boys had put in a big wheat planting, and now the seed had frozen in the ground. All that land would have to be plowed up and planted over again, planted in corn. It had happened before, but he was younger then, and he never worried about what had to be. He was sure of himself and of Mary; he knew they could bear what they had to bear, that they would always pull through somehow. But he was not so sure about the young ones, and he felt troubled because Rudolph and Polly were having such a hard start.

Sitting beside his flowering window while the panes rattled and the wind blew in under the door, Rosicky gave himself to reflection as he had not done since those Sundays in the loft of the furniture factory in New York, long ago. Then he was trying to find what he wanted in life for himself; now he was trying to find what he wanted for his boys, and why it was he so hungered to feel sure they would be here, working this very land, after he was gone.

They would have to work hard on the farm, and probably they would never do much more than make a living. But if he could think of them as staying here on the land, he wouldn't have to fear any great unkindness for them. Hardships, certainly; it was a hardship to have the wheat freeze in the ground when seed was so high; and to have to sell your stock because you had no feed. But there would be other years when everything came along right, and you caught up. And what you had was your own. You didn't have to choose between bosses and strikers, and go wrong either way. You didn't have to do with dishonest and cruel people. They were the only things in his experience he had found terrifying and horrible; the look in the eyes of a dishonest and crafty man, of a scheming and rapacious woman.

In the country, if you had a mean neighbor, you could keep off his land and make him keep off yours. But in the city, all the foulness and misery and brutality of your neighbors was part of your life. The worst things he had come upon in his journey through the world were human, — depraved and poisonous specimens of man. To this day he could recall certain terrible faces in the London streets. There were mean people everywhere, to be sure, even in their own country town here. But they weren't tempered, hardened, sharpened, like the treacherous people in cities who live by grinding or cheating or poisoning their fellow men. He had helped to bury two of his fellow workmen in the tailoring trade, and he was distrustful of the organized industries that see one out of the world in big cities.

Here, if you were sick, you had Doctor Ed to take care of you; and if you died, fat Mr. Haycock, the kindest man in the world, buried you.

It seemed to Rosicky that for good honest boys like his, the worst they could do on a farm was better than they would be likely to do in the city. If he'd had a mean boy, now, one who was crooked and sharp and tried to put anything over on his brothers, then town would be the place for him. But he had no such boy. As for Rudolph, the discontented one, he would give the shirt off his back to anyone who touched his heart. What Rosicky really hoped for his boys was that they would get through the world without knowing much about the cruelty of human beings. "Their mother and me ain't prepared them for that," he sometimes said to himself.

These thoughts brought him back to a grateful consideration of his own case. What an escape he had had, to be sure! He, too, in his time, had had to take money for repair work from the hand of a hungry child who let it go wistfully, because it was money due his boss. And now, in all these years, he had never had to take a cent from anyone in bitter need, — never had to look at the face of a woman become like a wolf's from struggle and famine. When he thought of these things, Rosicky would put on his cap and jacket and slip down to the barn and give his work horses a little extra oats, letting them eat it out of his hand in their slobbery fashion. It was his way of expressing what he felt, and made him chuckle with pleasure.

The spring came warm, with blue skies, — but dry, dry as a bone. The boys began plowing up the wheat fields to plant them over in corn. Rosicky would stand at the fence corner and watch them, and the earth was so dry it blew up in clouds of brown dust that hid the horses and the sulky plow and the driver. It was a bad outlook.

The big alfalfa field that lay between the home place and Rudolph's came up green, but Rosicky was worried because during that open windy winter a great many Russian thistle plants had blown in there and lodged. He kept asking the boys to rake them out; he was afraid their seed would root and "take the alfalfa." Rudolph said that was nonsense. The boys were working so hard planting corn, their father felt he couldn't insist about the thistles, but he set great store by that big alfalfa field. It was a feed you could depend on, — and there was some deeper reason, vague, but strong. The peculiar green of that clover woke early memories in old Rosicky, went back to something in his childhood in the old world. When he was a little boy, he had played in fields of that strong blue-green color.

One morning, when Rudolph had gone to town in the car, leaving a work team idle in his barn, Rosicky went over to his son's place, put the horses to the buggy rake, and set about quietly raking up those thistles. He behaved with guilty caution, and rather enjoyed stealing a march on Doctor Ed, who was just then taking his first vacation in seven years of practice and was attending a clinic in Chicago. Rosicky got the thistles raked up, but did not stop to burn them. That would take some time, and his breath was pretty short, so he thought he had better get the horses back to the barn.

He got them into the barn and to their stalls, but the pain had come on so sharp in his chest that he didn't try to take the harness off. He started for the house, bending lower with every step. The cramp in his chest was shutting him up like a jackknife. When he reached the windmill, he swayed and caught at the ladder. He saw Polly coming down the hill, running with the swiftness of a slim greyhound. In a flash she had her shoulder under his armpit.

"Lean on me, Father, hard! Don't be afraid. We can get to the house all right."

Somehow they did, though Rosicky became blind with pain; he could keep on his legs, but he couldn't steer his course. The next thing he was conscious of was lying on Polly's bed, and Polly bending over him wringing out bath towels in hot water and putting them on his chest. She stopped only to throw coal into the stove, and she kept the teakettle and the black pot going. She put these hot applications on him for nearly an hour, she told him afterwards, and all that time he was drawn up stiff and blue, with the sweat pouring off him.

As the pain gradually loosed its grip, the stiffness went out of his jaws, the black circles round his eyes disappeared, and a little of his natural color came back. When his daughter-in-law buttoned his shirt over his chest at last, he sighed.

"Da's fine, de way I feel now, Polly. It was a awful bad spell, an' I was so sorry it all come on you like it did."

Polly was flushed and excited. " Is the pain really gone? Can I leave you long enough to telephone over to your place? "

Rosicky's eyelids fluttered. " Don't telephone, Polly. It ain't no use to scare my wife. It's nice and quiet here, an' if I ain't too much trouble to you, just let me lay still till I feel like myself. I ain't got no pain now. It's nice here."

Polly bent over him and wiped the moisture from his face. " Oh, I'm so glad it's over! " she broke out impulsively. " It just broke my heart to see you suffer so, Father."

Rosicky motioned her to sit down on the chair where the tea-kettle had been, and looked up at her with that lively affectionate gleam in his eyes. " You was awful good to me, I won't never forgit dat. I hate it to be sick on you like dis. Down at de barn I say to myself, dat young girl ain't had much experience in sickness, I don't want to scare her, an' maybe she's got a baby comin' or somet'ing."

Polly took his hand. He was looking at her so intently and affectionately and confidingly; his eyes seemed to caress her face, to regard it with pleasure. She frowned with her funny streaks of eyebrows, and then smiled back at him.

" I guess maybe there is something of that kind going to happen. But I haven't told anyone yet, not my mother or Rudolph. You'll be the first to know."

His hand pressed hers. She noticed that it was warm again. The twinkle in his yellow-brown eyes seemed to come nearer.

" I like mighty well to see dat little child, Polly," was all he said. Then he closed his eyes and lay half smiling. But Polly sat still, thinking hard. She had a sudden feeling that nobody in the world, not her mother, not Rudolph, or anyone, really loved her as much as old Rosicky did. It perplexed her. She sat frowning and trying to puzzle it out. It was as if Rosicky had a special gift for loving people, something that was like an ear for music or an eye for color. It was quiet, unobtrusive; it was merely there. You saw it in his eyes,— perhaps that was why they were merry. You felt it in his hands, too. After he dropped off to sleep, she sat holding his warm, broad flexible brown hand. She had never seen another in the least like it. She wonder if it wasn't a kind of gypsy hand, it was so alive and quick and light in its communications,— very strange in a farmer. Nearly all the farmers she knew had huge lumps of fists, like mauls, or they were knotty and bony and uncomfortable-looking, with stiff fingers. But Rosicky's was like quicksilver, flexible, muscular, about the color of a pale cigar, with deep, deep creases across the palm. It wasn't nervous, it wasn't a stupid lump; it was a warm brown human hand, with some cleverness in it, a great deal of generosity, and something else which Polly could only call "gypsy-like," — something nimble and lively and sure, in the way that animals are.

Polly remembered that hour long afterwards; it had been like an awakening to her. It seemed to her that she had never learned so much about life from anything as from old Rosicky's hand. It brought her to herself; it communicated some direct and untranslatable message.

When she heard Rudolph coming in the car, she ran out to meet him.

"Oh, Rudy, your father's been awful sick! He raked up those thistles he's been worrying about, and afterwards he could hardly get to the house. He suffered so I was afraid he was going to die."

Rudolph jumped to the ground. "Where is he now?"

"On the bed. He's asleep. I was terribly scared, because, you know, I'm so fond of your father." She slipped her arm through his and they went into the house. That afternoon they took Rosicky home and put him to bed, though he protested that he was quite well again.

The next morning he got up and dressed and sat down to breakfast with his family. He told Mary that his coffee tasted better than usual to him, and he warned the boys not to bear any tales to Doctor Ed when he got home. After breakfast he sat down by his window to do some patching and asked Mary to thread several needles for him before she went to feed her chickens, — her eyes were better than his, and her hands steadier. He lit his pipe and took up John's overalls. Mary had been watching him anxiously all morning, and as she went out of the door with her bucket of scraps, she saw that he was smiling. He was thinking, indeed, about Polly, and how he might never have known what a tender heart she had if he hadn't got sick over there. Girls nowadays didn't wear their heart on their sleeve. But now he knew Polly would make a fine woman after the foolishness wore off. Either a woman had that sweetness at her heart or she hadn't. You couldn't always tell by the look of them; but if they had that, everything came out right in the end.

After he had taken a few stitches, the cramp began in his chest, like yesterday. He put his pipe cautiously down on the window sill and bent over to ease the pull. No use, – he had better try to get to his bed if he could. He rose and groped his way across the familiar floor, which was rising and falling like the deck of a ship. At the door he fell. When Mary came in, she found him lying there, and the moment she touched him she knew that he was gone.

Doctor Ed was away when Rosicky died, and for the first few weeks after he got home he was hard driven. Every day he said to himself that he must get out to see the family that had lost their father. One soft, warm moonlight night in early summer he started for the farm. His mind was on other things, and not until his road ran by the graveyard did he realize that Rosicky wasn't over there on the hill where the red lamplight shone, but here, in the moonlight. He stopped his car, shut off the engine, and sat there for a while.

A sudden hush had fallen on his soul. Everything here seemed strangely moving and significant, though signifying what, he did not know. Close by the wire fence stood Rosicky's mowing machine, where one of the boys had been cutting hay that afternoon; his own work horses had been going up and down there. The new-cut hay perfumed all the night air. The moonlight silvered the long, billowy grass that grew over the graves and hid the fence; the few little evergreens stood out black in it, like shadows in a pool. The sky was very blue and soft, the stars rather faint because the moon was full.

For the first time it struck Doctor Ed that this was really a beautiful graveyard. He thought of city cemeteries; acres of shrubbery and heavy stone, so arranged and lonely and unlike anything in the living world. Cities of the dead, indeed; cities of the forgotten, of the "put away." But this was open and free, this little square of long grass which the wind forever stirred. Nothing but the sky overhead, and the many-colored fields running on until they met that sky. The horses worked here in summer; the neighbors passed on their way to town; and over yonder, in the cornfield, Rosicky's own cattle would be eating fodder as winter came on. Nothing could be more undeathlike than this place; nothing could be more right for a man who had helped to do the work of great cities and had always longed for the open country and had got to it at last. Rosicky's life seemed to him complete and beautiful.

READING WITH INSIGHT

1. This is a character story, the kind of story in which the main business is to acquaint the reader with one or more characters. Rosicky is, of course, the main character. What do you remember about him? What single words would *you* use to characterize him, such as *courageous, wise*, etc.? Make your own list, but be prepared to support it from incidents in the story.

2. Perhaps the chief thing to learn from the story is how Miss Cather, a master of characterization, tells you what kind of person Rosicky is. Look at your list of characterizing words. Can you find any of them in the story? If not, can you figure out why the author did not use them?

3. If an author does not say in so many words that a character is honest, hard-working, clever, etc., how else can he give the reader an understanding of the character?

4. What did you learn from Rosicky from the things he said, set down by the author? Examine the points in the story where Rosicky is speaking. What do you learn about his attitude toward himself, toward other people, toward life, from what he says?

5. What do you learn about Rosicky from the things he does? From the things he tells of doing in his early days?

6. What is the attitude of the other characters in the story toward Rosicky? What do you learn about him from what they say and do? What is the attitude of the children toward Rosicky? What passages in the story tell you this?

7. Did you notice the description of Rosicky's hands? What did you learn about the man from this description?

8. Note the few points in the story where the author goes inside Rosicky's mind and tells his thoughts. What do you learn about him from those passages?

9. This story is told from the " omniscient " point of view. " Omniscient " means all-knowing. It is the point of view of a story told in the third person by a narrator who can enter into any character's thoughts. Which characters' minds does Miss Cather enter in this story?

10. What is the advantage, in this kind of story, of being able to enter into any character's thoughts at will? For example, would it have been harder to characterize Rosicky so thoroughly if the story were told from the viewpoint of one of the characters?

11. There is a conflict in the story, a plot that helps hold the story together. You can spot this conflict if you can state what problem worried Rosicky most. What did he do about this problem? Do you believe he solved it before the close of the story?

12. Is Rosicky too perfect? Is there anything unreal about him? Does Miss Cather say anything about his faults, or merely mention his good points?

13. Miss Cather tells us what kind of man Rosicky is, but the broader meaning of the story has to do with what is admirable in men. What in general terms is Miss Cather saying about people? You will find a clue in the sentence on page 209, " The worst things he had come upon in his journey through this world were human . . ."

If you like this story, you will be interested in

Cather. *The Sculptor's Funeral.*
My Ántonia (novel).
Death Comes for the Archbishop (novel).
Hamlin Garland. *Under the Lion's Paw.*
Ruth Suckow. *Golden Wedding.*
Uprooted.

SHERWOOD ANDERSON

Sophistication

SHERWOOD ANDERSON was born in Camden, Ohio in 1876. His parents were poor, and he had little chance to go far in school. In a way his jobs were his education. His family, he said, had been "a wandering gypsy sort of tribe, often moving from place to place just ahead of the bill collector." In various places, he worked as a stableboy, a factory laborer, a soldier in the Spanish-American War, manager of a paint factory, an advertising writer. Always he was terribly interested in people, trying to find out what they were thinking, why they acted as they did.

In 1919, he published just the kind of book you would have expected from a man with that interest. It was a collection of stories called *Winesburg, Ohio*. But these stories were not the usual kind. They hardly had plots. It was difficult to pick climaxes out of them. They were almost as much psychological studies as they were stories. But people read the book and realized that here was more of a portrait of a small town than had ever been put down in short stories. This was so because the people in the stories seemed so real, and because when one read the stories he could see below the surface of the people down into their thoughts and values. The stories were about the psychologies of people, more than their actions. Many times, the stories were mere incidents. But when you read them, you felt you understood why things happened as they did. "Sophistication" is one of the stories from *Winesburg, Ohio*. It is a story of mood and character, and you will notice how much more interested Anderson is in the things that happen below the surface than in surface actions.

In his later years, Anderson published two weekly newspapers at Marion, Virginia — one Democratic, one Republican. He died in 1941.

IT was early evening of a day in the late fall and the Winesburg County Fair had brought crowds of country people into town. The day had been clear and the night came on warm and pleasant. On the Trunion Pike, where the road after it left town stretched away between berry fields now covered with dry brown leaves, the dust from passing wagons arose in clouds. Children, curled into little balls, slept on the straw scattered on wagon beds. Their hair was full of dust and their fingers black and sticky. The dust rolled away over the fields and the departing sun set it ablaze with colors.

In the main street of Winesburg crowds filled the stores and the sidewalks. Night came on, horses whinnied, the clerks in the stores ran madly about, children became lost and cried lustily, an American town worked terribly at the task of amusing itself.

Pushing his way through the crowds in Main Street, young George Willard concealed himself in the stairway leading to Doctor Reefy's office and looked at the people. With feverish eyes he watched the faces drifting past under the store lights. Thoughts kept coming into his head and he did not want to think. He stamped impatiently on the wooden steps and looked sharply about. "Well, is she going to stay with him all day? Have I done all this waiting for nothing?" he muttered.

George Willard, the Ohio village boy, was fast growing into manhood and new thoughts had been coming into his mind. All that day, amid the jam of people at the Fair, he had gone about feeling lonely. He was about to leave Winesburg to go away to some city where he hoped to get work on a city newspaper and he felt grown up. The mood that had taken possession of him was a thing known to men and unknown to boys. He felt old and a little tired. Memories awoke in him. To his mind his new sense of maturity set him apart, made of him a half-tragic figure. He wanted someone to understand the feeling that had taken possession of him after his mother's death.

There is a time in the life of every boy when he for the first time takes the backward view of life. Perhaps that is the moment when he crosses the line into manhood. The boy is walking through the street of his town. He is thinking of the future and of the figure he will cut in the world. Ambitions and regrets awake within him. Suddenly something happens; he stops under a tree and waits as for a voice calling his name. Ghosts of old things creep into his consciousness; the voices outside of himself whisper a message concerning the limitations of life. From being quite sure of himself and his future he becomes not at all sure. If he be an imaginative boy a door is torn open and for the first time he looks out upon the world, seeing, as though they marched in procession before him, the countless figures of men who before his time have come out of nothingness into the world, lived their lives and again disappeared into nothingness. The sadness of sophistication has come to the boy. With a little gasp he sees himself as merely a leaf blown by the wind through the streets of his village. He knows that in spite of all the stout talk of his fellows he must live and die in uncertainty, a thing blown by the winds, a thing destined like corn to wilt in the sun. He shivers and looks eagerly about. The eighteen years he has lived seem but a moment, a breathing space in the long march of humanity. Already he hears death calling. With all his heart he wants to come close to some other human, touch someone with his hands, be touched by the hand of another. If he prefers that the other be a woman, that is because he believes that a woman will be gentle, that she will understand. He wants, most of all, understanding.

When the moment of sophistication came to George Willard his mind turned to Helen White, the Winesburg banker's daughter. Always he had been conscious of the girl growing into womanhood as he grew into manhood. Once on a summer night when he was eighteen, he had walked with her on a country road and in her presence had given way to an impulse to boast, to make himself appear big and significant in her eyes. Now he wanted to see her for another purpose. He wanted to tell her of the new impulses that had come to him. He had tried to make her think of him as a man when he knew nothing of manhood and now he wanted to be with her and to try to make her feel the change he believed had taken place in his nature.

As for Helen White, she also had come to a period of change. What George felt, she in her young woman's way felt also. She was no longer a girl and hungered to reach into the grace and beauty of womanhood. She had come home from Cleveland, where she was attending college, to spend a day at the Fair. She also had begun to have memories. During the day she sat in the grandstand with a young man, one of the instructors from the college, who was a guest of her mother's. The young man was of a pedantic turn of mind and she felt at once he would not do for her purpose. At the Fair she was glad to be seen in his company as he was well dressed and a stranger. She knew that the fact of his presence would create an impression. During the day she was happy, but when night came on she began to grow restless. She wanted to drive the instructor away, to get out of his presence. While they sat together in the grandstand and while the eyes of former schoolmates were upon them, she paid so much attention to her escort that he grew interested. " A scholar needs money. I should marry a woman with money," he mused.

Helen White was thinking of George Willard even as he wandered gloomily through the crowds thinking of her. She remembered the summer evening when they had walked together and wanted to walk with him again. She thought that the months she had spent in the city, the going to theaters and the seeing of great crowds wandering in lighted thoroughfares, had changed her profoundly. She wanted him to feel and be conscious of the change in her nature.

The summer evening together that had left its mark on the memory of both the young man and woman had, when looked at quite sensibly, been rather stupidly spent. They had walked out of town along a country road. Then they had stopped by a fence near a field of young corn and George had taken off his coat and let it hang on his arm. " Well, I've stayed here in Winesburg — yes — I've not yet gone away but I'm growing up," he had said. " I've been reading books and I've been thinking. I'm going to try to amount to something in life.

" Well," he explained, " that isn't the point. Perhaps I'd better quit talking."

The confused boy put his hand on the girl's arm. His voice trembled. The two started to walk back along the road toward town. In his desperation George boasted, " I'm going to be a big man, the biggest that ever lived here in Winesburg," he declared. " I want you to do something. I don't know what. Perhaps it is none of my business. I want you to try to be different from other women. You see the point. It's none of my business I tell you. I want you to be a beautiful woman. You see what I want."

The boy's voice failed and in silence the two came back into town and went along the street to Helen White's house. At the gate he tried to say something impressive. Speeches he had thought out came into his head, but they seemed utterly pointless. "I thought—I used to think—I had it in my mind you would marry Seth Richmond. Now I know you won't," was all he could find to say as she went through the gate and toward the door of her house.

On the warm fall evening as he stood in the stairway and looked at the crowd drifting through Main Street, George thought of the talk beside the field of young corn and was ashamed of the figure he had made of himself. In the street the people surged up and down like cattle confined in a pen. Buggies and wagons almost filled the narrow thoroughfare. A band played and small boys raced along the sidewalk, diving between the legs of men. Young men with shining red faces walked awkwardly about with girls on their arms. In a room above one of the stores, where a dance was to be held, the fiddlers tuned their instruments. The broken sounds floated down through an open window and out across the murmur of voices and the loud blare of the horns of the band. The medley of sounds got on young Willard's nerves. Everywhere, on all sides, the sense of crowding, moving life closed in about him. He wanted to run away by himself and think. "If she wants to stay with that fellow she may. Why should I care? What difference does it make to me?" he growled and went along Main Street and through Hern's grocery into a side street.

George felt so utterly lonely and dejected that he wanted to weep but pride made him walk rapidly along, swinging his arms. He came to Westley Moyer's livery barn and stopped in the shadows to listen to a group of men who talked of a race Westley's stallion, Tony Tip, had won at the Fair during the afternoon. A crowd had gathered in front of the barn and before the crowd walked Westley, prancing up and down and boasting. He held a whip in his hand and kept tapping the ground. Little puffs of dust arose in the lamplight. "Hell, quit your talking," Westley exclaimed. "I wasn't afraid, I knew I had 'em beat all the time. I wasn't afraid."

Ordinarily George Willard would have been intensely interested in the boasting of Moyer, the horseman. Now it made him angry.

He turned and hurried away along the street. " Old windbag," he sputtered. " Why does he want to be bragging? Why don't he shut up? "

George went into a vacant lot and as he hurried along, fell over a pile of rubbish. A nail protruding from an empty barrel tore his trousers. He sat down on the ground and swore. With a pin he mended the torn place and then arose and went on. " I'll go to Helen White's house, that's what I'll do. I'll walk right in. I'll say that I want to see her. I'll walk right in and sit down, that's what I'll do," he declared, climbing over a fence and beginning to run.

. . . .

On the veranda of Banker White's house Helen was restless and distraught. The instructor sat between the mother and daughter. His talk wearied the girl. Although he had also been raised in an Ohio town, the instructor began to put on the airs of the city. He wanted to appear cosmopolitan. " I like the chance you have given me to study the background out of which most of our girls come," he declared. " It was good of you, Mrs. White, to have me down for the day." He turned to Helen and laughed. " Your life is still bound up with the life of this town? " he asked. " There are people here in whom you are interested? " To the girl his voice sounded pompous and heavy.

Helen arose and went into the house. At the door leading to a garden at the back she stopped and stood listening. Her mother began to talk. " There is no one here fit to associate with a girl of Helen's breeding," she said.

Helen ran down a flight of stairs at the back of the house and into the garden. In the darkness she stopped and stood trembling. It seemed to her that the world was full of meaningless people saying words. Afire with eagerness she ran through a garden gate and turning a corner by the banker's barn, went into a little side street. " George! Where are you, George? " she cried, filled with nervous excitement. She stopped running, and leaned against a tree to laugh hysterically. Along the dark little street came George Willard, still saying words. " I'm going to walk right into her house. I'll go right in and sit down," he declared as he came up to her. He stopped and stared stupidly. " Come on," he said and took hold of her hand. With hanging heads they walked away along the street under the trees.

Dry leaves rustled under foot. Now that he had found her George wondered what he had better do and say.

At the upper end of the fairground, in Winesburg, there is a half-decayed old grandstand. It has never been painted and the boards are all warped out of shape. The fairground stands on top of a low hill rising out of the valley of Wine Creek and from the grandstand one can see at night, over a cornfield, the lights of the town reflected against the sky.

George and Helen climbed the hill to the fairground, coming by the path past Waterworks Pond. The feeling of loneliness and isolation that had come to the young man in the crowded streets of his town was both broken and intensified by the presence of Helen. What he felt was reflected in her.

In youth there are always two forces fighting in people. The warm unthinking little animal struggles against the thing that reflects and remembers, and the older, the more sophisticated thing had possession of George Willard. Sensing his mood, Helen walked beside him filled with respect. When they got to the grandstand they climbed up under the roof and sat down on one of the long benchlike seats.

There is something memorable in the experience to be had by going into a fairground that stands at the edge of a Middle Western town on a night after the annual fair has been held. The sensation is one never to be forgotten. On all sides are ghosts, not of the dead, but of living people. Here, during the day just passed, have come the people pouring in from the town and the country around. Farmers with their wives and children and all the people from the hundreds of little frame houses have gathered within these board walls. Young girls have laughed and men with beards have talked of the affairs of their lives. The place has been filled to overflowing with life. It has itched and squirmed with life and now it is night and the life has all gone away. The silence is almost terrifying. One conceals oneself standing silently beside the trunk of a tree and what there is of a reflective tendency in his nature is intensified. One shudders at the thought of the meaninglessness of life while at the same instant, and if the people of the town are his people, one loves life so intensely that tears come into the eyes.

In the darkness under the roof of the grandstand, George Willard sat beside Helen White and felt very keenly his own insignificance in the scheme of existence. Now that he had come out of town where the presence of the people stirring about, busy with a multitude of affairs, had been so irritating the irritation was all gone. The presence of Helen renewed and refreshed him. It was as though her woman's hand was assisting him to make some minute readjustment of the machinery of his life. He began to think of the people in the town where he had always lived with something like reverence. He had reverence for Helen. He wanted to love and to be loved by her, but he did not want at the moment to be confused by her womanhood. In the darkness he took hold of her hand and when she crept close put a hand on her shoulder. A wind began to blow and he shivered. With all his strength he tried to hold and to understand the mood that had come upon him. In that high place in the darkness the two oddly sensitive human atoms held each other tightly and waited. In the mind of each was the same thought. "I have come to this lonely place and here is this other," was the substance of the thing felt.

In Winesburg the crowded day had run itself out into the long night of the late fall. Farm horses jogged away along lonely country roads pulling their portion of weary people. Clerks began to bring samples of goods in off the sidewalks and lock the doors of stores. In the Opera House a crowd had gathered to see a show and further down Main Street the fiddlers, their instruments tuned, sweated and worked to keep the feet of youth flying over a dance floor.

In the darkness in the grandstand Helen White and George Willard remained silent. Now and then the spell that held them was broken and they turned and tried in the dim light to see into each other's eyes. They kissed but that impulse did not last. At the upper end of the fairground a half dozen men worked over horses that had raced during the afternoon. The men had built a fire and were heating kettles of water. Only their legs could be seen as they passed back and forth in the light. When the wind blew the little flames of the fire danced crazily about.

George and Helen arose and walked away into the darkness. They went along a path past a field of corn that had not yet been cut. The wind whispered among the dry corn blades. For a moment during the walk back into town the spell that held them was broken.

When they had come to the crest of Waterworks Hill they stopped by a tree and George again put his hands on the girl's shoulders. She embraced him eagerly and then again they drew quickly back from that impulse. They stopped kissing and stood a little apart. Mutual respect grew big in them. They were both embarrassed and to relieve their embarrassment dropped into the animalism of youth. They laughed and began to pull and haul at each other. In some way chastened and purified by the mood they had been in they became, not man and woman, not boy and girl, but excited little animals.

It was so they went down the hill. In the darkness they played like two splendid young things in a young world. Once, running swiftly forward, Helen tripped George and he fell. He squirmed and shouted. Shaking with laughter, he rolled down the hill. Helen ran after him. For just a moment she stopped in the darkness. There is no way of knowing what woman's thoughts went through her mind but, when the bottom of the hill was reached and she came up to the boy, she took his arm and walked beside him in dignified silence. For some reason they could not have explained they had both got from their silent evening together the thing needed. Man or boy, woman or girl, they had for a moment taken hold of the thing that makes the mature life of men and women in the modern world possible.

READING WITH INSIGHT

1. When critics talk about Anderson's Winesburg stories, they almost always marvel over the *reality* of the stories. Check this by your own experience. Are these *real* young people? Do their actions seem true to life? Does the town seem real? What details and incidents does the author use to get this effect?

2. Where does the interest lie in the story? Is there any suspense? Are you anxious over the outcome? Is there any exciting conflict? Any climax? Does a story have to have those qualities to interest its readers? How else can a story interest you?

3. This story would not be very interesting if told as an anecdote. What other stories in this book can you think of that would likewise not be interesting unless read entire?

[H]ow does the author's object in writing this nonanecdotal story [differ] from Jack London's object in his story "All-Gold Cañon"? London's story, of course, would still be interesting if told as an anecdote. What in general is the reason for writing a nonanecdotal story?

5. We said that the movement of a story was from problem to solution, or from tension to resolution. What is the problem or tension in this story, and what is the resolution?

6. How does the story obey Poe's rule as to what the first sentences of a story should do? Why do you think Anderson began it as he did, rather than with action?

7. Part of the effect of this story lies in the attitude of the author toward his characters. What would you say that attitude is? Is the author making fun of the young people, for example?

8. This is a story of character, rather than action. What other stories that you have read in this book would you likewise call stories of character?

9. What is the significance of George's and Helen's playing like children toward the end of the story? Have you ever had a feeling that you wanted to burst out of grown-up restraint and act like a youngster again?

10. What does the Professor contribute to the working out of the story?

11. Would you say that the last sentence sums up the story? How would you describe the meaning of the story?

12. Anderson has been a great influence on young writers. How would you expect his influence to differ from Poe's?

If you like this story, you will be interested in

Anderson. *Queer.*
Maureen Daly. *Sixteen.*
Martha Foley. *One with Shakespeare.*
Willa Cather. *Paul's Case.*
Ruth Suckow. *The Man of the Family.*

ERNEST HEMINGWAY

Now I Lay Me

PROBABLY more young Americans have tried to write like Ernest Hemingway than like any other living author. Together with Sherwood Anderson, Hemingway led the new kind of story which developed in this country in the 1920's, supplanting the long influence of Poe and Hawthorne. This new kind of story, you will find later in this book, is in the tradition of Chekov, rather than Poe. But American college students in the 20's, trying to learn to write fiction, did not read much Chekov; they read Hemingway. They tried to write like him and act like him.

Hemingway was born in 1898 in Oak Park, Illinois, the son of a physician. In high school he played football and boxed. He started to work for a newspaper, but the war came and he went into service on the French and Italian fronts. He was severely wounded, and the Italian government decorated him for conspicuous bravery. After the war, he went back into newspaper work, became a foreign correspondent, and joined the colony of young American artists in Paris. Here he published the first of the stories that made him famous, and the first of his much-read novels, *The Sun Also Rises*, *A Farewell to Arms*, and *For Whom the Bell Tolls*. He has lived out of this country almost as much as in it. He took part in the Spanish Civil War and in World War II. Now he divides his time between Florida and Cuba. Big and athletic, he loves bullfighting, deep-sea fishing, and outdoor life in general.

Young writers tried to copy Hemingway's method of telling a story. They tried to copy his "objective" kind of writing, in which he said little about his characters and nothing at all about their goodness or badness, and let the reader make up his own mind about them. They tried to copy his "underwriting"—his intentional playing down of exciting material so that it seemed all the more exciting by contrast with y he wrote about it. They tried to copy his use of dialogue written an idealized fashion as Hawthorne or Poe might have written it but flatly and sometimes banally as people really talk. All these characteristics are in this story, and you should notice them and see whether they appeal as much to you as they appealed to young readers thirty years ago.

But Hemingway's chief appeal was to the young people of his time who, after World War I, felt insecure and undirected. As has been said, Hemingway " expresses the aspirations of that portion of his generation which genuinely feels itself lost and is eager to admire a way of life which combines lostness with courage and color." The story that follows is about one member of that " lost generation."

THAT night we lay on the floor in the room and I listened to the silkworms eating. The silkworms fed in racks of mulberry leaves and all night you could hear them eating and a dropping sound in the leaves. I myself did not want to sleep because I had been living for a long time with the knowledge that if I ever shut my eyes in the dark and let myself go, my soul would go out of my body. I had been that way for a long time, ever since I had been blown up at night and felt it go out of me and go off and then come back. I tried never to think about it, but it had started to go since, in the nights, just at the moment of going off to sleep, and I could only stop it by a very great effort. So while now I am fairly sure that it would not really have gone out, yet then, that summer, I was unwilling to make the experiment.

I had different ways of occupying myself while I lay awake. I would think of a trout stream I had fished along when I was a boy and fish its whole length very carefully in my mind; fishing very carefully under all the logs, all the turns of the bank, the deep holes and the clear shallow stretches, sometimes catching trout and sometimes losing them. I would stop fishing at noon to eat my lunch; sometimes on a log over the stream; sometimes on a high bank under a tree, and I always ate my lunch very slowly and watched the stream below me while I ate. Often I ran out of bait because I would take only ten worms with me in a tobacco tin when I started. When I had used them all I had to find more worms, and sometimes it was very difficult digging in the bank of the stream where the cedar trees kept out the sun and there was no grass but only the bare moist earth and often I could find no worms. Always though I found some kind of bait, but one time in the swamp I could find no bait at all and had to cut up one of the trout I had caught and use him for bait.

Sometimes I found insects in the swamp meadows, in the grass or under ferns, and used them. There were beetles and insects with legs like grass stems, and grubs in old rotten logs; white grubs with brown pinching heads that would not stay on the hook and emptied into nothing in the cold water, and wood ticks under logs where sometimes I found angleworms that slipped into the ground as soon as the log was raised. Once I used a salamander from under an old log. The salamander was very small and neat and agile and a lovely color. He had tiny feet that tried to hold on to the hook, and after that one time I never used a salamander, although I found them very often. Nor did I use crickets, because of the way they acted about the hook.

Sometimes the stream ran through an open meadow, and in the dry grass I would catch grasshoppers and use them for bait and sometimes I would catch grasshoppers and toss them into the stream and watch them float along swimming on the stream and circling on the surface as the current took them and then disappear as a trout rose. Sometimes I would fish four or five different streams in the night; starting as near as I could get to their source and fishing them downstream. When I had finished too quickly and the time did not go, I would fish the stream over again, starting where it emptied into the lake and fishing back upstream, trying for all the trout I had missed coming down. Some nights too I made up streams, and some of them were very exciting, and it was like being awake and dreaming. Some of those streams I still remember and think that I have fished in them, and they are confused with streams I really know. I gave them all names and went to them on the train and sometimes walked for miles to get to them.

But some nights I could not fish, and on those nights I was cold-awake and said my prayers over and over and tried to pray for all the people I had ever known. That took up a great amount of time, for if you try to remember all the people you have ever known, going back to the earliest thing you remember — which was, with me, the attic of the house where I was born and my mother and father's wedding cake in a tin box hanging from one of the rafters, and, in the attic, jars of snakes and other specimens that my father had collected as a boy and preserved in alcohol, the alcohol sunken in the jars so the backs of some of the snakes and specimens were exposed and had turned white — if you thought back that far, you remembered a great many people. If you prayed for all of them, saying a Hail Mary and an Our Father for each one, it took a long time and finally it would be light, and then you could go to sleep, if you were in a place where you could sleep in the daylight.

On those nights I tried to remember everything that had ever happened to me, starting with just before I went to the war and remembering back from one thing to another. I found I could only remember back to that attic in my grandfather's house. Then I would start there and remember this way again, until I reached the war.

I remembered, after my grandfather died we moved away from that house and to a new house designed and built by my mother. Many things that were not to be moved were burned in the back yard and I remember those jars from the attic being thrown in the fire, and how they popped in the heat and the fire flamed up from the alcohol. I remember the snakes burning in the fire in the back yard. But there were no people in that, only things. I could not remember who burned the things, even, and I would go on until I came to people and then stop and pray for them.

About the new house I remembered how my mother was always cleaning things out and making a good clearance. One time when my father was away on a hunting trip she made a good thorough cleaning out in the basement and burned everything that should not have been there. When my father came home and got down from his buggy and hitched the horse, the fire was still burning in the road beside the house. I went out to meet him. He handed me his shotgun and looked at the fire. "What's this?" he asked.

"I've been cleaning out the basement, dear," my mother said from the porch. She was standing there smiling, to meet him. My father looked at the fire and kicked something. Then he leaned over and picked something out of the ashes. "Get a rake, Nick," he said to me. I went to the basement and brought a rake and my father raked very carefully in the ashes. He raked out stone axes and stone skinning knives and tools for making arrowheads and pieces of pottery and many arrowheads. They had all been blackened and chipped by the fire. My father raked them all out very carefully and spread them on the grass by the road. His shotgun in its leather case and his gamebags were on the grass where he had left them when he stepped down from the buggy.

"Take the gun and the bags in the house, Nick, and bring me a paper," he said. My mother had gone inside the house. I took the shotgun, which was heavy to carry and banged against my legs, and the two gamebags and started toward the house. "Take them one at a time," my father said. "Don't try and carry too much at once." I put down the gamebags and took in the shotgun and brought out a newspaper from the pile in my father's office. My father spread all the blackened, chipped stone implements on the paper and then wrapped them up. "The best arrowheads went all to pieces," he said. He walked into the house with the paper package and I stayed outside on the grass with the two gamebags. After a while I took them in. In remembering that, there were only two people, so I would pray for them both.

Some nights, though, I could not remember my prayers even. I could only get as far as "On earth as it is in heaven" and then have to start all over again and be absolutely unable to get past that. Then I would have to recognize that I could not remember and give up saying my prayers that night and try something else. So on some nights I would try to remember all the animals in the world by name and then the birds and then fishes and then countries and cities and then kinds of foods and the names of all the streets I could remember in Chicago, and when I could not remember anything at all any more I would just listen. And I do not remember a night on which you could not hear things. If I could have a light I was not afraid to sleep, because I knew my soul would only go out of me if it were dark. So, of course, many nights I was where I could have a light and then I slept because I was nearly always tired and often very sleepy. And I am sure many times too that I slept without knowing it — but I never slept knowing it, and on this night I listened to the silkworms. You can hear silkworms eating very clearly in the night and I lay with my eyes open and listened to them.

There was only one other person in the room and he was awake too. I listened to him being awake, for a long time. He could not lie as quietly as I could because, perhaps, he had not had as much practice being awake. We were lying on blankets spread over straw and when he moved the straw was noisy, but the silkworms were not frightened by any noise we made and ate on steadily. There were noises of night seven kilometers behind the lines outside but they were different from the small noises inside the room in the dark. The other man in the room tried lying quietly. Then he moved again. I moved too, so he would know I was awake. He had lived ten years in Chicago. They had taken him for a soldier in 1914 when he had come back to visit his family, and they had given him to me for an orderly because he spoke English. I heard him listening, so I moved again in the blankets.

"Can't you sleep, Signor Tenente?"[1] he asked.

"No."

"I can't sleep either."

"What's the matter?"

"I don't know. I can't sleep."

"You feel all right?"

"Sure. I feel good. I just can't sleep."

"You want to talk a while?" I asked.

"Sure. What can you talk about in this damn place."

"This place is pretty good," I said.

"Sure," he said. "It's all right."

"Tell me about out in Chicago," I said.

"Oh," he said, "I told you all that once."

"Tell me about how you got married."

"I told you that."

"Was the letter you got Monday – from her?"

"Sure. She writes me all the time. She's making good money with the place."

"You'll have a nice place when you go back."

"Sure. She runs it fine. She's making a lot of money."

"Don't you think we'll wake them up, talking?" I asked.

"No. They can't hear. Anyway, they sleep like pigs. I'm different," he said. "I'm nervous."

[1] **Signor Tenente:** Mr. Lieutenant.

"Talk quiet," I said. "Want a smoke?"

We smoked skillfully in the dark.

"You don't smoke much, Signor Tenente."

"No. I've just about cut it out."

"Well," he said, "it don't do you any good and I suppose you get so you don't miss it. Did you ever hear a blind man won't smoke because he can't see the smoke come out?"

"I don't believe it."

"I think it's all bull, myself," he said. "I just heard it somewhere. You know how you hear things."

We were both quiet and I listened to the silkworms.

"You hear those damn silkworms?" he asked. "You can hear them chew."

"It's funny," I said.

"Say, Signor Tenente, is there something really the matter that you can't sleep? I never see you sleep. You haven't slept nights ever since I been with you."

"I don't know, John," I said, "I got in pretty bad shape along early last spring and at night it bothers me."

"Just like I am," he said. "I shouldn't have ever got in this war. I'm too nervous."

"Maybe it will get better."

"Say, Signor Tenente, what did you get in this war for, anyway?"

"I don't know, John. I wanted to, then."

"Wanted to," he said. "That's a hell of a reason."

"We oughtn't to talk out loud," I said.

"They sleep just like pigs," he said. "They can't understand the English language, anyway. They don't know a damn thing. What are you going to do when it's over and we go back to the States?"

"I'll get a job on a paper."

"In Chicago?"

"Maybe."

"Do you ever read what this fellow Brisbane[1] writes? My wife cuts it out for me and sends it to me."

"Sure."

"Did you ever meet him?"

[1] **Arthur Brisbane**: a famous newspaper columnist.

"No, but I've seen him."

"I'd like to meet that fellow. He's a fine writer. My wife don't read English but she takes the paper just like when I was home and she cuts out the editorials and the sport page and sends them to me."

"How are your kids?"

"They're fine. One of the girls is in the fourth grade now. You know, Signor Tenente, if I didn't have the kids I wouldn't be your orderly now. They'd have made me stay in the line all the time."

"I'm glad you've got them."

"So am I. They're fine kids but I want a boy. Three girls and no boy. That's a hell of a note."

"Why don't you try and go to sleep."

"No, I can't sleep now. I'm wide awake, now, Signor Tenente. Say, I'm worried about you not sleeping though."

"It'll be all right, John."

"Imagine a young fellow like you not to sleep."

"I'll get all right. It just takes a while."

"You got to get all right. A man can't get along that don't sleep. Do you worry about anything? You got anything on your mind?"

"No, John, I don't think so."

"You ought to get married, Signor Tenente. Then you wouldn't worry."

"I don't know."

"You ought to get married. Why don't you pick out some nice Italian girl with plenty of money? You could get any one you want. You're young and you got good decorations and you look nice. You been wounded a couple of times."

"I can't talk the language well enough."

"You talk it fine. To hell with talking the language. You don't have to talk to them. Marry them."

"I'll think about it."

"You know some girls, don't you?"

"Sure."

"Well, you marry the one with the most money. Over here, the way they're brought up, they'll all make you a good wife."

"I'll think about it."

"Don't think about it, Signor Tenente. Do it."

"All right."

"A man ought to be married. You'll never regret it. Every man ought to be married."

"All right," I said. "Let's try and sleep a while."

"All right, Signor Tenente. I'll try it again. But you remember what I said."

"I'll remember it," I said. "Now let's sleep a while, John."

"All right," he said. "I hope you sleep, Signor Tenente."

I heard him roll in his blankets on the straw and then he was very quiet and I listened to him breathing regularly. Then he started to snore. I listened to him snore for a long time and then I stopped listening to him snore and listened to the silkworms eating. They ate steadily, making a dropping in the leaves. I had a new thing to think about and I lay in the dark with my eyes open and thought of all the girls I had ever known and what kind of wives they would make. It was a very interesting thing to think about and for a while it killed off trout fishing and interfered with my prayers. Finally, though, I went back to trout fishing, because I found that I could remember all the streams and there was always something new about them, while the girls, after I had thought about them a few times, blurred and I could not call them into my mind and finally they all blurred and all became rather the same and I gave up thinking about them almost altogether. But I kept on with my prayers and I prayed very often for John in the nights and his class was removed from active service before the October offensive. I was glad he was not there, because he would have been a great worry to me. He came to the hospital in Milan to see me several months after and was very disappointed that I had not yet married, and I know he would feel very badly if he knew that, so far, I have never married. He was going back to America and he was very certain about marriage and knew it would fix up everything.

READING WITH INSIGHT

1. Who is telling the story? Hemingway tells you nothing directly about him, but what do you learn about him indirectly?
2. Why can't the narrator sleep?
3. This story and Sherwood Anderson's "Sophistication" repre-

sent a considerable change in the American short story since the days of Poe and Hawthorne. Taking the Poe, Hawthorne, Anderson, and Hemingway stories in this volume as examples, how would you describe that change?

4. This story has tension, but would you say it has a plot? What is the problem? You can get at it by asking yourself what causes the tension – what is the reason for the main character's disquiet, and what is he seeking? Is the tension ever resolved? Does the story give you a sense of completeness and satisfaction? Does a story need to do that?

5. What do you think of the dialogue in this story? Is it real? How does it differ from the dialogue in some of the older stories in this book? Listen to a group of people talking, and try to write down afterward what they really said. Should fictional dialogue be an exact copy of the way people talk in real life?

6. How do you know this story takes place in World War I?

7. This is what is called "objective" writing. To see what is meant by that, compare what Hemingway tells you about these characters with what Harte tells you about his "Outcasts" or Miss Cather about her "Neighbor Rosicky."

8. Why is the other soldier in this story? What does he contribute to it? Is he merely someone for the main character to talk to? If not, what does he contribute to the meaning?

9. Are the scenes the soldier remembers out of the past merely there by chance, or has the author carefully selected them to mean something? Cite some evidence for your answer.

10. Why is there so much emphasis on the Lieutenant's boyhood? Recall that much of the story is memories of boyhood. The father and mother are remembered. The Lieutenant rejects the idea that he should get married, even quits thinking about possible wives and returns to memories of his childhood fishing. Is Hemingway trying to suggest that the soldier is just a boy after all, and that when he is scared and hurt he naturally tries to crawl back into the safe and protective and quiet life of his childhood? What other interpretation would you make of this?

11. You will agree that this is a vivid picture of one part of a soldier's life. What meaning has the story beyond being a good picture? What comment is Hemingway making about war?

If you like this story, you will be interested in

Hemingway. *In Another Country.*
The Undefeated.
The Killers.
J. P. Marquand. *Good Morning, Major.*
Richard Ely Danielson. *Corporal Hardy.*

STEPHEN VINCENT BENÉT

By the Waters of Babylon

STEPHEN BENÉT is best known as a poet, but he wrote a handful of stories which are full of imagination, humor, and poetry, and which in many ways are not surpassed in our time.

Benét was born in 1898 of an Army family, spent his boyhood in Army posts, graduated from Yale, and studied at the Sorbonne in Paris. When he was not quite 30, he wrote a poem that swept the country, sold thousands of copies, and won the Pulitzer Prize. This was *John Brown's Body*, a book-length poem about the War between the States. Benét published a number of other books of poetry, three not very well known novels, and a handful of unforgettable stories, before his untimely death in 1943.

This story, like "The Devil and Daniel Webster" and others of Benét's best, is fantasy. You will notice that it is realistic and believable except for one imaginary fact. In this case, the fact is that the story occurs after the end of our civilization. The secret of a story like this is to combine imaginative quality with realistic details.

THE north and the west and the south are good hunting ground, but it is forbidden to go east. It is forbidden to go to any of the Dead Places except to search for metal and then he who touches the metal must be a priest or the son of a priest. Afterward, both the man and the metal must be purified. These are the rules and the laws; they are well made. It is forbidden to cross the great river and look upon the place that was the Place of the Gods — this is most strictly forbidden. We do not even say its name though we know its name. It is there that spirits live, and demons — it is there that there are the ashes of the Great Burning. These things are forbidden — they have been forbidden since the beginning of time.

My father is a priest; I am the son of a priest. I have been in the Dead Places near us, with my father — at first, I was afraid. When my father went into the house to search for the metal, I stood by the door and my heart felt small and weak. It was a dead man's house, a spirit house. It did not have the smell of man, though there were old bones in a corner. But it is not fitting that a priest's son should show fear. I looked at the bones in the shadow and kept my voice still.

Then my father came out with the metal — a good, strong piece. He looked at me with both eyes but I had not run away. He gave me the metal to hold — I took it and did not die. So he knew that I was truly his son and would be a priest in my time. That was when I was very young — nevertheless, my brothers would not have done it, though they are good hunters. After that, they gave me the good piece of meat and the warm corner by the fire. My father watched over me — he was glad that I should be a priest. But when I boasted or wept without a reason, he punished me more strictly than my brothers. That was right.

After a time, I myself was allowed to go into the dead houses and search for metal. So I learned the ways of those houses — and if I saw bones, I was no longer afraid. The bones are light and old — sometimes they will fall into dust if you touch them. But that is a great sin.

I was taught the chants and the spells — I was taught how to stop the running of blood from a wound and many secrets. A priest must know many secrets — that was what my father said. If the hunters think we do all things by chants and spells, they may believe so — it does not hurt them. I was taught how to read in the old books and how to make the old writings — that was hard and took a long time. My knowledge made me happy — it was like a fire in my heart. Most of all, I liked to hear of the Old Days and the stories of the gods. I asked myself many questions that I could not answer, but it was good to ask them. At night, I would lie awake and listen to the wind — it seemed to me that it was the voice of the gods as they flew through the air.

We are not ignorant like the Forest People — our women spin wool on the wheel, our priests wear a white robe. We do not eat grubs from the tree, we have not forgotten the old writings, although they are hard to understand. Nevertheless, my knowledge and my lack of knowledge burned in me — I wished to know more. When I was a man at last, I came to my father and said, "It is time for me to go on my journey. Give me your leave."

He looked at me for a long time, stroking his beard, then he said at last, "Yes. It is time." That night, in the house of the priesthood, I asked for and received purification. My body hurt but my spirit was a cool stone. It was my father himself who questioned me about my dreams.

He bade me look into the smoke of the fire and see — I saw and told what I saw. It was what I have always seen — a river, and, beyond it, a great Dead Place and in it the gods walking. I have always thought about that. His eyes were stern when I told him — he was no longer my father but a priest. He said, "This is a strong dream."

"It is mine," I said, while the smoke waved and my head felt light. They were singing the Star song in the outer chamber and it was like the buzzing of bees in my head.

He asked me how the gods were dressed and I told him how they were dressed. We know how they were dressed from the book, but I saw them as if they were before me. When I had finished, he threw the sticks three times and studied them as they fell.

"This is a very strong dream," he said. "It may eat you up."

"I am not afraid," I said and looked at him with both eyes. My voice sounded thin in my ears but that was because of the smoke.

He touched me on the breast and the forehead. He gave me the bow and the three arrows.

"Take them," he said. "It is forbidden to travel east. It is forbidden to cross the river. It is forbidden to go to the Place of the Gods. All these things are forbidden."

"All these things are forbidden," I said, but it was my voice that spoke and not my spirit. He looked at me again.

"My son," he said. "Once I had young dreams. If your dreams do not eat you up, you may be a great priest. If they eat you, you are still my son. Now go on your journey."

I went fasting, as is the law. My body hurt but not my heart.

When the dawn came, I was out of sight of the village. I prayed and purified myself, waiting for a sign. The sign was an eagle. It flew east.

Sometimes signs are sent by bad spirits. I waited again on the flat rock, fasting, taking no food. I was very still — I could feel the sky above me and the earth beneath. I waited till the sun was beginning to sink. Then three deer passed in the valley going east — they did not mind me or see me. There was a white fawn with them — a very great sign.

I followed them, at a distance, waiting for what would happen. My heart was troubled about going east, yet I knew that I must go. My head hummed with my fasting — I did not even see the panther spring upon the white fawn. But, before I knew it, the bow was in my hand. I shouted and the panther lifted his head from the fawn. It is not easy to kill a panther with one arrow but the arrow went through his eye and into his brain. He died as he tried to spring — he rolled over, tearing at the ground. Then I knew I was meant to go east — I knew that was my journey. When the night came, I made my fire and roasted meat.

It is eight suns journey to the east and a man passes by many Dead Places. The Forest People are afraid of them but I am not. Once I made my fire on the edge of a Dead Place at night and, next morning, in the dead house, I found a good knife, little rusted. That was small to what came afterward but it made my heart feel big. Always when I looked for game, it was in front of my arrow, and twice I passed hunting parties of the Forest People without their knowing. So I knew my magic was strong and my journey clean, in spite of the law.

Toward the setting of the eighth sun, I came to the banks of the great river. It was half-a-day's journey after I had left the god-road — we do not use the god-roads now for they are falling apart into great blocks of stone, and the forest is safer going. A long way off, I had seen the water through trees but the trees were thick. At last, I came out upon an open place at the top of a cliff. There was the great river below, like a giant in the sun. It is very long, very wide. It could eat all the streams we know and still be thirsty. Its name is Ou-dis-sun, the Sacred, the Long. No man of my tribe had seen it, not even my father, the priest. It was magic and I prayed.

Then I raised my eyes and looked south. It was there, the Place of the Gods.

How can I tell what it was like — you do not know. It was there, in the red light, and they were too big to be houses. It was there with the red light upon it, mighty and ruined. I knew that in another moment the gods would see me. I covered my eyes with my hands and crept back into the forest.

Surely, that was enough to do, and live. Surely it was enough to spend the night upon the cliff. The Forest People themselves do not come near. Yet, all through the night, I knew that I should have to cross the river and walk in the places of the gods, although the gods ate me up. My magic did not help me at all and yet there was a fire in my bowels, a fire in my mind. When the sun rose, I thought, "My journey has been clean. Now I will go home from my journey." But, even as I thought so, I knew I could not. If I went to the Place of the Gods, I would surely die, if I did not go, I could never be at peace with my spirit again. It is better to lose one's life than one's spirit, if one is a priest and the son of a priest.

Nevertheless, as I made the raft, the tears ran out of my eyes. The Forest People could have killed me without fight, if they had come upon me then, but they did not come. When the raft was made, I said the sayings for the dead and painted myself for death. My heart was cold as a frog and my knees like water, but the burning in my mind would not let me have peace. As I pushed the raft from the shore, I began my death song — I had the right. It was a fine song.

"I am John, son of John," I sang. "My people are the Hill People.
They are the men.
I go into the Dead Places but I am not slain.
I take the metal from the Dead Places but I am not blasted.
I travel upon the god-roads and am not afraid. E-yah! I have killed the panther, I have killed the fawn!
E-yah! I have come to the great river. No man has come there before.
It is forbidden to go east, but I have gone, forbidden to go on the great river, but I am there.
Open your hearts, you spirits, and hear my song.

Now I go to the place of the gods, I shall not return.
My body is painted for death and my limbs weak, but my heart is big as I go to the place of the gods! "

All the same, when I came to the Place of the Gods, I was afraid, afraid. The current of the great river is very strong — it gripped my raft with its hands. That was magic, for the river itself is wide and calm. I could feel evil spirits about me, in the bright morning; I could feel their breath on my neck as I was swept down the stream. Never have I been so much alone — I tried to think of my knowledge, but it was a squirrel's heap of winter nuts. There was no strength in my knowledge any more and I felt small and naked as a new-hatched bird — alone upon the great river, the servant of the gods.

Yet, after a while, my eyes were opened and I saw. I saw both banks of the river — I saw that once there had been god-roads across it, though now they were broken and fallen like broken vines. Very great they were, and wonderful and broken — broken in the time of the Great Burning when the fire fell out of the sky. And always the current took me nearer to the Place of the Gods, and the huge ruins rose before my eyes.

I do not know the customs of rivers — we are the People of the Hills. I tried to guide my raft with the pole but it spun around. I thought the river meant to take me past the Place of the Gods and out into the Bitter Water of the legends. I grew angry then — my heart felt strong. I said aloud, " I am a priest and the son of a priest! " The gods heard me — they showed me how to paddle with the pole on one side of the raft. The current changed itself — I drew near to the Place of the Gods.

When I was very near, my raft struck and turned over. I can swim in our lakes — I swam to the shore. There was a great spike of rusted metal sticking out into the river — I hauled myself up upon it and sat there, panting. I had saved my bow and two arrows and the knife I found in the Dead Place but that was all. My raft went whirling downstream toward the Bitter Water. I looked after it, and thought if it had trod me under, at least I would be safely dead. Nevertheless, when I had dried my bowstring and re-strung it, I walked forward to the Place of the Gods.

It felt like ground underfoot; it did not burn me. It is not true what some of the tales say, that the ground there burns forever, for I have been there. Here and there were the marks and stains of the Great Burning, on the ruins, that is true. But they were old marks and old stains. It is not true either, what some of our priests say, that it is an island covered with fogs and enchantments. It is not. It is a great Dead Place — greater than any Dead Place we know. Everywhere in it there are god-roads, though most are cracked and broken. Everywhere there are the ruins of the high towers of the gods.

How shall I tell what I saw? I went carefully, my strung bow in my hand, my skin ready for danger. There should have been the wailings of spirits and the shrieks of demons, but there were not. It was very silent and sunny where I had landed — the wind and the rain and the birds that drop seeds had done their work — the grass grew in the cracks of the broken stone. It is a fair island — no wonder the gods built there. If I had come there, a god, I also would have built.

How shall I tell what I saw? The towers are not all broken — here and there one still stands, like a great tree in a forest, and the birds nest high. But the towers themselves look blind, for the gods are gone. I saw a fish hawk, catching fish in the river. I saw a little dance of white butterflies over a great heap of broken stones and columns. I went there and looked about me — there was a carved stone with cut-letters, broken in half. I can read letters but I could not understand these. They said UBTREAS. There was also the shattered image of a man or a god. It had been made of white stone and he wore his hair tied back like a woman's. His name was ASHING, as I read on the cracked half of a stone. I thought it wise to pray to ASHING, though I do not know that god.

How shall I tell what I saw? There was no smell of man left, on stone or metal. Nor were there many trees in that wilderness of stone. There are many pigeons, nesting and dropping in the towers — the gods must have loved them, or, perhaps, they used them for sacrifices. There are wild cats that roam the god-roads, green-eyed, unafraid of man. At night they wail like demons but they are not demons. The wild dogs are more dangerous, for they hunt in a pack, but them I did not meet till later. Everywhere there are the carved stones, carved with magical numbers or words.

I went north — I did not try to hide myself. When a god or a demon saw me, then I would die, but meanwhile I was no longer afraid. My hunger for knowledge burned in me — there was so much that I could not understand. After a while, I knew that my belly was hungry. I could have hunted for my meat, but I did not hunt. It is known that the gods did not hunt as we do — they got their food from enchanted boxes and jars. Sometimes these are still found in the Dead Places — once, when I was a child and foolish, I opened such a jar and tasted it and found the food sweet. But my father found out and punished me for it strictly, for, often, that food is death. Now, though, I had long gone past what was forbidden, and I entered the likeliest towers, looking for the food of the gods.

I found it at last in the ruins of a great temple in the mid-city. A mighty temple it must have been, for the roof was painted like the sky at night with its stars — that much I could see, though the colors were faint and dim. It went down into great caves and tunnels — perhaps they kept their slaves there. But when I started to climb down, I heard the squeaking of rats, so I did not go — rats are unclean, and there must have been many tribes of them, from the squeaking. But near there, I found food, in the heart of a ruin, behind a door that still opened. I ate only the fruits from the jars — they had a very sweet taste. There was drink, too, in bottles of glass — the drink of the gods was strong and made my head swim. After I had eaten and drunk, I slept on the top of a stone, my bow at my side.

When I woke, the sun was low. Looking down from where I lay, I saw a dog sitting on his haunches. His tongue was hanging out of his mouth; he looked as if he were laughing. He was a big dog, with a gray-brown coat, as big as a wolf. I sprang up and shouted at him but he did not move — he just sat there as if he were laughing. I did not like that. When I reached for a stone to throw, he moved swiftly out of the way of the stone. He was not afraid of me; he looked at me as if I were meat. No doubt I could have killed him with an arrow, but I did not know if there were others. Moreover, night was falling.

I looked about me — not far away there was a great, broken god-road, leading North. The towers were high enough, but not so high, and while many of the dead-houses were wrecked, there were some that stood. I went toward this god-road, keeping to the heights of the ruins, while the dog followed. When I had reached the god-road, I saw that there were others behind him. If I had slept later, they would have come upon me asleep and torn out my throat. As it was, they were sure enough of me; they did not hurry. When I went into the dead-house, they kept watch at the entrance — doubtless they thought they would have a fine hunt. But a dog cannot open a door and I knew, from the books, that the gods did not like to live on the ground but on high.

I had just found a door I could open when the dogs decided to rush. Ha! They were surprised when I shut the door in their faces — it was a good door, of strong metal. I could hear their foolish baying beyond it but I did not stop to answer them. I was in darkness — I found stairs and climbed. There were many stairs, turning around till my head was dizzy. At the top was another door — I found the knob and opened it. I was in a long small chamber — on one side of it was a bronze door that could not be opened, for it had no handle. Perhaps there was a magic word to open it but I did not have the word. I turned to the door in the opposite side of the wall. The lock of it was broken and I opened it and went in.

Within, there was a place of great riches. The god who lived there must have been a powerful god. The first room was a small anteroom — I waited there for some time, telling the spirits of the place that I came in peace and not as a robber. When it seemed to me that they had had time to hear me, I went on. Ah, what riches! Few, even, of the windows had been broken — it was all as it had been. The great windows that looked over the city had not been broken at all though they were dusty and streaked with many years. There were coverings on the floors, the colors not greatly faded, and the chairs were soft and deep. There were pictures upon the walls, very strange, very wonderful — I remember one of a bunch of flowers in a jar — if you came close to it, you could see nothing but bits of color, but if you stood away from it, the flowers might have been picked yesterday. It made my heart feel strange to look at this picture — and to look at the figure of a bird, in some hard clay, on a table and see it so like our birds. Everywhere there were books and writings, many in tongues that I could not read. The god who lived there must have been a wise god and full of knowledge. I felt I had right there, as I sought knowledge also.

Nevertheless, it was strange. There was a washing-place but no water — perhaps the gods washed in air. There was a cooking-place but no wood, and though there was a machine to cook food, there was no place to put fire in it. Nor were there candles or lamps — there were things that looked like lamps but they had neither oil nor wick. All these things were magic, but I touched them and lived — the magic had gone out of them. Let me tell one thing to show. In the washing-place, a thing said "Hot" but it was not hot to the touch — another thing said "Cold" but it was not cold. This must have been a strong magic but the magic was gone. I do not understand — they had ways — I wish that I knew.

It was close and dry and dusty in their house of the gods. I have said the magic was gone but that is not true — it had gone from the magic things but it had not gone from the place. I felt the spirits about me, weighing upon me. Nor had I ever slept in a Dead Place before — and yet, tonight, I must sleep there. When I thought of it, my tongue felt dry in my throat, in spite of my wish for knowledge. Almost I would have gone down again and faced the dogs, but I did not.

I had not gone through all the rooms when the darkness fell. When it fell, I went back to the big room looking over the city and made fire. There was a place to make fire and a box with wood in it, though I do not think they cooked there. I wrapped myself in a floor-covering and slept in front of the fire — I was very tired.

Now I tell what is very strong magic. I woke in the midst of the night. When I woke, the fire had gone out and I was cold. It seemed to me that all around me there were whisperings and voices. I closed my eyes to shut them out. Some will say that I slept again, but I do not think that I slept. I could feel the spirits drawing my spirit out of my body as a fish is drawn on a line.

Why should I lie about it? I am a priest and the son of a priest. If there are spirits, as they say, in the small Dead Places near us, what spirits must there not be in that great Place of the Gods? And would not they wish to speak? After such long years? I know that I felt myself drawn as a fish is drawn on a line. I had stepped out of my body — I could see my body asleep in front of the cold fire, but it was not I. I was drawn to look out upon the city of the gods.

It should have been dark, for it was night, but it was not dark. Everywhere there were lights — lines of light — circles and blurs of light — ten thousand torches would not have been the same. The sky itself was alight — you could barely see the stars for the glow in the sky. I thought to myself " This is strong magic " and trembled. There was a roaring in my ears like the rushing of rivers. Then my eyes grew used to the light and my ears to the sound. I knew that I was seeing the city as it had been when the gods were alive.

That was a sight indeed — yes, that was a sight: I could not have seen it in the body — my body would have died. Everywhere went the gods, on foot and in chariots — there were gods beyond number and counting and their chariots blocked the streets. They had turned night to day for their pleasure — they did not sleep with the sun. The noise of their coming and going was the noise of many waters. It was magic what they could do — it was magic what they did.

I looked out of another window — the great vines of their bridges were mended and the god-roads went east and west. Restless, restless, were the gods and always in motion! They burrowed tunnels under rivers — they flew in the air. With unbelievable tools they did giant works — no part of the earth was safe from them, for, if they wished for a thing, they summoned it from the other side of the world. And always, as they labored and rested, as they feasted and made love, there was a drum in their ears — the pulse of the giant city, beating and beating like a man's heart.

Were they happy? What is happiness to the gods? They were great, they were mighty, they were wonderful and terrible. As I looked upon them and their magic, I felt like a child — but a little more, it seemed to me, and they would pull down the moon from the sky. I saw them with wisdom beyond wisdom and knowledge beyond knowledge. And yet not all they did was well done — even I could see that — and yet their wisdom could not but grow until all was peace.

Then I saw their fate come upon them and that was terrible past speech. It came upon them as they walked the streets of their city. I have been in the fights with the Forest People — I have seen men die. But this was not like that. When gods war with gods, they use weapons we do not know. It was fire falling out of the sky and a mist that poisoned. It was the time of the Great Burning and the Destruction. They ran about like ants in the streets of their city—poor gods, poor gods! Then the towers began to fall. A few escaped—yes, a few. The legends tell it. But, even after the city had become a Dead Place, for many years the poison was still in the ground. I saw it happen, I saw the last of them die. It was darkness over the broken city and I wept.

All this, I saw. I saw it as I have told it, though not in the body. When I woke in the morning, I was hungry, but I did not think first of my hunger for my heart was perplexed and confused. I knew the reason for the Dead Places but I did not see why it had happened. It seemed to me it should not have happened, with all the magic they had. I went through the house looking for an answer. There was so much in the house I could not understand—and yet I am a priest and the son of a priest. It was like being on one side of the great river, at night, with no light to show the way.

Then I saw the dead god. He was sitting in his chair, by the window, in a room I had not entered before and, for the first moment, I thought that he was alive. Then I saw the skin on the back of his hand—it was like dry leather. The room was shut, hot and dry—no doubt that had kept him as he was. At first I was afraid to approach him—then the fear left me. He was sitting looking out over the city—he was dressed in the clothes of the gods. His age was neither young nor old—I could not tell his age. But there was wisdom in his face and great sadness. You could see that he would have not run away. He had sat at his window, watching his city die—then he himself had died. But it is better to lose one's life than one's spirit—and you could see from the face that his spirit had not been lost. I knew, that, if I touched him, he would fall into dust—and yet, there was something unconquered in the face.

That is all of my story, for then I knew he was a man—I knew then that they had been men, neither gods nor demons. It is a great knowledge, hard to tell and believe. They were men—they went a dark road, but they were men. I had no fear after that—I had no fear going home, though twice I fought off the dogs and once I was hunted for two days by the Forest People. When I saw my father again, I prayed and was purified. He touched my lips and my breast, he said, "You went away a boy. You come back a man and a priest." I said, "Father, they were men! I have been in the Place of the Gods and seen it! Now slay me, if it is the law — but still I know they were men."

He looked at me out of both eyes. He said, "The law is not always the same shape — you have done what you have done. I could not have done it in my time, but you come after me. Tell!"

I told and he listened. After that, I wished to tell all the people but he showed me otherwise. He said, "Truth is a hard deer to hunt. If you eat too much truth at once, you may die of the truth. It was not idly that our fathers forbade the Dead Places." He was right — it is better the truth should come little by little. I have learned that, being a priest. Perhaps, in the old days, they ate knowledge too fast.

Nevertheless, we make a beginning. It is not for the metal alone we go to the Dead Places now — there are the books and the writings. They are hard to learn. And the magic tools are broken — but we can look at them and wonder. At least, we make a beginning. And, when I am chief priest we shall go beyond the great river. We shall go to the Place of the Gods — the place newyork — not one man but a company. We shall look for the images of the gods and find the god ASHING and the others — the gods Licoln and Biltmore and Moses. But they were men who built the city, not gods or demons. They were men. I remember the dead man's face. They were men who were here before us. We must build again.

READING WITH INSIGHT

1. Where was the boy living? What was the river and what was the city? What were UBTREAS and ASHING? What are the Dead Places? What was the fire that fell from the skies?

2. This story, of course, was written before the atomic bomb was invented, but how does it apply to our new atomic age?

3. What would you say was the origin of the tribe from which the boy came?

4. How has Benét written this story to make it sound as though a boy in a primitive tribe were telling it? One example is his use of short sentences. What are others?

5. What is the chief source of interest in this story? Action? Character? Scenery? Atmosphere? Idea? Compare the relative interest of these things with their interest in such a story as, for instance, Harte's "The Outcasts of Poker Flat."

6. Does the thought of a future race looking at the ruins of our civilization give you a new outlook on the things around you? For example, suppose that all human beings were removed from this continent, and a stranger from another planet were to come to your town — what would he find and what would he decide about the kind of people who had built this town and lived in it? Suppose he came to your very home and your room — what would he be able to tell about you?

7. A shallow interpretation of this story's meaning might be, "They said it couldn't happen here!" In what ways is that inadequate to describe the meaning of the story? State your own idea of the meaning of the story.

8. In the city of the Dead Gods, the boy keeps wondering how the gods, with all their magic, could have let this happen to them. He never quite finds the answer, but his father says, "Maybe they ate knowledge too fast in those days." What does this sentence mean? What evidence is there that our civilization is "eating knowledge too fast"?

9. Granting that the destruction of our civilization had occurred, the first detail in the story which is not realistic is the boy's vision of the city as it used to be. Does the vision detract from or add to the effectiveness of the story? Was it necessary? Would you have preferred to imagine for yourself the city as it used to be? Give your reasons.

10. Would the story have been interesting to you even if it had no special application to the atomic age and to our civilization — that is, if it were just about a boy's adventures? How much of the effectiveness of the story is due to the historical implications and how much to the story itself?

11. What is the problem or tension and how is it resolved? What does the boy get out of his trip?

12. How does the author succeed in making this imaginative story seem real? What details make you say, "Yes, this could have happened"?

If you like this story, you will be interested in

Benét. *The Devil and Daniel Webster.*
Daniel Webster and the Sea-Serpent.
Freedom's a Hard-Bought Thing.
John Brown's Body (poem).
Eric Knight. *The Flying Yorkshireman.*
Wilbur Schramm. *Grandpa Hopewell Flies Again.*

JOHN STEINBECK

The Leader of the People

"I CAN'T understand why some reviewers persist in classing John Steinbeck as a hard-boiled writer," wrote a well-known critic. "Far from tough, he is exceptionally sensitive."

In a sense, Steinbeck is both tough and gentle. His novels, like the widely read *Grapes of Wrath*, deal with the seamy sides of life. His stories, like the one following, show people hurt, people not understood, people who are inadequate and misplaced and failures, and he writes about them almost as objectively as Hemingway. Yet throughout all his writing you feel that he loves the people he writes about. He is extraordinarily sensitive to their little problems, triumphs, and defeats. In "The Leader of the People" he presents a rather unlovely family situation. He shows an old man being hurt terribly. Yet he makes us understand and love that old man, and even appreciate why his son-in-law treats him as he does. And he is extraordinarily successful in recreating the world of the boy Jody. As you will notice, he has a remarkable understanding of both old age and youth, and his view of his characters as a whole is impartial and sympathetic.

Steinbeck was born in California in 1902, went to Stanford, wandered over the country working at many kinds of employment and meeting all kinds of men. He returned to California, moved to a farm, and began to write stories. Among them were half a dozen successful novels and a handful of remarkable short stories, like this one.

ON Saturday afternoon Billy Buck, the ranch hand, raked together the last of the old year's haystack and pitched small forkfuls over the wire fence to a few mildly interested cattle. High in the air small clouds like puffs of cannon smoke were driven eastward by the March wind. The wind could be heard whishing in the brush on the ridge crests, but no breath of it penetrated down into the ranch cup.

The little boy, Jody, emerged from the house eating a thick piece of buttered bread. He saw Billy working on the last of the haystack. Jody tramped down scuffing his shoes in a way he had been told was destructive to good shoe leather. A flock of white pigeons flew out of the black cypress tree as Jody passed, and circled the tree and landed again. A half-grown tortoise-shell cat leaped from the bunk-house porch, galloped on stiff legs across the road, whirled and galloped back again. Jody picked up a stone to help the game along, but he was too late, for the cat was under the porch before the stone could be discharged. He threw the stone into the cypress tree and started the white pigeons on another whirling flight.

Arriving at the used-up haystack, the boy leaned against the barbed-wire fence. "Will that be all of it, do you think?" he asked.

The middle-aged ranch hand stopped his careful raking and stuck his fork into the ground. He took off his black hat and smoothed down his hair. "Nothing left of it that isn't soggy from ground moisture," he said. He replaced his hat and rubbed his dry leathery hands together.

"Ought to be plenty mice," Jody suggested.

"Lousy with them," said Billy. "Just crawling with mice."

"Well, maybe, when you get all through, I could call the dogs and hunt the mice."

"Sure, I guess you could," said Billy Buck. He lifted a forkful of the damp ground-hay and threw it into the air. Instantly three mice leaped out and burrowed frantically under the hay again.

Jody sighed with satisfaction. Those plump, sleek, arrogant mice were doomed. For eight months they had lived and multiplied in the haystack. They had been immune from cats, from traps, from poison and from Jody. They had grown smug in their security, overbearing and fat. Now the time of disaster had come; they would not survive another day.

Billy looked up at the top of the hills that surrounded the ranch. "Maybe you better ask your father before you do it," he suggested.

"Well, where is he? I'll ask him now."

"He rode up to the ridge ranch after dinner. He'll be back pretty soon."

Jody slumped against the fence post. "I don't think he'd care."

As Billy went back to his work he said ominously, "You'd better ask him anyway. You know how he is."

Jody did know. His father, Carl Tiflin, insisted upon giving permission for anything that was done on the ranch, whether it was important or not. Jody sagged farther against the post until he was sitting on the ground. He looked up at the little puffs of wind-driven cloud. "Is it like to rain, Billy?"

"It might. The wind's good for it, but not strong enough."

"Well, I hope it don't rain until after I kill those damn mice." He looked over his shoulder to see whether Billy had noticed his mature profanity. Billy worked on without comment.

Jody turned back and looked at the sidehill where the road from the outside world came down. The hill was washed with lean March sunshine. Silver thistles, blue lupins and a few poppies bloomed among the sage bushes. Halfway up the hill Jody could see Doubletree Mutt, the black dog, digging in a squirrel hole. He paddled for a while and then paused to kick bursts of dirt out between his hind legs, and he dug with an earnestness which belied the knowledge he must have had that no dog had ever caught a squirrel by digging in a hole.

Suddenly, while Jody watched, the black dog stiffened, and backed out of the hole and looked up the hill toward the cleft in the ridge where the road came through. Jody looked up too. For a moment Carl Tiflin on horseback stood out against the pale sky and then he moved down the road toward the house. He carried something white in his hand.

The boy started to his feet. "He's got a letter," Jody cried. He trotted away toward the ranch house, for the letter would probably be read aloud and he wanted to be there. He reached the house before his father did, and ran in. He heard Carl Tiflin dismount from his creaking saddle and slap the horse on the side to send it to the barn where Billy would unsaddle it and turn it out.

Jody ran into the kitchen. "We got a letter!" he cried.

His mother looked up from a pan of beans. "Who has?"

"Father has, I saw it in his hand."

Carl strode into the kitchen then, and Jody's mother asked, "Who's the letter from, Carl?"

He frowned quickly. "How did you know there was a letter?"

She nodded her head in the boy's direction. "Big-Britches Jody told me."

Jody was embarrassed.

His father looked down at him contemptuously. "He *is* getting to be a Big-Britches," Carl said. "He's minding everybody's business but his own. Got his big nose into everything."

Mrs. Tiflin relented a little. "Well, he hasn't enough to keep him busy. Who's the letter from?"

Carl still frowned on Jody. "I'll keep him busy if he isn't careful." He held out a sealed letter. "I guess it's from your father."

Mrs. Tiflin took a hairpin from her head and slit open the flap. Her lips pursed judiciously. Jody saw her eyes snap back and forth over the lines. "He says," she translated, "he says he's going to drive out Saturday to stay for a little while. Why, this is Saturday. The letter must have been delayed." She looked at the postmark. "This was mailed day before yesterday. It should have been here yesterday." She looked up questioningly at her husband, and then her face darkened angrily. "Now what have you got that look on you for? He doesn't come often."

Carl turned his eyes away from her anger. He could be stern with her most of the time, but when occasionally her temper arose, he could not combat it.

"What's the matter with you?" she demanded again.

In his explanation there was a tone of apology Jody himself might have used. "It's just that he talks," Carl said lamely. "Just talks."

"Well, what of it? You talk yourself."

"Sure I do. But your father only talks about one thing."

"Indians!" Jody broke in excitedly. "Indians and crossing the plains!"

Carl turned fiercely on him. "You get out, Mr. Big-Britches! Go on, now! Get out!"

Jody went miserably out the back door and closed the screen with elaborate quietness. Under the kitchen window his shamed, downcast eyes fell upon a curiously shaped stone, a stone of such fascination that he squatted down and picked it up and turned it over in his hands.

The voices came clearly to him through the open kitchen window.

"Jody's damn well right," he heard his father say. "Just Indians and crossing the plains. I've heard that story about how the horses got driven off about a thousand times. He just goes on and on, and he never changes a word in the things he tells."

When Mrs. Tiflin answered, her tone was so changed that Jody, outside the window, looked up from his study of the stone. Her voice had become soft and explanatory. Jody knew how her face would have changed to match the tone. She said quietly, "Look at it this way, Carl. That was the big thing in my father's life. He led a wagon train clear across the plains to the coast, and when it was finished, his life was done. It was a big thing to do, but it didn't last long enough. Look!" she continued, "it's as though he were born to do that, and after he finished it, there wasn't anything more for him to do but think about it and talk about it. If there'd been any farther west to go, he'd have gone. He's told me so himself. But at last there was the ocean. He lives right by the ocean where he had to stop."

She had caught Carl, caught him and entangled him in her soft tone.

"I've seen him," he agreed quietly. "He goes down and stares off west over the ocean." His voice sharpened a little. "And then he goes up to the Horseshoe Club in Pacific Grove, and he tells people how the Indians drove off the horses."

She tried to catch him again. "Well, it's everything to him. You might be patient with him and pretend to listen."

Carl turned impatiently away. "Well, if it gets too bad, I can always go down to the bunkhouse and sit with Billy," he said irritably. He walked through the house and slammed the front door after him.

Jody ran to his chores. He dumped the grain to the chickens without chasing any of them. He gathered the eggs from the nests. He trotted into the house with the wood and interlaced it so carefully in the wood-box that two armloads seemed to fill it to overflowing.

His mother had finished the beans by now. She stirred up the fire and brushed off the stove-top with a turkey wing. Jody peered cautiously at her to see whether any rancor toward him remained. "Is he coming today?" Jody asked.

"That's what his letter said."

"Maybe I better walk up the road to meet him."

Mrs. Tiflin clanged the stove-lid shut. "That would be nice," she said. "He'd probably like to be met."

"I guess I'll just do it then."

Outside, Jody whistled shrilly to the dogs. "Come on up the hill," he commanded. The two dogs waved their tails and ran ahead. Along the roadside the sage had tender new tips. Jody tore off some pieces and rubbed them on his hands until the air was filled with the sharp wild smell. With a rush the dogs leaped from the road and yapped into the brush after a rabbit. That was the last Jody saw of them, for when they failed to catch the rabbit, they went back home.

Jody plodded on up the hill toward the ridge top. When he reached the little cleft where the road came through, the afternoon wind struck him and blew up his hair and ruffled his shirt. He looked down on the little hills and ridges below and then out at the huge green Salinas Valley. He could see the white town of Salinas far out in the flat and the flash of its windows under the waning sun. Directly below him, in an oak tree, a crow congress had convened. The tree was black with crows all cawing at once.

Then Jody's eyes followed the wagon road down from the ridge where he stood, and lost it behind a hill, and picked it up again on the other side. On that distant stretch he saw a cart slowly pulled by a bay horse. It disappeared behind the hill. Jody sat down on the ground and watched the place where the cart would reappear again. The wind sang on the hilltops and the puff-ball clouds hurried eastward.

Then the cart came into sight and stopped. A man dressed in black dismounted from the seat and walked to the horse's head. Although it was so far away, Jody knew he had unhooked the check-rein, for the horse's head dropped forward. The horse moved on, and the man walked slowly up the hill beside it. Jody gave a glad cry and ran down the road toward them. The squirrels bumped along off the road, and a road runner flirted its tail and raced over the edge of the hill and sailed out like a glider.

Jody tried to leap into the middle of his shadow at every step. A stone rolled under his foot and he went down. Around a little bend he raced, and there, a short distance ahead, were his grandfather and the cart. The boy dropped from his unseemly running and approached at a dignified walk.

The horse plodded stumble-footedly up the hill and the old man walked beside it. In the lowering sun their giant shadows flickered darkly behind them. The grandfather was dressed in a black broadcloth suit and he wore kid congress gaiters and a black tie on a short, hard collar. He carried his black slouch hat in his hand. His white beard was cropped close and his white eyebrows overhung his eyes like mustaches. The blue eyes were sternly merry. About the whole face and figure there was a granite dignity, so that every motion seemed an impossible thing. Once at rest, it seemed the old man would be stone, would never move again. His steps were slow and certain. Once made, no step could ever be retraced; once headed in a direction, the path would never bend nor the pace increase nor slow.

When Jody appeared around the bend, Grandfather waved his hat slowly in welcome, and he called, "Why, Jody! Come down to meet me, have you?"

Jody sidled near and turned and matched his step to the old man's step and stiffened his body and dragged his heels a little. "Yes, sir," he said. "We got your letter only today."

"Should have been here yesterday," said Grandfather. "It certainly should. How are all the folks?"

"They're fine, sir." He hesitated and then suggested shyly, "Would you like to come on a mouse hunt tomorrow, sir?"

"Mouse hunt, Jody?" Grandfather chuckled. "Have the people of this generation come down to hunting mice? They aren't very strong, the new people, but I hardly thought mice would be game for them."

"No, sir. It's just play. The haystack's gone. I'm going to drive out the mice to the dogs. And you can watch, or even beat the hay a little."

The stern, merry eyes turned down on him. "I see. You don't eat them, then. You haven't come to that yet."

Jody explained, "The dogs eat them, sir. It wouldn't be much like hunting Indians, I guess."

"No, not much—but then later, when the troops were hunting Indians and shooting children and burning tepees, it wasn't much different from your mouse hunt."

They topped the rise and started down into the ranch cup, and they lost the sun from their shoulders. "You've grown," Grandfather said. "Nearly an inch, I should say."

"More," Jody boasted. "Where they mark me on the door, I'm up more than an inch since Thanksgiving even."

Grandfather's rich throaty voice said, "Maybe you're getting too much water and turning to pith and stalk. Wait until you head out, and then we'll see."

Jody looked quickly into the old man's face to see whether his feelings should be hurt, but there was no will to injure, no punishing nor putting-in-your-place light in the keen blue eyes. "We might kill a pig," Jody suggested.

"Oh, no! I couldn't let you do that. You're just humoring me. It isn't the time and you know it."

"You know Riley, the big boar, sir?"

"Yes, I remember Riley well."

"Well, Riley ate a hole into that same haystack, and it fell down on him and smothered him."

"Pigs do that when they can," said Grandfather.

"Riley was a nice pig, for a boar, sir. I rode him sometimes, and he didn't mind."

A door slammed at the house below them, and they saw Jody's mother standing on the porch waving her apron in welcome. And they saw Carl Tiflin walking up from the barn to be at the house for the arrival.

The sun had disappeared from the hills by now. The blue smoke from the house chimney hung in flat layers in the purpling ranch cup. The puff-ball clouds, dropped by the falling wind, hung listlessly in the sky.

Billy Buck came out of the bunkhouse and flung a washbasin of soapy water on the ground. He had been shaving in mid-week, for Billy held Grandfather in reverence, and Grandfather said that Billy was one of the few men of the new generation who had not gone soft. Although Billy was in middle age, Grandfather considered him a boy. Now Billy was hurrying toward the house too.

When Jody and Grandfather arrived, the three were waiting for them in front of the yard gate.

Carl said, "Hello, sir. We've been looking for you."

Mrs. Tiflin kissed Grandfather on the side of his beard, and stood still while his big hand patted her shoulder. Billy shook hands solemnly, grinning under his straw mustache. "I'll put up your horse," said Billy, and he led the rig away.

Grandfather watched him go, and then, turning back to the group, he said as he had said a hundred times before, "There's a good boy. I knew his father, old Mule-tail Buck. I never knew why they called him Mule-tail except he packed mules."

Mrs. Tiflin turned and led the way into the house. "How long are you going to stay, Father? Your letter didn't say."

"Well, I don't know. I thought I'd stay about two weeks. But I never stay as long as I think I'm going to."

In a short while they were sitting at the white oilcloth table eating their supper. The lamp with the tin reflector hung over the table. Outside the dining-room windows the big moths battered softly against the glass.

Grandfather cut his steak into tiny pieces and chewed slowly. "I'm hungry," he said. "Driving out here got my appetite up. It's like when we were crossing. We all got so hungry every night we could hardly wait to let the meat get done. I could eat about five pounds of buffalo meat every night."

"It's moving around does it," said Billy. "My father was a government packer. I helped him when I was a kid. Just the two of us could about clean up a deer's ham."

"I knew your father, Billy," said Grandfather. "A fine man he was. They called him Mule-tail Buck. I don't know why except he packed mules."

"That was it," Billy agreed. "He packed mules."

Grandfather put down his knife and fork and looked around the table. "I remember one time we ran out of meat—" His voice dropped to a curious low singsong, dropped into a tonal groove the story had worn for itself. "There was no buffalo, no antelope, not even rabbits. The hunters couldn't even shoot a coyote. That was the time for the leader to be on the watch. I was the leader, and I kept my eyes open. Know why? Well, just the minute the people began to get hungry they'd start slaughtering the team oxen. Do you believe that? I've heard of parties that just ate up their draft cattle. Started from the middle and worked toward the ends. Finally they'd eat the lead pair, and then the wheelers. The leader of a party had to keep them from doing that."

In some manner a big moth got into the room and circled the hanging kerosene lamp. Billy got up and tried to clap it between his hands. Carl struck with a cupped palm and caught the moth and broke it. He walked to the window and dropped it out.

"As I was saying," Grandfather began again, but Carl interrupted him. "You'd better eat some more meat. All the rest of us are ready for our pudding."

Jody saw a flash of anger in his mother's eyes. Grandfather picked up his knife and fork. "I'm pretty hungry, all right," he said. "I'll tell you about that later."

When supper was over, when the family and Billy Buck sat in front of the fireplace in the other room, Jody anxiously watched Grandfather. He saw the signs he knew. The bearded head leaned forward, the eyes lost their sternness and looked wonderingly into the fire; the big lean fingers laced themselves on the black knees. "I wonder," he began, "I just wonder whether I ever told you how those thieving Piutes drove off thirty-five of our horses."

"I think you did," Carl interrupted. "Wasn't it just before you went up into the Tahoe country?"

Grandfather turned quickly toward his son-in-law. "That's right, I guess I must have told you that story."

"Lots of times," Carl said cruelly, and he avoided his wife's eyes. But he felt the angry eyes on him, and he said, "'Course I'd like to hear it again."

Grandfather looked back at the fire. His fingers unlaced and laced again. Jody knew how he felt, how his insides were collapsed and empty. Hadn't Jody been called a Big-Britches that very afternoon? He arose to heroism and opened himself to the term Big-Britches again. "Tell about Indians," he said softly.

Grandfather's eyes grew stern again. "Boys always want to hear about Indians. It was a job for men, but boys want to hear about it. Well, let's see. Did I ever tell you how I wanted each wagon to carry a long iron plate?"

Everyone but Jody remained silent. Jody said, "No. You didn't."

"Well, when the Indians attacked, we always put the wagons in a circle and fought from between the wheels. I thought that if every wagon carried a long plate with rifle holes, the men could stand the plates on the outside of the wheels when the wagons were in the circle and they would be protected. It would save lives and that would make up for the extra weight of the iron. But of course the party wouldn't do it. No party had done it before and they couldn't see why they should go to the expense. They lived to regret it, too."

Jody looked at his mother, and knew from her expression that she was not listening at all. Carl picked at a callus on his thumb and Billy Buck watched a spider crawling up the wall.

Grandfather's tone dropped into its narrative groove again. Jody knew in advance exactly what words would fall. The story droned on, speeded up for the attack, grew sad over the wounds, struck a dirge at the burials on the great plains. Jody sat quietly watching Grandfather. The stern blue eyes were detached. He looked as though he were not very interested in the story himself.

When it was finished, when the pause had been politely respected as the frontier of the story, Billy Buck stood up and stretched and hitched his trousers. "I guess I'll turn in," he said. Then he faced Grandfather. "I've got an old powder horn and a cap and ball pistol down to the bunkhouse. Did I ever show them to you?"

Grandfather nodded slowly. "Yes, I think you did, Billy. Reminds me of a pistol I had when I was leading the people across." Billy stood politely until the little story was done, and then he said, "Good night," and went out of the house.

Carl Tiflin tried to turn the conversation then. "How's the country between here and Monterey? I've heard it's pretty dry."

"It is dry," said Grandfather. "There's not a drop of water in the Laguna Seca. But it's a long pull from '87. The whole country was powder then, and in '61 I believe all the coyotes starved to death. We had fifteen inches of rain this year."

"Yes, but it all came too early. We could do with some now." Carl's eye fell on Jody. "Hadn't you better be getting to bed?"

Jody stood up obediently. "Can I kill the mice in the old haystack, sir?"

"Mice? Oh! sure, kill them all off. Billy said there isn't any good hay left."

Jody exchanged a secret and satisfying look with Grandfather. "I'll kill every one tomorrow," he promised.

Jody lay in his bed and thought of the impossible world of Indians and buffaloes, a world that had ceased to be forever. He wished he could have been living in the heroic time, but he knew he was not of heroic timber. No one living now, save possibly Billy Buck, was worthy to do the things that had been done. A race of giants had lived then, fearless men, men of a staunchness unknown in his day. Jody thought of the wide plains and of the wagons moving across like centipedes. He thought of Grandfather on a huge white horse, marshaling the people. Across his mind marched the great phantoms, and they marched off the earth and were gone.

He came back to the ranch for a moment, then. He heard the dull rushing sound that space and silence make. He heard one of the dogs, out in the doghouse, scratching a flea and bumping his elbow against the floor with every stroke. Then the wind arose again and the black cypress groaned and Jody went to sleep.

He was up half an hour before the triangle sounded for breakfast. His mother was rattling the stove to make the flames roar when Jody went through the kitchen. "You're up early," she said. "Where are you going?"

"Out to get a good stick. We're going to kill the mice today."

"Who is 'we'?"

"Why, Grandfather and I."

"So you've got him in it. You always like to have someone in with you in case there's blame to share."

"I'll be right back," said Jody. "I just want to have a good stick ready for after breakfast."

He closed the screen door after him and went out into the cool blue morning. The birds were noisy in the dawn and the ranch cats came down from the hill like blunt snakes. They had been hunting gophers in the dark, and although the four cats were full of gopher meat, they sat in a semicircle at the back door and mewed piteously for milk. Doubletree Mutt and Smasher moved sniffing along the edge of the brush, performing the duty with rigid ceremony, but when Jody whistled, their heads jerked up and their tails waved. They plunged down to him, wriggling their skins and yawning. Jody patted their heads seriously, and moved on to the weathered scrap pile. He selected an old broom handle and a short piece of inch-square scrap wood. From his pocket he took a shoelace and tied the ends of the sticks loosely together to make a flail. He whistled his new weapon through the air and struck the ground experimentally, while the dogs leaped aside and whined with apprehension.

Jody turned and started down past the house toward the old haystack ground to look over the field of slaughter, but Billy Buck, sitting patiently on the back steps, called to him. "You better come back. It's time for breakfast."

Jody changed his course and moved toward the house. He leaned his flail against the steps. "That's to drive the mice out," he said. "I'll bet they're fat. I'll bet they don't know what's going to happen to them today."

"No, nor you either," Billy remarked philosophically, "nor me, nor any one."

Jody was staggered by this thought. He knew it was true. His imagination twitched away from the mouse hunt. Then his mother came out on the back porch and struck the triangle, and all thoughts fell in a heap.

Grandfather hadn't appeared at the table when they sat down. Billy nodded at the empty chair. "He's all right? He isn't sick?"

"He takes a long time to dress," said Mrs. Tiflin. "He combs his whiskers and rubs up his shoes and brushes his clothes."

Carl scattered sugar on his mush. "A man that's led a wagon train across the plains has got to be pretty careful how he dresses."

Mrs. Tiflin turned on him. "Don't do that, Carl! Please don't!" There was more of threat than of request in her tone. And the threat irritated Carl.

"Well, how many times do I have to listen to the story of the iron plates, and the thirty-five horses? That time's done. Why can't he forget it, now it's done?" He grew angrier while he talked, and his voice rose. "Why does he have to tell them over and over? He came across the plains. All right! Now it's finished. Nobody wants to hear about it over and over."

The door of the kitchen closed softly. The four at the table sat frozen. Carl laid his mush spoon on the table and touched his chin with his fingers.

Then the kitchen door opened and Grandfather walked in. His mouth smiled tightly and his eyes were squinted. "Good morning," he said, and he sat down and looked at his mush dish.

Carl could not leave it there. "Did—did you hear what I said?"

Grandfather jerked a little nod.

"I don't know what got into me, sir. I didn't mean it. I was just being funny."

Jody glanced in shame at his mother, and he saw that she was looking at Carl, and that she wasn't breathing. It was an awful thing that he was doing. He was tearing himself to pieces to talk like that. It was a terrible thing to him to retract a word, but to retract it in shame was infinitely worse.

Grandfather looked sidewise. "I'm trying to get right side up," he said gently. "I'm not being mad. I don't mind what you said, but it might be true, and I would mind that."

"It isn't true," said Carl. "I'm not feeling well this morning. I'm sorry I said it."

"Don't be sorry, Carl. An old man doesn't see things sometimes. Maybe you're right. The crossing is finished. Maybe it should be forgotten, now it's done."

Carl got up from the table. "I've had enough to eat. I'm going to work. Take your time, Billy!" He walked quickly out of the dining room. Billy gulped the rest of his food and followed soon after. But Jody could not leave his chair.

"Won't you tell any more stories?" Jody asked.

"Why, sure I'll tell them, but only when—I'm sure people want to hear them."

"I like to hear them, sir."

"Oh! Of course you do, but you're a little boy. It was a job for men, but only little boys like to hear about it."

Jody got up from his place. "I'll wait outside for you, sir, I've got a good stick for those mice."

He waited by the gate until the old man came out on the porch. "Let's go down and kill the mice now," Jody called.

"I think I'll just sit down in the sun, Jody. You go kill the mice."

"You can use my stick if you like."

"No, I'll just sit here awhile."

Jody turned disconsolately away, and walked down toward the haystack. He tried to whip up his enthusiasm with thoughts of the fat juicy mice. He beat the ground with his flail. The dogs coaxed and whined about him, but he could not go. Back at the house he could see Grandfather sitting on the porch, looking small and thin and black.

Jody gave up and went to sit on the steps at the old man's feet.

"Back already? Did you kill the mice?"

"No, sir. I'll kill them some other day."

The morning flies buzzed close to the ground and the ants dashed about in front of the steps. The heavy smell of sage slipped down the hill. The porch boards grew warm in the sunshine.

Jody hardly knew when Grandfather started to talk. "I shouldn't stay here, feeling the way I do." He examined his strong old hands. "I feel as though the crossing wasn't worth doing." His eyes moved up the sidehill and stopped on a motionless hawk perched on a dead limb. "I tell those old stories, but they're not what I want to tell. I only know how I want people to feel when I tell them.

"It wasn't Indians that were important, nor adventures, nor even getting out here. It was a whole bunch of people made into one big crawling beast. And I was the head. It was westering and westering. Every man wanted something for himself, but the big beast that was all of them wanted only westering. I was the leader, but if I hadn't been there, someone else would have been the head. The thing had to have a head.

"Under the little bushes the shadows were black at white noonday. When we saw the mountains at last, we cried—all of us. But it wasn't getting here that mattered, it was movement and westering.

"We carried life out here and set it down the way those ants carry eggs. And I was the leader. The westering was as big as God, and the slow steps that made the movement piled up and piled up until the continent was crossed.

"Then we came down to the sea, and it was done." He stopped and wiped his eyes until the rims were red. "That's what I should be telling instead of stories."

When Jody spoke, Grandfather started and looked down at him. "Maybe I could lead the people some day," Jody said.

The old man smiled. "There's no place to go. There's the ocean to stop you. There's a line of old men along the shore hating the ocean because it stopped them."

"In boats I might, sir."

"No place to go, Jody. Every place is taken. But that's not the worst — no, not the worst. Westering has died out of the people. Westering isn't a hunger any more. It's all done. Your father is right. It is finished." He laced his fingers on his knee and looked at them.

Jody felt very sad, "If you'd like a glass of lemonade I could make it for you."

Grandfather was about to refuse, and then he saw Jody's face. "That would be nice," he said. "Yes, it would be nice to drink a lemonade."

Jody ran into the kitchen where his mother was wiping the last of the breakfast dishes. "Can I have a lemon to make a lemonade for Grandfather?"

His mother mimicked — "And another lemon to make a lemonade for you."

"No, ma'am. I don't want one."

"Jody! You're sick!" Then she stopped suddenly. "Take a lemon out of the cooler," she said softly. "Here, I'll reach the squeezer down to you."

READING WITH INSIGHT

1. In what respects could this story be called tough? What examples can you find of the author's sensitivity and sympathy for his characters?

2. Steinbeck builds up his characters from tiny details. Take several of the characters in this story, and try to remember what Steinbeck has told you about them. You will probably find that he has given you a number of small facts rather than broad statements about what kind of people they are. What other authors in this book have used such a method of characterizing?

3. What does the act of unhooking the checkrein tell you about the Grandfather? Pick out other such details which tell you much about the characters without ever characterizing them directly.

4. Pick out some examples of vivid pictures in this story. For example, the "clouds like puffs of cannon smoke."

5. Would you say that Carl is justified in being irritated by his

father-in-law? What examples can you find in this story of how the old man might be irritating?

6. What kind of man was Carl? Unpleasant? Cruel? Insensitive? Self-centered? Why does he act as he does?

7. Why does Grandfather tell his stories of the westward movement? Did he know that people were tired of them? Did he think he hadn't told them before? Had he nothing else worth talking about? What was behind his compulsion to tell the stories over and over again?

8. What kind of woman was Jody's mother? Did she like the stories, or did she merely feel the obligation of being nice to her father? Did she understand Jody better than his father did? In fact, did she understand all the other characters better than any other person in the story did? What evidence can you find for your answers to these questions?

9. Why did Billy Buck feel a reverence for Grandfather?

10. From your own experience, would you say that the character of Jody is a realistic picture of a boy? What are some of the specially real or unreal things he does?

11. What is going to happen now in this family? Will this event break the old man's spirit? Will he stop telling the stories? Will Carl treat him better? What effect will these happenings have on Jody?

12. One part of the meaning of this story has to do with the relation of different generations to each other. Does the story say that the old generation lives in the past, the adult generation in the present, and the childhood generation in the future? How true is that?

13. Another part of the meaning has to do with "westering." Does the story mean that modern people are too soft or too disinterested to follow frontiers as the older generations did? And is that true? Does the story mean that there are no more frontiers or unknown places to be conquered? What are the new frontiers that could take the place of the West? Or does the story simply mean that there is a point in a man's life when he has done his exciting work — he has done his "westering," crossed his frontiers, been a leader — and after that he must resign himself to boredom and memories? And do you think that is true?

14. You will probably agree that this is a remarkable story of character. How important is plot in the story? Do you feel tension

building up? Where is the climax? Would this story be any good as an anecdote? In what ways would you say this story follows the lead of Anderson and Hemingway, rather than the lead of Poe?

If you like this story, you will be interested in

Steinbeck. *The Red Pony.*
Willa Cather. *Double Birthday.*
Ring Lardner. *Golden Honeymoon.*
Ruth Suckow. *Golden Wedding.*
Wallace Stegner. *Bugle Song.*
William Saroyan. *The Summer of the Beautiful White Horse.*

WILLIAM FAULKNER

The Bear

WILLIAM FAULKNER was born in 1897 into a family which had been known for a long line of Southern generals and statesmen. He grew up in Oxford, Mississippi, was for a time postmaster of Oxford, and still lives in an old plantation house near Oxford. During World War I he served in the Canadian Air Corps and was wounded in action. After the war he went to the University of Mississippi for two years, then made his living as a newspaperman until he proved himself an artist in fiction and could afford to move into the plantation house and give all his time to writing.

The story that follows is about the Southern woods, an old plantation house like Faulkner's own, and a boy who had some of the same experiences Faulkner himself must have had as a boy. This story, on the surface, is simply an account of a boy's learning to hunt. It has beautiful descriptions of the woods, and exciting action. But as you begin to ask why the characters did what they did — for example, why the boy did as he did about shooting the bear — you will begin to see new meaning in the story. And as you dig into these deeper levels of meaning you will discover that the story says rather profound things which you might miss entirely if you thought of it merely as an adventure story. You will also discover that the bear is a symbol. Try to decide what it symbolizes.

HE was ten. But it had already begun, long before that day when at last he wrote his age in two figures and he saw for the first time the camp where his father and Major de Spain and old General Compson and the others spent two weeks each November and two weeks again each June. He had already inherited then, without ever having seen it, the tremendous bear with one trap-ruined foot which, in an area almost a hundred miles deep, had earned for itself a name, a definite designation like a living man.

He had listened to it for years: the long legend of corncribs rifled, of shoats and grown pigs and even calves carried bodily into the woods and devoured, of traps and deadfalls overthrown and dogs mangled and slain, and shotgun and even rifle charges delivered at point-blank range and with no more effect than so many peas blown through a tube by a boy — a corridor of wreckage and destruction beginning back before he was born, through which sped, not fast but rather with the ruthless and irresistible deliberation of a locomotive, the shaggy tremendous shape.

It ran in his knowledge before ever he saw it. It looked and towered in his dreams before he even saw the unaxed woods where it left its crooked print, shaggy, huge, red-eyed, not malevolent but just big — too big for the dogs which tried to bay it, for the horses which tried to ride it down, for the men and the bullets they fired into it, too big for the very country which was its constricting scope. He seemed to see it entire with a child's complete divination before he ever laid eyes on either — the doomed wilderness whose edges were being constantly and punily gnawed at by men with axes and plows who feared it because it was wilderness, men myriad and nameless even to one another in the land where the old bear had earned a name, through which ran not even a mortal animal but an anachronism, indomitable and invincible, out of an old dead time, a phantom, epitome and apotheosis of the old wild life at which the puny humans swarmed and hacked in a fury of abhorrence and fear, like pygmies about the ankles of a drowsing elephant: the old bear solitary, indomitable and alone, widowered, childless, and absolved of mortality — old Priam [1] reft of his old wife and having outlived all his sons.

Until he was ten, each November he would watch the wagon containing the dogs and the bedding and food and guns and his father and Tennie's Jim, the Negro, and Sam Fathers, the Indian, son of a slave woman and a Chickasaw chief, depart on the road to town, to

[1] **Priam**: the king of Troy. His sons were killed in the battle to defend the city against the Greeks, and Priam himself died when the Greeks captured the city.

Jefferson, where Major de Spain and the others would join them. To the boy, at seven, eight, and nine, they were not going into the Big Bottom to hunt bear and deer, but to keep yearly rendezvous with the bear which they did not even intend to kill. Two weeks later they would return, with no trophy, no head and skin. He had not expected it. He had not even been afraid it would be in the wagon. He believed that even after he was ten and his father would let him go too, for those two weeks in November, he would merely make another one, along with his father and Major de Spain and General Compson and the others, the dogs which feared to bay at it and the rifles and shotguns which failed even to bleed it, in the yearly pageant of the old bear's furious immortality.

Then he heard the dogs. It was in the second week of his first time in the camp. He stood with Sam Fathers against a big oak beside the faint crossing where they had stood each dawn for nine days now, hearing the dogs. He had heard them once before, one morning last week — a murmur, sourceless, echoing through the wet woods, swelling presently into separate voices which he could recognize and call by name. He had raised and cocked the gun as Sam told him and stood motionless again while the uproar, the invisible course, swept up and past and faded; it seemed to him that he could actually see the deer, the buck, blond, smoke-colored, elongated with speed, fleeing, vanishing, the woods, the gray solitude, still ringing even when the cries of the dogs had died away.

"Now let the hammers down," Sam said.

"You knew they were not coming here too," he said.

"Yes," Sam said. "I want you to learn how to do when you didn't shoot. It's after the chance for the bear or the deer has done already come and gone that men and dogs get killed."

"Anyway," he said, "it was just a deer."

Then on the tenth morning he heard the dogs again. And he readied the too-long, too-heavy gun as Sam had taught him, before Sam even spoke. But this time it was no deer, no ringing chorus of dogs running strong on a free scent, but a moiling yapping an octave too high, with something more than indecision and even abjectness in it, not even moving very fast, taking a long time to pass completely out of hearing, leaving even then somewhere in the air that echo, thin, slightly hysterical, abject, almost grieving, with no sense of a fleeing, unseen, smoke-colored, grass-eating shape ahead of it, and Sam, who had taught him first of all to cock the gun and take position where he could see everywhere and then never move again, had himself moved up beside him; he could hear Sam breathing at his shoulder and he could see the arched curve of the old man's inhaling nostrils.

"Hah," Sam said. "Not even running. Walking."

"Old Ben!" the boy said. "But up here!" he cried. "Way up here!"

"He do it every year," Sam said. "Once. Maybe to see who in camp this time, if he can shoot or not. Whether we got the dog yet that can bay and hold him. He'll take them to the river, then he'll send them back home. We may as well go back, too; see how they look when they come back to camp."

When they reached the camp the hounds were already there, ten of them crouching back under the kitchen, the boy and Sam squatting to peer back into the obscurity where they huddled, quiet, the eyes luminous, glowing at them and vanishing, and no sound, only that effluvium of something more than dog, stronger than dog and not just animal, just beast, because still there had been nothing in front of that abject and almost painful yapping save the solitude, the wilderness, so that when the eleventh hound came in at noon and with all the others watching — even old Uncle Ash, who called himself first a cook — Sam daubed the tattered ear and the raked shoulder with turpentine and axle grease, to the boy it was still no living creature, but the wilderness which, leaning for the moment down, had patted lightly once the hound's temerity.

"Just like a man," Sam said. "Just like folks. Put off as long as she could having to be brave, knowing all the time that sooner or later she would have to be brave to keep on living with herself, and knowing all the time beforehand what was going to happen to her when she done it."

That afternoon, himself on the one-eyed wagon mule which did not mind the smell of blood nor, as they told him, of bear, and with Sam on the other one, they rode for more than three hours through the rapid, shortening winter day. They followed no path, no trail even that he could see; almost at once they were in a country which he had never seen before. Then he knew why Sam had made him ride the mule which would not spook. The sound one stopped short and tried to whirl and bolt even as Sam got down, blowing its breath, jerking and wrenching at the rein, while Sam held it, coaxing it forward with his voice, since he could not risk tying it, drawing it forward while the boy got down from the marred one.

Then, standing beside Sam in the gloom of the dying afternoon, he looked down at the rotted over-turned log, gutted and scored with claw marks and, in the wet earth beside it, the print of the enormous warped two-toed foot. He knew now what he had smelled when he peered under the kitchen where the dogs huddled. He realized for the first time that the bear which had run in his listening and loomed in his dreams since before he could remember to the contrary, and which, therefore, must have existed in the listening and dreams of his father and Major de Spain and even old General Compson, too, before they began to remember in their turn, was a mortal animal, and that if they had departed for the camp each November without any actual hope of bringing its trophy back, it was not because it could not be slain, but because so far they had had no actual hope to.

"Tomorrow," he said.

"We'll try tomorrow," Sam said. "We ain't got the dog yet."

"We've got eleven. They ran him this morning."

"It won't need but one," Sam said. "He ain't here. Maybe he ain't nowhere. The only other way will be for him to run by accident over somebody that has a gun."

"That wouldn't be me," the boy said. "It will be Walter or Major or——"

"It might," Sam said. "You watch close in the morning. Because he's smart. That's how come he has lived this long. If he gets hemmed up and has to pick out somebody to run over, he will pick out you."

"How?" the boy said. "How will he know——" He ceased. "You mean he already knows me, that I ain't never been here before, ain't had time to find out yet whether I——" He ceased again, looking at Sam, the old man whose face revealed nothing until it smiled. He said humbly, not even amazed, "It was me he was watching. I don't reckon he did need to come but once."

The next morning they left the camp three hours before daylight. They rode this time because it was too far to walk, even the dogs in the wagon; again the first gray light found him in a place which he had never seen before, where Sam had placed him and told him to stay and then departed. With the gun which was too big for him, which did not even belong to him, but to Major de Spain, and which he had fired only once — at a stump on the first day, to learn the recoil and how to reload it — he stood against a gum tree beside a little bayou whose black still water crept without movement out of a canebrake and crossed a small clearing and into cane again, where, invisible, a bird — the big woodpecker called Lord-to-God by Negroes — clattered at a dead limb.

It was a stand like any other, dissimilar only in incidentals to the one where he had stood each morning for ten days; a territory new to him, yet no less familiar than that other one which, after almost two weeks, he had come to believe he knew a little — the same solitude, the same loneliness through which human beings had merely passed without altering it, leaving no mark, no scar, which looked exactly as it must have looked when the first ancestor of Sam Fathers' Chickasaw predecessors crept into it and looked about, club or stone ax or bone arrow drawn and poised; different only because, squatting at the edge of the kitchen, he smelled the hounds huddled and cringing beneath it and saw the raked ear and shoulder of the one who, Sam said, had had to be brave once in order to live with herself, and saw yesterday in the earth beside the gutted log the print of the living foot.

He heard no dogs at all. He never did hear them. He only heard the drumming of the woodpecker stop short off and knew that the bear was looking at him. He never saw it. He did not know whether it was in front of him or behind him. He did not move, holding the useless gun, which he had not even had warning to cock and which even now he did not cock, tasting in his saliva that taint as of brass which he knew now because he had smelled it when he peered under the kitchen at the huddled dogs.

Then it was gone. As abruptly as it had ceased, the woodpecker's dry, monotonous clatter set up again, and after a while he even believed he could hear the dogs — a murmur, scarce a sound even, which he had probably been hearing for some time before he even remarked it, drifting into hearing and then out again, dying away. They came nowhere near him. If it was a bear they ran, it was another bear. It was Sam himself who came out of the cane and crossed the bayou, followed by the injured bitch of yesterday. She was almost at heel, like a bird dog, making no sound. She came and crouched against his leg, trembling, staring off into the cane.

"I didn't see him," he said. "I didn't, Sam!"

"I know it," Sam said. "He done the looking. You didn't hear him neither, did you?"

"No," the boy said. "I——"

"He's smart," Sam said. "Too smart." He looked down at the hound, trembling faintly and steadily against the boy's knee. From the raked shoulder a few drops of fresh blood oozed and clung. "Too big. We ain't got the dog yet. But maybe someday. Maybe not next time. But someday."

So I must see him, he thought. *I must look at him.* Otherwise, it seemed to him that it would go on like this forever, as it had gone on with his father and Major de Spain, who was older than his father, and even with old General Compson, who had been old enough to be a brigade commander in 1865. Otherwise, it would go on so forever, next time and next time, after and after and after. It seemed to him that he could see the two of them, himself and the bear, shadowy in the limbo from which time emerged, becoming time; the old bear absolved of mortality and himself partaking, sharing a little of it, enough of it. And he knew now what he had smelled in the huddled dogs and tasted in his saliva. He recognized fear. *So I will have to see him,* he thought, without dread or even hope. *I will have to look at him.*

It was in June of the next year. He was eleven. They were in camp again, celebrating Major de Spain's and General Compson's birthdays. Although the one had been born in September and the other in the depth of winter and in another decade, they had met for two weeks to fish and shoot squirrels and turkey and run coons and wildcats with the dogs at night. That is, he and Boon Hoggenbeck and the Negroes fished and shot squirrels and ran the coons and cats, because the proved hunters, not only Major de Spain and old General Compson, who spent those two weeks sitting in a rocking chair before a tremendous iron pot of Brunswick stew, stirring and tasting, with old Ash to quarrel with about how he was making it and Tennie's Jim to pour from the demijohn into the tin dipper from which he drank, but even the boy's father and Walter Ewell, who were still young enough, scorned such, other than shooting the wild gobblers with pistols for wagers on their marksmanship.

Or, that is, his father and the others believed he was hunting squirrels. Until the third day, he thought that Sam Fathers believed that too. Each morning he would leave the camp right after breakfast. He had his own gun now, a Christmas present. He went back to the tree beside the bayou where he had stood that morning. Using the compass which old General Compson had given him, he ranged from that point; he was teaching himself to be a better-than-fair woodsman without knowing he was doing it. On the second day he even found the gutted log where he had first seen the crooked print. It was almost completely crumbled now, healing with unbelievable speed, a passionate and almost visible relinquishment, back into the earth from which the tree had grown.

He ranged the summer woods now, green with gloom; if anything, actually dimmer than in November's gray dissolution, where, even at noon, the sun fell only in intermittent dappling upon the earth, which never completely dried out and which crawled with snakes — moccasins and water snakes and rattlers, themselves the color of the dappled gloom, so that he would not always see them until they moved, returning later and later, first day, second day, passing in the twilight of the third evening the little log pen enclosing the log stable where Sam was putting up the horses for the night.

"You ain't looked right yet," Sam said.

He stopped. For a moment he didn't answer. Then he said peacefully, in a peaceful rushing burst as when a boy's miniature dam in a little brook gives way, "All-right. But how? I went to the bayou. I even found that log again. I ——"

"I reckon that was all right. Likely he's been watching you. You never saw his foot?"

"I," the boy said — "I didn't — I never thought ——"

"It's the gun," Sam said. He stood beside the fence, motionless — the old man, the Indian, in the battered faded overalls and the frayed five-cent straw hat which in the Negro's race had been the badge of his enslavement and was now the regalia of his freedom. The camp — the clearing, the house, the barn and its tiny lot with which Major de Spain in his turn had scratched punily and evanescently at the wilderness — faded in the dusk, back into the immemorial darkness of the woods. *The gun*, the boy thought. *The gun.*

"Be scared," Sam said. "You can't help that. But don't be afraid. Ain't nothing in the woods going to hurt you unless you corner it, or it smells that you are afraid. A bear or a deer, too, has got to be scared of a coward the same as a brave man has got to be."

The gun, the boy thought.

"You will have to choose," Sam said.

He left the camp before daylight, long before Uncle Ash would wake in his quilts on the kitchen floor and start the fire for breakfast. He had only the compass and a stick for snakes. He could go almost a mile before he would begin to need the compass. He sat on a log, the invisible compass in his invisible hand, while the secret night sounds, fallen still at his movements, scurried again and then ceased for good, and the owls ceased and gave over to the waking of day birds, and he could see the compass. Then he went fast yet still quietly; he was becoming better and better as a woodsman, still without having yet realized it.

He jumped a doe and a fawn at sunrise, walked them out of the bed, close enough to see them — the crash of undergrowth, the white scut, the fawn scudding behind her faster than he had believed it could run. He was hunting right, upwind, as Sam had taught him; not that it mattered now. He had left the gun; of his own will and relinquishment he had accepted not a gambit, not a choice, but a condition in which not only the bear's heretofore inviolable anonymity but all the old rules and balances of hunter and hunted had been abrogated. He would not even be afraid, not even in the moment when the fear would take him completely — blood, skin, bowels, bones, memory from the long time before it became his memory — all save that thin, clear, immortal lucidity which alone differed him from this bear and from all the other bear and deer he would ever kill in the humility and pride of his skill and endurance, to which Sam had spoken when he leaned in the twilight on the lot fence yesterday.

By noon he was far beyond the little bayou, farther into the new and alien country than he had ever been. He was traveling now not only by the old, heavy, biscuit-thick silver watch which had belonged to his grandfather. When he stopped at last, it was for the first time since he had risen from the log at dawn when he could see the compass. It was far enough. He had left the camp nine hours ago; nine hours from now, dark would have already been an hour old. But he didn't think that. He thought, *All right. Yes. But what?* and stood for a moment, alien and small in the green and topless solitude, answering his own question before it had formed and ceased. It was the watch, the compass, the stick — the three lifeless mechanicals with which for nine hours he had fended the wilderness off; he hung the watch and compass carefully on a bush and leaned the stick beside them and relinquished completely to it.

He had not been going very fast for the last two or three hours. He went no faster now, since distance would not matter even if he could have gone fast. And he was trying to keep a bearing on the tree where he had left the compass, trying to complete a circle which would bring him back to it or at least intersect itself, since direction would not matter now either. But the tree was not there, and he did as Sam had schooled him — made the next circle in the opposite direction, so that the two patterns would bisect somewhere, but crossing no print of his own feet, finding the tree at last, but in the wrong place — no bush, no compass, no watch — and the tree not even the tree, because there was a down log beside it and he did what Sam Fathers had told him was the next thing and the last.

As he sat down on the log he saw the crooked print — the warped, tremendous, two-toed indentation which, even as he watched it, filled with water. As he looked up, the wilderness coalesced, solidified — the glade, the tree he sought, the bush, the watch and the compass glinting where a ray of sunlight touched them. Then he saw the bear. It did not emerge, appear; it was just there, immobile, solid, fixed in the hot dappling of the green and windless noon, not as big as he had dreamed it, but as big as he had expected it, bigger, dimensionless against the dappled obscurity, looking at him where he sat quietly on the log and looked back at it.

Then it moved. It made no sound. It did not hurry. It crossed the glade, walking for an instant into the full glare of the sun; when it reached the other side it stopped again and looked back at him across one shoulder while his quiet breathing inhaled and exhaled three times.

Then it was gone. It didn't walk into the woods, the undergrowth. It faded, sank back into the wilderness as he had watched a fish, a huge old bass, sink and vanish into the dark depths of its pool without even any movement of its fins.

He thought, *It will be next fall.* But it was not next fall, nor the next nor the next. He was fourteen then. He had killed his buck, and Sam Fathers had marked his face with the hot blood, and in the next year he killed a bear. But even before that accolade he had become as competent in the woods as many grown men with the same experience; by his fourteenth year he was a better woodsman than most grown men with more. There was no territory within thirty miles of the camp that he did not know — bayou, ridge, brake, landmark, tree and path. He could have led anyone to any point in it without deviation, and brought them out again. He knew the game trails that even Sam Fathers did not know; in his thirteenth year he found a buck's bedding place, and unbeknown to his father he borrowed Walter Ewell's rifle and lay in wait at dawn and killed the buck when it walked back to the bed, as Sam had told him how the old Chickasaw fathers did.

But not the old bear, although by now he knew its footprints better than he did his own, and not only the crooked one. He could see any one of the three sound ones and distinguish it from any other, and not only by its size. There were other bears within these thirty miles which left tracks almost as large, but this was more than that. If Sam Fathers had been his mentor and the back-yard rabbits and squirrels at home his kindergarten, then the wilderness the old bear ran was his college, the old male bear itself, so long unwifed and childless as to have become its own ungendered progenitor, was his alma mater. But he never saw it.

He could find the crooked print now almost whenever he liked, fifteen or ten or five miles, or sometimes nearer the camp than that. Twice while on stand during the three years he heard the dogs strike its trail by accident; on the second time they jumped it seemingly, the voices high, abject, almost human in hysteria, as on that first morning two years ago. But not the bear itself. He would remember that noon three years ago, the glade, himself and the bear fixed during that moment in the windless and dappled blaze, and it would seem to him that it had never happened, that he had dreamed that too. But it had happened. They had looked at each other, they had emerged from the wilderness old as earth, synchronized to that instant by something more than the blood that moved the flesh and bones which bore them, and touched, pledged something, affirmed something more lasting than the frail web of bones and flesh which any accident could obliterate.

Then he saw it again. Because of the very fact that he thought of nothing else, he had forgotten to look for it. He was still-hunting with Walter Ewell's rifle. He saw it cross the end of a long blowdown, a corridor where a tornado had swept, rushing through rather than over the tangle of trunks and branches as a locomotive would have, faster than he had ever believed it could move, almost as fast as a deer even, because a deer would have spent most of that time in the air, faster than he could bring the rifle sights up to it, so that he believed the reason he never let off the shot was that he was still behind it, had never caught up with it. And now he knew what had been wrong during all the three years. He sat on a log, shaking and trembling as if he had never seen the woods before nor anything that ran them, wondering with incredulous amazement how he could have forgotten the very thing which Sam Fathers had told him and which the bear itself had proved the next day and had now returned after three years to reaffirm.

And now he knew what Sam Fathers had meant about the right dog, a dog in which size would mean less than nothing. So when he returned alone in April — school was out then, so that the sons of farmers could help with the land's planting, and at last his father had granted him permission, on his promise to be back in four days — he had the dog. It was his own, a mongrel of the sort called by Negroes a fyce, a ratter, itself not much bigger than a rat and possessing that bravery which had long since stopped being courage and had become foolhardiness.

It did not take four days. Alone again, he found the trail on the first morning. It was not a stalk; it was an ambush. He timed the meeting almost as if it were an appointment with a human being. Himself holding the fyce muffled in a feed sack and Sam Fathers with two of the hounds on a piece of a plowline rope, they lay down wind of the trail at dawn of the second morning. They were so close that the bear turned without even running, as if in surprised amazement at the shrill and frantic uproar of the released fyce, turning at bay against the trunk of a tree, on its hind feet; it seemed to the boy that it would never stop rising, taller and taller, and even the two hounds seemed to take a desperate and despairing courage from the fyce, following it as it went in.

Then he realized that the fyce was actually not going to stop. He flung, threw the gun away, and ran; when he overtook and grasped the frantically pin-wheeling little dog, it seemed to him that he was directly under the bear.

He could smell it, strong and hot and rank. Sprawling, he looked up to where it loomed and towered over him like a cloudburst and colored like a thunderclap, quite familiar, peacefully and even lucidly familiar, until he remembered: This was the way he had used to dream about it. Then it was gone. He didn't see it go. He knelt, holding the frantic fyce with both hands, hearing the abashed wailing of the hounds drawing farther and farther away, until Sam came up. He carried the gun. He laid it down quietly beside the boy and stood looking down at him.

"You've done seed him twice now with a gun in your hands," he said. "This time you couldn't have missed him."

The boy rose. He still held the fyce. Even in his arms and clear of the ground, it yapped frantically, straining and surging after the fading uproar of the two hounds like a tangle of wire springs. He was panting a little, but he was neither shaking nor trembling now.

"Neither could you!" he said. "You had the gun! Neither did you!"

"And you didn't shoot," his father said. "How close were you?"

"I don't know, sir," he said. "There was a big wood tick inside his right hind leg. I saw that. But I didn't have the gun then."

"But you didn't shoot when you had the gun," his father said. "Why?"

But he didn't answer, and his father didn't wait for him to, rising and crossing the room, across the pelt of the bear which the boy had killed two years ago and the larger one which his father had killed before he was born, to the bookcase beneath the mounted head of the boy's first buck. It was the room which his father called the office, from which all the plantation business was transacted; in it for the fourteen years of his life he had heard the best of all talking. Major de Spain would be there and sometimes old General Compson, and Walter Ewell and Boon Hoggenbeck and Sam Fathers and Tennie's Jim, too, were hunters, knew the woods and what ran them.

He would hear it, not talking himself but listening — the wilderness, the big woods, bigger and older than any recorded document of white man fatuous enough to believe he had bought any fragment of it or Indian ruthless enough to pretend that any fragment of it had been his to convey. It was of the men, not white nor black nor red, but men, hunters with the will and hardihood to endure and the humility and skill to survive, and the dogs and the bear and deer juxtaposed and reliefed against it, ordered and compelled by and within the wilderness in the ancient and unremitting contest by the ancient and immitigable rules which voided all regrets and brooked no quarter, the voices quiet and weighty and deliberate for retrospection and recollection and exact remembering, while he squatted in the blazing firelight.

His father returned with the book and sat down again and opened it. "Listen," he said. He read the five stanzas aloud, his voice quiet and deliberate in the room where there was no fire now because it was already spring. Then he looked up. The boy watched him. "All right," his father said. "Listen." He read again, but only the second stanza this time, to the end of it, the last two lines, and closed the book and put it on the table beside him. "She cannot fade, though thou hast not thy bliss, for ever wilt thou love, and she be fair," he said.

"He's talking about a girl," the boy said.

"He had to talk about something," his father said. Then he said, "He was talking about truth. Truth doesn't change. Truth is one thing. It covers all things which touch the heart — honor and pride and pity and justice and courage and love. Do you see now?"

He didn't know. Somehow it was simpler than that. There was an old bear, fierce and ruthless, not merely just to stay alive, but with the fierce pride of liberty and freedom, proud enough of that liberty and freedom to see it threatened without fear or even alarm; nay, who at times even seemed deliberately to put that freedom and liberty in jeopardy in order to savor them, to remind his old strong bones and flesh to keep supple and quick to defend and preserve them. There was an old man, son of a Negro slave and an Indian king, inheritor on the one side of the long chronicle of a people who had learned humility through suffering, and pride through the endurance which survived the suffering and injustice, and on the other side, the chronicle of a people even longer in the land than the first, yet who no longer existed in the land at all save in the solitary brotherhood of an old Negro's alien blood and the wild and invincible spirit of an old bear. There was a boy who wished to learn humility and pride in order to become skillful and worthy in the woods, who suddenly found himself becoming so skillful so rapidly that he feared he would never become worthy because he had not learned humility and pride, although he had tried to, until one day and as suddenly he discovered that an old man who could not have defined either had led him, as though by the hand, to that point where an old bear and a little mongrel dog showed him that, by possessing one thing other, he would possess them both.

And a little dog, nameless and mongrel and many-fathered, grown, yet weighing less than six pounds, saying as if to itself, " I can't be dangerous, because there's nothing much smaller than I am; I can't be fierce, because they would call it just noise; I can't be humble, because I'm already too close to the ground to genuflect; I can't be proud, because I wouldn't be near enough to it for anyone to know who was casting that shadow, and I don't even know that I'm not going to heaven, because they have already decided that I don't possess an immortal soul. So all I can be is brave. But it's all right. I can be that, even if they still call it just noise."

That was all. It was simple, much simpler than somebody talking in a book about a youth and a girl he would never need to grieve over, because he could never approach any nearer her and would never have to get any farther away. He had heard about a bear, and finally got big enough to trail it, and he trailed it four years and at last met it with a gun in his hands and he didn't shoot. Because a little dog —— But he could have shot long before the little dog covered the twenty yards to where the bear waited, and Sam Fathers could have shot at any time during that interminable minute while Old Ben stood on his hind feet over them. He stopped. His father was watching him gravely across the spring-rife twilight of the room; when he spoke, his words were as quiet as the twilight, too, not loud, because they did not need to be because they would last. " Courage, and honor, and pride," his father said, " and pity, and love of justice and of liberty. They all touch the heart, and what the heart holds to becomes truth, as far as we know the truth. Do you see now? "

Sam, and Old Ben, and Nip, he thought. And himself too. He had been all right too. His father had said so. " Yes, sir," he said.

READING WITH INSIGHT

" The Bear " is a good example of what is meant by " richness " in stories. (See the Introduction, p. 43.) It is rich in every way listed there. Particularly it is rich in meaning. It makes you think, and the more you think, the more you find in the story. There are several layers of meaning, as you will see.

1. The first layer of meaning lies in the account of the physical action in the story. It is important to get this absolutely straight. The following questions may help you:

a) How many times did the boy see the bear?
b) How many chances did he have to shoot the bear?
c) Was the boy's dog afraid of the bear?
d) Was the bear afraid when the boy, the dog, and the man suddenly came upon it?
e) Did the boy wonder whether it was right for him not to have shot the bear?
f) Did the boy's father think it was right for the boy not to have shot the bear?

2. On the surface this is an exciting adventure story — the story of a boy's hunt for a big bear. The problem is: Will the boy get the bear? Trace the rising action. What is the climax? If the story were merely an adventure story, without much symbolic meaning, would the climax be satisfying? Why or why not?

3. Think back over the story and recall what kind of information you have been told about the boy. Do you know his name? Whether he is tall or short, fat or thin, blond or brunet, freckled or tanned? What *do* you know about him? Can you imagine him vividly even without details?

4. The two main characters, of course, are the boy and the bear. The other characters are in the story merely as the wilderness is there — to provide a setting for the boy's experiences, to help him in his quest, to help him learn what he has to learn. List the steps by which Faulkner brings the two main characters closer together toward the climax.

5. If you were to summarize the story briefly, you might say, "It is a story of a boy who spent four years hunting a bear. When he finally came face to face with it, he decided not to shoot it." Now the central question about the story is this: Why didn't the boy shoot the bear? If you can answer this question, you will be getting at a deeper layer of meaning.

6. What change occurs in the boy's attitude toward the bear as the story progresses? What change, if any, occurs in your own feeling toward the bear?

7. What did the boy learn from the bear?

8. At the outset of the story, you might say that the boy and the bear are opposing forces. The conflict lies between them. The question is whether the boy is going to get the bear. Suddenly on page 277 comes the paragraph beginning "*So I must see him . . .*" From this point, the conflict is no longer between boy and bear. The conflict is *inside* the boy. What is that conflict? The boy must overcome more than one thing. Can you name those things? Why did the boy feel that he must see the bear face to face?

9. How had the boy changed by the end of the story? The answer to this question will give you a clue to the real conflict in the story.

10. On page 279 Sam says, "Be scared. You can't help that. But don't be afraid. Ain't nothing in the woods going to hurt you unless you corner it, or it smells that you are afraid. A bear or a deer, too, has got to be scared of a coward the same as a brave man has got to be." Why must a brave man be scared of a coward with a gun? Why must a bear be scared of a coward with a gun? With Sam's statement in mind, can you explain (a) why the boy went looking for the bear without a gun? (b) why the boy hung his watch and compass on the tree?

11. What is the advantage of telling this story in the third person, rather than in the first?

If you like this story, you will be interested in

Joseph Conrad. *The Secret Sharer.*
James Street. *Biscuit Eater.*
Wallace Stegner. *Bugle Song.*
John Steinbeck. *The Red Pony.*

KATHERINE ANNE PORTER

The Jilting of Granny Weatherall

MISS PORTER was born in Texas in 1894. She was educated in private schools, and for most of her adult life has lived in New York or abroad. She has written comparatively little, and mostly in the form of short stories and novelettes, but she has always written like an artist, and her work has gained an increasing popularity among readers who appreciate delicate and artistic writing.

This particular story is in the form we call stream-of-consciousness. In a sense, it turns the traditional story upside down: instead of being concerned mostly with the physical events of an incident, it is concerned hardly at all with the physical events; in place of describing action as a way of illuminating mental life, it describes mental life as a way of illuminating behavior. The entire story takes place in Granny Weatherall's mind, and the great events are not what happen around her, but the thoughts that sweep like a stream through her mind.

Miss Porter is a master of suggestion. You will be interested in comparing her in this respect with Katherine Mansfield. Both writers have attained great skill in making a few words stand for much, and in choosing the few suggestive words or the suggestive picture which will open deeper meanings to the reader. In a Mansfield or a Porter story, very few words are ever wasted.

SHE flicked her wrist neatly out of Doctor Harry's pudgy careful fingers and pulled the sheet up to her chin. The brat ought to be in knee breeches. Doctoring around the country with spectacles on his nose! " Get along now, take your schoolbooks and go. There's nothing wrong with me."

Doctor Harry spread a warm paw like a cushion on her forehead where the forked green vein danced and made her eyelids twitch. " Now, now, be a good girl, and we'll have you up in no time."

" That's no way to speak to a woman nearly eighty years old just because she's down. I'd have you respect your elders, young man."

" Well, Missy, excuse me." Doctor Harry patted her cheek. " But I've got to warn you, haven't I? You're a marvel, but you must be careful or you're going to be good and sorry."

" Don't tell me what I'm going to be. I'm on my feet now, morally speaking. It's Cornelia. I had to go to bed to get rid of her."

Her bones felt loose, and floated around in her skin, and Doctor Harry floated like a balloon around the foot of the bed. He floated and pulled down his waistcoat and swung his glasses on a cord. " Well, stay where you are, it certainly can't hurt you."

" Get along and doctor your sick," said Granny Weatherall. " Leave a well woman alone. I'll call for you when I want you. . . . Where were you forty years ago when I pulled through milk leg and double pneumonia? You weren't even born. Don't let Cornelia lead you on," she shouted, because Doctor Harry appeared to float up to the ceiling and out. " I pay my own bills, and I don't throw my money away on nonsense! "

She meant to wave good-by, but it was too much trouble. Her eyes closed of themselves, it was like a dark curtain drawn around the bed. The pillow rose and floated under her, pleasant as a hammock in a light wind. She listened to the leaves rustling outside the window. No, somebody was swishing newspapers: no, Cornelia and Doctor Harry were whispering together. She leaped broad awake, thinking they whispered in her ear.

" She was never like this, *never* like this! " " Well, what can we expect? " " Yes, eighty years old. . . ."

Well, and what if she was? She still had ears. It was like Cornelia to whisper around doors. She always kept things secret in such a public way. She was always being tactful and kind. Cornelia was dutiful; that was the trouble with her. Dutiful and good: " So good and dutiful," said Granny, " that I'd like to spank her." She saw herself spanking Cornelia and making a fine job of it.

" What'd you say, Mother? "

Granny felt her face tying up in hard knots.

" Can't a body think, I'd like to know? "

"I thought you might want something."

"I do. I want a lot of things. First off, go away and don't whisper."

She lay and drowsed, hoping in her sleep that the children would keep out and let her rest a minute. It had been a long day. Not that she was tired. It was always pleasant to snatch a minute now and then. There was always so much to be done, let me see: tomorrow.

Tomorrow was far away and there was nothing to trouble about. Things were finished somehow when the time came; thank God there was always a little margin over for peace: then a person could spread out the plan of life and tuck in the edges orderly. It was good to have everything clean and folded away, with the hairbrushes and tonic bottles sitting straight on the white embroidered linen: the day started without fuss and the pantry shelves laid out with rows of jelly glasses and brown jugs and white stone-china jars with blue whirligigs and words painted on them: coffee, tea, sugar, ginger, cinnamon, allspice: and the bronze clock with the lion on top nicely dusted off. The dust that lion could collect in twenty-four hours! The box in the attic with all those letters tied up, well, she'd have to go through that tomorrow. All those letters — George's letters and John's letters and her letters to them both — lying around for the children to find afterwards made her uneasy. Yes, that would be tomorrow's business. No use to let them know how silly she had been once.

While she was rummaging around she found death in her mind and it felt clammy and unfamiliar. She had spent so much time preparing for death there was no need for bringing it up again. Let it take care of itself now. When she was sixty she had felt very old, finished, and went around making farewell trips to see her children and grandchildren, with a secret in her mind: This is the very last of your mother, children! Then she made her will and came down with a long fever. That was all just a notion like a lot of other things, but it was lucky too, for she had once for all got over the idea of dying for a long time. Now she couldn't be worried. She hoped she had better sense now. Her father had lived to be one hundred and two years old and had drunk a noggin of strong hot toddy on his last birthday. He told the reporters it was his daily habit, and he owed his long life to that. He had made quite a scandal and was very pleased about it. She believed she'd just plague Cornelia a little.

" Cornelia! Cornelia! " No footsteps, but a sudden hand on her cheek. " Bless you, where have you been? "

" Here, Mother."

" Well, Cornelia, I want a noggin of hot toddy."

" Are you cold, darling? "

" I'm chilly, Cornelia. Lying in bed stops the circulation. I must have told you that a thousand times."

Well, she could just hear Cornelia telling her husband that Mother was getting a little childish and they'd have to humor her. The thing that most annoyed her was that Cornelia thought she was deaf, dumb, and blind. Little hasty glances and tiny gestures tossed around her and over her head saying, " Don't cross her, let her have her way, she's eighty years old," and she sitting there as if she lived in a thin glass cage. Sometimes Granny almost made up her mind to pack up and move back to her own house where nobody could remind her every minute that she was old. Wait, wait, Cornelia, till your own children whisper behind your back!

In her day she had kept a better house and had got more work done. She wasn't too old yet for Lydia to be driving eighty miles for advice when one of the children jumped the track, and Jimmy still dropped in and talked things over: " Now, Mammy, you've a good business head, I want to know what you think of this? . . ." Old. Cornelia couldn't change the furniture around without asking. Little things, little things! They had been so sweet when they were little. Granny wished the old days were back again with the children young and everything to be done over. It had been a hard pull, but not too much for her. When she thought of all the food she had cooked, and all the clothes she had cut and sewed, and all the gardens she had made – well, the children showed it. There they were, made out of her, and they couldn't get away from that. Sometimes she wanted to see John again and point to them and say, Well, I didn't do so badly, did I? But that would have to wait. That was for tomorrow. She used to think of him as a man, but now all the children were older than their father, and he would be a child beside her if she saw him now. It seemed strange and there was something wrong in the idea. Why, he couldn't possibly recognize her. She had fenced in a hundred acres once, digging the postholes herself and clamping the wires with just a Negro boy to help. That changed a woman.

John would be looking for a young woman with the peaked Spanish comb in her hair and the painted fan. Digging postholes changed a woman. Riding country roads in the winter when women had their babies was another thing: sitting up nights with sick horses and sick Negroes and sick children and hardly ever losing one. John, I hardly ever lost one of them! John would see that in a minute, that would be something he could understand, she wouldn't have to explain anything!

It made her feel like rolling up her sleeves and putting the whole place to rights again. No matter if Cornelia was determined to be everywhere at once, there were a great many things left undone on this place. She would start tomorrow and do them. It was good to be strong enough for everything, even if all you made melted and changed and slipped under your hands, so that by the time you finished you almost forgot what you were working for. What was it I set out to do? she asked herself intently, but she could not remember. A fog rose over the valley, she saw it marching across the creek swallowing the trees and moving up the hill like an army of ghosts. Soon it would be at the near edge of the orchard, and then it was time to go in and light the lamps. Come in, children, don't stay out in the night air.

Lighting the lamps had been beautiful. The children huddled up to her and breathed like little calves waiting at the bars in the twilight. Their eyes followed the match and watched the flame rise and settle in a blue curve, then they moved away from her. The lamp was lit, they didn't have to be scared and hang on to mother any more. Never, never, never more. God, for all my life I thank Thee. Without Thee, my God, I could never have done it. Hail, Mary, full of grace.[1]

I want you to pick all the fruit this year and see that nothing is wasted. There's always someone who can use it. Don't let good things rot for want of using. You waste life when you waste good food. Don't let things get lost. It's bitter to lose things. Now, don't let me get to thinking, not when I am tired and taking a little nap before supper. . . .

The pillow rose about her shoulders and pressed against her heart

[1] **Hail, Mary, full of grace:** first line of the prayer often called by its Latin name, Ave Maria.

and the memory was being squeezed out of it: oh, push down the pillow, somebody: it would smother her if she tried to hold it. Such a fresh breeze blowing and such a green day with no threats in it. But he had not come, just the same. What does a woman do when she has put on the white veil and set out the white cake for a man and he doesn't come? She tried to remember. No, I swear he never harmed me but in that. He never harmed me but in that . . . and what if he did? There was the day, the day, but a whirl of dark smoke rose and covered it, crept up and over into the bright field where everything was planted so carefully in orderly rows. That was hell, she knew hell when she saw it. For sixty years she had prayed against remembering him and against losing her soul in the deep pit of hell, and now the two things were mingled in one and the thought of him was a smoky cloud from hell that moved and crept in her head when she had just got rid of Doctor Harry and was trying to rest a minute. Wounded vanity, Ellen, said a sharp voice in the top of her mind. Don't let your wounded vanity get the upper hand of you. Plenty of girls get jilted. You were jilted, weren't you? Then stand up to it. Her eyelids wavered and let in streamers of blue-gray light like tissue paper over her eyes. She must get up and pull the shades down or she'd never sleep. She was in bed again and the shades were not down. How could that happen? Better turn over, hide from the light, sleeping in the light gave you nightmares. " Mother, how do you feel now? " and a stinging wetness on her forehead. But I don't like having my face washed in cold water!

Hapsy? George? Lydia? Jimmy? No, Cornelia, and her features were swollen and full of little puddles. " They're coming, darling, they'll all be here soon." Go wash your face, child, you look funny.

Instead of obeying, Cornelia knelt down and put her head on the pillow. She seemed to be talking but there was no sound. " Well, are you tongue-tied? Whose birthday is it? Are you going to give a party? "

Cornelia's mouth moved urgently in strange shapes. " Don't do that, you bother me, daughter."

" Oh, no, Mother. Oh, no. . . ."

Nonsense. It was strange about children. They disputed your every word. " No what, Cornelia? "

" Here's Doctor Harry."

"I won't see that boy again. He just left five minutes ago."

"That was this morning, Mother. It's night now. Here's the nurse."

"This is Doctor Harry, Mrs. Weatherall. I never saw you look so young and happy!"

"Ah, I'll never be young again — but I'd be happy if they'd let me lie in peace and get rested."

She thought she spoke up loudly, but no one answered. A warm weight on her forehead, a warm bracelet on her wrist, and a breeze went on whispering, trying to tell her something. A shuffle of leaves in the everlasting hand of God, He blew on them and they danced and rattled. "Mother, don't mind, we're going to give you a little hypodermic." "Look here, daughter, how do ants get in this bed? I saw sugar ants yesterday." Did you send for Hapsy too?

It was Hapsy she really wanted. She had to go a long way back through a great many rooms to find Hapsy standing with a baby on her arm. She seemed to herself to be Hapsy also, and the baby on Hapsy's arm was Hapsy and himself and herself, all at once, and there was no surprise in the meeting. Then Hapsy melted from within and turned flimsy as gray gauze and the baby was a gauzy shadow, and Hapsy came up close and said. "I thought you'd never come," and looked at her very searchingly and said, "You haven't changed a bit!" They leaned forward to kiss, when Cornelia began whispering from a long way off, "Oh, is there anything you want to tell me? Is there anything I can do for you?"

Yes, she had changed her mind after sixty years and she would like to see George. I want you to find George. Find him and be sure to tell him I forgot him. I want him to know I had my husband just the same and my children and my house like any other woman. A good house too and a good husband that I loved and fine children out of him. Better than I hoped for even. Tell him I was given back everything he took away and more. Oh, no, oh, no, there was something else besides the house and the man and the children. Oh, surely they were not all? What was it? Something not given back. . . . Her breath crowded down under her ribs and grew into a monstrous frightening shape with cutting edges; it bored up into her head, and the agony was unbelievable: Yes, John, get the Doctor now, no more talk, my time has come.

When this one was born it should be the last. The last. It should have been born first, for it was the one she had truly wanted. Everything came in good time. Nothing left out, left over. She was strong, in three days she would be as well as ever. Better. A woman needed milk in her to have her full health.

"Mother, do you hear me?"

"I've been telling you —"

"Mother, Father Connolly's here."

"I went to Holy Communion only last week. Tell him I'm not so sinful as all that."

"Father just wants to speak to you."

He could speak as much as he pleased. It was like him to drop in and inquire about her soul as if it were a teething baby, and then stay on for a cup of tea and a round of cards and gossip. He always had a funny story of some sort, usually about an Irishman who made his little mistakes and confessed them, and the point lay in some absurd thing he would blurt out in the confessional showing his struggles between native piety and original sin. Granny felt easy about her soul. Cornelia, where are your manners? Give Father Connolly a chair. She had her secret comfortable understanding with a few favorite saints who cleared a straight road to God for her. All as surely signed and sealed as the papers for the new Forty Acres. Forever . . . heirs and assigns forever. Since the day the wedding cake was not cut, but thrown out and wasted. The whole bottom dropped out of the world, and there she was blind and sweating with nothing under her feet and the walls falling away. His hand had caught her under the breast, she had not fallen, there was the freshly polished floor with the green rug on it, just as before. He had cursed like a sailor's parrot and said, "I'll kill him for you." Don't lay a hand on him, for my sake leave something to God. "Now, Ellen, you must believe what I tell you. . . ."

So there was nothing, nothing to worry about any more, except sometimes in the night one of the children screamed in a nightmare, and they both hustled out shaking and hunting for the matches and calling, "There, wait a minute, here we are!" John, get the doctor now, Hapsy's time has come. But there was Hapsy standing by the bed in a white cap. "Cornelia, tell Hapsy to take off her cap. I can't see her plain."

Her eyes opened very wide and the room stood out like a picture she had seen somewhere. Dark colors with the shadows rising toward the ceiling in long angles. The tall black dresser gleamed with nothing on it but John's picture, enlarged from a little one, with John's eyes very black when they should have been blue. You never saw him, so how do you know how he looked? But the man insisted the copy was perfect, it was very rich and handsome. For a picture, yes, but it's not my husband. The table by the bed had a linen cover and a candle and a crucifix. The light was blue from Cornelia's silk lamp shades. No sort of light at all, just frippery. You had to live forty years with kerosene lamps to appreciate honest electricity. She felt very strong and she saw Doctor Harry with a rosy nimbus around him.

"You look like a saint, Doctor Harry, and I vow that's as near as you'll ever come to it."

"She's saying something."

"I heard you, Cornelia. What's all this carrying-on?"

"Father Connolly's saying —"

Cornelia's voice staggered and bumped like a cart in a bad road. It rounded corners and turned back again and arrived nowhere. Granny stepped up in the cart very lightly and reached for the reins, but a man sat beside her and she knew him by his hands, driving the cart. She did not look in his face, for she knew without seeing, but looked instead down the road where the trees leaned over and bowed to each other and a thousand birds were singing a Mass. She felt like singing too, but she put her hand in the bosom of her dress and pulled out a rosary, and Father Connolly murmured Latin in a very solemn voice and tickled her feet. Will you stop that nonsense? I'm a married woman. What if he did run away and leave me to face the priest by myself? I found another a whole world better. I wouldn't have exchanged my husband for anybody except St Michael himself, and you may tell him that for me with a thank you in the bargain.

Light flashed on her closed eyelids, and a deep roaring shook her. Cornelia, is that lightning? I hear thunder. There's going to be a storm. Close all the windows. Call the children in. . . . "Mother, here we are, all of us." "Is that you, Hapsy?" "Oh, no, I'm Lydia. We drove as fast as we could." Their faces drifted above her, drifted away. The rosary fell out of her hands and Lydia put it back. Jimmy tried to help, their hands fumbled together, and Granny closed two fingers around Jimmy's thumb. Beads wouldn't do, it must be something alive. She was so amazed her thoughts ran round and round. So, my dear Lord, this is my death and I wasn't even thinking about it. My children have come to see me die. But I can't, it's not time. Oh, I always hated surprises. I wanted to give Cornelia the amethyst set—Cornelia, you're to have the amethyst set, but Hapsy's to wear it when she wants, and, Doctor Harry, do shut up. Nobody sent for you. Oh, my dear Lord, do wait a minute. I meant to do something about the Forty Acres, Jimmy doesn't need it and Lydia will later on, with that worthless husband of hers. I meant to finish the altar cloth and send six bottles of wine to Sister Borgia for her dyspepsia. I want to send six bottles of wine to Sister Borgia, Father Connolly, now don't let me forget.

Cornelia's voice made short turns and tilted over and crashed. "Oh, Mother, oh, Mother, oh, Mother. . . ."

"I'm not going, Cornelia. I'm taken by surprise. I can't go."

You'll see Hapsy again. What about her? "I thought you'd never come." Granny made a long journey outward, looking for Hapsy. What if I don't find her? What then? Her heart sank down and down, there was no bottom to death, she couldn't come to the end of it. The blue light from Cornelia's lamp shade drew into a tiny point in the center of her brain, it flickered and winked like an eye, quietly it fluttered and dwindled. Granny lay curled down within herself, amazed and watchful, staring at the point of light that was herself; her body was now only a deeper mass of shadow in an endless darkness and this darkness would curl around the light and swallow it up. God, give a sign!

For the second time there was no sign. Again no bridegroom and the priest in the house. She could not remember any other sorrow because this grief wiped them all away. Oh, no, there's nothing more cruel than this—I'll never forgive it. She stretched herself with a deep breath and blew out the light.

READING WITH INSIGHT

1. The first question to ask of a story like this is: Do you find it believable? You can't check up on Granny Weatherall's thoughts, but you have the right to ask whether Granny Weatherall might have thought them. Can you mention anything in Granny Weatherall's stream-of-consciousness which seems unconvincing to you? What can you mention that seems to be especially real and authentic?

2. What happens around the dying woman? How many people come into the room, and what do they do? Summarize the physical action that takes place in the room.

3. You might call this story a variation on the idea that a drowning man remembers his life. Many scenes in Granny Weatherall's life return to her as she lies dying. What do you think determines which memories come back to a person in a situation like this? What makes the unpleasant memories so insistent?

4. What does the fact that Granny Weatherall remembers the jilting so vividly tell you about her?

5. The jilting comes to be a symbol for something in the story. To see what it means, read the last paragraph again. How has Granny again been jilted, this time on her deathbed?

6. There is a theory that any moment or any tiny thing in life is a miniature of everything in life. If you know enough about that tiny thing, you can expand it until you know everything about everything. If you know enough about an atom, you can come to know everything about the universe; if you know enough about one man, you can come to know everything about history. And so this story is constructed on the principle that one incident in the life of a woman described in a very sensitive way will enable the reader to know a great deal about the woman's whole life and character. What do you know about Granny as a result of reading this incident in her last hours?

7. What does Granny Weatherall's orderliness tell you about her?

8. What does her concern for her children tell you about her?

9. Compare this story with Hemingway's "Now I Lay Me," which is also centered mostly in the mind of a character. How have

the two authors approached the problem differently? Which would you say is the more objective? Which fills in the picture more fully?

10. Miss Porter is known for the exquisite care with which she polishes and finishes a story. Pick out some examples of telling descriptions like, for example, Cornelia's keeping "things secret in a public sort of way."

11. In the ordinary sense of the word, there is no rising action, no falling action, no climax in this story. Is there, however, any progress from tension to resolution? Try to describe the structure of this story.

12. Writing an introduction to her best-known book of short stories, Miss Porter said: "All the conscious and recollected years of my life have been lived to this day under the heavy threats of world catastrophe. . . . In the face of such shape and weight of present misfortune, the voice of the individual artist may seem perhaps of no more consequence than the whirring of a cricket in the grass; but the arts do live continuously, and they live literally by faith; their names and their shapes and their uses and their basic meanings survive unchanged in all that matters through times of interruption, diminishment, neglect; they outlive governments and creeds and the societies, even the very civilizations that produce them. They cannot be destroyed altogether because they represent the substance of faith and the only reality. They are what we find again when the ruins are cleared away. And even the smallest and most incomplete offering at this time can be a proud act in defense of that faith." [1]

Considering what Miss Porter has said here, what would you say are the reasons why we need great writers — even in a time of tension and war?

If you like this story, you will be interested in

Ambrose Bierce. *Occurrence at Owl Creek Bridge.*
James Joyce. *Eveline.*
Caroline Gordon. *The Last Day in the Field.*
Anton Chekov. *The Lament.*
Willa Cather. *Neighbor Rosicky.*

[1] From the Modern Library edition of *Flowering Judas.* Used by permission of the author and of Random House, Inc.

WILLIAM SAROYAN

The Summer of the Beautiful White Horse

WILLIAM SAROYAN was born in 1908 near Fresno, California. His family was Armenian, and he grew up amidst the Armenian-American characters with whom he fills stories like this one. He was unable to go to college, but very early started to write for publication. For some years, his only acceptances were from the Armenian magazines and papers published in this country. Then in 1934 *Story* magazine published "The Daring Young Man on the Flying Trapeze," and critics and readers alike realized that a great new talent had been discovered. Thereafter he published in many magazines, his stories were collected into books, and he wrote and published a number of plays.

To a critic who contended that Saroyan's pieces were not short stories, the author answered: "What I write is not a story; very good. It doesn't matter in the slightest. I dislike bickering. Whatever it is, it is not dead." No one ever wrote a better thumbnail description of Saroyan's stories: they are not dead! Most of them are certainly not in the orthodox form of stories, but they are excitingly, movingly alive. The characters are alive. The mood is rich and poetic. The incidents are real and vivid. Perhaps they succeed in spite of, rather than because of, their form, but a person who reads them has the experience of meeting life and imagination and color. Two words more often than any others have been applied to Saroyan's stories: original and alive.

Speaking of his intentions as a writer, Saroyan said that he wanted in his stories to "restore man to his natural dignity and gentleness." As you read, you can decide whether he achieves that goal in this story.

ONE day back there in the good old days when I was nine and the world was full of every imaginable kind of magnificence, and life was still a delightful and mysterious dream, my cousin Mourad, who was considered crazy by everybody who knew him except me, came to my house at four in the morning and woke me up tapping on the window of my room.

Aram, he said.

I jumped out of bed and looked out the window.

I couldn't believe what I saw.

It wasn't morning yet, but it was summer and with daybreak not many minutes around the corner of the world it was light enough for me to know I wasn't dreaming.

My cousin Mourad was sitting on a beautiful white horse.

I stuck my head out of the window and rubbed my eyes.

Yes, he said in Armenian. It's a horse. You're not dreaming. Make it quick if you want to ride.

I knew my cousin Mourad enjoyed being alive more than anybody else who had ever fallen into the world by mistake, but this was more than even I could believe.

In the first place, my earliest memories had been memories of horses and my first longings had been longings to ride.

This was the wonderful part.

In the second place, we were poor.

This was the part that wouldn't permit me to believe what I saw.

We were poor. We had no money. Our whole tribe was poverty-stricken. Every branch of the Garoghlanian family was living in the most amazing and comical poverty in the world. Nobody could understand where we ever got money enough to keep us with food in our bellies, not even the old men of the family. Most important of all, though, we were famous for our honesty. We had been famous for our honesty for something like eleven centuries, even when we had been the wealthiest family in what we liked to think was the world. We were proud first, honest next, and after that we believed in right and wrong. None of us would take advantage of anybody in the world, let alone steal.

Consequently, even though I could *see* the horse, so magnificent; even though I could *smell* it, so lovely; even though I could *hear* it breathing, so exciting; I couldn't *believe* the horse had anything to do with my cousin Mourad or with me or with any of the other members of our family, asleep or awake, because I *knew* my cousin Mourad couldn't have *bought* the horse, and if he couldn't have bought it he must have *stolen* it, and I refused to believe he had stolen it.

No member of the Garoghlanian family could be a thief.

I stared first at my cousin and then at the horse. There was a pious stillness and humor in each of them which on the one hand delighted me and on the other frightened me.

Mourad, I said, where did you steal this horse?

Leap out of the window, he said, if you want to ride.

It was true, then. He *had* stolen the horse. There was no question about it. He had come to invite me to ride or not, as I chose.

Well, it seemed to me stealing a horse for a ride was not the same thing as stealing something else, such as money. For all I knew, maybe it wasn't stealing at all. If you were crazy about horses the way my cousin Mourad and I were, it wasn't stealing. It wouldn't become stealing until we offered to sell the horse, which of course, I knew we would never do.

Let me put on some clothes, I said.

All right, he said, but hurry.

I leaped into my clothes.

I jumped down to the yard from the window and leaped up onto the horse behind my cousin Mourad.

That year we lived at the edge of town, on Walnut Avenue. Behind our house was the country: vineyards, orchards, irrigation ditches, and country roads. In less than three minutes we were on Olive Avenue, and then the horse began to trot. The air was new and lovely to breathe. The feel of the horse running was wonderful. My cousin Mourad who was considered one of the craziest members of our family began to sing. I mean, he began to roar.

Every family has a crazy streak in it somewhere, and my cousin Mourad was considered the natural descendant of the crazy streak in our tribe. Before him was our uncle Khosrove, an enormous man with a powerful head of black hair and the largest mustache in the San Joaquin Valley,[1] a man so furious in temper, so irritable, so im-

[1] **San Joaquin Valley: one of the long interior valleys of California.**

patient that he stopped anyone from talking by roaring, *It is no harm; pay no attention to it.*

That was all, no matter what anybody happened to be talking about. Once it was his own son Arak running eight blocks to the barber shop where his father was having his mustache trimmed to tell him their house was on fire. This man Khosrove sat up in the chair and roared, It is no harm; pay no attention to it. The barber said, But the boy says your house is on fire. So Khosrove roared, Enough, it is no harm, I say.

My cousin Mourad was considered the natural descendant of this man, although Mourad's father was Zorab, who was practical and nothing else. That's how it was in our tribe. A man could be the father of his son's flesh, but that did not mean that he was also the father of his spirit. The distribution of the various kinds of spirit of our tribe had been from the beginning capricious and vagrant.

We rode and my cousin Mourad sang. For all anybody knew we were still in the old country where, at least according to some of our neighbors, we belonged. We let the horse run as long as it felt like running.

At last my cousin Mourad said, Get down. I want to ride alone.

Will you let me ride alone? I asked.

That is up to the horse, my cousin said. Get down.

The *horse* will let me ride, I said.

We shall see, he said. Don't forget that I have a way with a horse.

Well, I said, any way you have with a horse, I have also.

For the sake of your safety, he said, let us hope so. Get down.

All right, I said, but remember you've got to let me try to ride alone.

I got down and my cousin Mourad kicked his heels into the horse and shouted, *Vazire*, run. The horse stood on its hind legs, snorted, and burst into a fury of speed that was the loveliest thing I had ever seen. My cousin Mourad raced the horse across a field of dry grass to an irrigation ditch, crossed the ditch on the horse, and five minutes later returned, dripping wet.

The sun was coming up.

Now it's my turn to ride, I said.

My cousin Mourad got off the horse.

Ride, he said.

I leaped to the back of the horse and for a moment knew the awfulest fear imaginable. The horse did not move.

Kick into his muscles, my cousin Mourad said. What are you waiting for? We've got to take him back before everybody in the world is up and about.

I kicked into the muscles of the horse. Once again it reared and snorted. Then it began to run. I didn't know what to do. Instead of running across the field to the irrigation ditch the horse ran down the road to the vineyard of Dikran Halabian where it began to leap over vines. The horse leaped over seven vines before I fell. Then it continued running.

My cousin Mourad came running down the road.

I'm not worried about you, he shouted. We've got to get that horse. You go this way and I'll go this way. If you come upon him, be kindly. I'll be near.

I continued down the road and my cousin Mourad went across the field toward the irrigation ditch.

It took him half an hour to find the horse and bring him back.

All right, he said, jump on. The whole world is awake now.

What will we do? I said.

Well, he said, we'll either take him back or hide him until tomorrow morning.

He didn't sound worried and I knew he'd hide him and not take him back. Not for a while, at any rate.

Where will we hide him? I said.

I know a place, he said.

How long ago did you steal this horse? I said.

It suddenly dawned on me that he had been taking these early morning rides for some time and had come for me this morning only because he knew how much I longed to ride.

Who said anything about stealing a horse? he said.

Anyhow, I said, how long ago did you begin riding every morning?

Not until this morning, he said.

Are you telling the truth? I said.

Of course not, he said, but if we are found out, that's what you're to say. I don't want both of us to be liars. All you know is that we started riding this morning.

All right, I said.

He walked the horse quietly to the barn of a deserted vineyard which at one time had been the pride of a farmer named Fetvajian. There were some oats and dry alfalfa in the barn.

We began walking home.

It wasn't easy, he said, to get the horse to behave so nicely. At first it wanted to run wild, but, as I've told you, I have a way with a horse. I can get it to want to do anything I want it to do. Horses understand me.

How do you do it? I said.

I have an understanding with a horse, he said.

Yes, but what sort of an understanding? I said.

A simple and honest one, he said.

Well, I said, I wish I knew how to reach an understanding like that with a horse.

You're still a small boy, he said. When you get to be thirteen you'll know how to do it.

I went home and ate a hearty breakfast.

That afternoon my uncle Khosrove came to our house for coffee and cigarettes. He sat in the parlor, sipping and smoking and remembering the old country. Then another visitor arrived, a farmer named John Byro, an Assyrian who, out of loneliness, had learned to speak Armenian. My mother brought the lonely visitor coffee and tobacco and he rolled a cigarette and sipped and smoked, and then at last, sighing sadly, he said, My white horse which was stolen last month is still gone, I cannot understand it.

My uncle Khosrove became very irritated and shouted, It's no harm. What is the loss of a horse? Haven't we all lost the homeland? What is this crying over a horse?

That may be all right for you, a city dweller, to say, John Byro said, but what of my surrey? What good is a surrey without a horse?

Pay no attention to it, my uncle Khosrove roared.

I walked ten miles to get here, John Byro said.

You have legs, my uncle Khosrove shouted.

My left leg pains me, the farmer said.

Pay no attention to it, my uncle Khosrove roared.

That horse cost me sixty dollars, the farmer said.

I spit on money, my uncle Khosrove said.

He got up and stalked out of the house, slamming the screen door.

My mother explained.

He has a gentle heart, she said. It is simply that he is homesick and such a large man.

The farmer went away and I ran over to my cousin Mourad's house.

He was sitting under a peach tree, trying to repair the hurt wing of a young robin which could not fly. He was talking to the bird.

What is it? he said.

The farmer, John Byro, I said. He visited our house. He wants his horse. You've had it a month. I want you to promise not to take it back until I learn to ride.

It will take you *a year* to learn to ride, my cousin Mourad said.

We could keep the horse a year, I said.

My cousin Mourad leaped to his feet.

What? he roared. Are you inviting a member of the Garoghlanian family to steal? The horse must go back to its true owner.

When? I said.

In six months at the latest, he said.

He threw the bird into the air. The bird tried hard, almost fell twice, but at last flew away, high and straight.

Early every morning for two weeks my cousin Mourad and I took the horse out of the barn of the deserted vineyard where we were hiding it and rode it, and every morning the horse, when it was my turn to ride alone, leaped over grape vines and small trees and threw me and ran away. Nevertheless, I hoped in time to learn to ride the way my cousin Mourad rode.

One morning on the way to Fetvajian's deserted vineyard we ran into the farmer John Byro who was on his way to town.

Let me do the talking, my cousin Mourad said. I have a way with farmers.

Good morning, John Byro, my cousin Mourad said to the farmer.

The farmer studied the horse eagerly.

Good morning, son of my friends, he said. What is the name of your horse?

My Heart, my cousin Mourad said in Armenian.

A lovely name, John Byro said, for a lovely horse. I could swear it is the horse that was stolen from me many weeks ago. May I look into his mouth?

Of course, Mourad said.

The farmer looked into the mouth of the horse.

Tooth for tooth, he said. I would swear it *is* my horse if I didn't know your parents. The fame of your family for honesty is well known to me. Yet the horse is the twin of my horse. A suspicious man would believe his eyes instead of his heart. Good day, my young friends.

Good day, John Byro, my cousin Mourad said.

Early the following morning we took the horse to John Byro's vineyard and put it in the barn. The dogs followed us around without making a sound.

The dogs, I whispered to my cousin Mourad. I thought they would bark.

They would at somebody else, he said. I have a way with dogs.

My cousin Mourad put his arms around the horse, pressed his nose into the horse's nose, patted it, and then we went away.

That afternoon John Byro came to our house in his surrey and showed my mother the horse that had been stolen and returned.

I do not know what to think, he said. The horse is stronger than ever. Better-tempered, too. I thank God. My uncle Khosrove, who was in the parlor, became irritated and shouted, Quiet, man, quiet. Your horse has been returned. Pay no attention to it.

READING WITH INSIGHT

1. Would you call this a plot story, a character story, or a mood story?

2. If this story moves from problem to solution, what is the problem?

3. Do the characters stay in your memory? Are you interested in what happens to them? Can you name any things the boys do that seem to you especially boylike? Anything that does not seem true to boy psychology?

4. How would you describe the mood of this story? If you were

asked to pick out of the first sentence a word that seems to describe the mood or atmosphere, what word would you choose?

5. You will probably agree that this story does not have breathless adventure and exciting action. Then what is the source of its interest?

6. There is a difference between quaintness and reality. Would you say the people in this story are real or merely quaint?

7. Can you remember feeling like the narrator of this story? What incidents can you recall out of your childhood that might make stories?

8. Do you think this story would be as effective if told in the third person? Why?

9. The story pretends to be a reminiscence out of childhood — the sort of story a person might tell when he sees an old photograph or remembers an old friend. How does Saroyan make it more than reminiscence?

10. Does Byro know that the white horse is his? If so, why doesn't he say so? Does he realize, after the horse is returned, who had stolen the animal? What evidence have you for your answer to that question? What do you think of the ethics of the two boys? Did they return the horse because they were conscience-stricken or because they were afraid?

11. There is very little formal description in this story, and the writing is almost as simple as in a children's book. Yet, see how many pictures from the story you can remember vividly.

12. Saroyan's stories have been described in many ways: "live," "original," "fresh," "unspoiled," "natural," "egotistic," "full of love of mankind," "fake," "highly conscious art," "unconscious art," and many others. How would you describe this kind of story in a word or a phrase?

If you like this story, you will be interested in

Saroyan. *Inhale, Exhale.*
Locomotive 38, The Ojibway.
A Nice Old-Fashioned Romance.
Jesse Stuart. *Split Cherry Tree.*
Wallace Stegner. *Bugle Song.*

The Short Story in Great Britain

JOSEPH CONRAD

The Secret Sharer

WHEN the British writer John Galsworthy was a young man, he took a trip around the world. On his way to Cape Town by sailing ship, he made the acquaintance of the first mate, a bearded Pole. The acquaintance became a lifelong friendship, but it was more than that. For Galsworthy came back and told everybody that a Pole named Korzeniowski, who had never spoken English until he was 20, was writing the best sea stories ever written in English!

Korzeniowski, of course, was the Polish name of Joseph Conrad, whose life story is one of the most remarkable among authors. He was born in Poland, in 1857, of a noble family. He was educated in good schools and by private tutors, but decided to go to sea, and became a master mariner in the British merchant marine. Although he had grown up speaking no English, he began to write fiction in English. At first his stories did not sell. Then a few writers like Galsworthy found the stories and realized their unusual quality. They recommended Conrad to their friends. Before long, Conrad's novels were sweeping the literary world. One success after another they came—*Almayer's Folly, Lord Jim,* "Typhoon," "Youth," *Victory*. When he died in 1924 he had 16 novels and several books of shorter pieces to his credit.

"The Secret Sharer" is one of the great adventure stories in English. It is full of the magic and loneliness of the sea. As you read it, you will doubtless reflect on the strange kind of literary miracle by which a man born in Poland and speaking only Polish throughout his formative years should become able to write literature like this in English.

ON my right hand there were lines of fishing stakes resembling a mysterious system of half-submerged bamboo fences, incomprehensible in its division of the domain of tropical fishes, and crazy of aspect as if abandoned forever by some nomad tribe of fishermen now gone to the other end of the ocean; for there was no sign of human habitation as far as the eye could reach. To the left a group of barren islets, suggesting ruins of stone walls, towers, and blockhouses, had its foundations set in a blue seat that itself looked solid, so still and stable did it lie below my feet; even the track of light from the westering sun shone smoothly, without that animated glitter which tells of an imperceptible ripple. And when I turned my head to take a parting glance at the tug which had just left us anchored outside the bar, I saw the straight line of the flat shore joined to the stable sea, edge to edge, with a perfect and unmarked closeness, in one leveled floor half brown, half blue under the enormous dome of the sky. Corresponding in their insignificance to the islets of the sea, two small clumps of trees, one on each side of the only fault in the impeccable joint, marked the mouth of the river Meinam [1] we had just left on the first preparatory stage of our homeward journey; and, far back on the inland level, a larger and loftier mass, the grove surrounding the great Paknam pagoda, was the only thing on which the eye could rest from the vain task of exploring the monotonous sweep of the horizon. Here and there gleams as of a few scattered pieces of silver marked the windings of the great river; and on the nearest of them, just within the bar, the tug steaming right into the land became lost to my sight, hull and funnel and masts, as though the impassive earth had swallowed her up without an effort, without a tremor. My eye followed the light cloud of her smoke, now here, now there, above the plain, according to the devious curves of the stream, but always

[1] **Meinam:** you will find most of the places mentioned in this story along the south coast of Siam or the west coast of Indo-China. The Meinam is the river which flows through Bangkok and empties into the Gulf of Siam. Paknam is on the river near the gulf.

fainter and farther away, till I lost it at last behind the miter-shaped hill of the great pagoda. And then I was left alone with my ship, anchored at the head of the Gulf of Siam.

She floated at the starting point of a long journey, very still in an immense stillness, the shadows of her spars flung far to the eastward by the setting sun. At that moment I was alone on her decks. There was not a sound in her — and around us nothing moved, nothing lived, not a canoe on the water, not a bird in the air, not a cloud in the sky. In this breathless pause at the threshold of a long passage we seemed to be measuring our fitness for a long and arduous enterprise, the appointed task of both our existences to be carried out far from all human eyes, with only sky and sea for spectators and for judges.

There must have been some glare in the air to interfere with one's sight, because it was only just before the sun left us that my roaming eyes made out beyond the highest ridge of the principal islet of the group something which did away with the solemnity of perfect solitude. The tide of darkness flowed on swiftly; and with tropical suddenness a swarm of stars came out above the shadowy earth, while I lingered yet, my hand resting lightly on my ship's rail as if on the shoulder of a trusted friend. But, with all that multitude of celestial bodies staring down at one, the comfort of quiet communion with her was gone for good. And there were also disturbing sounds by this time — voices, footsteps forward; the steward flitted along the main deck, a busily ministering spirit; a hand bell tinkled urgently under the poop deck.[1] . . .

I found my two officers waiting for me near the supper table, in the lighted cuddy.[2] We sat down at once, and as I helped the chief mate, I said:

"Are you aware that there is a ship anchored inside the islands? I saw her mastheads above the ridge as the sun went down."

He raised sharply his simple face, overcharged by a terrible growth of whisker, and emitted his usual ejaculations: "Bless my soul, sir! You don't say so!"

My second mate was a round-cheeked, silent young man, grave beyond his years, I thought; but as our eyes happened to meet I de-

[1] **poop deck:** a deck above the main deck, toward the rear of the ship.
[2] **cuddy:** the ship's kitchen or a small dining room opening off it.

tected a slight quiver on his lips. I looked down at once. It was not my part to encourage sneering on board my ship. It must be said, too, that I knew very little of my officers. In consequence of certain events of no particular significance, except to myself, I had been appointed to the command only a fortnight before. Neither did I know much of the hands forward. All these people had been together for eighteen months or so, and my position was that of the only stranger on board. I mention this because it has some bearing on what is to follow. But what I felt most was my being a stranger to the ship; and if all the truth must be told, I was somewhat of a stranger to myself. The youngest man on board (barring the second mate), and untried as yet by a position of the fullest responsibility, I was willing to take the adequacy of the others for granted. They had simply to be equal to their tasks; but I wondered how far I should turn out faithful to that ideal conception of one's own personality every man sets up for himself secretly.

Meantime the chief mate, with an almost visible effect of collaboration on the part of his round eyes and frightful whiskers, was trying to evolve a theory of the anchored ship. His dominant trait was to take all things into earnest consideration. He was of a painstaking turn of mind. As he used to say, he "liked to account to himself" for practically everything that came in his way, down to a miserable scorpion he had found in his cabin a week before. The why and the wherefore of that scorpion — how it got on board and came to select his room rather than the pantry (which was a dark place and more what a scorpion would be partial to), and how on earth it managed to drown itself in the inkwell of his writing desk — had exercised him infinitely. The ship within the islands was much more easily accounted for; and just as we were about to rise from table he made his pronouncement. She was, he doubted not, a ship from home lately arrived. Probably she drew too much water to cross the bar[1] except at the top of spring tides. Therefore she went into that natural harbor to wait for a few days in preference to remaining in an open roadstead.

"That's so," confirmed the second mate, suddenly, in his slightly hoarse voice. "She draws over twenty feet. She's the Liverpool ship

[1] **bar: sand bar. The bottom of the ship would have scraped the sand bar.**

Sephora with a cargo of coal. Hundred and twenty-three days from Cardiff."

We looked at him in surprise.

"The tugboat skipper told me when he came on board for your letters, sir," explained the young man. "He expects to take her up the river the day after tomorrow."

After thus overwhelming us with the extent of his information he slipped out of the cabin. The mate observed regretfully that he "could not account for that young fellow's whims." What prevented him telling us all about it at once, he wanted to know.

I detained him as he was making a move. For the last two days the crew had had plenty of hard work, and the night before they had very little sleep. I felt painfully that I — a stranger — was doing something unusual when I directed him to let all hands turn in without setting an anchor watch. I proposed to keep on deck myself till one o'clock or thereabouts. I would get the second mate to relieve me at that hour.

"He will turn out the cook and the steward at four," I concluded, "and then give you a call. Of course at the slightest sign of any sort of wind we'll have the hands up and make a start at once."

He concealed his astonishment. "Very well, sir." Outside the cuddy he put his head in the second mate's door to inform him of my unheard-of caprice to take a five hours' anchor watch on myself. I heard the other raise his voice incredulously — "What? The Captain himself?" Then a few more murmurs, a door closed, then another. A few moments later I went on deck.

My strangeness, which had made me sleepless, had prompted that unconventional arrangement, as if I had expected in those solitary hours of the night to get on terms with the ship of which I knew nothing, manned by men of whom I knew very little more. Fast alongside a wharf, littered like any ship in port with a tangle of unrelated things, invaded by unrelated shore people, I had hardly seen her yet properly. Now, as she lay cleared for sea, the stretch of her main deck seemed to me very fine under the stars. Very fine, very roomy for her size, and very inviting. I descended the poop and paced the waist, my mind picturing to myself the coming passage through the Malay Archipelago, down the Indian Ocean, and up the Atlantic All its phases were familiar enough to me, every characteristic, all the alternatives which were likely to face me on the high seas — everything! . . . except the novel responsibility of command. But I took heart from the reasonable thought that the ship was like other ships, the men like other men, and that the sea was not likely to keep any special surprises expressly for my discomfiture.

Arrived at that comforting conclusion, I bethought myself of a cigar and went below to get it. All was still down there. Everybody at the after end of the ship was sleeping profoundly. I came out again on the quarter-deck,[1] agreeably at ease in my sleeping suit on that warm breathless night, barefooted, a glowing cigar in my teeth, and, going forward, I was met by the profound silence of the fore end of the ship. Only as I passed the door of the forecastle I heard a deep, quiet, trustful sigh of some sleeper inside. And suddenly I rejoiced in the great security of the sea as compared with the unrest of the land, in my choice of that untempted life presenting no disquieting problems, invested with an elementary moral beauty by the absolute straightforwardness of its appeal and by the singleness of its purpose.

The riding light in the forerigging [2] burned with a clear, untroubled, as if symbolic, flame, confident and bright in the mysterious shades of the night. Passing on my way aft along the other side of the ship, I observed that the rope side-ladder, put over, no doubt, for the master of the tug when he came to fetch away our letters, had not been hauled in as it should have been. I became annoyed at this, for exactitude in small matters is the very soul of discipline. Then I reflected that I had myself peremptorily dismissed my officers from duty, and by my own act had prevented the anchor watch being formally set and things properly attended to. I asked myself whether it was wise ever to interfere with the established routine of duties even from the kindest of motives. My action might have made me appear eccentric. Goodness only knew how that absurdly whiskered mate would "account" for my conduct, and what the whole ship thought of that informality of their new captain. I was vexed with myself.

Not from compunction certainly, but, as it were mechanically, I

[1] **quarter-deck:** a part of the upper deck reserved for officers.

[2] **riding light in the forerigging:** the light that is carried toward the front of the ship to warn approaching vessels.

proceeded to get the ladder in myself. Now a side-ladder of that sort is a light affair and comes in easily, yet my vigorous tug, which should have brought it flying on board, merely recoiled upon my body in a totally unexpected jerk. What the devil! . . . I was so astounded by the immovableness of that ladder that I remained stock-still, trying to account for it to myself like that imbecile mate of mine. In the end, of course, I put my head over the rail.

The side of the ship made an opaque belt of shadow on the darkling glassy shimmer of the sea. But I saw at once something elongated and pale floating very close to the ladder. Before I could form a guess a faint flash of phosphorescent light, which seemed to issue suddenly from the naked body of a man, flickered in the sleeping water with the elusive, silent play of summer lightning in a night sky. With a gasp I saw revealed to my stare a pair of feet, the long legs, a broad livid back immersed right up to the neck in a greenish cadaverous glow. One hand, awash, clutched the bottom rung of the ladder. He was complete but for the head. A headless corpse! The cigar dropped out of my gaping mouth with a tiny plop and a short hiss quite audible in the absolute stillness of all things under heaven. At that I suppose he raised up his face, a dimly pale oval in the shadow of the ship's side. But even then I could only barely make out down there the shape of his black-haired head. However, it was enough for the horrid, frost-bound sensation which had gripped me about the chest to pass off. The moment of vain exclamations was past, too. I only climbed on the spare spar and leaned over the rail as far as I could, to bring my eyes nearer to that mystery floating alongside.

As he hung by the ladder, like a resting swimmer, the sea-lightning played about his limbs at every stir; and he appeared in it ghastly, silvery, fishlike. He remained as mute as a fish, too. He made no motion to get out of the water, either. It was inconceivable that he should not attempt to come on board, and strangely troubling to suspect that perhaps he did not want to. And my first words were prompted by just that troubled incertitude.

"What's the matter?" I asked in my ordinary tone, speaking down to the face upturned exactly under mine.

"Cramp," it answered, no louder. Then slightly anxious, "I say, no need to call anyone."

" I was not going to," I said.

" Are you alone on deck? "

" Yes."

I had somehow the impression that he was on the point of letting go the ladder to swim away beyond my ken — mysterious as he came. But, for the moment, this being appearing as if he had risen from the bottom of the sea (it was certainly the nearest land to the ship) wanted only to know the time. I told him. And he, down there, tentatively:

" I suppose your captain's turned in? "

" I am sure he isn't," I said.

He seemed to struggle with himself, for I heard something like the low, bitter murmur of doubt. " What's the good? " His next words came out with a hesitating effort.

" Look here, my man. Could you call him out quietly? "

I thought the time had come to declare myself.

" *I* am the captain."

I heard a " By Jove! " whispered at the level of the water. The phosphorescence flashed in the swirl of the water all about his limbs, his other hand seized the ladder.

" My name's Leggatt."

The voice was calm and resolute. A good voice. The self-possession of that man had somehow induced a corresponding state in myself. It was very quietly that I remarked:

" You must be a good swimmer."

" Yes. I've been in the water practically since nine o'clock. The question for me now is whether I am to let go this ladder and go on swimming till I sink from exhaustion, or — to come on board here."

I felt this was no mere formula of desperate speech, but a real alternative in the view of a strong soul. I should have gathered from this that he was young; indeed, it is only the young who are ever confronted by such clear issues. But at the time it was pure intuition on my part. A mysterious communication was established already between us two — in the face of that silent, darkened tropical sea. I was young, too; young enough to make no comment. The man in the water began suddenly to climb up the ladder, and I hastened away from the rail to fetch some clothes.

Before entering the cabin I stood still, listening in the lobby at the foot of the stairs. A faint snore came through the closed door of the chief mate's room. The second mate's door was on the hook, but the darkness in there was absolutely soundless. He, too, was young and could sleep like a stone. Remained the steward, but he was not likely to wake up before he was called. I got a sleeping suit out of my room and, coming back on deck, saw the naked man from the sea sitting on the main hatch, glimmering white in the darkness, his elbows on his knees and his head in his hands. In a moment he had concealed his damp body in a sleeping suit of the same gray-stripe pattern as the one I was wearing and followed me like my double on the poop. Together we moved right aft, barefoot, silent.

"What is it?" I asked in a deadened voice, taking the lighted lamp out of the binnacle,[1] and raising it to his face.

"An ugly business."

He had rather regular features; a good mouth; light eyes under somewhat heavy, dark eyebrows; a smooth, square forehead; no growth on his cheeks; a small, brown mustache, and a well-shaped round chin. His expression was concentrated, meditative, under the inspecting light of the lamp I held up to his face; such as a man thinking hard in solitude might wear. My sleeping suit was just right for his size. A well-knit young fellow of twenty-five at most. He caught his lower lip with the edge of white, even teeth.

"Yes," I said, replacing the lamp in the binnacle. The warm, heavy tropical night closed upon his head again.

"There's a ship over there," he murmured.

"Yes, I know. The *Sephora*. Did you know of us?"

"Hadn't the slightest idea. I am the mate of her——" He paused and corrected himself. "I should say I *was*."

"Aha! Something wrong?"

"Yes. Very wrong indeed. I've killed a man."

"What do you mean? Just now?"

"No, on the passage. Weeks ago. Thirty-nine south. When I say a man——"

"Fit of temper," I suggested, confidently.

The shadowy, dark head, like mine, seemed to nod imperceptibly above the ghostly gray of my sleeping suit. It was, in the night, as

1 **binnacle: the compass stand. At night a lighted lamp is kept there for use when it is necessary to read the compass.**

though I had been faced by my own reflection in the depths of a somber and immense mirror.

"A pretty thing to have to own up to for a Conway [1] boy," murmured my double, distinctly.

"You're a Conway boy?"

"I am," he said, as if startled. Then, slowly . . . "Perhaps you too ——"

It was so; but being a couple of years older I had left before he joined. After a quick interchange of dates a silence fell; and I thought suddenly of my absurd mate with his terrific whiskers and the "Bless my soul – you don't say so" type of intellect. My double gave me an inkling of his thoughts by saying: "My father's a parson in Norfolk. Do you see me before a judge and jury on that charge? For myself I can't see the necessity. There are fellows that an angel from heaven —— And I am not that. He was one of those creatures that are just simmering all the time with a silly sort of wickedness. Miserable devils that have no business to live at all. He wouldn't do his duty and wouldn't let anybody else do theirs. But what's the good of talking! You know well enough the sort of ill-conditioned snarling cur ——"

He appealed to me as if our experiences had been identical as our clothes. And I knew well enough the pestiferous danger of such a character where there are no means of legal repression. And I knew well enough also that my double there was no homicidal ruffian. I did not think of asking him for details, and he told me the story roughly in brusque, disconnected sentences. I needed no more. I saw it all going on as though I were myself inside that other sleeping suit.

"It happened while we were setting a reefed foresail,[2] at dusk. Reefed foresail! You understand the sort of weather. The only sail we had left to keep the ship running; so you may guess what it had been like for days. Anxious sort of job, that. He gave me some of his cursed insolence at the sheet. I tell you I was overdone with this

[1] **Conway:** a naval school.

[2] **reefed foresail:** a rolled or folded sail at the front of the ship. The sheet is the rope or chain that controls the angle of the sail in relation to the wind. They were apparently trying to set this foresail so that the ship could ride with the wind and not be swamped by waves from the side.

terrific weather that seemed to have no end to it. Terrific, I tell you — and a deep ship. I believe the fellow himself was half-crazed with funk. It was no time for gentlemanly reproof, so I turned round and felled him like an ox. He up and at me. We closed just as an awful sea made for the ship. All hands saw it coming and took to the rigging, but I had him by the throat, and went on shaking him like a rat, the men above us yelling, 'Look out! Look out!' Then a crash as if the sky had fallen on my head. They say that for over ten minutes hardly anything was to be seen of the ship — just the three masts and a bit of the forecastle head and of the poop all awash driving along in a smother of foam. It was a miracle that they found us, jammed together behind the forebits. It's clear that I meant business, because I was holding him by the throat still when they picked us up. He was black in the face. It was too much for them. It seems they rushed us aft together, gripped as we were, screaming 'Murder!' like a lot of lunatics, and broke into the cuddy. And the ship running for her life, touch and go all the time, any minute her last in a sea fit to turn your hair gray only a-looking at it. I understand that the skipper, too, started raving like the rest of them. The man had been deprived of sleep for more than a week, and to have this sprung on him at the height of a furious gale nearly drove him out of his mind. I wonder they didn't fling me overboard after getting the carcass of their precious shipmate out of my fingers. They had rather a job to separate us, I've been told. A sufficiently fierce story to make an old judge and a respectable jury sit up a bit. The first thing I heard when I came to myself was the maddening howling of that endless gale, and on that the voice of the old man. He was hanging on to my bunk, staring into my face out of his sou'wester.

"'Mr. Leggatt, you have killed a man. You can act no longer as chief mate of this ship.'"

His care to subdue his voice made it sound monotonous. He rested a hand on the end of the skylight to steady himself with, and all that time did not stir a limb, so far as I could see. "Nice little tale for a quiet tea party," he concluded in the same tone.

One of my hands, too, rested on the end of the skylight; neither did I stir a limb, so far as I knew. We stood less than a foot from each other. It occurred to me that if old "Bless my soul — you don't say so" were to put his head up the companion and catch sight of us, he would think he was seeing double, or imagine himself come upon a scene of weird witchcraft; the strange captain having a quiet confabulation by the wheel with his own gray ghost. I became very much concerned to prevent anything of the sort. I heard the other's soothing undertone.

"My father's a parson in Norfolk," it said. Evidently he had forgotten he had told me this important fact before. Truly a nice little tale.

"You had better slip down into my stateroom now," I said, moving off stealthily. My double followed my movements; our bare feet made no sound; I let him in, closed the door with care, and, after giving a call to the second mate, returned on deck for my relief.

"Not much sign of any wind yet," I remarked when he approached.

"No, sir. Not much," he assented, sleepily, in his hoarse voice, with just enough deference, no more, and barely suppressing a yawn.

"Well, that's all you have to look out for. You have got your orders."

"Yes, sir."

I paced a turn or two on the poop and saw him take up his position face forward with his elbow in the ratlines of the mizzen-rigging before I went below. The mate's faint snoring was still going on peacefully. The cuddy lamp was burning over the table on which stood a vase with flowers, a polite attention from the ship's provision merchant — the last flowers we should see for the next three months at the very least. Two bunches of bananas hung from the beam symmetrically, one on each side of the rudder-casing. Everything was as before in the ship — except that two of her captain's sleeping suits were simultaneously in use, one motionless in the cuddy, the other keeping very still in the captain's stateroom.

It must be explained here that my cabin had the form of the capital letter L the door being within the angle and opening into the short part of the letter. A couch was to the left, the bed-place to the right; my writing desk and the chronometers' table faced the door. But anyone opening it, unless he stepped right inside, had no view of what I call the long (or vertical) part of the letter. It contained some lockers surmounted by a bookcase; and a few clothes, a thick jacket or two, caps, oilskin coat, and suchlike, hung on hooks.

There was at the bottom of that part a door opening into my bathroom, which could be entered also directly from the saloon. But that way was never used.

The mysterious arrival had discovered the advantage of this particular shape. Entering my room, lighted strongly by a big bulkhead lamp swung on gimbals [1] above my writing desk, I did not see him anywhere till he stepped out quietly from behind the coats hung in the recessed part.

"I heard somebody moving about, and went in there at once," he whispered.

I, too, spoke under my breath.

"Nobody is likely to come in here without knocking and getting permission."

He nodded. His face was thin and the sunburn faded, as though he had been ill. And no wonder. He had been, I heard presently, kept under arrest in his cabin for nearly seven weeks. But there was nothing sickly in his eyes or in his expression. He was not a bit like me, really; yet, as we stood leaning over my bed-place, whispering side by side, with our dark heads together and our backs to the door, anybody bold enough to open it stealthily would have been treated to the uncanny sight of a double captain busy talking in whispers with his other self.

"But all this doesn't tell me how you came to hang on to our side-ladder," I inquired, in the hardly audible murmurs we used, after he had told me something more of the proceedings on board the *Sephora* once the bad weather was over.

"When we sighted Java Head [2] I had had time to think all those matters out several times over. I had six weeks of doing nothing else, and with only an hour or so every evening for a tramp on the quarter-deck."

[1] **gimbals**: pivots. A bulkhead on a ship is a partition between compartments. Lamps were hung on pivots to let them tip in any direction and still remain level when the ship rocked.

[2] **Java Head**: you will find the places here mentioned on maps of the Malay Archipelago. Sunda Straits lie between Java and Sumatra. The *Sephora* had apparently gone south from Cardiff, Wales, around the Cape of Good Hope, and up through the Indian Ocean, between Java and Sumatra, to the Gulf of Siam. Somewhere near the Cape of Good Hope, in latitude 39 south, it encountered the fierce storm described in the story.

He whispered, his arms folded on the side of my bed-place, staring through the open port. And I could imagine perfectly the manner of this thinking out — a stubborn if not a steadfast operation; something of which I should have been perfectly incapable.

"I reckoned it would be dark before we closed with the land," he continued, so low that I had to strain my hearing, near as we were to each other, shoulder touching shoulder almost. "So I asked to speak to the old man. He always seemed very sick when he came to see me — as if he could not look me in the face. You know, that foresail saved the ship. She was too deep to have run long under bare poles. And it was I that managed to set it for him. Anyway, he came. When I had him in my cabin — he stood by the door looking at me as if I had the halter around my neck already — I asked him right away to leave my cabin door unlocked at night while the ship was going through Sunda Straits. There would be the Java coast within two or three miles, off Angier Point. I wanted nothing more. I've had a prize for swimming my second year in the Conway."

"I can believe it," I breathed out.

"God only knows why they locked me in every night. To see some of their faces you'd have thought they were afraid I'd go about at night strangling people. Am I a murdering brute? Do I look it? By Jove! If I had been, he wouldn't have trusted himself like that into my room. You'll say I might have chucked him aside and bolted out, there and then — it was dark already. Well, no. And for the same reason I wouldn't think of trying to smash the door. There would have been a rush to stop me at the noise, and I did not mean to get into a confounded scrimmage. Somebody else might have got killed — for I would not have broken out only to get chucked back, and I did not want any more of that work. He refused, looking more sick than ever. He was afraid of the men, and also of that old second mate of his who had been sailing with him for years — a gray-headed old humbug; and his steward, too, had been with him devil knows how long — seventeen years or more — a dogmatic sort of loafer who hated me like poison, just because I was the chief mate. No chief mate ever made more than one voyage in the *Sephora*, you know. Those two old chaps ran the ship. Devil only knows what the skipper wasn't afraid of (all his nerve went to pieces altogether in that hellish spell of bad weather we had) — of what the law would do to him — of his wife, perhaps. Oh, yes! she's on board. Though I don't think she would have meddled. She would have been only too glad to have me out of the ship in any way. The 'brand of Cain'[1] business, don't you see. That's all right. I was ready enough to go off wandering on the face of the earth — and that was price enough to pay for an Abel of that sort. Anyhow, he wouldn't listen to me. 'This thing must take its course. I represent the law here.' He was shaking like a leaf. 'So you won't?' 'No!' 'Then I hope you will be able to sleep on that,' I said, and turned my back on him. 'I wonder that *you* can,' cries he, and locks the door.

"Well, after that, I couldn't. Not very well. That was three weeks ago. We have had a slow passage through the Java Sea; drifted about Carimata[2] for ten days. When we anchored here they thought, I suppose, it was all right. The nearest land (and that's five miles) is the ship's destination; the consul would soon set about catching me; and there would have been no object in bolting to these islets there. I don't suppose there's a drop of water on them. I don't know how it was, but tonight that steward, after bringing me my supper, went out to let me eat it, and left the door unlocked. And I ate it — all there was, too. After I had finished I strolled out on the quarter-deck. I don't know that I meant to do anything. A breath of fresh air was all I wanted, I believe. Then a sudden temptation came over me. I kicked off my slippers and was in the water before I had made up my mind fairly. Somebody heard the splash and they raised an awful hullabaloo. 'He's gone! Lower the boats! He's committed suicide! No, he's swimming.' Certainly I was swimming. It's not so easy for a swimmer like me to commit suicide by drowning. I landed on the nearest islet before the boat left the ship's side. I heard them pulling about in the dark, hailing, and so on, but after a bit they gave up. Everything quieted down and the anchorage became as still as death. I sat down on a stone and began to think. I felt certain they would start searching for me at daylight. There was no place to hide on those stony things — and if there had been, what would have been the good? But now I was clear of that ship, I was not going back. So

[1] **brand of Cain**: Cain was branded on the forehead so that all men would know he had murdered Abel.

[2] **Carimata**: between Sumatra and Borneo.

after a while I took off all my clothes, tied them up in a bundle with a stone inside, and dropped them in the deep water on the outer side of that islet. That was suicide enough for me. Let them think what they liked, but I didn't mean to drown myself. I meant to swim till I sank—but that's not the same thing. I struck out for another of these little islands, and it was from that one that I first saw your riding light. Something to swim for. I went on easily, and on the way I came upon a flat rock a foot or two above water. In the daytime, I dare say, you might make it out with a glass from your poop. I scrambled up on it and rested myself for a bit. Then I made another start. That last spell must have been over a mile."

His whisper was getting fainter and fainter, and all the time he stared straight out through the porthole, in which there was not even a star to be seen. I had not interrupted him. There was something that made comment impossible in his narrative, or perhaps in himself; a sort of feeling, a quality, which I can't find a name for. And when he ceased, all I found was a futile whisper: "So you swam for our light?"

"Yes—straight for it. It was something to swim for. I couldn't see any stars low down because the coast was in the way, and I couldn't see the land, either. The water was like glass. One might have been swimming in a confounded thousand-feet deep cistern with no place for scrambling out anywhere; but what I didn't like was the notion of swimming round and round like a crazed bullock before I gave out; and as I didn't mean to go back . . . No. Do you see me being hauled back, stark naked, off one of these little islands by the scruff of the neck and fighting like a wild beast? Somebody would have got killed for certain, and I did not want any of that. So I went on. Then your ladder——"

"Why didn't you hail the ship?" I asked, a little louder.

He touched my shoulder lightly. Lazy footsteps came right over our heads and stopped. The second mate had crossed from the other side of the poop and might have been hanging over the rail, for all we knew.

"He couldn't hear us talking—could he?" My double breathed into my very ear, anxiously.

His anxiety was an answer, a sufficient answer, to the question I had put to him. An answer containing all the difficulty of that situation. I closed the porthole quietly, to make sure. A louder word might have been overheard.

"Who's that?" he whispered then.

"My second mate. But I don't know much more of the fellow than you do."

And I told him a little about myself. I had been appointed to take charge while I least expected anything of the sort, not quite a fortnight ago. I didn't know either the ship or the people. Hadn't had the time in port to look about me or size anybody up. And as to the crew, all they knew was that I was appointed to take the ship home. For the rest, I was almost as much of a stranger on board as himself, I said. And at the moment I felt it most acutely. I felt that it would take very little to make me a suspect person in the eyes of the ship's company.

He had turned about meantime; and we, the two strangers in the ship, faced each other in identical attitudes.

"Your ladder ——" he murmured, after a silence. "Who'd have thought of finding a ladder hanging over at night in a ship anchored out here! I felt just then a very unpleasant faintness. After the life I've been leading for nine weeks, anybody would have got out of condition. I wasn't capable of swimming round as far as your rudder chains. And, lo and behold! there as a ladder to get hold of. After I gripped it I said to myself, 'What's the good?' When I saw a man's head looking over I thought I would swim away presently and leave him shouting — in whatever language it was. I didn't mind being looked at. I — I liked it. And then you speaking to me so quietly — as if you had expected me — made me hold on a little longer. It had been a confounded lonely time — I don't mean while swimming. I was glad to talk a little to somebody that didn't belong to the *Sephora*. As to asking for the captain, that was a mere impulse. It could have been no use, with all the ship knowing about me and the other people pretty certain to be round here in the morning. I don't know — I wanted to be seen, to talk to somebody, before I went on. I don't know what I would have said. . . . 'Fine night, isn't it?' or something of the sort."

"Do you think they will be round here presently?" I asked with some incredulity.

"Quite likely," he said, faintly.

He looked extremely haggard all of a sudden. His head rolled on his shoulders.

"H'm. We shall see then. Meantime get into that bed," I whispered. "Want help? There."

It was a rather high bed-place with a set of drawers underneath. This amazing swimmer really needed the lift I gave him by seizing his leg. He tumbled in, rolled over on his back, and flung one arm across his eyes. And then, with his face nearly hidden, he must have looked exactly as I used to look in that bed. I gazed upon my other self for a while before drawing across carefully the two green serge curtains, which ran on a brass rod. I thought for a moment of pinning them together for greater safety, but I sat down on the couch, and once there I felt unwilling to rise and hunt for a pin. I would do it in a moment. I was extremely tired, in a peculiarly intimate way, by the strain of stealthiness, by the effort of whispering and the general secrecy of this excitement. It was three o'clock by now and I had been on my feet since nine, but I was not sleepy; I could not have gone to sleep. I sat there, fagged out, looking at the curtains, trying to clear my mind of the confused sensation of being in two places at once, and greatly bothered by an exasperating knocking in my head. It was a relief to discover suddenly that it was not in my head at all, but on the outside of the door. Before I could collect myself, the words "Come in" were out of my mouth, and the steward entered with a tray, bringing in my morning coffee. I had slept, after all, and I was so frightened that I shouted, "This way! I am here, Steward," as though he had been miles away. He put down the tray on the table next the couch and only then said, very quietly, "I can see you are here, sir." I felt him give me a keen look, but I dared not meet his eyes just then. He must have wondered why I had drawn the curtains of my bed before going to sleep on the couch. He went out, hooking the door open as usual.

I heard the crew washing decks above me. I knew I would have been told at once if there had been any wind. Calm, I thought, and I was doubly vexed. Indeed, I felt dual more than ever. The steward reappeared suddenly in the doorway. I jumped up from the couch so quickly that he gave a start.

"What do you want here?"

"Close your port, sir—they are washing decks."

"It is closed," I said, reddening.

"Very well, sir." But he did not move from the doorway and returned my stare in an extraordinary, equivocal manner for a time. Then his eyes wavered, all his expression changed, and in a voice unusually gentle, almost coaxingly:

"May I come in to take the empty cup away, sir?"

"Of course!" I turned my back on him while he popped in and out. Then I unhooked and closed the door and even pushed the bolt. This sort of thing could not go on very long. The cabin was as hot as an oven, too. I took a peep at my double, and discovered that he had not moved, his arm was still over his eyes; but his chest heaved; his hair was wet; his chin glistened with perspiration. I reached over him and opened the port.

"I must show myself on deck," I reflected.

Of course, theoretically, I could do what I liked, with no one to say nay to me within the whole circle of the horizon; but to lock my cabin door and take the key away I did not dare. Directly I put my head out of the companion I saw the group of my two officers, the second mate barefooted, the chief mate in long India-rubber boots, near the break of the poop, and the steward halfway down the poop ladder talking to them eagerly. He happened to catch sight of me and dived, the second ran down on the main deck shouting some order or other, and the chief mate came to meet me, touching his cap.

There was a sort of curiosity in his eye that I did not like. I don't know whether the steward had told them that I was "queer" only, or downright drunk, but I know the man meant to have a good look at me. I watched him coming with a smile which, as he got into point-blank range, took effect and froze his very whiskers. I did not give him time to open his lips.

"Square the yards by lifts and braces before the hands go to breakfast."

It was the first particular order I had given on board that ship; and I stayed on deck to see it executed, too. I had felt the need of asserting myself without loss of time. That sneering young cub got taken down a peg or two on that occasion, and I also seized the opportunity of having a good look at the face of every foremast man as they filed past me to go to the after braces. At breakfast time, eating nothing myself, I presided with such frigid dignity that the two mates were only too glad to escape from the cabin as soon as decency permitted; and all the time the dual working of my mind distracted me almost to the point of insanity. I was constantly watching myself, my secret self, as dependent on my actions as my own personality, sleeping in that bed, behind that door which faced me as I sat at the head of the table. It was very much like being mad, only it was worse because one was aware of it.

I had to shake him for a solid minute, but when at last he opened his eyes it was in the full possession of his senses, with an inquiring look.

" All's well so far," I whispered. " Now you must vanish into the bathroom."

He did so, as noiseless as a ghost, and then I rang for the steward, and facing him boldly, directed him to tidy up my stateroom while I was having my bath — " and be quick about it." As my tone admitted of no excuses, he said, " Yes, sir," and ran off to fetch his dustpan and brushes. I took a bath and did most of my dressing, splashing, and whistling softly for the steward's edification, while the secret sharer of my life stood drawn up bolt upright in that little space, his face looking very sunken in daylight, his eyelids lowered under the stern, dark line of his eyebrows drawn together by a slight frown.

When I left him there to go back to my room the steward was finishing dusting. I sent for the mate and engaged him in some insignificant conversation. It was, as it were, trifling with the terrific character of his whiskers; but my object was to give him an opportunity for a good look at my cabin. And then I could at last shut, with a clear conscience, the door of my stateroom and get my double back into the recessed part. There was nothing else for it. He had to sit still on a small folding stool, half smothered by the heavy coats hanging there. We listened to the steward going into the bathroom out of the saloon, filling the water bottles there, scrubbing the bath, setting things to rights, whisk, bang, clatter — out again into the saloon — turn the key — click. Such was my scheme for keeping my second self invisible. Nothing better could be contrived under the circumstances. And there we sat; I at my writing desk ready to appear busy with some papers, he behind me out of sight of the door.

It would not have been prudent to talk in daytime; and I could not have stood the excitement of that queer sense of whispering to myself. Now and then, glancing over my shoulder, I saw him far back there, sitting rigidly on the low stool, his bare feet close together, his arms folded, his head hanging on his breast — and perfectly still. Anybody would have taken him for me.

I was fascinated by it myself. Every moment I had to glance over my shoulder. I was looking at him when a voice outside the door said:

"Beg pardon, sir."

"Well!" . . . I kept my eyes on him, and so, when the voice outside the door announced, "There's a ship's boat coming our way, sir," I saw him give a start — the first movement he had made for hours. But he did not raise his bowed head.

"All right. Get the ladder over."

I hesitated. Should I whisper something to him? But what? His immobility seemed to have been never disturbed. What could I tell him he did not know already? . . . Finally I went on deck.

II

The skipper of the *Sephora* had a thin red whisker all round his face, and the sort of complexion that goes with hair of that color; also the particular, rather smeary shade of blue in the eyes. He was not exactly a showy figure; his shoulders were high, his stature but middling — one leg slightly more bandy than the other. He shook hands, looking vaguely around. A spiritless tenacity was his main characteristic, I judged. I behaved with a politeness which seemed to disconcert him. Perhaps he was shy. He mumbled to me as if he were ashamed of what he was saying; gave his name (it was something like Archbold — but at this distance of years I hardly am sure), his ship's name, and a few other particulars of that sort, in the manner of a criminal making a reluctant and doleful confession. He had had terrible weather on the passage out — terrible — terrible — wife aboard, too.

By this time we were seated in the cabin and the steward brought in a tray with a bottle and glasses. "Thanks! No." Never took liquor. Would have some water, though. He drank two tumblerfuls.

Terrible thirsty work. Ever since daylight had been exploring the islands round his ship.

"What was that for — fun?" I asked, with an appearance of polite interest.

"No!" He sighed. "Painful duty."

As he persisted in his mumbling and I wanted my double to hear every word, I hit upon the notion of informing him that I regretted to say I was hard of hearing.

"Such a young man, too!" he nodded, keeping his smeary blue, unintelligent eyes fastened upon me. "What was the cause of it — some disease?" he inquired, without the least sympathy and as if he thought that, if so, I'd got no more than I deserved.

"Yes; disease," I admitted in a cheerful tone which seemed to shock him. But my point was gained, because he had to raise his voice to give me his tale. It is not worth while to record that version. It was just over two months since all this had happened, and he had thought so much about it that he seemed completely muddled as to its bearings, but still immensely impressed.

"What would you think of such a thing happening on board your own ship? I've had the *Sephora* for these fifteen years. I am a well-known shipmaster."

He was densely distressed — and perhaps I should have sympathized with him if I had been able to detach my mental vision from the unsuspected sharer of my cabin as though he were my second self. There he was on the other side of the bulkhead, four or five feet from us, no more, as we sat in the saloon. I looked politely at Captain Archbold (if that was his name), but it was the other I saw, in a gray sleeping suit, seated on a low stool, his bare feet close together, his arms folded, and every word said between us falling into the ears of his dark head bowed on his chest.

"I have been at sea now, man and boy, for seven-and-thirty years, and I've never heard of such a thing happening in an English ship. And that it should be my ship. Wife on board, too."

I was hardly listening to him.

"Don't you think," I said, "that the heavy sea which, you told me, came aboard just then might have killed the man? I have seen the sheer weight of a sea kill a man very neatly, by simply breaking his neck."

"Good God!" he uttered, impressively, fixing his smeary blue eyes on me. "The sea! No man killed by the sea ever looked like that." He seemed positively scandalized at my suggestion. And as I gazed at him, certainly not prepared for anything original on his part, he advanced his head close to mine and thrust his tongue out at me so suddenly that I couldn't help starting back.

After scoring over my calmness in this graphic way he nodded wisely. If I had seen the sight, he assured me, I would never forget it as long as I lived. The weather was too bad to give the corpse a proper sea burial. So next day at dawn they took it up on the poop, covering its face with a bit of bunting; he read a short prayer, and then, just as it was, in its oilskins and long boots, they launched it amongst those mountainous seas that seemed ready every moment to swallow up the ship herself and the terrified lives on board of her.

"That reefed foresail saved you," I threw in.

"Under God—it did," he exclaimed fervently. "It was by a special mercy, I firmly believe, that it stood some of those hurricane squalls."

"It was the setting of that sail which——" I began.

"God's own hand in it," he interrupted me. "Nothing less could have done it. I don't mind telling you that I hardly dared give the order. It seemed impossible that we could touch anything without losing it, and then our last hope would have been gone."

The terror of that gale was on him yet. I let him go on for a bit, then said, casually—as if returning to a minor subject:

"You were very anxious to give up your mate to the shore people, I believe?"

He was. To the law. His obscure tenacity on that point had in it something incomprehensible and a little awful; something, as it were, mystical, quite apart from his anxiety that he should not be suspected of "countenancing any doings of that sort." Seven-and-thirty virtuous years at sea, of which over twenty of immaculate command, and the last fifteen in the *Sephora,* seemed to have laid him under some pitiless obligation.

"And you know," he went on, groping shamefacedly amongst his feelings, "I did not engage that young fellow. His people had some interest with my owners. I was in a way forced to take him on. He looked very smart, very gentlemanly, and all that. But do you know — I never liked him, somehow. I am a plain man. You see he wasn't exactly the sort for the chief mate of a ship like the *Sephora*."

I had become so connected in thoughts and impressions with the secret sharer of my cabin that I felt as if I, personally, were being given to understand that I, too, was not the sort that would have done for the chief mate of a ship like the *Sephora*. I had no doubt of it in my mind.

"Not at all the style of man. You understand," he insisted, superfluously, looking hard at me.

I smiled urbanely. He seemed at a loss for a while.

"I suppose I must report a suicide."

"Beg pardon? "

"Sui-cide! That's what I'll have to write to my owners directly I get in."

"Unless you manage to recover before tomorrow," I assented, dispassionately. . . . "I mean, alive."

He mumbled something which I really did not catch, and I turned my ear to him in a puzzled manner. He fairly bawled:

"The land — I say, the mainland is at least seven miles off my anchorage."

"About that."

My lack of excitement, of curiosity, of surprise, of any sort of pronounced interest, began to arouse his distrust. But except for the felicitous pretence of deafness I had not tried to pretend anything. I had felt utterly incapable of playing the part of ignorance properly, and therefore was afraid to try. It is also certain that he had brought some ready-made suspicions with him, and that he viewed my politeness as a strange and unnatural phenomenon. And yet how else could I have received him? Not heartily! That was impossible for psychological reasons, which I need not state here. My only object was to keep off his inquiries. Surlily? Yes, but surliness might have provoked a point-blank question. From its novelty to him and from its nature, punctilious courtesy was the manner best calculated to restrain the man. But there was the danger of his breaking through my defense bluntly. I could not, I think, have met him by a direct lie, also for psychological (not moral) reasons. If he had only known how afraid I was of his putting my feeling of identity with the other to the test! But, strangely enough — (I thought of it only afterward) — I believe that he was not a little disconcerted by the reverse side of that weird situation, by something in me that reminded him of the man he was seeking — suggested a mysterious similitude to the young fellow he had distrusted and disliked from the first.

However that might have been, the silence was not very prolonged. He took another oblique step.

"I reckon I had no more than a two-mile pull to your ship. Not a bit more."

"And quite enough, too, in this awful heat," I said.

Another pause full of mistrust followed. Necessity, they say, is mother of invention, but fear, too, is not barren of ingenious suggestions. And I was afraid he would ask me point-blank for news of my other self.

"Nice little saloon, isn't it?" I remarked, as if noticing for the first time the way his eyes roamed from one closed door to the other. "And very well fitted out, too. Here, for instance," I continued, reaching over the back of my seat negligently and flinging the door open, "is my bathroom."

He made an eager movement, but hardly gave it a glance. I got up, shut the door of the bathroom, and invited him to have a look round, as if I were very proud of my accommodation. He had to rise and be shown round, but he went through the business without any raptures whatever.

"And now we'll have a look at my stateroom," I declared, in a voice as loud as I dared to make it, crossing the cabin to the starboard side with purposely heavy steps.

He followed me in and gazed around. My intelligent double had vanished. I played my part.

"Very convenient — isn't it?"

"Very nice. Very comf . . ." He didn't finish, and went out brusquely as if to escape from some unrighteous wiles of mine. But it was not to be. I had been too frightened not to feel vengeful; I felt I had him on the run, and I meant to keep him on the run. My polite insistence must have had something menacing in it, because he gave in suddenly. And I did not let him off a single item; mate's room, pantry, storerooms, the very sail locker which was also under the poop — he had to look into them all. When at last I showed him out on the quarter-deck he drew a long, spiritless sigh, and mumbled dismally that he must really be going back to his ship now. I desired my mate, who had joined us, to see to the captain's boat.

The man of whiskers gave a blast on the whistle which he used to wear hanging round his neck, and yelled, "*Sephora's* away!" My double down there in my cabin must have heard, and certainly could not feel more relieved than I. Four fellows came running out from somewhere forward and went over the side, while my own men, appearing on deck too, lined the rail. I escorted my visitor to the gangway ceremoniously, and nearly overdid it. He was a tenacious beast. On the very ladder he lingered, and in that unique, guiltily conscientious manner of sticking to the point:

"I say . . . you . . . you don't think that——"

I covered his voice loudly:

"Certainly not. . . . I am delighted. Good-by."

I had an idea of what he meant to say, and just saved myself by the privilege of defective hearing. He was too shaken generally to insist, but my mate, close witness of that parting, looked mystified and his face took on a thoughtful cast. As I did not want to appear as if I wished to avoid all communication with my officers, he had the opportunity to address me.

"Seems a very nice man. His boat's crew told our chaps a very extraordinary story, if what I am told by the steward is true. I suppose you had it from the captain, sir?"

"Yes. I had a story from the captain."

"A very horrible affair – isn't it, sir?"

"It is."

"Beats all these tales we hear about murders in Yankee ships."

"I don't think it beats them. I don't think it resembles them in the least."

"Bless my soul – you don't say so! But of course I've no acquaintance whatever with American ships, not I, so I couldn't go against your knowledge. It's horrible enough for me. . . . But the queerest part is that those fellows seemed to have some idea the man was hidden aboard here. They had really. Did you ever hear of such a thing?"

"Preposterous – isn't it?"

We were walking to and fro athwart the quarter-deck. No one

of the crew forward could be seen (the day was Sunday), and the mate pursued:

"There was some little dispute about it. Our chaps took offense. 'As if we would harbor a thing like that,' they said. 'Wouldn't you like to look for him in our coalhole?' Quite a tiff. But they made it up in the end. I suppose he did drown himself. Don't you, sir?"

"I don't suppose anything."

"You have no doubt in the matter, sir?"

"None whatever."

I left him suddenly. I felt I was producing a bad impression, but with my double down there it was most trying to be on deck. And it was almost as trying to be below. Altogether a nerve-trying situation. But on the whole I felt less torn in two when I was with him. There was no one in the whole ship whom I dared to take into my confidence. Since the hands had got to know his story, it would have been impossible to pass him off for anyone else, and an accidental discovery was to be dreaded now more than ever. . . .

The steward being engaged in laying the table for dinner, we could talk only with our eyes when I first went down. Later in the afternoon we had a cautious try at whispering. The Sunday quietness of the ship was against us; the stillness of air and water around her was against us; the elements, the men were against us – everything was against us in our secret partnership; time itself – for this could not go on forever. The very trust in Providence was, I suppose, denied to his guilt. Shall I confess that this thought cast me down very much? And as to the chapter of accidents which counts for so much in the book of success, I could only hope that it was closed. For what favorable accident could be expected?

"Did you hear everything?" were my first words as soon as we took up our position side by side, leaning over my bed-place.

He had. And the proof of it was his earnest whisper, "The man told you he hardly dared to give the order."

I understood the reference to be to that saving foresail.

"Yes. He was afraid of it being lost in the setting."

"I assure you he never gave the order. He may think he did, but he never gave it. He stood there with me on the break of the poop after the main-topsail blew away, and whimpered about our last hope – positively whimpered about it and nothing else – and the night coming on! To hear one's skipper go on like that in such weather was enough to drive any fellow out of his mind. It worked me up into a sort of desperation. I just took it into my own hands and went away from him, boiling, and —— But what's the use telling you? *You* know! . . . Do you think that if I had not been pretty fierce with them I should have got the men to do anything? Not it! The bo's'n perhaps? Perhaps! It wasn't a heavy sea – it was a sea gone mad! I suppose the end of the world will be something like that; and a man may have the heart to see it coming once and be done with it – but to have to face it day after day —— I don't blame anybody. I was precious little better than the rest. Only – I was an officer of that old coal wagon, anyhow —— "

"I quite understand," I conveyed that sincere assurance into his ear. He was out of breath with whispering; I could hear him pant slightly. It was all very simple. The same strung-up force which had given twenty-four men a chance, at least, for their lives, had, in a sort of recoil, crushed an unworthy mutinous existence.

But I had no leisure to weigh the merits of the matter – footsteps in the saloon, a heavy knock. "There's enough wind to get under way with, sir." Here was the call of a new claim upon my thoughts and even upon my feelings.

"Turn the hands up," I cried through the door. "I'll be on deck directly."

I was going out to make the acquaintance of my ship. Before I left the cabin our eyes met – the eyes of the only two strangers on board. I pointed to the recessed part where the little camp-stool awaited him and laid my finger on my lips. He made a gesture – somewhat vague – a little mysterious, accompanied by a faint smile, as if of regret.

This is not the place to enlarge upon the sensations of a man who feels for the first time a ship move under his feet to his own independent word. In my case they were not unalloyed. I was not wholly alone with my command; for there was that stranger in my cabin. Or rather, I was not completely and wholly with her. Part of me was absent. That mental feeling of being in two places at once affected me physically as if the mood of secrecy had penetrated my very soul. Before an hour had elapsed since the ship had begun to move, having occasion to ask the mate (he stood by my side) to take a compass bearing of the pagoda, I caught myself reaching up to his ear in whispers. I say I caught myself, but enough had escaped to startle the man. I can't describe it otherwise than by saying that he shied. A grave, preoccupied manner, as though he were in possession of some perplexing intelligence, did not leave him henceforth. A little later I moved away from the rail to look at the compass with such a stealthy gait that the helmsman noticed it—and I could not help noticing the unusual roundness of his eyes. These are trifling instances, though it's to no commander's advantage to be suspected of ludicrous eccentricities. But I was also more seriously affected. There are to a seaman certain words, gestures, that should in given conditions come as naturally, as instinctively as the winking of a menaced eye. A certain order should spring on to his lips without thinking; a certain sign should get itself made, so to speak, without reflection. But all unconscious alertness had abandoned me. I had to make an effort of will to recall myself back (from the cabin) to the conditions of the moment. I felt that I was appearing an irresolute commander to those people who were watching me more or less critically.

And, besides, there were the scares. On the second day out, for instance, coming off the deck in the afternoon (I had straw slippers on my bare feet) I stopped at the open pantry door and spoke to the steward. He was doing something there with his back to me. At the sound of my voice he nearly jumped out of his skin, as the saying is, and incidentally broke a cup.

"What on earth's the mater with you?" I asked, astonished.

He was extremely confused. "Beg your pardon, sir. I made sure you were in your cabin."

"You see I wasn't."

"No, sir. I could have sworn I had heard you moving in there not a moment ago. It's most extraordinary . . . very sorry, sir."

I passed on with an inward shudder. I was so identified with my secret double that I did not even mention the fact in those scanty, fearful whispers we exchanged. I suppose he had made some slight noise of some kind or other. It would have been miraculous if he hadn't at one time or another. And yet, haggard as he appeared, he looked always perfectly self-controlled, more than calm—almost invulnerable. On my suggestion he remained almost entirely in the bathroom, which, upon the whole, was the safest place. There could be really no shadow of an excuse for anyone ever wanting to go in there, once the steward had done with it. It was a very tiny place. Sometimes he reclined on the floor, his legs bent, his head sustained on one elbow. At others I would find him on the camp-stool, sitting in his gray sleeping suit and with his cropped dark hair like a patient, unmoved convict. At night I would smuggle him into my bed-place, and we would whisper together, with the regular footfalls of the officer of the watch passing and repassing over our heads. It was an infinitely miserable time. It was lucky that some tins of fine preserves were stowed in a locker in my stateroom; hard bread I could always get hold of; and so he lived on stewed chicken, *pâté de foie gras,* asparagus, cooked oysters, sardines — on all sorts of abominable sham delicacies out of tins. My early morning coffee he always drank; and it was all I dared do for him in that respect.

Every day there was the horrible maneuvering to go through so that my room and then the bathroom should be done in the usual way. I came to hate the sight of the steward, to abhor the voice of that harmless man. I felt that it was he who would bring on the disaster of discovery. It hung like a sword over our heads.

The fourth day out, I think (we were then working down the east side of the Gulf of Siam, tack for tack, in light winds and smooth water) — the fourth day, I say, of this miserable juggling with the unavoidable, as we sat at our evening meal, that man, whose slightest movement I dreaded, after putting down the dishes ran up on deck busily. This could not be dangerous. Presently he came down again; and then it appeared that he had remembered a coat of mine which I had thrown over a rail to dry after having been wetted in a shower which had passed over the ship in the afternoon. Sitting stolidly at the head of the table I became terrified at the sight of the garment on his arm. Of course he made for my door. There was no time to lose.

"Steward," I thundered. My nerves were so shaken that I could not govern my voice and conceal my agitation. This was the sort of thing that made my terrifically whiskered mate tap his forehead with his forefinger. I had detected him using that gesture while talking on deck with a confidential air to the carpenter. It was too far to hear a word, but I had no doubt that this pantomime could only refer to the strange new captain.

"Yes, sir," the pale-faced steward turned resignedly to me. It was this maddening course of being shouted at, checked without rhyme or reason, arbitrarily chased out of my cabin, suddenly called into it, sent flying out of his pantry on incomprehensible errands, that accounted for the growing wretchedness of his expression.

"Where are you going with that coat?"

"To your room, sir."

"Is there another shower coming?"

"I'm sure I don't know, sir. Shall I go up again and see, sir?"

"No! never mind."

My object was attained, as of course my other self in there would have heard everything that passed. During this interlude my two officers never raised their eyes off their respective plates; but the lip of that confounded cub, the second mate, quivered visibly.

I expected the steward to hook my coat on and come out at once. He was very slow about it; but I dominated my nervousness sufficiently not to shout after him. Suddenly I became aware (it could be heard plainly enough) that the fellow for some reason or other was opening the door of the bathroom. It was the end. The place was literally not big enough to swing a cat in. My voice died in my throat and I went stony all over. I expected to hear a yell of surprise and terror, and made a movement, but had not the strength to get on my legs. Everything remained still. Had my second self taken the poor wretch by the throat? I don't know what I could have done next moment if I had not seen the steward come out of my room, close the door, and then stand quietly by the sideboard.

"Saved," I thought. "But, no! Lost! Gone! He was gone!"

I laid my knife and folk down and leaned back in my chair. My head swam. After a while, when sufficiently recovered to speak in a steady voice, I instructed my mate to put the ship round at eight o'clock himself.

"I won't come on deck," I went on. "I think I'll turn in, and unless the wind shifts I don't want to be disturbed before midnight. I feel a bit seedy."

"You did look middling bad a little while ago," the chief mate remarked without showing any great concern.

They both went out, and I stared at the steward clearing the table. There was nothing to be read on that wretched man's face. But why did he avoid my eyes I asked myself. Then I thought I should like to hear the sound of his voice.

"Steward!"

"Sir!" Startled as usual.

"Where did you hang up that coat?"

"In the bathroom, sir." The usual anxious tone. "It's not quite dry yet, sir."

For some time longer I sat in the cuddy. Had my double vanished as he had come? But for his coming there was an explanation, whereas his disappearance would be inexplicable. . . . I went slowly into my dark room, shut the door, lighted the lamp, and for a time dared not turn round. When at last I did I saw him standing bolt upright in the narrow recessed part. It would not be true to say I had a shock, but an irresistible doubt of his bodily existence flitted through my mind. Can it be, I asked myself, that he is not visible to other eyes than mine? It was like being haunted. Motionless, with a grave face, he raised his hands slightly at me in a gesture which meant clearly, "Heavens! What a narrow escape!" Narrow indeed. I think I had come creeping quietly as near insanity as any man who has not actually gone over the border. That gesture restrained me, so to speak.

The mate with the terrific whiskers was now putting the ship on the other tack. In the moment of profound silence which follows upon the hands going to their stations I heard on the poop his raised voice: "Hard alee!" and the distant shout of the order repeated on the main deck. The sails, in that light breeze, made but a faint fluttering noise. It ceased. The ship was coming round slowly; I held my breath in the renewed stillness of expectation; one wouldn't have thought that there was a single living soul on her decks. A sudden brisk shout, "Mainsail haul!" broke the spell, and in the noisy cries and rush overhead of the men running away with the main brace [1] we two, down in my cabin, came together in our usual position by the bed-place.

He did not wait for my question. "I heard him fumbling here and just managed to squat myself down in the bath," he whispered to

[1] **main brace:** rope holding the yardarm of the mainsail.

me. "The fellow only opened the door and put his arm in to hang the coat up. All the same——"

"I never thought of that," I whispered back, even more appalled than before at the closeness of the shave, and marveling at that something unyielding in his character which was carrying him through so finely. There was no agitation in his whisper. Whoever was being driven distracted, it was not he. He was sane. And the proof of his sanity was continued when he took up the whispering again.

"It would never do for me to come to life again."

It was something that a ghost might have said. But what he was alluding to was his old captain's reluctant admission of the theory of suicide. It would obviously serve his turn—if I had understood at all the view which seemed to govern the unalterable purpose of his action.

"You must maroon me as soon as ever you can get amongst these islands off the Cambodge[1] shore," he went on.

"Maroon you! We are not living in a boy's adventure tale," I protested. His scornful whispering took me up.

"We aren't indeed! There's nothing of a boy's tale in this. But there's nothing else for it. I want no more. You don't suppose I am afraid of what can be done to me? Prison or gallows or whatever they may please. But you don't see me coming back to explain such things to an old fellow in a wig and twelve respectable tradesmen, do you? What can they know whether I am guilty or not—or of *what* I am guilty, either? That's my affair. What does the Bible say? 'Driven off the face of the earth.' Very well. I am off the face of the earth now. As I came at night so I shall go."

"Impossible!" I murmured. "You can't."

"Can't? . . . Not naked like a soul on the Day of Judgment. I shall freeze on to this sleeping suit. The Last Day is not yet—and . . . you have understood thoroughly. Didn't you?"

I felt suddenly ashamed of myself. I may say truly that I understood—and my hesitation in letting that man swim away from my ship's side had been a mere sham sentiment, a sort of cowardice.

"It can't be done now till next night," I breathed out. "The ship is on the off-shore tack and the wind may fail us."

"As long as I know that you understand," he whispered. "But

[1] **Cambodge: Cambodia, the west coast of Indo-China.**

of course you do. It's a great satisfaction to have got somebody to understand. You seem to have been there on purpose." And in the same whisper, as if we two whenever we talked had to say things to each other which were not fit for the world to hear, he added, " It's very wonderful."

We remained side by side talking in our secret way—but sometimes silent or just exchanging a whispered word or two at long intervals. And as usual he stared through the port. A breath of wind came now and again into our faces. The ship might have been moored in dock, so gently and on an even keel she slipped through the water, that did not murmur even at our passage, shadowy and silent like a phantom sea.

At midnight I went on deck, and to my mate's great surprise put the ship round on the other tack. His terrible whiskers flitted round me in silent criticism. I certainly should not have done it if it had been only a question of getting out of that sleepy gulf as quickly as possible. I believe he told the second mate, who relieved him, that it was a great want of judgment. The other only yawned. That intolerable cub shuffled about so sleepily and lolled against the rails in such a slack, improper fashion that I came down on him sharply.

" Aren't you properly awake yet? "

" Yes, sir! I am awake."

" Well, then, be good enough to hold yourself as if you were. And keep a lookout. If there's any current we'll be closing with some islands before daylight."

The east side of the gulf is fringed with islands, some solitary, others in groups. On the blue background of the high coast they seem to float on silvery patches of calm water, arid and gray, or dark green and rounded like clumps of evergreen bushes, with the larger ones, a mile or two long, showing the outlines of ridges, ribs of gray rock under the dank mantle of matted leafage. Unknown to trade, to travel, almost to geography, the manner of life they harbor is an unsolved secret. There must be villages—settlements of fishermen at least—on the largest of them, and some communication with the world is probably kept up by native craft. But all that forenoon, as we headed for them, fanned along by the faintest of breezes, I saw no sign of man or canoe in the field of the telescope I kept on pointing at the scattered group.

At noon I gave no orders for a change of course, and the mate's whiskers became much concerned and seemed to be offering themselves unduly to my notice. At last I said:

"I am going to stand right in. Quite in—as far as I can take her."

The stare of extreme surprise imparted an air of ferocity also to his eyes, and he looked truly terrific for a moment.

"We're not doing well in the middle of the gulf," I continued, casually. "I am going to look for the land breezes tonight."

"Bless my soul! Do you mean, sir, in the dark amongst the lot of all them islands and reefs and shoals?"

"Well—if there are any regular land breezes at all on this coast one must get close inshore to find them, mustn't one?"

"Bless my soul!" he exclaimed again under his breath. All that afternoon he wore a dreamy, contemplative appearance which in him was a mark of perplexity. After dinner I went into my stateroom as if I meant to take some rest. There we two bent our dark heads over a half-unrolled chart lying on my bed.

"There," I said. "It's got to be Koh-ring.[1] I've been looking at it ever since sunrise. It has got two hills and a low point. It must be inhabited. And on the coast opposite there is what looks like the mouth of a biggish river—with some town, no doubt, not far up. It's the best chance for you that I can see."

"Anything. Koh-ring let it be."

He looked thoughtfully at the chart as if surveying chances and distances from a lofty height—and following with his eyes his own figure wandering on the blank land of Cochin China, and then passing off that piece of paper clean out of sight into uncharted regions. And it was as if the ship had two captains to plan her course for her. I had been so worried and restless running up and down that I had not had the patience to dress that day. I had remained in my sleeping suit, with straw slippers and a soft floppy hat. The closeness of the heat in the gulf had been most oppressive, and the crew were used to see me wandering in that airy attire.

"She will clear the south point as she heads now," I whispered into his ear. "Goodness only knows when, though, but certainly

[1] **Koh-ring: you will find the Kohs, or islands, off the west coast of Indo-China.**

after dark. I'll edge her in to half a mile, as far as I may be able to judge in the dark —— "

"Be careful," he murmured, warningly — and I realized suddenly that all my future, the only future for which I was fit, would perhaps go irretrievably to pieces in any mishap to my first command.

I could not stop a moment longer in the room. I motioned him to get out of sight and made my way on the poop. That unplayful cub had the watch. I walked up and down for a while thinking things out, then beckoned him over.

"Send a couple of hands to open the two quarter-deck ports," I said, mildly.

He actually had the impudence, or else so forgot himself in his wonder at such an incomprehensible order, as to repeat:

"Open the quarter-deck ports! What for, sir? "

"The only reason you need concern yourself about is because I tell you to do so. Have them open wide and fastened properly."

He reddened and went off, but I believe made some jeering remark to the carpenter as to the sensible practice of ventilating a ship's quarter-deck. I know he popped into the mate's cabin to impart the fact to him because the whiskers came on deck, as it were by chance, and stole glances at me from below — for signs of lunacy or drunkenness, I suppose.

A little before supper, feeling more restless than ever, I rejoined, for a moment, my second self. And to find him sitting so quietly was surprising, like something against nature, inhuman.

I developed my plan in a hurried whisper.

"I shall stand in as close as I dare and then put her round. I will presently find means to smuggle you out of here into the sail locker, which communicates with the lobby. But there is an opening, a sort of square for hauling the sails out, which gives straight on the quarter-deck and which is never closed in fine weather, so as to give air to the sails. When the ship's way is deadened in stays [1] and all the hands are aft at the main-braces you will have a clear road to slip out and get overboard through the open quarter-deck port. I've had them both fastened up. Use a rope's end to lower yourself

[1] **When the ship's way is deadened in stays:** when the ship is going slowly while sails are changed from one direction to another. The ship is turning at the time.

into the water so as to avoid a splash — you know. It could be heard and cause some beastly complication."

He kept silent for a while, then whispered, "I understand."

"I won't be there to see you go," I began with an effort. "The rest . . . I only hope I have understood, too."

"You have. From first to last" — and for the first time there seemed to be a faltering, something strained in his whisper. He caught hold of my arm, but the ringing of the supper bell made me start. He didn't, though; he only released his grip.

After supper I didn't come below again till well past eight o'clock. The faint, steady breeze was loaded with dew; and the wet, darkened sails held all there was of propelling power in it. The night, clear and starry, sparkled darkly, and the opaque, lightless patches shifting slowly against the low stars were the drifting islets. On the port bow there was a big one more distant and shadowily imposing by the great space of sky it eclipsed.

On opening the door I had a back view of my very own self looking at a chart. He had come out of the recess and was standing near the table.

"Quite dark enough," I whispered.

He stepped back and leaned against my bed with a level, quiet glance. I sat on the couch. We had nothing to say to each other. Over our heads the officer of the watch moved here and there. Then I heard him move quickly. I knew what that meant. He was making for the companion; and presently his voice was outside my door.

"We are drawing in pretty fast, sir. Land looks rather close."

"Very well," I answered. "I am coming on deck directly."

I waited till he was gone out of the cuddy, then rose. My double moved too. The time had come to exchange our last whispers, for neither of us was ever to hear each other's natural voice.

"Look here! " I opened a drawer and took out three sovereigns. "Take this anyhow. I've got six and I'd give you the lot, only I must keep a little money to buy some fruit and vegetables for the crew from native boats as we go through Sunda Straits."

He shook his head.

"Take it," I urged him, whispering desperately. "No one can tell what —— "

He smiled and slapped meaningly the only pocket of the sleeping jacket. It was not safe, certainly. But I produced a large old silk handkerchief of mine, and tying the three pieces of gold in a corner, pressed it on him. He was touched, I suppose, because he took it at last and tied it quickly round his waist under the jacket, on his bare skin.

Our eyes met; several seconds elapsed, till, our glances still mingled, I extended my hand and turned the lamp out. Then I passed through the cuddy, leaving the door of my room wide open. . . . "Steward!"

He was still lingering in the pantry in the greatness of his zeal, giving a rub-up to a plated cruet stand the last thing before going to bed. Being careful not to wake up the mate, whose room was opposite, I spoke in an undertone.

He looked round anxiously. "Sir!"

"Can you get me a little hot water from the galley?"

"I am afraid, sir, the galley fire's been out for some time now."

"Go and see."

He fled up the stairs.

"Now," I whispered, loudly, into the saloon — too loudly, perhaps, but I was afraid I couldn't make a sound. He was by my side in an instant — the double captain slipped past the stairs — through the tiny dark passage . . . a sliding door. We were in the sail locker, scrambling on our knees over the sails. A sudden thought struck me. I saw myself wandering barefooted, bareheaded, the sun beating on my dark poll. I snatched off my floppy hat and tried hurriedly in the dark to ram it on my other self. He dodged and fended off silently. I wonder what he thought had come to me before he understood and suddenly desisted. Our hands met gropingly, lingered united in a steady, motionless clasp for a second. . . . No word was breathed by either of us when they separated.

I was standing quietly by the pantry door when the steward returned.

"Sorry, sir. Kettle barely warm. Shall I light the spirit lamp?"

"Never mind."

I came out on deck slowly. It was now a matter of conscience to shave the land as close as possible — for now he must go overboard whenever the ship was put in stays. Must! There could be no going back for him. After a moment I walked over to leeward and my heart flew into my mouth at the nearness of the land on the bow. Under any other circumstances I would not have held on a minute longer. The second mate had followed me anxiously.

I looked on till I felt I could command my voice.

"She will weather," I said then in a quiet tone.

"Are you going to try that, sir?" he stammed out incredulously.

I took no notice of him and raised my tone just enough to be heard by the helmsman.

"Keep her good full."

"Good full, sir."

The wind fanned my cheek, the sails slept, the world was silent. The strain of watching the dark loom of the land grow bigger and denser was too much for me. I had shut my eyes—because the ship must go closer. She must! The stillness was intolerable. Were we standing still?

When I opened my eyes the second view started my heart with a thump. The black southern hill of Koh-ring seemed to hang right over the ship like a towering fragment of the everlasting night. On that enormous mass of blackness there was not a gleam to be seen, not a sound to be heard. It was gliding irresistibly toward us, and yet seemed already within reach of the hand. I saw the vague figures of the watch grouped in the waist, gazing in awed silence.

"Are you going on, sir?" inquired an unsteady voice at my elbow.

I ignored it. I had to go on.

"Keep her full. Don't check her way. That won't do now," I said warningly.

"I can't see the sails very well," the helmsman answered me, in strange, quavering tones.

Was she close enough? Already she was, I won't say in the shadow of the land, but in the very blackness of it, already swallowed up, as it were, gone too close to be recalled, gone from me altogether.

"Give the mate a call," I said to the young man who stood at my elbow as still as death. "And turn all hands up."

My tone had a borrowed loudness reverberated from the height of the land. Several voices cried out together: "We are all on deck, sir."

Then stillness again, with the great shadow gliding closer, towering higher, without a light, without a sound. Such a hush had fallen on the ship that she might have been a bark of the dead floating in slowly under the very gate of Erebus.[1]

"My God! Where are we?"

It was the mate moaning at my elbow. He was thunderstruck, and as it were deprived of the moral support of his whiskers. He clapped his hands and absolutely cried out, "Lost!"

"Be quiet," I said, sternly.

He lowered his tone, but I saw the shadowy gesture of his despair. "What are we doing here?"

"Looking for the land wind."

He made as if to tear his hair, and addressed me recklessly.

"She will never get out. You have done it, sir. I knew it'd end in something like this. She will never weather, and you are too close now to stay. She'll drift ashore before she's round. O my God!"

I caught his arm as he was raising it to batter his poor devoted head, and shook it violently.

"She's ashore already," he wailed, trying to tear himself away.

"Is she? . . . Keep good full there!"

"Good full, sir," cried the helmsman in a frightened, thin, child-like voice.

I hadn't let go the mate's arm and went on shaking it. "Ready about, do you hear? You go forward" — shake — "and stop there" — shake — "and hold your noise" — shake — "and see these head-sheets properly overhauled" — shake, shake — shake.

And all the time I dared not look toward the land lest my heart should fail me. I released my grip at last and he ran forward as if fleeing for dear life.

I wondered what my double there in the sail locker thought of this commotion. He was able to hear everything — and perhaps he was able to understand why, on my conscience, it had to be thus close — no less. My first order "Hard alee!" re-echoed ominously under the towering shadow of Koh-ring as if I had shouted in a mountain gorge. And then I watched the land intently. In that smooth water and light wind it was impossible to feel the ship coming-to. No! I could not feel her. And my second self was making

[1] **Erebus:** in Greek mythology, the dark and gloomy place on the way to Hades.

now ready to slip out and lower himself overboard. Perhaps he was gone already . . . ?

The great black mass brooding over our very mastheads began to pivot away from the ship's side silently. And now I forgot the secret stranger ready to depart, and remembered only that I was a total stranger to the ship. I did not know her. Would she do it? How was she to be handled?

I swung the main yard [1] and waited helplessly. She was perhaps stopped, and her very fate hung in the balance, with the black mass of Koh-ring like the gate of the everlasting night towering over her taffrail.[2] What would she do now? Had she way on her yet? I stepped to the side swiftly, and on the shadowy water I could see nothing except a faint phosphorescent flash revealing the glassy smoothness of the sleeping surface. It was impossible to tell — and I had not learned yet the feel of my ship. Was she moving? What I needed was something easily seen, a piece of paper, which I could throw overboard and watch. I had nothing on me. To run down for it I didn't dare. There was no time. All at once my strained, yearning stare distinguished a white object floating within a yard of the ship's side. White on the black water. A phosphorescent flash passed under it. What was that thing? . . . I recognized my own floppy hat. It must have fallen off his head . . . and he didn't bother. Now I had what I wanted — the saving mark for my eyes. But I hardly thought of my other self, now gone from the ship, to be hidden forever from all friendly faces, to be a fugitive and a vagabond on the earth, with no brand of the curse on his sane forehead to stay a slaying hand . . . too proud to explain.

And I watched the hat — the expression of my sudden pity for his mere flesh. It had been meant to save his homeless head from the dangers of the sun. And now — behold — it was saving the ship, by serving me for a mark to help out the ignorance of my strangeness. Ha! It was drifting forward, warning me just in time that the ship had gathered sternway.

"Shift the helm," I said in a low voice to the seaman standing still like a statue.

1 **main yard:** the spar or pole which swings out from the mast and holds the bottom of the mainsail.

2 **taffrail:** rail at the stern of the ship.

The man's eyes glistened wildly in the binnacle light as he jumped round to the other side and spun round the wheel.

I walked to the break of the poop. On the overshadowed deck all hands stood by the forebraces waiting for my order. The stars ahead seemed to be gliding from right to left. And all was so still in the world that I heard the quiet remark "She's round," passed in a tone of intense relief between two seamen.

"Let go and haul."

The foreyards ran round with a great noise, amidst cheery cries. And now the frightful whiskers made themselves heard giving various orders. Already the ship was drawing ahead. And I was alone with her. Nothing! no one in the world should stand now between us, throwing a shadow on the way of silent knowledge and mute affection, the perfect communion of a seaman with his first command.

Walking to the taffrail, I was in time to make out, on the very edge of a darkness thrown by a towering black mass like the very gateway of Erebus—yes, I was in time to catch an evanescent glimpse of my white hat left behind to mark the spot where the secret sharer of my cabin and of my thoughts, as though he were my second self, had lowered himself into the water to take his punishment: a free man, a proud swimmer striking out for a new destiny.

READING WITH INSIGHT

1. Why does the captain keep the presence of the fugitive a secret? Why can't he simply tell the crew that he has taken another person on board?

2. If you try to locate the climax of the story, you will see that there are two climaxes, rather than one. What are they?

3. The two climaxes suggest that there are two lines of action in this story, two problems and two solutions about which Conrad holds you in suspense. The first concerns the refugee. How would you state that problem and the line of action that grows out of it?

4. The second problem is the captain's. How would you state it? You will see this part of the story more clearly if you can state how

the captain has changed by the end of the story. What does he know about himself and his ship at the start of the story? What at the end?

5. If you understand the captain's part of the story, you can see the real importance of his daring maneuver in moving the ship close to the shore. Was he confident that he could keep the ship afloat and moving in the offshore winds? Why did he go into such danger? Why did he take a chance?

6. What would have happened to the captain if the refugee had been discovered on the ship? Why did he take the chance of shielding and hiding the refugee? To put it another way, why did he not turn over the refugee to police or to the captain of the other ship?

7. Why did the captain speak so often of the refugee as his "double"? In what way was he the captain's double?

8. There are at least two possible explanations of the captain's attitude toward the refugee: (a) the captain felt that he might have done the same thing under the same circumstances, (b) the captain sees in the refugee a kind of "other self" who has the same problem as the captain. Decide on evidence in the story which explanation you prefer.

9. The captain is presented as a lonely man at the start of the story. How does this loneliness bear on the meaning of the story? Here is a quotation from Conrad's own definition of the artist. "The artist," says Conrad, "speaks to our capacity for delight, for wonder, to the sense of mystery surrounding our lives; to our sense of pity, and beauty, and pain; to the latent feeling of fellowship with all creation – and to the subtle but invincible conviction of solidarity that knits together the loneliness of innumerable hearts; to the solidarity in dreams, in joy, in sorrow, in aspirations, in illusions, in hope, in fear, which binds men to each other, which binds together all humanity . . ." Notice the emphasis on loneliness and fellowship and mystery. How does this quotation help you to understand the actions of the captain?

10. Conrad uses the hat floating on the sea as a kind of symbol. What does it stand for? How does it become a repayment by the refugee for his great debt to the captain?

11. *Whose* story is it? Are you more interested in what happens to the captain or to the refugee?

12. Why does Conrad have the captain tell the story? How would the story have been different if the refugee had told it?

13. Would you call the refugee a murderer? Does he get more or less punishment than he deserves?

14. Point out some passages in this story that are especially successful in helping you to understand the appearance, the sound, and the atmosphere of the sea.

If you like this story, you will be interested in

Conrad. *Youth.*
Typhoon.
The Lagoon.
Gaspar Ruiz.
Lord Jim (novel).
Stephen Crane. *The Open Boat.*
Wilbur Daniel Steele. *The Yellow Cat.*

RUDYARD KIPLING

The Incarnation of Krishna Mulvaney

Rudyard Kipling was one of the greatest storytellers that ever lived. He was not a philosophic writer like Hawthorne, or a writer interested in social problems like Wells or Galsworthy, or a writer who thought out every word of his story in advance and polished it and perfected it as did Katherine Anne Porter or Katherine Mansfield. But he could tell a story as none of these could. He came as close as any great writer to being a *natural* storyteller. He was the present-day version of the fireside narrator of primitive times who helped pass the cold and lonely nights by recalling the great days of the tribe, the adventures, the humor, and the strangeness of faraway times and places. In Kipling's hands, anything became a story. His imagination was so fertile, his sense of drama and humor and human interest was so sure, that he never told a poor story. He wrote equally well for children and for adults, and occasionally (as in his story "The Man Who Would Be King") he produced one of the great stories of all times.

India gave him many of his greatest characters and stories. He was born in India in 1865 and educated in England. He married an American woman and lived four years in Vermont, then traveled and resided in many parts of the world until his death in 1936. But India remained home base. Here he saw the drama of England's colonial expansion, the meeting of two races, the exotic life of a distant country, the mystery of the jungle, the robust and salty life of professional soldiers. He put all this into many of his greatest stories—like the one mentioned above, his novel *Kim*, the *Jungle Books*, *Plain Tales from the Hills*, and *Soldiers Three*. The following story is a fine example of Kipling's India stories.

Kipling's India, of course, was the India of the late nineteenth century

— long before the time of Gandhi and Nehru and the movement for freedom. India was a British crown colony in those years, and it was necessary to keep it garrisoned with English troops. These troops were not often called upon for severe or prolonged fighting, and the life they lived was often as happy-go-lucky as Kipling here describes it.

ONCE upon a time, very far from England, there lived three men who loved each other so greatly that neither man nor woman could come between them. They were in no sense refined, nor to be admitted to the outer door mats of decent folk, because they happened to be private soldiers in Her Majesty's Army; and private soldiers of our service have small time for self-culture. Their duty is to keep themselves and their accouterments specklessly clean, to refrain from getting drunk more often than is necessary, to obey their superiors, and to pray for a war. All these things my friends accomplished; and of their own motion threw in some fighting-work for which the Army Regulations did not call. Their fate sent them to serve in India, which is not a golden country, though poets have sung otherwise. There men die with great swiftness, and those who live suffer many and curious things. I do not think that my friends concerned themselves much with the social or political aspects of the East. They attended a not unimportant war on the northern frontier, another one on our western boundary, and a third in Upper Burma. Then their regiment sat still to recruit, and the boundless monotony of cantonment life was their portion. They were drilled morning and evening in the same dusty parade ground. They wandered up and down the same stretch of dusty white road, attended the same church and the same grogshop, and slept in the same lime-washed barn of a barrack for two long years. There was Mulvaney, the father in the craft, who had served with various regiments from Bermuda to Halifax, old in war, scarred, reckless, resourceful, and in his pious hours an unequaled soldier. To him turned for help and comfort six and a half feet of slow-moving, heavy-footed Yorkshireman, born on the wolds, bred in the dales, and educated chiefly among the carriers' carts at the back of York railway station. His name was Learoyd, and his chief virtue an unmitigated patience which helped him to win fights. How Ortheris, a fox terrier or a Cockney, ever came to be one of the trio, is a mystery which even today I cannot explain. "There was always three av us," Mulvaney used to say. "An' by the grace av God, so long as our service last, three av us they'll always be. 'Tis better so."

They desired no companionship beyond their own, and it was evil for any man of the regiment who attempted dispute with them Physical argument was out of the question as regarded Mulvaney and the Yorkshireman; and assault on Ortheris meant a combined attack from these twain — a business which no five men were anxious to have on their hands. Therefore they flourished, sharing their drinks, their tobacco, and their money; good luck and evil; battle and the chances of death, life and the chances of happiness from Calicut in southern, to Peshawur in northern India.[1]

Through no merit of my own it was my good fortune to be in a measure admitted to their friendship — frankly by Mulvaney from the beginning, sullenly and with reluctance by Learoyd, and suspiciously by Ortheris, who held to it that no man not in the army could fraternize with a redcoat.[2] "Like to like," said he. "I'm a bloomin' sodger — he's a bloomin' civilian. 'Taint natural — that's all."

But that was not all. They thawed progressively, and in the thawing told me more of their lives and adventures than I am ever likely to write.

Omitting all else, this tale begins with the Lamentable Thirst that was at the beginning of First Causes. Never was such a thirst — Mulvaney told me so. They kicked against their compulsory virtue, but the attempt was only successful in the case of Ortheris. He, whose talents were many, went forth into the highways and stole a dog from a "civilian" — *videlicet,*[3] some one, he knew not who, not in the Army. Now that civilian was but newly connected by marriage with the colonel of the regiment, and outcry was made

1 **northern India:** Calicut is Calcutta, near the eastern tip of India. Peshawar is at the northern tip, near the Khyber Pass, at the border of Afghanistan. The soldiers are apparently stationed at a cantonment in northwest India, perhaps in the Punjab.

2 **redcoat:** the British soldier wore a red uniform until near the time of World War I.

3 **videlicet:** that is to say, or namely.

from quarters least anticipated by Ortheris, and, in the end, he was forced, lest a worse thing should happen, to dispose at ridiculously unremunerative rates of as promising a small terrier as ever graced one end of a leading string. The purchase money was barely sufficient for one small outbreak which led him to the guardroom. He escaped, however, with nothing worse than a severe reprimand, and a few hours of punishment drill. Not for nothing had he acquired the reputation of being "the best soldier of his inches" in the regiment. Mulvaney had taught personal cleanliness and efficiency as the first articles of his companion's creed. "A dhirty man," he was used to say, in the speech of his kind, "goes to Clink [1] for a weakness in the knees, an' is coort-martialed for a pair av socks missin'; but a clane man, such as is an ornament to his service—a man whose buttons are gold, whose coat is wax upon him, an' whose 'couterments are widout a speck—*that* man may, spakin' in reason, do fwhat he likes an' dhrink from day to divil. That's the pride av bein' dacint."

We sat together, upon a day, in the shade of a ravine far from the barracks, where a watercourse used to run in rainy weather. Behind us was the scrub jungle, in which jackals, peacocks, the gray wolves of the Northwestern Provinces, and occasionally a tiger estrayed from Central India, were supposed to dwell. In front lay the cantonment, glaring white under a glaring sun; and on either side ran the broad road that led to Delhi.

It was the scrub that suggested to my mind the wisdom of Mulvaney taking a day's leave and going upon a shooting tour. The peacock is a holy bird throughout India, and he who slays one is in danger of being mobbed by the nearest villagers; but on the last occasion that Mulvaney had gone forth, he had contrived, without in the least offending local religious susceptibilities, to return with six beautiful peacock skins which he sold to profit. It seemed just possible then—

"But fwhat manner av use is ut to me goin' out widout a dhrink? The ground's powdher-dhry underfoot, an' ut gets unto the throat fit to kill," wailed Mulvaney, looking at me reproachfully. "An' a peacock is not a bird you can catch the tail av onless ye run. Can a man run on wather—an' jungle-wather too?"

[1] **Clink**: jail.

Ortheris had considered the question in all its bearings. He spoke, chewing his pipestem meditatively the while:

> " Go forth, return in glory,
> To Clusium's royal 'ome:
> An' round these bloomin' temples 'ang
> The bloomin' shields o' Rome.

You better go. You ain't like to shoot yourself. Me an' Learoyd 'll stay at 'ome an' keep shop — 'case of anythin' turnin' up. But you go out with a gas-pipe gun an' ketch the little peacockses or somethin'. You kin get one day's leave easy as winkin'. Go along an' get it, an' get peacockses or somethin'."

" Jock," said Mulvaney, turning to Learoyd, who was half-asleep under the shadow of the bank. He roused slowly.

" Sitha, Mulvaaney, go," said he.

And Mulvaney went; cursing his allies with Irish fluency and barrack-room point.

" Take note," said he, when he had won his holiday, and appeared dressed in his roughest clothes with the only other regimental fowling piece in his hand. " Take note, Jock, an' you Orth'ris, I am goin' in the face av my own will — all for to please you. I misdoubt anythin' will come av permiscuous huntin' afther peacockses in a desolit lan'; an' I know that I will lie down an' die wid thirrst. Me catch peacockses for you, ye lazy scutts — an' be sacrificed by the peasanthry — Ugh! "

He waved a huge paw and went away.

At twilight, long before the appointed hour, he returned empty-handed, much begrimed with dirt.

" Peacockses? " queried Ortheris from the safe rest of a barrack-room table whereon he was smoking cross-legged, Learoyd fast asleep on a bench.

" Jock," said Mulvaney, without answering, as he stirred up the sleeper. " Jock, can ye fight? Will ye fight? "

Very slowly the meaning of the words communicated itself to the half-roused man. He understood — and again — what might these things mean? Mulvaney was shaking him savagely. Meantime the men in the room howled with delight. There was war in the confederacy at last — war and the breaking of bonds.

Barrack-room etiquette is stringent. On the direct challenge must follow the direct reply. This is more binding than the ties of tried friendship. Once again Mulvaney repeated the question. Learoyd answered by the only means in his power, and so swiftly that the Irishman had barely time to avoid the blow. The laughter around increased. Learoyd looked bewilderedly at his friend — himself as greatly bewildered. Ortheris dropped from the table because his world was falling.

"Come outside," said Mulvaney, and as the occupants of the barrack room prepared joyously to follow, he turned and said furiously, "There will be no fight this night — onless any wan av you is wishful to assist. The man that does, follows on."

No man moved. The three passed out into the moonlight, Learoyd fumbling with the buttons of his coat. The parade ground was deserted except for the scurrying jackals. Mulvaney's impetuous rush carried his companions far into the open ere Learoyd attempted to turn round and continue the discussion.

"Be still now. 'Twas my fault for beginning things in the middle av an end, Jock. I should ha' comminst wid an explanation; but Jock, dear, on your sowl are ye fit, think you, for the finest fight that iver was — betther than fightin' me? Considher before ye answer."

More than ever puzzled, Learoyd turned round two or three times, felt an arm, kicked tentatively, and answered, "Ah'm fit." He was accustomed to fight blindly at the bidding of the superior mind.

They sat them down, the men looking on from afar, and Mulvaney untangled himself in mighty words.

"Followin' your fools' scheme I wint out into the thrackless desert beyond the barricks. An' there I met a pious Hindu dhriving a bullock-kyart. I tuk it for granted he wud be delighted for to convoy me a piece, an' I jumped in" —

"You long, lazy, black-haired swine," drawled Ortheris, who would have done the same thing under similar circumstances.

"'Twas the height av policy. That man dhruv miles an' miles — as far as the new railway line they're buildin' now back av the Tavi river. ''Tis a kyart for dhirt only,' says he now an' again timoreously, to get me out av ut. 'Dhirt I am,' sez I, 'an' the dhryest that you iver kyarted. Dhrive on, me son, an' glory be wid you.' At that I wint to slape, an' took no heed till he pulled up on the embankmint av the line where the coolies [1] were pilin' mud. There was a matther av two thousand coolies on that line — you remimber that. Prisintly a bell rang, an' they throops off to a big payshed. 'Where's the white man in charge? ' sez I to my kyart dhriver. 'In the shed,' sez he, 'engaged on a riffle.' — 'A fwhat? ' sez I. 'Riffle,' sez he. 'You take ticket. He take money. You get nothin'.' — 'Oho! ' sez I, 'that's fwhat the shuperior an' cultivated man calls a raffle, me misbeguided child av darkness an' sin. Lead on to that raffle, though fwhat the mischief 'tis doin' so far away from uts home — which is the charity bazaar at Christmas, an' the colonel's wife grinnin' behind the tea table — is more than I know.' Wid that I wint to the shed an' found 'twas payday among the coolies. Their wages was on a table forninst a big, fine, red buck av a man — sivun fut high, four fut wide, an' three fut thick, wid a fist on him like a corn-sack. He was payin' the coolies fair an' easy, but he wud ask each man if he wud raffle that month, an' each man sez, 'Yes,' av course. Thin he wud deduct from their wages accordin'. Whin all was paid, he filled an ould cigar box full av gun-wads an' scatthered ut among the coolies. They did not take much joy av that performince, an' small wondher. A man close to me picks up a black gun-wad an' sings out, 'I have ut.' — 'Good may ut do you,' sez I. The coolie wint forward to this big, fine, red man, who threw a cloth off av the most sumpshus, jooled, enameled an' variously bediviled sedan chair [2] I iver saw."

"Sedan chair! Put your 'ead in a bag. That was a palanquin. Don't yer know a palanquin when you see it? " said Ortheris with great scorn.

"I chuse to call ut sedan chair, an' chair ut shall be, little man," continued the Irishman. " 'Twas a most amazin' chair — all lined wid pink silk an' fitted wid red silk curtains. 'Here ut is,' sez the red man. 'Here ut is,' sez the coolie; then he grinned weakly-ways. 'Is ut any use to you? ' sez the red man. 'No,' sez the coolie; 'I'd like to make a prisint av ut to you.' — 'I am graciously pleased to accept that same,' sez the red man; an' at that all the coolies cried aloud in fwhat was mint for cheerful notes, an' wint back to their diggin', lavin' me alone in the shed. The red man saw me, an' his face grew

[1] **coolies:** native workers. Does not necessarily mean Chinese.

[2] **sedan chair:** a covered chair usually carried on poles by two men.

blue on his big, fat neck. 'Fwhat d'you want here? ' sez he. 'Standin' room an' no more,' sez I, 'onless it may be fwhat ye niver had, an' that's manners, ye raffling ruffian,' for I was not goin' to have the Service throd upon. 'Out of this,' sez he. 'I'm in charge av this section av construction.' — 'I'm in charge av mesilf,' sez I, 'an' it's like I will stay a while. D'ye raffle much in these parts? ' — 'Fwhat's that to you? ' sez he. 'Nothin',' sez I, 'but a great dale to you, for begad I'm thinkin' you get the full half av your revenue from that sedan chair. Is ut always raffled so? ' I sez, an' wid that I wint to a coolie to ask questions. Bhoys, that man's name is Dearsley, an' he's ben rafflin' that ould sedan chair monthly this matther av nine months. Ivry coolie on the section takes a ticket — or he gives 'em the go — wanst a month on payday. Ivry coolie that wins ut gives ut back to him, for 'tis too big to carry away, an' he'd sack the man that thried to sell ut. That Dearsley has been makin' the rowlin' wealth av Roshus by nefarious rafflin'. Think av the burning shame to the sufferin' coolie-man that the army in Injia are bound to protect an' nourish in their bosoms! Two thousand coolies defrauded wanst a month! "

"Dom t' coolies. Has't gotten t' cheer, man? " said Learoyd.

"Hould on. Havin' onearthed this amazin' an' stupenjus fraud committed by the man Dearsley, I hild a council av war; he thryin' all the time to sejuce me into a fight wid opprobrious language. That sedan chair niver belonged by right to any foreman av coolies. 'Tis a king's chair or a quane's. There's gold on ut an' silk an' all manner av trapesemints. Bhoys, 'tis not for me to countenance any sort av wrongdoin' — me bein' the ould man — but — anyway he has had ut nine months, an' he dare not make throuble av ut was taken from him. Five miles away, or ut may be six " —

There was a long pause and the jackals howled merrily. Learoyd bared one arm, and contemplated it in the moonlight. Then he nodded partly to himself and partly to his friends. Ortheris wriggled with suppressed emotion.

"I thought ye wud see the reasonableness av ut," said Mulvaney. "I make bould to say as much to the man before. He was for a direct front attack — fut, horse, an' guns — an' all for nothin', seein' that I had no thransport to convey the machine away. 'I will not argue wid you,' sez I, 'this day, but subsequintly, Mister Dearsley, one rafflin' jool, we talk ut out lengthways. 'Tis no good policy to swindle the coolie av his heard-earned emolumints, an' by presint informashin'—'twas the kyart man that tould me—'ye've been perpethrating that same for nine months. But I'm a just man,' sez I, 'an' overlookin' the presumpshin that yondher settee wid the gilt top was not come by honust'—at that he turned sky-green, so I knew things was more thrue than tellable—'not come by honust, I'm willin' to compound the felony for this month's winnin's.' "

"Ah! Ho!" from Learoyd and Ortheris.

"That man Dearsley's rushin' on his fate," continued Mulvaney, solemnly wagging his head. "All Hell had no name bad enough for me that tide. Faith, he called me a robber! Me! that was savin' him from continuin' in his evil ways widout a remonstrince—an' to a man av conscience a remonstrince may change the chune av his life. ''Tis not for me to argue,' sez I, 'fwhatever ye are, Mister Dearsley, but, by my hand, I'll take away the temptation for you that lies in that sedan chair.'—'You will have to fight me for ut,' sez he, 'for well I know you will never dare make report to any-one.'—'Fight I will,' sez I, 'but not this day, for I'm rejuced for want av nourishment.'—'Ye're an ould bould hand,' sez he, sizin' me up an' down; 'an' a jool av a fight we will have. Eat now an' dhrink, an' go your way.' Wid that he gave me some hump—an' we talked av this an' that the while. 'It goes hard on me now,' sez I, wipin' my mouth, 'to confiscate that piece av furniture, but justice is justice.'—'Ye've not got ut yet,' sez he; 'there's the fight between.' —'There is,' sez I, 'an' a good fight. Ye shall have the pick av the best quality in my rigimint for the dinner you have given this day.' Thin I came hotfoot to you two. Hould your tongue, the both. 'Tis this way. Tomorrow we three will go there an' he shall have his pick betune me an' Jock. Jock's a deceivin' fighter, for he is all fat to the eye, an' he moves slow. Now I'm all beef to the look, an' I move quick. By my reckonin' the Dearsley man won't take me; so me an' Orth'ris 'll see fair play. Jock, I tell you, 'twill be big fightin'—whipped, wid the cream above the jam. Afther the business 'twill take a good three av us—Jock'll be very hurt—to haul away that sedan chair."

"Palanquin." This from Ortheris.

"Fwhatever ut is, we must have ut. 'Tis the only sellin' piece av property widin reach that we can get so cheap. An' fwhat's a fight afther all? He has robbed the coolie, dishonust. We rob him honust."

"But wot'll we do with the bloomin' article when we've got it? Them palanquins are as big as 'ouses, an' uncommon 'ard to sell, as McCleary said when ye stole the sentry box."

"Who's goin' to do t' fightin'?" said Learoyd, and Ortheris subsided. The three returned to barracks without a word. Mulvaney's last argument clinched the matter. This palanquin was property, vendible, and to be attained in the simplest and least embarrassing fashion. It would eventually become beer. Great was Mulvaney.

Next afternoon a procession of three formed itself and disappeared into the scrub in the direction of the new railway line. Learoyd alone was without care, for Mulvaney dived darkly into the future, and little Ortheris feared the unknown. What befell at that interview in the lonely payshed by the side of the half-built embankment, only a few hundred coolies know, and their tale is a confusing one, running thus —

"We were at work. Three men in red coats came. They saw the Sahib [1] — Dearsley Sahib. They made oration; and noticeably the small man among the redcoats. Dearsley Sahib also made oration, and used many very strong words. Upon this talk they departed together to an open space, and there the fat man in the red coat fought with Dearsley Sahib after the custom of white men — with his hands, making no noise, and never at all pulling Dearsley Sahib's hair. Such of us as were not afraid beheld these things for just so long a time as a man needs to cook the midday meal. The small man in the red coat had possessed himself of Dearsley Sahib's watch. No, he did not steal that watch. He held it in his hand, and at certain seasons made outcry, and the twain ceased their combat, which was like the combat of young bulls in spring. Both men were soon all red, but Dearsley Sahib was much more red than the other. Seeing this, and fearing for his life — because we greatly loved him — some fifty of us made shift to rush upon the redcoats. But a certain man — very black as to the hair, and in no way to be confused with the small man, or the fat man who fought — that man, we affirm, ran upon us, and of us he embraced some ten or fifty in both arms,

[1] Sahib: the title used by natives when addressing, or speaking of, a European gentleman.

and beat our heads together, so that our livers turned to water, and we ran away. It is not good to interfere in the fightings of white men. After that Dearsley Sahib fell and did not rise, these men jumped upon his stomach and despoiled him of all his money, and attempted to fire the payshed, and departed. Is it true that Dearsley Sahib makes no complaint of these latter things having been done? We were senseless with fear, and do not at all remember. There was no palanquin near the payshed. What do we know about palanquins? Is it true that Dearsley Sahib does not return to this place, on account of his sickness, for ten days? This is the fault of those bad men in the red coats, who should be severely punished; for Dearsley Sahib is both our father and mother, and we love him much. Yet, if Dearsley Sahib does not return to this place at all, we will speak the truth. There was a palanquin, for the upkeep of which we were forced to pay nine-tenths of our monthly wage. On such mulctings Dearsley Sahib allowed us to make obeisance to him before the palanquin. What could we do? We were poor men. He took a full half of our wages. Will the Government repay us those moneys? Those three men in red coats bore the palanquin upon their shoulders and departed. All the money that Dearsley Sahib had taken from us was in the cushions of that palanquin. Therefore they stole. Thousands of rupees were there—all our money. It was our bank box, to fill which we cheerfully contributed to Dearsley Sahib three-sevenths of our monthly wage. Why does the white man look upon us with the eye of disfavor? There was a palanquin, and now there is no palanquin; and if they send the police here to make inquisition, we can only say that there never has been any palanquin. Why should a palanquin be near these works? We are poor men, and we know nothing."

Such is the simplest version of the simplest story connected with the descent upon Dearsley. From the lips of the coolies I received it. Dearsley himself was in no condition to say anything, and Mulvaney preserved a massive silence, broken only by the occasional licking of the lips. He had seen a fight so gorgeous that even his power of speech was taken from him. I respected that reserve until, three days after the affair, I discovered in a disused stable in my quarters a palanquin of unchastened splendor—evidently in past days the litter of a queen. The pole whereby it swung between the shoulders of the bearers was rich with the painted papier-mâché of Cashmere. The shoulder pads were of yellow silk. The panels of the litter itself were ablaze with the loves of all the gods and goddesses of the Hindu Pantheon — lacquer on cedar. The cedar sliding doors were fitted with hasps of translucent Jaipur enamel and ran in grooves shod with silver. The cushions were of brocaded Delhi silk, and the curtains which once hid any glimpse of the beauty of the king's palace were stiff with gold. Closer investigation showed that the entire fabric was everywhere rubbed and discolored by time and wear; but even thus it was sufficiently gorgeous to deserve housing on the threshold of a royal zenana.[1] I found no fault with it, except that it was in my stable. Then, trying to lift it by the silver-shod shoulder pole, I laughed. The road from Dearsley payshed to the cantonment was a narrow and uneven one, and, traversed by three very inexperienced palanquin-bearers, one of whom was sorely battered about the head, must have been a path of torment. Still I did not quite recognize the right of the three musketeers to turn me into a "fence" for stolen property.

"I'm askin' you to warehouse ut," said Mulvaney when he was brought to consider the question. "There's no steal in ut. Dearsley tould us we cud have ut if we fought. Jock fought — an', oh, sorr, when the throuble was at uts finest an' Jock was bleedin' like a stuck pig, an' little Orth'ris was shquealin' on one leg chewin' big bites out ab Dearsley's watch, I ud ha' given my place at the fight to have had you see wan round. He tuk Jock, as I suspicioned he would, an' Jock was deceptive. Nine roun's they were even matched, an' at the tenth — About that palanquin now. There's not the least throuble in the world, or we wud not ha' brought ut here. You will ondherstand that the Queen — God bless her! — does not reckon for a private soldier to kape elephints an' palanquins an' sich in barracks. Afther we had dhragged ut down from Dearsley's through that cruel scrub that near broke Orth'ris's heart, we set ut in the ravine for a night; an' a thief av a porcupine an' a civet cat av a jackal roosted in ut, as well we knew in the mornin'. I put ut to you, sorr, is an elegint palanquin, fit for the princess, the natural abidin' place av all the vermin in cantonmints? We brought ut to you afther dark, and put ut in your sthable. Do not

[1] **zenana**: the women's residence in a Hindu palace.

let your conscience prick. Think av the rejoicin' men in the payshed yonder — lookin' at Dearsley wid his head tied up in a towel — an' well knowin' that they can dhraw their pay ivry month widout stoppages for riffles. Indirectly, sorr, you have rescued from an onprincipled son av a nighthawk the peasanthry av a numerous village. An' besides, will I let that sedan chair rot on our hands? Not I. 'Tis not every day a piece av pure joolry comes into the market. There's not a king widin these forty miles" — he waved his hand round the dusty horizon — "not a king wud not be glad to buy ut. Some day meself, when I have leisure, I'll take ut up along the road an' dishpose av ut."

"How?" said I, for I knew the man was capable of anything.

"Get unto ut, av coorse, and keep wan eye open through the curtains. Whin I see a likely man av the native persuasion, I will descind blushin' from my canopy and say, 'Buy a palanquin, ye scutt?' I will have to hire four men to carry me first, though; and that's impossible till next payday."

Curiously enough, Learoyd, who had fought for the prize, and in the winning secured the highest pleasure life had to offer him, was altogether disposed to undervalue it, while Ortheris openly said it would be better to break the thing up. Dearsley, he argued, might be a many-sided man, capable, despite his magnificent fighting qualities, of setting in motion the machinery of the civil law — a thing much abhorred by the soldier. Under any circumstances their fun had come and passed; the next payday was close at hand, when there would be beer for all. Wherefore longer conserve the painted palanquin?

"A first-class rifleshot an' a good little man av your inches you are," said Mulvaney. "But you niver had a head worth a soft-boiled egg. 'Tis me has to lie awake av nights schamin' an' plottin' for the three av us. Orth'ris, me son, 'tis no matther av a few gallons av beer — no, nor twenty gallons — but tubs an' vats an' firkins in that sedan chair. Who ut was, an' what ut was, an' how ut got there, we do not know; but I know in my bones that you an' me an' Jock wid his sprained thumb will get a fortune thereby. Lave me alone, an' let me think."

Meantime the palanquin stayed in my stall, the key of which was in Mulvaney's hands.

Payday came, and with it beer. It was not in experience to hope that Mulvaney, dried by four weeks' drought, would avoid excess. Next morning he and the palanquin had disappeared. He had taken the precaution of getting three days' leave "to see a friend on the railway," and the colonel, well knowing that the seasonal outburst was near, and hoping it would spend its force beyond the limits of his jurisdiction, cheerfully gave him all he demanded. At this point Mulvaney's history, as recorded in the messroom, stopped.

Ortheris carried it not much further. "No, 'e wasn't drunk," said the little man loyally, "the liquor was no more than feelin' its way round inside of 'im; but 'e went an' filled that ole bloomin' palanquin with bottles 'fore he went off. 'E's gone an' 'ired six men to carry 'im, an' I 'ad to 'elp 'im in 'cause 'e wouldn't 'ear reason. 'E's gone off in 'is shirt an' trousies, swearin' tremenjus — gone down the road in the palanquin, wavin' 'is legs out o' windy."

"Yes," said I, "but where?"

"Now you arx me a question. 'E said 'e was goin' to sell that palanquin, but from observations what happened when I was stuffin' 'im through the door, I fancy 'e's gone to the new embankment to mock at Dearsley. 'Soon as Jock's off duty I'm goin' there to see if 'e's safe — not Mulvaney, but t'other man. My saints, but I pity 'im as 'elps Terence out o' the palanquin when 'e's once fair drunk!"

"He'll come back without harm," I said.

"'Corse 'e will. On'y question is, what'll 'e be doin' on the road? Killing Dearsley, like as not. 'E shouldn't 'a gone without Jock or me."

Reinforced by Learoyd, Ortheris sought the foreman of the coolie-gang. Dearsley's head was still embellished with towels. Mulvaney, drunk or sober, would have struck no man in that condition, and Dearsley indignantly denied that he would have taken advantage of the intoxicated brave.

"I had my pick o' you two," he explained to Learoyd, "and you got my palanquin — not before I'd made my profit on it. Why'd I do harm when everything's settled? Your man *did* come here — drunk as Davy's sow on a frosty night — came a-purpose to mock me — stuck his head out of the door an' called me a hodman. I made him drunker, an' sent him along. But I never touched him."

To these things Learoyd, slow to perceive the evidences of sincerity, answered only, "If owt comes to Mulvaney 'long o' you, I'll gripple you, clouts or no clouts on your ugly head, an' I'll draw t' throat twistways, man. See there, now."

The embassy removed itself, and Dearsley, the battered, laughed alone over his supper that evening.

Three days passed—a fourth and a fifth. The week drew to a close and Mulvaney did not return. He, his royal palanquin, and his six attendants, had vanished into air. A very large and very tipsy soldier, his feet sticking out of the litter of a reigning princess, is not a thing to travel along the ways without comment. Yet no man of all the country round had seen any such wonder. He was, and he was not; and Learoyd suggested the immediate smashment of Dearsley as a sacrifice to his ghost. Ortheris insisted that all was well, and in the light of past experience his hopes seemed reasonable.

"When Mulvaney goes up the road," said he, "'e's like to go a very long ways up. But what gits me 'is not bein' 'eard of pullin' wool off the natives somewheres about. That don't look good. The drink must ha' died out in 'im by this, unless 'e's broke a bank, an' then—Why don't 'e come back? 'E didn't ought to ha' gone off without us."

Even Ortheris's heart sank at the end of the seventh day, for half the regiment were out scouring the countryside, and Learoyd had been forced to fight two men who hinted openly that Mulvaney had deserted. To do him justice, the colonel laughed at the notion, even when it was put forward by his much-trusted adjutant.

"Mulvaney would as soon think of deserting as you would," said he. "No; he's either fallen into a mischief among the villagers—and yet that isn't likely, for he'd blarney himself out of the Pit;[1] or else he is engaged on urgent private affairs—some stupendous devilment that we shall hear of at mess after it has been the round of the barrack rooms. The worst of it is that I shall have to give him twenty-eight days' confinement at least for being absent without leave, just when I most want him to lick the new batch of recruits into shape. I never knew a man who could put a polish on young soldiers as quickly as Mulvaney can. How does he do it?"

"With blarney and the buckle-end of a belt, sir," said the adjutant. "He is worth a couple of non-commissioned officers when we are

[1] **the Pit:** Hades.

dealing with an Irish draft, and the London lads seem to adore him. The worst of it is that if he goes to the cells the other two are neither to hold nor to bind till he comes out again. I believe Ortheris preaches mutiny on those occasions, and I know that the mere presence of Learoyd mourning for Mulvaney kills all the cheerfulness of his room. The sergeants tell me that he allows no man to laugh when he feels unhappy. They are a queer gang."

"For all that, I wish we had a few more of them. I like a well-conducted regiment, but these pasty-faced, shifty-eyed, mealy-mouthed young slouchers from the depot worry me sometimes with their offensive virtue. They don't seem to have backbone enough to do anything but play cards and prowl around the married quarters. I believe I'd forgive that old villain on the spot if he turned up with any sort of explanation that I could in decency accept."

"Not likely to be much difficulty about that, sir," said the adjutant. "Mulvaney's explanations are only one degree less wonderful than his performances. They say that when he was in the Black Tyrone,[1] before he came to us, he was discovered on the banks of the Liffey trying to sell his colonel's charger to a Donegal dealer as a perfect lady's hack. Shackbolt commanded the Tyrone then."

"Shackbolt must have had apoplexy at the thought of his ramping war horses answering to that description. He used to buy unbacked devils, and tame them on some pet theory of starvation. What did Mulvaney say?"

"That he was a member of the Society for the Prevention of Cruelty to Animals, anxious to 'sell the poor baste where he would get something to fill out his dimples.' Shackbolt laughed, but I fancy that was why Mulvaney exchanged to ours."

"I wish he were back," said the colonel; "for I like him and believe he likes me."

That evening, to cheer our souls, Learoyd, Ortheris, and I went into the waste to smoke out a porcupine. All the dogs attended, but even their clamor — and they began to discuss the shortcomings of porcupines before they left cantonments — could not take us out of ourselves. A large, low moon turned the tops of the plume grass to silver, and the stunted camel's-thorn bushes and sour tamarisks into the likeness of trooping devils. The smell of the sun had not left the

[1] **Black Tyrone:** an Irish regiment. The Liffey and Donegal are in Ireland.

earth, and little aimless winds blowing across the rose gardens to the southward brought the scent of dried roses and water. Our fire once started, and the dogs craftily disposed to wait the dash of the porcupine, we climbed to the top of a rain-scarred hillock of earth, and looked across the scrub seamed with cattle paths, white with long grass, and dotted with spots of level pond-bottom, where the snipe would gather in winter.

" This," said Ortheris, with a sigh, as he took in the unkempt desolation of it all, " this is sanguinary. This is unusually sanguinary. Sort o' mad country. Like a grate when the fire's put out by the sun." He shaded his eyes against the moonlight. " An' there's a loony dancin' in the middle of it all. Quite right. I'd dance too if I wasn't so downheart."

There pranced a Portent in the face of the moon — a huge and ragged spirit of the waste, that flapped its wings from afar. It had risen out of the earth; it was coming toward us, and its outline was never twice the same. The toga, tablecloth, or dressing gown, whatever the creature wore, took a hundred shapes. Once it stopped on a neighboring mound and flung all its legs and arms to the winds.

" My, but that scarecrow 'as got 'em bad! " said Ortheris. " Seems like if 'e comes any furder we'll 'ave to argify with 'im."

Learoyd raised himself from the dirt as a bull clears his flanks of the wallow. And as a bull bellows, so he, after a short minute at gaze, gave tongue to the stars.

" MULVAANEY! MULVAANEY! A-hoo! "

Oh then it was that we yelled, and the figure dipped into the hollow, till, with a crash of rending grass, the lost one strode up to the light of the fire, and disappeared to the waist in a wave of joyous dogs! Then Learoyd and Ortheris gave greeting, bass and falsetto together, both swallowing a lump in the throat.

" You fool! " said they, and severally pounded him with their fists.

" Go easy! " he answered; wrapping a huge arm around each. " I would have you to know that I am a god, to be treated as such — tho', by my faith, I fancy I've got to go to the guardroom just like a privit soldier."

The latter part of the sentence destroyed the suspicions raised by the former. Anyone would have been justified in regarding Mulvaney as mad. He was hatless and shoeless, and his shirt and trousers were dropping off him. But he wore one wondrous garment — a gigantic cloak that fell from collarbone to heel — of pale pink silk wrought all over in cunningest needlework of hands long since dead, with the loves of the Hindu gods. The monstrous figures leaped in and out of the light of the fire as he settled the folds round him.

Ortheris handled the stuff respectfully for a moment while I was trying to remember where I had seen it before. Then he screamed, "What *'ave* you done with the palanquin? You're wearin' the linin'."

"I am," said the Irishman, "an' by the same token the 'broidery is scrapin' my hide off. I've lived in this sumpshus counterpane for four days. Me son, I begin to ondherstand why the native is no use. Widout me boots, an' me trousies like an openwork stocking on a gyurl's leg at a dance, I begin to feel like a native — all fearful an' timoreous. Give me a pipe an' I'll tell on."

He lit a pipe, resumed his grip of his two friends, and rocked to and fro in a gale of laughter.

"Mulvaney," said Ortheris sternly, "'tain't no time for laughin'. You've given Jock an' me more trouble than you're worth. You 'ave been absent without leave an' you'll go into cells for that; an' you 'ave come back disgustin'ly dressed an' most improper in the linin' o' that bloomin' palanquin. Instid of which you laugh. An' *we* thought you was dead all the time."

"Bhoys," said the culprit, still shaking gently, "whin I've done my tale you may cry if you like, an' little Orth'ris here can thrample my inside out. Ha' done an' listen. My performinces have been stupenjus: my luck has been the blessed luck av the British Army — an' there's no betther than that. I have come back a pink god. Did any of you go to Dearsley afther my time was up? He was at the bottom of ut all."

"Ah said so," murmured Learoyd. "Tomorrow ah'll smash t' face in upon his heead."

"Ye will not. Dearsley's a jool av a man. Afther Ortheris had put me into the palanquin an' the six bearer-men were gruntin' down the road, I tuk thought to mock Dearsley for that fight. So I tould thim, 'Go to the embankmint,' and there, bein' most amazin' full, I shtuck my head out av the concern an' passed compliments wid Dearsley. I must ha' miscalled him outrageous, for whin I am that way the power av the tongue comes on me. I can bare remimber tellin' him that his mouth opened endways like the mouth av a skate which was thrue afther Learoyd had handled ut; an' I clear remimber his takin' no manner nor matter av offense, but givin' me a big dhrink of beer. 'Twas the beer did the thrick, for I crawled back into the palanquin, steppin' on me right ear wid me left foot, an' thin I slept like the dead. Wanst I half-roused, an', begad the noise in my head was tremenjus — roarin' and rattlin' an' poundin', such as was quite new to me. 'Mother av Mercy,' thinks I, 'phwat a concertina I will have on my shoulders whin I wake! ' An' wid that I curls mysilf up to sleep before ut should get hold on me. Bhoys, that noise was not dhrink, 'twas the rattle av a thrain! "

There followed an impressive pause.

"Yes, he had put me on a thrain — put me, palanquin an' all, an' six av his own coolies that was in his nefarious confidence, on the flat av a ballast thruck, and we were rowlin' an' bowlin' along to Benares. Glory be to that I did not wake up thin an' introjuce mysilf to the coolies. As I was sayin', I slept for the betther part av a day an' a night. But remimber you, that that man Dearsley had packed me off on wan av his material-thrains to Benares, all for to make me overstay my leave an' get into the cells."

The explanation was an eminently rational one. Benares lay at least ten hours by rail from the cantonments, and nothing in the world could have saved Mulvaney from arrest as a deserter had he appeared there in the apparel of his orgies. Dearsley had not forgotten to take revenge. Learoyd, drawing back a little, began to place soft blows over selected portions of Mulvaney's body. His thoughts were away on the embankment, and they meditated evil for Dearsley. Mulvaney continued —

"Whin I was full awake the palanquin was set down in a street, I suspicioned, for I cud hear people passin' an' talkin'. But I knew well I was far from home. There is a queer smell upon our cantonments — a smell av dried earth an' brick kilns wid whiffs of cavalry stable-litter. This place smelt marigold flowers an' bad water, an' wanst somethin' alive came an' blew heavy with his muzzle at the chink av the shutter. 'It's in a village I am,' thinks I to myself, 'an' the parochial buffalo is investigatin' the palanquin.' But anyways I had no desire to move. Only lie still whin you're in foregin parts an' the standin' luck av the British Army will carry ye through. That is an epigram. I made ut.

"Thin a lot av whisperin' divils surrounded the palanquin. 'Take ut up,' sez wan man. 'But who'll pay us?' sez another. 'The Maharanee's [1] minister, av coorse,' sez the man. 'Oho!' sez I to myself, 'I'm a quane in me own right, wid a minister to pay me expenses. I'll be an emperor if I lie still long enough; but this is no village I've found.' I lay quiet, but I gummed me right eye to a crack av the shutters, an' I saw that the whole street was crammed with palanquins an' horses, an' a sprinklin' av naked priests all yellow powder an' tigers' tails. But I may tell you, Orth'ris, an' you, Learoyd, that av all the palanquins ours was the most imperial an' magnificent. Now a palanquin means a native lady all the world over, except whin a soldier av the Quane happens to be takin' a ride. 'Women an' priests!' sez I. 'Your father's son is in the right pew this time, Terence. There will be proceedin's.' Six divils in pink muslin tuk up the palanquin, an' oh! but the rowlin' and' the rockin' made me sick. Thin we got fair jammed among the palanquins — not more than fifty av them — an' we grated an' bumped like Queenstown potato-smacks in a runnin' tide. I cud hear the women gigglin' and squirkin' in their palanquins, but mine was the royal equipage. They made way for ut, an', begad the pink muslin men o' mine were howlin', 'Room for the Maharanee av Gokral-Seetarum.' Do you know aught av the lady, sorr?"

"Yes," said I. "She is a very estimable old queen of the Central Indian States, and they say she is fat. How on earth could she go to Benares without all the city knowing her palanquin?"

"'Twas the eternal foolishness of the natives. They saw the palanquin lying loneful an' forlornsome, an' the beauty av ut, after Dearsley's men had dhropped ut and gone away, an' they gave us the best name that occurred to thim. Quite right too. For aught we know the ould lady was travelin' *incog* [2] — like me. I'm glad to hear she's fat. I was no light weight myself, an' my men were mortial anxious to dhrop me under a great big archway."

"The temple of Prithi-Devil," I murmured, remembering the monstrous horrors of that sculptured archway at Benares.

[1] **Maharanee:** wife of a maharajah.

[2] **incog:** incognito; that is, with identity concealed.

"Pretty Devilskins, savin' your presence, sorr! There was nothin' pretty about it, except me. 'Twas all half dhark, an' whin the coolies left they shut a big black gate behind av us, an' half a company av fat yellow priests began pully-haulin' the palanquins into a dharker place yet—a big stone wall full av pillars, an' gods, an' incense, an' all manner av similar thruck. The gate disconcerted me, for I perceived I wud have to go forward to get out, my retreat bein' cut off. By the same token a good priest makes a bad palanquin-coolie. Begad! they nearly turned me inside out draggin' the palanquin to the temple. Now the disposishin av the forces inside was this way. The Maharanee av Gokral-Seetarum—that was me—lay by the favor av Providence on the far left flank behind the dhark av a pillar carved with elephants' heads. The remainder av the palanquins was in a big half circle facing in to the biggest, fattest, an' most amazin' she-god that iver I dreamed av. Her head ran up into the black above us, an' her feet stuck out in the light av a little fire av melted butter that a priest was feedin' out av a butter dish. Thin a man began to sing an' play on somethin' back in the dhark, an' 'twas a queer song. Ut made my hair lift on the back av my neck. Thin the doors av all the palanquins slid back, an' the women bundled out. I saw what I'll niver see again. 'Twas more glorious than thransformation at a pantomime, for they was in pink an' blue an' silver an' red an' grass green, wid di'monds an' im'ralds an' great red rubies all over thim. But that was the least part av the glory. O bhoys, they were more lovely than the like av any loveliness in hiven; ay, their little bare feet were better than the white hands av a lord's lady, an' their mouths were like puckered roses, an' their eyes were bigger an' dharker than the eyes av any livin' women I've see. Ye may laugh, but I'm speakin' truth. I niver saw the like, an' niver I will again."

"Seeing that in all probability you were watching the wives and daughters of most of the kings of India, the chances are that you won't," I said, for it was dawning on me that Mulvaney had stumbled upon a big Queen's Praying at Benares.

"I niver will," he said, mournfully. "That sight doesn't come twist to any man. It made me ashamed to watch. A fat priest knocked at my door. I didn't think he'd have the insolince to disturb the Maharanee av Gokral-Seetarum, so I lay still. 'The old cow's asleep,' sez he to another. 'Let her be,' sez that. ''Twill be long before she has a calf! ' I might ha' known before he spoke that all a woman prays for in Injia — an' for matter o' that in England too — is childher. That made me more sorry I'd come, me bein', as you well know, a childless man."

He was silent for a moment, thinking of his little son, dead many years ago.

" They prayed, an' the butter-fires blazed up an' the incense turned everything blue, an' between that an' the fires the women looked as tho' they were all ablaze an' twinklin'. They took hold av the she-god's knees, they cried out an' they threw themselves about, an' that world-without-end-amen music was dhrivin' thim mad. Mother av Hiven! how they cried, an' the ould she-god grinnin' above thim all so scornful! The dhrink was dyin' out in me fast, an' I was thinkin' harder than the thoughts wud go through my head — thinkin' how to get out, an' all manner of nonsense as well. The women were rockin' in rows, their di'mond belts clickin', an' the tears runnin' out betune their hands, an' the lights were goin' lower an' dharker. Thin there was a blaze like lightnin' from the roof, an' that showed me the inside av the palanquin, an' at the end where my foot was, stood the livin' spit an' image o' mysilf worked on the linin'. This man here, ut was."

He hunted in the folds of his pink cloak, ran a hand under one, and thrust into the firelight a foot-long embroidered presentment of the great god Krishna, playing on a flute. The heavy jowl, the staring eye, and the blue-black mustache of the god made up a far-off resemblance to Mulvaney.

" The blaze was gone in a wink, but the whole schame came to me thin. I believe I was mad too. I slid the off-shutter open an' rowled out into the dhark behind the elephint-head pillar, tucked up my trousies to my knees, slipped off my boots an' tuk a general hold av all the pink linin' av the palanquin. Glory be, ut ripped out like a woman's dhriss whin you tread on ut at a sergeant's ball, an' a bottle came with ut. I tuk the bottle an' the next minit I was out av the dhark av the pillar, the pink linin' wrapped round me most graceful, the music thunderin' like kettledrums, an' a could draft blowin' round my bare legs. By this hand that did ut, I was Khrishna tootlin' on the flute — the god that the rig'mental chaplain talks about. A sweet sight I must ha' looked. I knew my eyes were big, and my face was wax-white, an' at the worst I must ha' looked like a ghost. But they took me for the livin' god. The music stopped, and the women were dead dumb an' I crooked my legs like a shepherd on a china basin, an' I did the ghost-waggle with my feet as I had done ut at the rig'mental theater many times, an' I slid acrost the width av that temple in front av the she-god tootlin' on the beer bottle."

"Wot did you toot?" demanded Ortheris the practical.

"Me? Oh!" Mulvaney sprang up, suiting the action to the word, and sliding gravely in front of us, a dilapidated but imposing deity in the half light. "I sang —

"Only say
You'll be Mrs. Brallaghan.
Don't say nay,
Charmin' Judy Callaghan.

I didn't know me own voice when I sang. An' oh! 'twas pitiful to see the women. The darlin's were down on their knees. When I passed the last wan I cud see her poor little fingers workin' one in another as if she wanted to touch my feet. So I dhrew the tail av this pink overcoat over her head for the greater honor, an' I slid into the dhark on the other side av the temple, and fetched up in the arms of a big fat priest. All I wanted was to get away clear. So I tuk him by his greasy throat an' shut the speech out av him. 'Out!' sez I 'Which way, ye fat heathen?' — 'Oh!' sez he. 'Man,' sez I. 'White man, soldier man, common soldier man. Where in the name av confusion is the back door?' The women in the temple were still on their faces, an' a young priest was holdin' out his arms above their heads.

"'This way,' sez my fat friend, duckin' behind a big bull-god an' divin' into a passage. Thin I remimbered that I must ha' made the miraculous reputation av that temple for the next fifty years. 'Not so fast,' I sez, an' I held out both my hands with a wink. That ould thief smiled like a father. I took him by the back av the neck in case he should be wishful to put a knife unto me unbeknownst, an' I ran him up and down the passage twice to collect his sensibilities! 'Be quiet,' sez he, in English. 'Now you talk sense,' I sez. 'Fwhat'll you give me for the use av that most illigant palanquin I have no time to take away? ' — 'Don't tell,' sez he. 'Is ut like? ' sez I. 'But ye might give me my railway fare. I'm far from home an' I've done you a service.' Bhoys, 'tis a good thing to be a priest. The old man niver throubled himself to dhraw from a bank. As I will prove to you subsequint, he philandered all round the slack av his clothes an' began dribblin' ten-rupee notes, old gold mohurs, and rupees into my hand till I could hould no more."

"You lie! " said Ortheris. "You're mad or sunstrook. A native don't give coin unless you cut it out o' 'im. 'Tain't nature."

"Then my lie an' my sunstroke is concealed under that lump av sod yonder," retorted Mulvaney, unruffled, nodding across the scrub. "An' there's a dale more in nature than your squidgy little legs have iver taken you to, Orth'ris, me son. Four hundred an' thirty-four rupees by my reckonin', *an'* a big fat gold necklace that I took from him as a remimbrancer, was our share in that business."

"An' 'e give it to you for love," said Ortheris.

"We were alone in that passage. Maybe I was a trifle too pressin', but considher fwhat I had done for the good av the temple, and the iverlasting joy av those women. 'Twas cheap at the price. I wud ha' taken more if I cud ha' found ut. I turned the ould man upside down at the last, but he was milked dhry. Thin he opened a door in another passage an' I found mysilf up to my knees in Benares river water, an' bad smellin' ut is. More by token I had come out on the riverline close to the burnin' ghat and contagious to a cracklin' corpse. This was in the heart av the night, for I had been four hours in the temple. There was a crowd of boats tied up, so I tuk wan an' wint across the river. Thin I came home acrost country, lyin' up by day."

"How on earth did you manage? " I said.

"How did Sir Frederick Roberts get from Cabul to Candahar? He marched an' he niver tould how near he was to breakin' down. That's why he is fwhat he is. An' now " — Mulvaney yawned portentously. "Now I will go an' give myself up for absince widout leave. It's eight an' twenty days an' the rough end of the colonel's tongue in orderly room, any way you look at ut. But 'tis cheap at the price."

"Mulvaney," said I, softly. "If there happens to be any sort of excuse that the colonel can in any way accept, I have a notion that you'll get nothing more than the dressing down. The new recruits are in, and" —

"Not a word more, sorr. Is ut excuses the old man wants? 'Tis not my way, but he shall have thim. I'll tell him I was engaged in financial operations connected with a church," and he flapped his way to cantonments and the cells, singing lustily —

> "So they sent a corp'ril's file,
> And they put me in the gyard-room
> For conduck unbecomin' of a soldier."

And when he was lost in the midst of the moonlight we could hear the refrain —

> "Bang upon the big drum, bash upon the cymbals,
> As we go marchin' along, boys, oh!
> For although in this campaign
> There's no whisky nor champagne,
> We'll keep our spirits goin' with a song, boys!"

Therewith he surrendered himself to the joyful and almost weeping guard, and was made much of by his fellows. But to the colonel he said that he had been smitten with sunstroke and had lain insensible on a villager's cot for untold hours; and between laughter and good will the affair was smoothed over, so that he could, next day, teach the new recruits how to "Fear God, Honor the Queen, Shoot Straight, and Keep Clean."

READING WITH INSIGHT

1. What do you like about this story? A rich story will often have many sources of interest and pleasure. What sources of pleasure can you identify in this story?

2. This is an adventure story. Describe the movement of the story in terms of rising action, climax, falling action.

3. This story is told from the point of view of a minor character who takes little part in the action but is able to view it from a broader

viewpoint than any of the participants. Just who is the narrator? What do you find out about him?

4. How do the three musketeers differ in character and personality? How do they complement each other? Have you known any groups of friends like these?

5. Mulvaney is rough, sometimes crude, often undependable as a soldier. Why is he so likable?

6. What do you learn about Mulvaney's character from other characters in the story? For example, the narrator? The Colonel? The other soldiers? His two friends?

7. What do you learn about Mulvaney's character from his own actions?

8. Do you like to read Mulvaney's Irish dialect? What other kinds of dialect are there in the story?

9. What does this story show you about the meeting of two different civilizations in India? Does it give a very complimentary picture of the natives? This, of course, is before the days of Gandhi, Nehru, and the movement for a free India and Pakistan. Could Kipling have written such a story if he had known India in our time?

10. On two occasions Kipling takes us away from *looking at* the action and lets us hear what happened in the words of one of the participants. This happens at two of the most important scenes — the fight with Dearsley, and the scene in the temple. Would you say this is a defect in the story? Would the story have been more effective if told entirely in the third person? What reason might Kipling have had for using several characters to tell the story?

11. One of the attributes of a good story is richness. Would you say this is a richer story than, for example, Harte's "Outcasts of Poker Flat" or London's "All-Gold Cañon"? If so, how? In what way is its richness different from that of another great adventure story, Conrad's "The Secret Sharer"? One critic has said that the difference between these two stories is the difference between the life of colonial India and the life of the sea. How much of the difference seems to you to be caused by this difference in subject matter, and how much would you attribute to the author's attitude toward his characters?

12. Kipling is often praised for his "fertile invention" and his

use of " unsuspected turns " of action. Illustrate these qualities from this story.

13. In what respects is this story " dated "? For example, is it dated in its picture of India? Its picture of an army? Its picture of colonialism? Are characters like Mulvaney dated, or are there Mulvaneys in all periods? Is it possible to have adventures like these in any time of history?

If you like this story, you will be interested in

Kipling. *The Drums of the Fore and Aft.*
The Man Who Would Be King.
In the Matter of a Private.
The Sending of Dana Da.
Prosper Merimee. *Mateo Falcone.*
Booth Tarkington. *Henry the Great.*
James Thurber. *The Night the Ghost Got In.*

A. CONAN DOYLE

The Red-Headed League

IN 1891 Dr. A. Conan Doyle set up offices as an eye specialist in London. Few patients came. In his first year of practice his total income was about $600. When he filed this sum on his income tax report, the suspicious tax collector returned his report with the words "Most unsatisfactory" written over it. Doyle cheerfully sent the document back with the written comment, "I entirely agree."

But because the young doctor was not very busy, he had time to try his hand at writing. And so we have to thank those patients who never came for the most popular series of detective stories ever written.

Dr. Watson, in the stories, is partly modeled on Doyle's own experiences as a physician. Sherlock Holmes is also partly Doyle; partly he is one of Doyle's famous medical teachers, Dr. Joseph Bell, whose abilities to diagnose from tiny facts and to reconstruct the whole history of a patient from tiny observations, amounted almost to intuition. But he is more than either of those; he has become a living legend with readers of detective stories. Doyle enthusiasts still argue over where Holmes went to college, and why he handled his archenemy, the criminal Moriarty, as he did.

Doyle was born in Edinburgh in 1859. After his literary reputation was established, he spent much of his time lecturing and writing. He was knighted in recognition of his writing. Doyle was known, not only for his detective stories, but also for his novels — *The White Company, The Lost World,* and others. But his chief claim to fame was the shelf of Sherlock Holmes stories that gradually lengthened as his medical practice grew less. These stories went all over the world. They were not the first dectective stories; Poe, rather than Doyle, must be given credit for developing the form. Doyle was perhaps no more ingenious than Poe, although he wrote many more detective stories and therefore had more chance to prove the dimensions of his ingenuity. But he made one great change in the story as Poe had told it. Doyle made the story revolve around a central character so real, so interesting, that he carried through all the stories. Poe's detective stories were built on problem and plot. Doyle's were built on problem, plot, and *character.*

One incident was a dramatic testimony to the living quality of that central character. Doyle himself once became tired of Holmes, and at the end of a story had him die. Such a clamor arose around the world that Doyle had to revive his character. The report of his death was erroneous, he explained. *The Return of Sherlock Holmes* began to appear. And in the hearts of detective-story readers Holmes is still living today.

I HAD called upon my friend, Mr. Sherlock Holmes, one day in the autumn of last year, and found him in deep conversation with a very stout, florid-faced, elderly gentleman, with fiery red hair. With an apology for my intrusion, I was about to withdraw when Holmes pulled me abruptly into the room, and closed the door behind me. "You could not possibly have come at a better time, my dear Watson," he said, cordially.

"I was afraid that you were engaged."

"So I am. Very much so."

"Then I can wait in the next room."

"Not at all. This gentleman, Mr. Wilson, has been my partner and helper in many of my most successful cases, and I have no doubt that he will be of the utmost use to me in yours also."

The stout gentleman half rose from his chair and gave a bob of greeting, with a quick, little, questioning glance from his small, fat-encircled eyes.

"Try the settee," said Holmes, relapsing into his armchair, and putting his finger tips together, as was his custom when in judicial moods. "I know, my dear Watson, that you share my love of all that is bizarre and outside the conventions and humdrum routine of everyday life. You have shown your relish for it by the enthusiasm which has prompted you to chronicle, and, if you will excuse my saying so, somewhat to embellish so many of my own little adventures."

"Your cases have indeed been of the greatest interest to me," I observed.

"You will remember that I remarked the other day, just before we went into the very simple problem presented by Miss Mary

Sutherland, that for strange effects and extraordinary combinations we must go to life itself, which is always far more daring than any effort of the imagination."

"A proposition which I took the liberty of doubting."

"You did, doctor, but none the less you must come round to my view, for otherwise I shall keep on piling fact upon fact on you, until your reason breaks down under them and acknowledges me to be right. Now, Mr. Jabez Wilson here has been good enough to call upon me this morning, and to begin a narrative which promises to be one of the most singular which I have listened to for some time. You have heard me remark that the strangest and most unique things are very often connected not with the larger but with the smaller crimes, and occasionally, indeed, where there is room for doubt whether any positive crime has been committed. As far as I have heard, it is impossible for me to say whether the present case is an instance of crime or not, but the course of events is certainly among the most singular that I have ever listened to. Perhaps, Mr. Wilson, you would have the great kindness to recommence your narrative. I ask you, not merely because my friend Dr. Watson has not heard the opening part, but also because the peculiar nature of the story makes me anxious to have every possible detail from your lips. As a rule, when I have heard some slight indication of the course of events, I am able to guide myself by the thousands of other similar cases which occur to my memory. In the present instance I am forced to admit that the facts are, to the best of my belief, unique."

The portly client puffed out his chest with an appearance of some little pride and pulled a dirty and wrinkled newspaper from the inside pocket of his greatcoat. As he glanced down the advertisement column, with his head thrust forward and the paper flattened out upon his knee, I took a good look at the man and endeavored, after the fashion of my companion, to read the indications which might be presented by his dress or appearance.

I did not gain very much, however, by my inspection. Our visitor bore every mark of being an average commonplace British tradesman, obese, pompous, and slow. He wore rather baggy gray shepherd's check trousers, a not overclean black frock coat, unbuttoned in the front, and a drab waistcoat with a heavy brassy Albert chain, and a square pierced bit of metal dangling down as an ornament. A frayed top hat and a faded brown overcoat with a wrinkled velvet collar lay upon a chair beside him. Altogether, look as I would, there was nothing remarkable about the man save his blazing red head, and the expression of extreme chagrin and discontent upon his features.

Sherlock Holmes's quick eye took in my occupation, and he shook his head with a smile as he noticed my questioning glances. " Beyond the obvious facts that he has at some time done manual labor, that he takes snuff, that he is a Freemason, that he has been in China, and that he has done a considerable amount of writing lately, I can deduce nothing else."

Mr. Jabez Wilson started up in his chair, with his forefinger upon the paper, but his eyes upon my companion.

" How, in the name of good-fortune, did you know all that, Mr. Holmes? " he asked. " How did you know, for example, that I did manual labor? It's as true as gospel, for I began as a ship's carpenter."

" Your hands, my dear sir. Your right hand is quite a size larger than your left. You have worked with it, and the muscles are more developed."

" Well, the snuff, then, and the Freemasonry? "

" I won't insult your intelligence by telling you how I read that, especially as, rather against the strict rules of your order, you use an arc-and-compass breastpin."

" Ah, of course, I forgot that. But the writing? "

" What else can be indicated by that right cuff so very shiny for five inches, and the left one with the smooth patch near the elbow where you rest it upon the desk? "

" Well, but China? "

" The fish that you have tattooed immediately above your right wrist could only have been done in China. I have made a small study of tattoo marks and have even contributed to the literature of the subject. That trick of staining the fishes' scales of a delicate pink is quite peculiar to China. When, in addition, I see a Chinese coin hanging from your watch chain, the matter becomes even more simple."

Mr. Jabez Wilson laughed heavily. " Well, I never! " said he. " I thought at first that you had done something clever, but I see that there was nothing in it, after all."

" I begin to think, Watson," said Holmes, " that I make a mistake in explaining. '*Omne ignotum pro magnifico*,'[1] you know, and my poor little reputation, such as it is, will suffer shipwreck if I am so candid. Can you not find the advertisement, Mr. Wilson? "

"Yes, I have got it now," he answered with his thick red finger planted halfway down the column. "Here it is. This is what began it all. You just read it for yourself, sir."

I took the paper from him and read as follows:

TO THE RED-HEADED LEAGUE:

On account of the bequest of the late Ezekiah Hopkins, of Lebanon, Pennsylvania, U. S. A., there is now another vacancy open which entitles a member of the League to a salary of £4 a week for purely nominal services. All red-headed men who are sound in body and mind, and above the age of twenty-one years, are eligible. Apply in person on Monday, at eleven o'clock, to Duncan Ross, at the offices of the League, 7 Pope's Court, Fleet Street.

"What on earth does this mean? " I ejaculated, after I had twice read over the extraordinary announcement.

Holmes chuckled, and wriggled in his chair, as was his habit when in high spirits. "It is a little off the beaten track, isn't it? " said he. "And now, Mr. Wilson, off you go at scratch, and tell us all about yourself, your household, and the effect which this advertisement had upon your fortunes. You will first make a note, doctor, of the paper and the date."

"It is *The Morning Chronicle* of August 9, 1890. Just two months ago."

"Very good. Now, Mr. Wilson? "

"Well, it is just as I have been telling you, Mr. Sherlock Holmes," said Jabez Wilson, mopping his forehead, "I have a small pawnbroker's business at Coburg Square, near the City.[2] It's not a very large affair, and of late years it has not done more than just give me a living. I used to be able to keep two assistants, but now I only keep one; and I would have a job to pay him, but that he is willing to come for half wages, so as to learn the business."

[1] **Omne ignotum pro magnifico**: Anything unknown is likely to seem marvelous. (Latin.)

[2] **the City**: the old city, the central part of London.

"What is the name of this obliging youth?" asked Sherlock Holmes.

"His name is Vincent Spaulding, and he's not such a youth, either. It's hard to say his age. I should not wish a smarter assistant, Mr. Holmes; and I know very well that he could better himself, and earn twice what I am able to give him. But, after all, if he is satisfied, why should I put ideas in his head?"

"Why, indeed? You seem most fortunate in having an employee who comes under the full market price. It is not a common experience among employers in this age. I don't know that your assistant is not as remarkable as your advertisement."

"Oh, he has his faults, too," said Mr. Wilson. "Never was such a fellow for photography. Snapping away with a camera when he ought to be improving his mind, and then diving down into the cellar like a rabbit into its hole to develop his pictures. That is his main fault, but on the whole he's a good worker. There's no vice in him."

"He is still with you, I presume?"

"Yes, sir. He and a girl of fourteen, who does a bit of simple cooking and keeps the place clean — that's all I have in the house, for I am a widower and never had any family. We live very quietly, sir, the three of us; and we keep a roof over our heads and pay our debts, if we do nothing more.

"The first thing that put us out was that advertisement. Spaulding, he came down into the office just this day eight weeks, with this very paper in his hand, and he says:

"'I wish to the Lord, Mr. Wilson, that I was a red-headed man.'

"'Why that?' I asks.

"'Why,' says he, 'here's another vacancy on the League of the Red-headed Men. It's worth quite a little fortune to any man who gets it, and I understand that there are more vacancies than there are men, so that the trustees are at their wits' end what to do with the money. If my hair would only change color, here's a nice little crib all ready for me to step into.'

"'Why, what is it, then?' I asked. You see, Mr. Holmes, I am a very stay-at-home man, and as my business came to me instead of my having to go to it, I was often weeks on end without putting my foot over the door mat. In that way I didn't know much of what was going on outside, and I was always glad of a bit of news.

"'Have you never heard of the League of the Red-headed Men?' he asked with his eyes open.

"'Never.'

"'Why, I wonder at that, for you are eligible yourself for one of the vacancies.'

"'And what are they worth?' I asked.

"'Oh, merely a couple of hundred a year, but the work is slight, and it need not interfere very much with one's other occupations.'

"Well, you can easily think that that made me prick up my ears, for the business has not been over-good for some years, and an extra couple of hundred would have been very handy.

"'Tell me all about it,' said I.

"'Well,' said he, showing me the advertisement, 'you can see for yourself that the League has a vacancy, and there is the address where you should apply for particulars. As far as I can make out, the League was founded by an American millionaire, Ezekiah Hopkins, who was very peculiar in his ways. He was himself red-headed, and he had a great sympathy for all red-headed men; so, when he died, it was found that he had left his enormous fortune in the hands of trustees, with instructions to apply the interest to the providing of easy berths to men whose hair is of that color. From all I hear it is splendid pay, and very little to do.'

"'But,' said I, 'there would be millions of red-headed men who would apply.'

"'Not so many as you might think,' he answered. 'You see it is really confined to Londoners, and to grown men. This American had started from London when he was young, and he wanted to do the old town a good turn. Then, again, I have heard it is no use your applying if your hair is light red, or dark red, or anything but real bright, blazing, fiery red. Now, if you cared to apply, Mr. Wilson, you would just walk in; but perhaps it would hardly be worth your while to put yourself out of the way for the sake of a few hundred pounds.'

"Now, it is a fact, gentlemen, as you may see for yourselves, that my hair is of a very full and rich tint, so that it seemed to me that, if there was to be any competition in the matter, I stood as good a chance as any man that I had ever met. Vincent Spaulding seemed to know so much about it that I thought he might prove useful, so I just ordered him to put up the shutters for the day, and to come right away with me. He was very willing to have a holiday, so we shut the business up, and started off for the address that was given us in the advertisement.

"I never hope to see such a sight as that again, Mr. Holmes. From north, south, east, and west every man who had a shade of red in his hair had tramped into the City to answer the advertisement. Fleet Street was choked with red-headed folk, and Pope's Court looked like a coster's orange barrow. I should not have thought there were so many in the whole country as were brought together by that single advertisement. Every shade of color they were – straw, lemon, orange, brick, Irish-setter, liver, clay; but, as Spaulding said, there were not many who had the real vivid flame-colored tint. When I saw how many were waiting, I would have given it up in despair; but Spaulding would not hear of it. How he did it I could not imagine, but he pushed and pulled and butted until he got me through the crowd, and right up to the steps which led to the office. There was a double stream upon the stair, some going up in hope, and some coming back dejected; but we wedged in as well as we could and soon found ourselves in the office."

"Your experience has been a most entertaining one," remarked Holmes as his client paused and refreshed his memory with a huge pinch of snuff. "Pray continue your very interesting statement."

"There was nothing in the office but a couple of wooden chairs and a deal table, behind which sat a small man with a head that was even redder than mine. He said a few words to each candidate as he came up, and then he always managed to find some fault in them which would disqualify them. Getting a vacancy did not seem to be such a very easy matter, after all. However, when our turn came the little man was much more favorable to me than to any of the others, and he closed the door as we entered, so that he might have a private word with us.

"'This is Mr. Jabez Wilson,' said my assistant, 'and he is willing to fill a vacancy in the League.'

"'And he is admirably suited for it,' the other answered. 'He has every requirement. I cannot recall when I have seen anything so fine.' He took a step backward, cocked his head on one side, and gazed at my hair until I felt quite bashful. Then suddenly he plunged forward, wrung my hand, and congratulated me warmly on my success.

" 'It would be injustice to hesitate,' said he. 'You will, however, I am sure, excuse me for taking an obvious precaution.' With that he seized my hair in both his hands, and tugged until I yelled with the pain. 'There is water in your eyes,' said he, as he released me. 'I perceive that all is as it should be. But we have to be careful, for we have twice been deceived by wigs and once by paint. I could tell you tales of cobbler's wax which would disgust you with human nature.'

"He stepped over to the window, and shouted through it at the top of his voice that the vacancy was filled. A groan of disappointment came up from below, and the folk all trooped away in different directions, until there was not a red-head to be seen except my own and that of the manager.

" 'My name,' said he, 'is Mr. Duncan Ross, and I am myself one of the pensioners upon the fund left by our noble benefactor. Are you a married man, Mr. Wilson? Have you a family?'

"I answered that I had not.

"His face fell immediately.

" 'Dear me!' he said, gravely, 'that is very serious indeed! I am sorry to hear you say that. The fund was, of course, for the propagation and spread of the red-heads as well as for their maintenance. It is exceedingly unfortunate that you should still be a bachelor.'

"My face lengthened at this, Mr. Holmes, for I thought that I was not to have the vacancy after all; but after thinking it over for a few minutes he said that it would be all right.

" 'In the case of another,' said he, 'the objection might be fatal, but we must stretch a point in favor of a man with such a head of hair as yours. When shall you be able to enter upon your new duties?'

" 'Well, it is a little awkward, for I have a business already,' said I.

" 'Oh, never mind about that, Mr. Wilson!' said Vincent Spaulding. 'I should be able to look after that for you.'

" 'What would be the hours?' I asked.

" 'Ten to two.'

"Now a pawnbroker's business is mostly done of an evening, Mr. Holmes, especially Thursday and Friday evening, which is just before payday; so it would suit me very well to earn a little in the mornings. Besides, I knew that my assistant was a good man, and that he would see to anything that turned up.

"'That would suit me very well,' said I. 'And the pay?'

"'Is £4 a week.'

"'And the work?'

"'Is purely nominal.'

"'What do you call purely nominal?'

"'Well, you have to be in the office, or at least in the building, the whole time. If you leave, you forfeit your whole position forever. The will is very clear upon that point. You don't comply with the conditions if you budge from the office during that time.'

"'It's only four hours a day, and I should not think of leaving,' said I.

"'No excuse will avail,' said Mr. Duncan Ross; 'neither sickness nor business nor anything else. There you must stay, or you lose your billet.'

"'And the work?'

"'Is to copy out the *Encyclopædia Britannica*. There is the first volume of it in that press.[1] You must find your own ink, pens, and blotting paper, but we provide this table and chair. Will you be ready tomorrow?'

"'Certainly,' I answered.

"'Then, good-by, Mr. Jabez Wilson, and let me congratulate you once more on the important position which you have been fortunate enough to gain.' He bowed me out of the room, and I went home with my assistant, hardly knowing what to say or do, I was so pleased at my own good fortune.

"Well, I thought over the matter all day, and by evening I was in low spirits again for I had quite persuaded myself that the whole affair must be some great hoax or fraud, though what its object might be I could not imagine. It seemed altogether past belief that anyone could make such a will, or that they would pay such a sum for doing anything so simple as copying out the *Encyclopædia Britannica*. Vincent Spaulding did what he could to cheer me up, but

[1] **press:** bookcase or cupboard.

by bedtime I had reasoned myself out of the whole thing. However, in the morning I determined to have a look at it anyhow, so I bought a penny bottle of ink, and with a quill pen and seven sheets of foolscap paper, I started off for Pope's Court.

"Well, to my surprise and delight, everything was as right as possible. The table was set out ready for me, and Mr. Duncan Ross was there to see that I got fairly to work. He started me off upon the letter A, and then he left me; but he would drop in from time to time to see that all was right with me. At two o'clock he bade me good day, complimented me upon the amount that I had written, and locked the door of the office after me.

"This went on day after day, Mr. Holmes, and on Saturday the manager came in and planked down four golden sovereigns for my week's work. It was the same next week, and the same the week after. Every morning I was there at ten, and every afternoon I left at two. By degrees Mr. Duncan Ross took to coming in only once of a morning, and then, after a time, he did not come in at all. Still, of course, I never dared to leave the room for an instant, for I was not sure when he might come, and the billet was such a good one, and suited me so well, that I would not risk the loss of it.

"Eight weeks passed away like this, and I had written about Abbots and Archery and Armor and Architecture and Attica, and hoped with diligence that I might get on to the B's before very long. It cost me something in foolscap, and I had pretty nearly filled a shelf with my writings. And then suddenly the whole business came to an end."

"To an end?"

"Yes, sir. And no later than this morning. I went to my work as usual at ten o'clock, but the door was shut and locked, with a little square of cardboard hammered on to the middle of the panel with a tack. Here it is, and you can read for yourself."

He held up a piece of white cardboard about the size of a sheet of note paper. It read in this fashion:

THE RED-HEADED LEAGUE

IS

DISSOLVED

October 9, 1890.

Sherlock Holmes and I surveyed this curt announcement and the rueful face behind it, until the comical side of the affair so completely overtopped every other consideration that we both burst out into a roar of laughter.

"I cannot see that there is anything very funny," cried our client, flushing up to the roots of his flaming head. "If you can do nothing better than laugh at me, I can go elsewhere."

"No, no," cried Holmes, shoving him back into the chair from which he had half risen. "I really wouldn't miss your case for the world. It is most refreshingly unusual. But there is, if you will excuse my saying so, something just a little funny about it. Pray, what steps did you take when you found the card upon the door?"

"I was staggered, sir. I did not know what to do. Then I called at the offices round, but none of them seemed to know anything about it. Finally, I went to the landlord, who is an accountant living on the ground floor, and I asked him if he could tell me what had become of the Red-headed League. He said that he had never heard of any such body. Then I asked him who Mr. Duncan Ross was. He answered that the name was new to him.

"'Well,' said I, 'the gentleman at No. 4.'

"'What, the red-headed man?'

"'Yes.'

"'Oh,' said he, 'his name was William Morris. He was a solicitor, and was using my room as a temporary convenience until his new premises were ready. He moved out yesterday.'

"'Where could I find him?'

"'Oh, at his new offices. He did tell me the address. Yes, 17 King Edward Street, near St. Paul's.'

"I started off, Mr. Holmes, but when I got to that address it was a manufactory of artificial kneecaps, and no one in it had ever heard of either Mr. William Morris or Mr. Duncan Ross."

"And what did you do then?"

"I went home to Saxe-Coburg Square, and I took the advice of my assistant. But he could not help me in any way. He could only say that if I waited I should hear by post. But that was not quite good enough, Mr. Holmes. I did not wish to lose such a place without a struggle; so, as I have heard that you were good enough to give advice to poor folk who were in need of it, I came right away to you."

"And you did very wisely," said Holmes. "Your case is an exceedingly remarkable one, and I shall be happy to look into it. From what you have told me I think that it is possible that graver issues hang from it than might at first sight appear."

"Grave enough!" said Mr. Jabez Wilson. "Why, I have lost four pound a week."

"As far as you are personally concerned," remarked Holmes, "I do not see that you have any grievance against this extraordinary league. On the contrary, you are, as I understand, richer by some £30, to say nothing of the minute knowledge which you have gained on every subject which comes under the letter A. You have lost nothing by them."

"No, sir. But I want to find out about them, and who they are, and what their object was in playing this prank – if it was a prank – upon me. It was a pretty expensive joke for them, for it cost them two and thirty pounds."

"We shall endeavor to clear up these points for you. And, first, one or two questions, Mr. Wilson. This assistant of yours who first called your attention to the advertisement – how long had he been with you?"

"About a month then."

"How did he come?"

"In answer to an advertisement."

"Was he the only applicant?"

"No, I had a dozen."

"Why did you pick him?"

"Because he was handy and would come cheap."

"At half wages, in fact."

"Yes."

"What is he like, this Vincent Spaulding?"

"Small, stout-built, very quick in his ways, no hair on his face, though he's not short of thirty. Has a white splash of acid upon his forehead."

Holmes sat up in his chair in considerable excitement. "I thought as much," said he. "Have you ever observed that his ears are pierced for earrings?"

"Yes, sir. He told me that a gypsy had done it for him when he was a lad."

"Hum!" said Holmes, sinking back in deep thought. "He is still with you?"

"Oh, yes, sir; I have only just left him."

"And has your business been attended to in your absence?"

"Nothing to complain of, sir. There's never very much to do of a morning."

"That will do, Mr. Wilson. I shall be happy to give you an opinion upon the subject in the course of a day or two. Today is Saturday, and I hope that by Monday we may come to a conclusion."

"Well, Watson," said Holmes, when our visitor had left us, "what do you make of it all?"

"I make nothing of it," I answered, frankly. "It is a most mysterious business."

"As a rule," said Holmes, "the more bizarre a thing is, the less mysterious it proves to be. It is your commonplace, featureless crimes which are really puzzling, just as a commonplace face is the most difficult to identify. But I must be prompt over this matter."

"What are you going to do, then?" I asked.

"To smoke," he answered. "It is quite a three-pipe problem, and I beg that you won't speak to me for fifty minutes." He curled himself up in his chair, with his thin knees drawn up to his hawk-like nose, and there he sat with his eyes closed and his black clay pipe thrusting out like the bill of some strange bird. I had come to the conclusion that he had dropped asleep, and indeed was nodding myself, when he suddenly sprang out of his chair with the gesture of a man who has made up his mind, and put his pipe down upon the mantelpiece.

"Sarasate [1] plays at the St. James's Hall this afternoon," he remarked. "What do you think, Watson? Could your patients spare you for a few hours?"

"I have nothing to do today. My practice is never very absorbing."

"Then put on your hat and come. I am going through the City first, and we can have some lunch on the way. I observe that there is a good deal of German music on the program, which is rather more

[1] **Sarasate: a famous Spanish violinist.**

to my taste than Italian or French. It is introspective, and I want to introspect. Come along!"

We traveled by the Underground as far as Aldersgate; and a short walk took us to Saxe-Coburg Square, the scene of the singular story which we had listened to in the morning. It was a poky, little, shabby-genteel place, where four lines of dingy two-storied brick houses looked out into a small railed-in enclosure, where a lawn of weedy grass and a few clumps of faded laurel bushes made a hard fight against a smoke-laden and uncongenial atmosphere. Three gilt balls and a brown board with "JABEZ WILSON" in white letters, upon a corner house, announced the place where our red-headed client carried on his business. Sherlock Holmes stopped in front of it with his head on one side and looked it all over, with his eyes shining brightly between puckered lids. Then he walked slowly up the street, and then down again to the corner, still looking keenly at the houses. Finally he returned to the pawnbroker's, and, having thumped vigorously upon the pavement with his stick two or three times, he went up to the door and knocked. It was instantly opened by a bright-looking, clean-shaven young fellow, who asked him to step in.

"Thank you," said Holmes, "I only wished to ask you how you would go from here to the Strand."

"Third right, fourth left," answered the assistant promptly, closing the door.

"Smart fellow, that," observed Holmes as we walked away. "He is, in my judgment, the fourth smartest man in London, and for daring I am not sure that he has not a claim to be third. I have known something of him before."

"Evidently," said I, "Mr. Wilson's assistant counts for a good deal in this mystery of the Red-headed League. I am sure that you inquired your way merely in order that you might see him."

"Not him."

"What then?"

"The knees of his trousers."

"And what did you see?"

"What I expected to see."

"Why did you beat the pavement?"

"My dear doctor, this is a time for observation, not for talk.

We are spies in an enemy's country. We know something of Saxe-Coburg Square. Let us now explore that which lies behind it."

The road in which we found ourselves as we turned round the corner from the retired Saxe-Coburg Square presented as great a contrast to it as the front of a picture does to the back. It was one of the main arteries which convey the traffic of the City to the north and west. The roadway was blocked with the immense stream of commerce flowing in a double tide inward and outward, while the footpaths were black with the hurrying swarm of pedestrians. It was difficult to realize, as we looked at the line of fine shops and stately business premises, that they really abutted on the other side upon the faded and stagnant square which we had just quitted.

"Let me see," said Holmes, standing at the corner, and glancing along the line, "I should like just to remember the order of the houses here. It is a hobby of mine to have an exact knowledge of London. There is Mortimer's, the tobacconist, the little newspaper shop, the Coburg branch of the City and Suburban Bank, the Vegetarian Restaurant, and McFarlane's carriage-building depot. That carries us right on to the other block. And now, doctor, we've done our work, so it's time we had some play. A sandwich and a cup of coffee, and then off to violin-land, where all is sweetness and delicacy and harmony, and there are no red-headed clients to vex us with their conundrums."

My friend was an enthusiastic musician, being himself not only a very capable performer but a composer of no ordinary merit. All the afternoon he sat in the stalls wrapped in the most perfect happiness, gently waving his long, thin fingers in time to the music, while his gently smiling face and his languid, dreamy eyes were as unlike those of Holmes, the sleuth-hound, Holmes the relentless, keen-witted, ready-handed criminal agent, as it was possible to conceive. In his singular character the dual nature alternately asserted itself, and his extreme exactness and astuteness represented, as I have often thought, the reaction against the poetic and contemplative mood which occasionally predominated in him. The swing of his nature took him from extreme languor to devouring energy; and, as I knew well, he was never so truly formidable as when, for days on end, he had been lounging in his armchair amid his improvisations and his black-letter editions. Then it was that the lust of the chase would suddenly come upon him, and that his brilliant reasoning power would rise to the level of intuition, until those who were unacquainted with his methods would look askance at him as on a man whose knowledge was not that of other mortals. When I saw him that afternoon so enwrapped in the music at St. James's Hall I felt that an evil time might be coming upon those whom he had set himself to hunt down.

"You want to go home, no doubt, Doctor," he remarked as we emerged.

"Yes, it would be as well."

"And I have some business to do which will take some hours. This business at Coburg Square is serious."

"Why serious?"

"A considerable crime is in contemplation. I have every reason to believe that we shall be in time to stop it. But today being Saturday rather complicates matters. I shall want your help tonight."

"At what time?"

"Ten will be early enough."

"I shall be at Baker Street at ten."

"Very well. And, I say, doctor, there may be some little danger, so kindly put your army revolver in your pocket." He waved his hand, and disappeared in an instant among the crowd.

I trust that I am not more dense than my neighbors, but I was always oppressed with a sense of my own stupidity in my dealings with Sherlock Holmes. Here I had heard what he had heard, I had seen what he had seen, and yet from his words it was evident that he saw clearly not only what had happened, but what was about to happen, while to me the whole business was still confused and grotesque. As I drove home to my house in Kensington I thought over it all from the extraordinary story of the red-headed copier of the *Encyclopædia* down to the visit to Saxe-Coburg Square, and the ominous words with which he had parted from me. What was this nocturnal expedition, and why should I go armed? Where were we going, and what were we to do? I had the hint from Holmes that this smooth-faced pawnbroker's assistant was a formidable man – a man who might play a deep game. I tried to puzzle it out, but gave it up in despair, and set the matter aside until night should bring an explanation.

It was a quarter past nine when I started from home and made my way across the Park, and so through Oxford Street to Baker Street. Two hansoms were standing at the door, and, as I entered the passage, I heard the sound of voices from above. On entering his room I found Holmes in animated conversation with two men, one of whom I recognized as Peter Jones, the official police agent, while the other was a long, thin, sad-faced man, with a very shiny hat and oppressively respectable frock coat.

"Ha! our party is complete," said Holmes, buttoning up his pea jacket,[1] and taking his heavy hunting crop from the rack. "Watson, I think you know Mr. Jones, of Scotland Yard? [2] Let me introduce you to Mr. Merryweather, who is to be our companion in tonight's adventure."

"We're hunting in couples again, doctor, you see," said Jones, in his consequential way. "Our friend here is a wonderful man for starting a chase. All he wants is an old dog to help him to do the running down."

"I hope a wild goose may not prove to be the end of our chase," observed Mr. Merryweather gloomily.

"You may place considerable confidence in Mr. Holmes, sir," said the police agent loftily. "He has his own little methods, which are, if he won't mind my saying so, just a little too theoretical and fantastic, but he has the makings of a detective in him. It is not too much to say that once or twice, as in that business of the Sholto murder and the Agra treasure, he has been more nearly correct than the official force."

"Oh, if you say so, Mr. Jones, it is all right," said the stranger with deference. "Still, I confess that I miss my rubber. It is the first Saturday night for seven-and-twenty years that I have not had my rubber."

"I think you will find," said Sherlock Holmes, "that you will play for a higher stake tonight than you have ever done yet, and that the play will be more exciting. For you, Mr. Merryweather, the stake will be some £30,000; and for you, Jones, it will be the man upon whom you wish to lay your hands."

[1] **pea jacket:** a coarse woolen coat.

[2] **Scotland Yard:** the British Metropolitan Police, famous for its detective bureau.

"John Clay, the murderer, thief, smasher, and forger. He's a young man, Mr. Merryweather, but he is at the head of his profession, and I would rather have my bracelets on him than on any criminal in London. He's a remarkable man, is young John Clay. His grandfather was a royal duke, and he himself has been to Eton and Oxford. His brain is as cunning as his fingers, and though we meet signs of him at every turn, we never know where to find the man himself. He'll crack a crib in Scotland one week, and be raising money to build an orphanage in Cornwall the next. I've been on his track for years and have never set eyes on him yet."

"I hope that I may have the pleasure of introducing you tonight. I've had one or two little turns also with Mr. John Clay, and I agree with you that he is at the head of his profession. It is past ten, however, and quite time that we started. If you two will take the first hansom, Watson and I will follow in the second."

Sherlock Holmes was not very communicative during the long drive, and lay back in the cab humming the tunes which he had heard in the afternoon. We rattled through an endless labyrinth of gaslit streets until we emerged into Farringdon Street.

"We are close there now," my friend remarked. "This fellow Merryweather is a bank director, and personally interested in the matter. I thought it as well to have Jones with us also. He is not a bad fellow, though an absolute imbecile in his profession. He has one positive virtue. He is as brave as a bulldog, and as tenacious as a lobster if he gets his claws upon anyone. Here we are, and they are waiting for us."

We had reached the same crowded thoroughfare in which we had found ourselves in the morning. Our cabs were dismissed, and, following the guidance of Mr. Merryweather, we passed down a narrow passage and through a side door, which he opened for us. Within there was a small corridor, which ended in a very massive iron gate. This also was opened, and led down a flight of winding stone steps, which terminated at another formidable gate. Mr. Merryweather stopped to light a lantern, and then conducted us down a dark, earth-smelling passage, and so, after opening a third door, into a huge vault or cellar, which was piled all round with crates and massive boxes.

"You are not very vulnerable from above," Holmes remarked as he held up the lantern and gazed about him.

"Nor from below," said Mr. Merryweather, striking his stick upon the flags which line the floor. "Why, dear me, it sounds quite hollow!" he remarked, looking up in surprise.

"I must really ask you to be a little more quiet!" said Holmes severely. "You have already imperiled the whole success of our expedition. Might I beg that you would have the goodness to sit down upon one of those boxes, and not to interfere?"

The solemn Mr. Merryweather perched himself upon a crate, with a very injured expression upon his face, while Holmes fell upon his knees upon the floor and, with the lantern and a magnifying lens, began to examine minutely the cracks between the stones. A few seconds sufficed to satisfy him, for he sprang to his feet again and put his glass in his pocket.

"We have at least an hour before us," he remarked, "for they can hardly take any steps until the good pawnbroker is safely in bed. Then they will not lose a minute, for the sooner they do their work the longer time they will have for their escape. We are at present, Doctor — as no doubt you have divined — in the cellar of the City branch of one of the principal London banks. Mr. Merryweather is the chairman of directors, and he will explain to you that there are reasons why the more daring criminals of London should take a considerable interest in this cellar at present."

"It is our French gold," whispered the director. "We have had several warnings that an attempt might be made upon it."

"Your French gold?"

"Yes. We had occasion some months ago to strengthen our resources and borrowed for that purpose 30,000 leons [1] from the Bank of France. It has become known that we have never had occasion to unpack the money, and that it is still lying in our cellar. The crate upon which I sit contains two thousand napoleons packed between layers of lead foil. Our reserve of bullion is much larger at present than is usually kept in a single branch office, and we have had misgivings upon the subject."

"Which were very well justified," observed Holmes. "And now it is time that we arranged our little plans. I expect that within an

[1] **leons: French coins of large denomination.**

hour matters will come to a head. In the meantime, Mr. Merryweather, we must put the screen over that dark lantern."

"And sit in the dark?"

"I am afraid so. I had brought a pack of cards in my pocket, and I thought that, as we were a *partie carrée*,[1] you might have your rubber after all. But I see that the enemy's preparations have gone so far that we cannot risk the presence of a light. And, first of all, we must choose our positions. These are daring men, and though we shall take them at a disadvantage, they may do us some harm unless we are careful. I shall stand behind this crate, and do you conceal yourselves behind those. Then when I flash a light upon them, close in swiftly. If they fire, Watson, have no compunction about shooting them down."

I placed my revolver, cocked, upon the top of the wooden case behind which I crouched. Holmes shot the slide across the front of his lantern, and left us in pitch darkness—such an absolute darkness as I have never before experienced. The smell of hot metal remained to assure us that the light was still there, ready to flash out at a moment's notice. To me, with my nerves worked up to a pitch of expectancy, there was something depressing and subduing in the sudden gloom, and in the cold, dank air of the vault.

"They have but one retreat," whispered Holmes. "That is back through the house into Saxe-Coburg Square. I hope that you have done what I asked you, Jones?"

"I have an inspector and two officers waiting at the front door."

"Then we have stopped all the holes. And now we must be silent and wait."

What a time it seemed! From comparing notes afterward it was but an hour and a quarter, yet it appeared to me that the night must have almost gone, and the dawn be breaking above us. My limbs were weary and stiff, for I feared to change my position; yet my nerves were worked up to the highest pitch of tension, and my hearing was so acute that I could not only hear the gentle breathing of my companions, but I could distinguish the deeper, heavier in-breath of the bulky Jones from the thin, sighing note of the bank director. From my position I could look over the case in the direction of the floor. Suddenly my eyes caught the glint of a light.

[1] partie carrée: party of four. (French.)

At first it was but a lurid spark upon the stone pavement. Then it lengthened out until it became a yellow line, and then, without any warning or sound, a gash seemed to open and a hand appeared; a white, almost womanly hand, which felt about in the center of the little area of light. For a minute or more the hand, with its writhing fingers, protruded out of the floor. Then it was withdrawn as suddenly as it appeared, and all was dark again save the single lurid spark which marked a chink between the stones.

Its disappearance, however, was but momentary. With a rending, tearing sound, one of the broad, white stones turned over upon its side and left a square, gaping hole, through which streamed the light of a lantern. Over the edge there peeped a clean-cut, boyish face, which looked keenly about it, and then, with a hand on either side of the aperture, drew itself shoulder-high and waist-high, until one knee rested upon the edge. In another instant he stood at the side of the hole and was hauling after him a companion, lithe and small like himself, with a pale face and a shock of very red hair.

"It's all clear," he whispered. "Have you the chisel and the bags? Great Scott! Jump, Archie, jump, and I'll swing for it!"

Sherlock Holmes had sprung out and seized the intruder by the collar. The other dived down the hole, and I heard the sound of rending cloth as Jones clutched at his skirts.[1] The light flashed upon the barrel of a revolver, but Holmes's hunting crop came down on the man's wrist, and the pistol clinked upon the stone floor.

"It's no use, John Clay," said Holmes blandly. "You have no chance at all."

"So I see," the other answered with the utmost coolness. "I fancy that my pal is all right, though I see you have got his coattails."

"There are three men waiting for him at the door," said Holmes.

"Oh, indeed! You seem to have done the thing very completely. I must compliment you."

"And I you," Holmes answered. "Your red-headed idea was very new and effective."

"You'll see your pal again presently," said Jones. "He's quicker at climbing down holes than I am. Just hold out while I fix the derbies."[2]

"I beg that you will not touch me with your filthy hands," re-

1 **skirts**: coattails.

2 **derbies**: handcuffs.

marked our prisoner, as the handcuffs clattered upon his wrists. "You may not be aware that I have royal blood in my veins. Have the goodness, also, when you address me always to say 'sir' and 'please.'"

"All right," said Jones, with a stare and a snigger. "Well, would you please, sir, march upstairs, where we can get a cab to carry your highness to the police station?"

"That is better," said John Clay, serenely. He made a sweeping bow to the three of us and walked quietly off in the custody of the detective.

"Really, Mr. Holmes," said Mr. Merryweather as we followed them from the cellar, "I do not know how the bank can thank you or repay you. There is no doubt that you have detected and defeated in the most complete manner one of the most determined attempts at bank robbery that have ever come within my experience."

"I have had one or two little scores of my own to settle with Mr. John Clay," said Holmes. "I have been at some small expense over this matter, which I shall expect the bank to refund, but beyond that I am amply repaid by having had an experience which is in many ways unique, and by hearing the very remarkable narrative of the Red-headed League."

"You see, Watson," he explained, in the early hours of the morning, as we sat over a glass of whisky and soda in Baker Street, "it was perfectly obvious from the first that the only possible object of this rather fantastic business of the advertisement of the League, and the copying of the *Encyclopædia*, must be to get this not overbright pawnbroker out of the way for a number of hours every day. It was a curious way of managing it, but, really, it would be difficult to suggest a better. The method was no doubt suggested to Clay's ingenious mind by the color of his accomplice's hair. The four pounds a week was a lure which must draw him, and what was it to them, who were playing for thousands? They put in the advertisement, one rogue has the temporary office, the other rogue incites the man to apply for it, and together they manage to secure his absence every morning in the week. From the time that I heard of the assistant having come for half wages, it was obvious to me that he had some strong motive for securing the situation."

"But how could you guess what the motive was?"

"Had there been women in the house, I should have suspected a mere vulgar intrigue. That, however, was out of the question. The man's business was a small one, and there was nothing in his house which could account for such elaborate preparations, and such an expenditure as they were at. It must, then, be something out of the house. What could it be? I thought of the assistant's fondness for photography, and his trick of vanishing into the cellar. The cellar! There was the end of this tangled clue. Then I made inquiries as to this mysterious assistant and found that I had to deal with one of the coolest and most daring criminals in London. He was doing something in the cellar – something which took many hours a day for months on end. What could it be, once more? I could think of nothing save that he was running a tunnel to some other building.

"So far I had got when we went to visit the scene of action. I surprised you by beating upon the pavement with my stick. I was ascertaining whether the cellar stretched out in front or behind. It was not in front. Then I rang the bell, and, as I hoped, the assistant answered it. We have had some skirmishes, but we had never set eyes upon each other before. I hardly looked at his face. His knees were what I wished to see. You must yourself have remarked how worn, wrinkled, and stained they were. They spoke of those hours of burrowing. The only remaining point was what they were burrowing for. I walked round the corner, saw that the City and Suburban Bank abutted on our friend's premises, and felt that I had solved my problem. When you drove home after the concert I called upon Scotland Yard and upon the chairman of the bank directors, with the result that you have seen."

"And how could you tell that they would make their attempt tonight?" I asked.

"Well, when they closed their League offices that was a sign that they cared no longer about Mr. Jabez Wilson's presence – in other words, that they had completed their tunnel. But it was essential that they should use it soon, as it might be discovered, or the bullion might be removed. Saturday would suit them better than any other day, as it would give them two days for their escape. For all these reasons I expected them to come tonight."

"You reasoned it out beautifully," I exclaimed in unfeigned admiration. "It is so long a chain, and yet every link rings true."

"It saved me from ennui," he answered, yawning. "Alas! I already feel it closing in upon me. My life is spent in one long effort to escape from the commonplaces of existence. These little problems help me to do so."

"And you are a benefactor of the race," said I.

He shrugged his shoulders. "Well, perhaps, after all, it is of some little use," he remarked. "'*L'homme c'est rien – l'œuvre c'est tout,*'[1] as Gustave Flaubert wrote to George Sand."

READING WITH INSIGHT

1. The technique of detective-story writing is to give the reader the information needed to solve the problem, but to keep the solution hard to guess. Look back over the story and notice all the information Doyle has given you from which you might have deduced the answer. For example, recall that Holmes pounded the pavement in front of the shop with his cane.

2. Another device of the detective story is to give certain false leads, in order to hide the real answer. What false leads are there in this story?

3. As detective stories go, this is not a very difficult story. Did you guess the right answer? If so, when? What gave you the hint you needed? At what point in the story, do you think, did Holmes arrive at the solution? Did he have more information at that point than you had?

4. In what different ways does a detective story appeal to you as compared to another kind of story? Do you like to read a detective story a second time? If so, for what?

5. What qualities make Holmes a good detective?

6. What did you learn in this story about Holmes as a person? Do you agree with the statement that Doyle employs character as an element in his detective stories? Support your answer by evidence from this story.

7. What part does Dr. Watson play in the story? Would the

[1] **L'homme c'est rien — l'œuvre c'est tout:** Man is nothing, his work is everything. (French.)

story be as interesting without him? What are the advantages of having him tell the story (as compared to having it told entirely in the third person)?

8. Where does the falling action begin in this story? Most detective stories end with an explanation of how the detective solved the problem. Why is this?

9. Atmosphere in mystery stories is important because it is often used to build up tension. Notice that in this story the climactic scene happens at night, in the darkness, underground. What kind of atmosphere is Doyle trying to create?

10. What is the difference between the detective of Holmes's type and the modern scientific crime fighter? Would Holmes have liked to use modern crime laboratory equipment, or would he have found it uninteresting and unchallenging?

If you like this story, you will be interested in

Doyle. *The Adventure of the Bruce-Partington Plans.*
The Speckled Band.
The Adventures of Sherlock Holmes (book of stories).
Edgar Allan Poe. *The Purloined Letter.*
Murders in the Rue Morgue.

H. H. MUNRO (SAKI)

The Storyteller

FEW writers, says Christopher Morley, are less profitable than Saki to write *about;* Saki exists only to be read.

There is not much to write about him. He was born in Burma in 1870, son of a British Army officer, and was brought up mostly in England, in the care of female relatives. He appears to have spent a peculiarly " aunty " childhood, and all his life he loved to write stories, like this one, of aunts being discomfited, or aunts being eaten by werewolves or meeting some other such well-deserved fate. He traveled in Europe and served for a short time in the Burma police. Then he had to come back to England to protect his health, and found he could earn a living by writing for the newspapers and magazines. He enlisted in the British Army at the beginning of World War I, and was killed in action in 1916.

He left behind him the charming, sometimes malicious, always whimsical little stories to which he signed the pen name Saki, borrowed from *The Rubáiyát* of Omar Khayyám, in which the cupbearer was named Saki. This English Saki was disarmingly light and simple. He made no attempt to be philosophic or weighty. But hardly a writer in his time could poke a sharp finger more skillfully into weak spots and false spots. With a few sentences he could show up the fatuousness of Victorian ways of bringing up children, or the emptiness of tea-table conversation, or the stiff artificiality of English party and club life. Yet it was a kind satire, a chuckling satire, which makes it a joy to read his stories aloud and which takes away their sting without removing their truth.

IT was a hot afternoon, and the railway carriage[1] was correspondingly sultry, and the next stop was at Templecombe, nearly an hour ahead. The occupants of the carriage were a small girl and a smaller girl and a small boy. An aunt belonging to the children occupied one corner seat, and the further corner seat on the opposite side was occupied by a bachelor who was a stranger to their party, but the small girls and the small boy emphatically occupied the compartment. Both the aunt and the children were conversational in a limited, persistent way, reminding one of the attentions of a housefly that refused to be discouraged. Most of the aunt's remarks seemed to begin with "Don't," and nearly all of the children's remarks began with "Why?" The bachelor said nothing out loud.

"Don't, Cyril, don't," exclaimed the aunt, as the small boy began smacking the cushions of the seat, producing a cloud of dust at each blow.

"Come and look out of the window," she added.

The child moved reluctantly to the window. "Why are those sheep being driven out of that field?" he asked.

"I expect they are being driven to another field where there is more grass," said the aunt weakly.

"But there is lots of grass in that field," protested the boy; "there's nothing else but grass there. Aunt, there's lots of grass in that field."

"Perhaps the grass in the other field is better," suggested the aunt fatuously.

"Why is it better?" came the swift, inevitable question.

"Oh, look at those cows!" exclaimed the aunt. Nearly every field along the line had contained cows or bullocks, but she spoke as though she were drawing attention to a rarity.

"Why is the grass in the other field better?" persisted Cyril.

The frown on the bachelor's face was deepening to a scowl. He was a hard, unsympathetic man, the aunt decided in her mind. She was utterly unable to come to any satisfactory decision about the grass in the other field.

The smaller girl created a diversion by beginning to recite "On

[1] **carriage: a compartment in railway coach.**

the Road to Mandalay." [1] She only knew the first line, but she put her limited knowledge to the fullest possible use. She repeated the line over and over again in a dreamy but resolute and very audible voice; it seemed to the bachelor as though someone had had a bet with her that she could not repeat the line aloud two thousand times without stopping. Whoever it was who had made the wager was likely to lose his bet.

"Come over here and listen to a story," said the aunt, when the bachelor had looked twice at her and once at the communication cord.

The children moved listlessly toward the aunt's end of the carriage. Evidently her reputation as a storyteller did not rank high in their estimation.

In a low, confidential voice, interrupted at frequent intervals by loud, petulant questions from her listeners, she began an unenterprising and deplorably uninteresting story about a little girl who was good, and made friends with everyone on account of her goodness, and was finally saved from a mad bull by a number of rescuers who admired her moral character.

"Wouldn't they have saved her if she hadn't been good?" demanded the bigger of the small girls. It was exactly the question that the bachelor had wanted to ask.

"Well, yes," admitted the aunt lamely, "but I don't think they would have run quite so fast to her help if they had not liked her so much."

"It's the stupidest story I've ever heard," said the bigger of the small girls, with immense conviction.

"I didn't listen after the first bit, it was so stupid," said Cyril.

The smaller girl made no actual comment on the story, but she had long ago recommenced a murmured repetition of her favorite line.

"You don't seem to be a success as a storyteller," said the bachelor suddenly from his corner.

The aunt bristled in instant defense at this unexpected attack.

"It's a very difficult thing to tell stories that children can both understand and appreciate," she said stiffly.

[1] **"On the Road to Mandalay"**: poem by Kipling, set to music and for many years a favorite concert song for baritones.

"I don't agree with you," said the bachelor.

"Perhaps *you* would like to tell them a story," was the aunt's retort.

"Tell us a story," demanded the bigger of the small girls.

"Once upon a time," began the bachelor, "there was a little girl called Bertha, who was extraordinarily good."

The children's momentarily aroused interest began at once to flicker; all stories seemed dreadfully alike, no matter who told them.

"She did all that she was told, she was always truthful, she kept her clothes clean, ate milk puddings as though they were jam tarts, learned her lessons perfectly, and was polite in her manners."

"Was she pretty?" asked the bigger of the small girls.

"Not as pretty as any of you," said the bachelor, "but she was horribly good."

There was a wave of reaction in favor of the story; the word horrible in connection with goodness was a novelty that commended itself. It seemed to introduce a ring of truth that was absent from the aunt's tales of infant life.

"She was so good," continued the bachelor, "that she won several medals for goodness, which she always wore, pinned on to her dress. There was a medal for obedience, another medal for punctuality, and a third for good behavior. They were large metal medals and they clicked against one another as she walked. No other child in the town where she lived had as many as three medals, so everybody knew that she must be an extra good child."

"Horribly good," quoted Cyril.

"Everybody talked about her goodness, and the Prince of the country got to hear about it, and he said that as she was so very good she might be allowed once a week to walk in his park, which was just outside the town. It was a beautiful park, and no children were ever allowed in it, so it was a great honor for Bertha to be allowed to go there."

"Were there any sheep in the park?" demanded Cyril.

"No," said the bachelor, "there were no sheep."

"Why weren't there any sheep?" came the inevitable question arising out of that answer.

The aunt permitted herself a smile, which might almost have been described as a grin.

"There were no sheep in the park," said the bachelor, "because the Prince's mother had once had a dream that her son would either be killed by a sheep or else by a clock falling on him. For that reason the Prince never kept a sheep in his park or a clock in his palace."

The aunt suppressed a gasp of admiration.

"Was the Prince killed by a sheep or by a clock?" asked Cyril.

"He is still alive, so we can't tell whether the dream will come true," said the bachelor unconcernedly; "anyway, there were no sheep in the park, but there were lots of little pigs running all over the place."

"What color were they?"

"Black with white faces, white with black spots, black all over, gray with white patches, and some were white all over."

The storyteller paused to let a full idea of the park's treasures sink into the children's imaginations; then he resumed:

"Bertha was rather sorry to find that there were no flowers in the park. She had promised her aunts, with tears in her eyes, that she would not pick any of the kind Prince's flowers, and she had meant to keep her promise, so of course it made her feel silly to find that there were no flowers to pick."

"Why weren't there any flowers?"

"Because the pigs had eaten them all," said the bachelor promptly. "The gardeners had told the Prince that you couldn't have pigs and flowers, so he decided to have pigs and no flowers."

There was a murmur of approval at the excellence of the Prince's decision; so many people would have decided the other way.

"There were lots of other delightful things in the park. There were ponds with gold and blue and green fish in them, and trees with beautiful parrots that said clever things at a moment's notice, and hummingbirds that hummed all the popular tunes of the day. Bertha walked up and down and enjoyed herself immensely, and thought to herself: 'If I were not so extraordinarily good I should not have been allowed to come into this beautiful park and enjoy all that there is to be seen in it,' and her three medals clinked against one another as she walked and helped to remind her how very good she really was. Just then an enormous wolf came prowling into the park to see if it could catch a fat little pig for its supper."

"What color was it?" asked the children, amid an immediate quickening of interest.

"Mud color all over, with a black tongue and pale gray eyes that gleamed with unspeakable ferocity. The first thing that it saw in the park was Bertha; her pinafore was so spotlessly white and clean that it could be seen from a great distance. Bertha saw the wolf and saw that it was stealing toward her, and she began to wish that she had never been allowed to come into the park. She ran as hard as she could, and the wolf came after her with huge leaps and bounds. She managed to reach a shrubbery of myrtle bushes and she hid herself in one of the thickest of the bushes. The wolf came sniffing among the branches, its black tongue lolling out of its mouth and its pale gray eyes glaring with rage. Bertha was terribly frightened, and thought to herself: 'If I had not been so extraordinarily good I should have been safe in the town at this moment.' However, the scent of the myrtle was so strong that the wolf could not sniff out where Bertha was hiding, and the bushes were so thick that he might have hunted about in them for a long time without catching sight of her, so he thought he might as well go off and catch a little pig instead. Bertha was trembling very much at having the wolf prowling and sniffing so near her, and as she trembled, the medal for obedience clinked against the medals for good conduct and punctuality. The wolf was just moving away when he heard the sound of the medals clinking and stopped to listen; they clinked again in a bush quite near him. He dashed into the bush, his pale gray eyes gleaming with ferocity and triumph, and dragged Bertha out and devoured her to the last morsel. All that was left of her were her shoes, bits of clothing, and the three medals for goodness."

"Were any of the little pigs killed?"

"No, they all escaped."

"The story began badly," said the smaller of the small girls, "but it had a beautiful ending."

"It is the most beautiful story that I ever heard," said the bigger of the small girls, with immense decision.

"It is the *only* beautiful story I have ever heard," said Cyril.

A dissentient opinion came from the aunt.

"A most improper story to tell to young children! You have undermined the effect of years of careful teaching."

"At any rate," said the bachelor, collecting his belongings preparatory to leaving the carriage, "I kept them quiet for ten minutes, which was more than you were able to do."

"Unhappy woman!" he observed to himself as he walked down the platform of Templecombe station; "for the next six months or so those children will assail her in public with demands for an improper story!"

READING WITH INSIGHT

1. If you have ever tried to figure out why something is funny, you have probably noticed that there are many different kinds of humor. There is fun that comes from play upon words, using them in strange and unusual ways. There is fun in the quick and smart retort, the wisecrack. There is fun in exaggeration such as you find in many of Mark Twain's stories. Then there is an entirely different kind of humor which comes from funny situations. Mark Twain was skillful in this kind of humor. James Thurber is at his best in this humor of situation. So was Robert Benchley, as you know if you have read "The Treasurer's Report."

Sometimes the humorist gets you to laugh at him, sometimes to laugh with him. Satire is the kind of fun in which you laugh at others.

On the basis of this description, discuss the humor of "The Storyteller." How does the author get you to laugh? What makes you laugh? What kind of humor is there in this story?

2. Compare Kipling's Mulvaney story with "The Storyteller." In what ways are they alike and different?

3. In order to make his point, Saki gives two examples of storytelling — that of the aunt and that of the bachelor. In what ways are they contrasted? How do they differ?

4. What is the reason for including the children's interruptions? How do they serve to contrast the two kinds of storytelling?

5. Saki uses two different methods of giving you the children's reactions to the stories. What are the two methods?

6. Are these children real? Are their questions real? From your experience, would you say that children are interested in stories of

bloodshed and the downfall of heroes and heroines? What kinds of stories do children like? In what respects do they like or dislike the same kinds of stories adults do? Do children usually want many details in their stories — for instance, the color of the wolf? Why? And what kind of details?

7. Would you have liked the story as well without the last paragraph?

8. What is the meaning of the story? What point does it have beyond the delight of its unexpected turns, and the discomfiture of a placid, proper, unimaginative person (a kind of person Saki thoroughly detested)?

9. Describe this story, if you can, in terms of rising action, climax, and falling action.

10. Most of this story is carried by dialogue. What important contributions are made by setting? By action?

11. *How* was the bachelor a good storyteller?

If you like this story, you will be interested in

Saki. *The Open Door.*
The Lumber Room.
Mrs. Packletide's Tiger.
Tobermory.

Leonard Q. Ross. Any of the stories in *The Education of H*Y*M*A*N K*A*P*L*A*N.*

Stephen Leacock. *A Hero in Homespun.*

Robert Benchley. *The Treasurer's Report.*

James Thurber. *The Night the Ghost Got In.*
The Secret Life of Walter Mitty.

JOHN GALSWORTHY

Timber

JOHN GALSWORTHY, son of a lawyer and himself an Oxford graduate in law, never enjoyed the practice of law and soon gave it up. To this fact we are indebted for a number of fine novels, plays, stories, essays, and poems.

He was born in a suburb of London in 1867, educated at Harrow and Oxford, and admitted to the bar. He had independent means, and therefore could afford to give up his law practice before it was well started and spend several years traveling around the world. It was on one of these trips that he met Joseph Conrad, who was then a seaman and just beginning to write. The young Galsworthy encouraged the young Conrad. They became friends, and both went on to become famous.

Galsworthy's most famous work is *The Forsyte Saga*, a collection of novels and interludes dealing with an English family, the Forsytes, through several generations. The number and richness of character portraits in the *Saga* is a remarkable accomplishment. Essentially, though, the *Saga* is a penetrating social criticism of what was happening to England between the Victorian era and years following World War I, and especially of the importance of property and changing attitudes toward property. The story in this book is cut from the same cloth as *The Forsyte Saga*. It too deals with an upperclass Englishman's attitude toward property, and it is quite as critical, and at the same time quite as detached and apparently impartial, as the novels.

Galsworthy died in 1933.

SIR Arthur Hirries, Baronet, of Hirriehugh, in a northern county, came to the decision to sell his timber in that state of mind — common during the War [1] — which may be called patrio-profiteering. Like newspaper proprietors, writers on strategy, shipbuilders, owners of works, makers of arms and the rest of the working classes at large, his mood was: "Let me serve my

[1] **the War:** World War I.

country, and if thereby my profits are increased, let me put up with it, and invest in National Bonds."

With an encumbered estate and some of the best coverts in that northern county, it had not become practical politics to sell his timber till the Government wanted it at all costs. To let his shooting [1] had been more profiable, till now, when a patriotic action and a stroke of business had become synonymous. A man of sixty-five, but not yet gray, with a reddish tinge in his mustache, cheeks, lips, and eyelids, slightly knock-kneed, and with large, rather spreading feet, he moved in the best circles in a somewhat embarrassed manner. At the enhanced price, the timber at Hirriehugh would enfranchise him for the remainder of his days. He sold it therefore one day of April when the War news was bad, to a Government official on the spot. He sold it at half past five in the afternoon, practically for cash down, and drank a stiff whisky and soda to wash away the taste of the transaction; for, though no sentimentalist, his great-great-grandfather had planted most of it, and his grandfather the rest. Royalty too had shot there in its time; and he himself (never much of a sportsman) had missed more birds in the rides and hollows of his fine coverts than he cared to remember. But the country was in need, and the price considerable. Bidding the Government official good-by, he lighted a cigar, and went across the Park to take a farewell stroll among his timber.

He entered the home covert by a path leading through a group of pear trees just coming into bloom. Sir Arthur Hirries had not much sense of natural beauty. But those pear trees impressed him, greenish-white against blue sky and fleecy thick clouds which looked as if they had snow in them. They were deuced pretty, and promised a good year for fruit, if they escaped the late frosts, though it certainly looked like freezing tonight! He paused a moment at the wicket gate to glance back at them — like scantily-clothed maidens posing on the outskirts of his timber. Such, however, was not the vision of Sir Arthur Hirries, who was considering how he should invest the balance of the cash down after paying off his mortgages. National Bonds — the country was in need!

Passing through the gate he entered the ride of the home covert.

[1] **to let his shooting:** to rent his land to hunting parties during the hunting seasons.

Variety lay like color on his woods. They stretched for miles, and his ancestors had planted almost every kind of tree – beech, oak, birch, sycamore, ash, elm, hazel, holly, pine; a lime tree and a hornbeam here and there, and further in among the winding coverts, spinneys and belts of larch. The evening air was sharp, and sleet showers came whirling from those bright clouds; he walked briskly, drawing at his richly fragrant cigar, the whisky still warm within him. He walked thinking, with a gentle melancholy slowly turning a little sulky, that he would never again be pointing out with his shooting stick to such or such a guest where he was to stand to get the best birds over him. The pheasants had been let down during the War, but he put up two or three old cocks who went clattering and whirring out to left and right; and rabbits crossed the rides quietly to and fro, within easy shot. He came to where Royalty had stood fifteen years ago during the last drive. He remembered Royalty saying: "Very pretty shooting at that last stand, Hirries; birds just about as high as I like them." The ground indeed rose rather steeply there, and the timber was oak and ash, with a few pines sprinkled into the bare grayish twiggery of the oaks, always costive in spring, and the just greening feather of the ashes.

"They'll be cutting those pines first," he thought – strapping trees, straight as the lines of Euclid,[1] and free of branches, save at their tops. In the brisk wind those tops swayed a little and gave forth soft complaint. "Three times my age," he thought; "prime timber." The ride wound sharply and entered a belt of larch, whose steep rise entirely barred off the rather sinister sunset – a dark and wistful wood, delicate dun and gray, whose green shoots and crimson tips would have perfumed the evening coolness, but for the cigar smoke in his nostrils. "They'll have this spinney for pit props,"[2] he thought; and, taking a cross ride through it, he emerged in a heathery glen of birch trees. No forester, he wondered if they would make anything of those whitened, glistening shapes. His cigar had gone out now, and he leaned against one of the satin-smooth stems, under the lacery of twig and bud, sheltering the flame of a relighting match. A hare lopped away among the bilberry shoots; a jay, painted like a fan, squawked and flustered past him up the glen.

[1] **Euclid:** the founder of geometry.

[2] **pit props:** supports for underground coal mines.

Interested in birds, and wanting just one more jay to complete a fine stuffed group of them, Sir Arthur, though devoid of a gun, followed, to see where "The beggar's" nest was. The glen dipped rapidly, and the character of the timber changed, assuming greater girth and solidity. There was a lot of beech here — a bit he did not know, for though taken in by the beaters, no guns could be stationed there because of the lack of undergrowth. The jay had vanished, and light had begun to fail. "I must get back," he thought, "or I shall be late for dinner." He debated for a moment whether to retrace his steps or to cut across the beeches and regain the home covert by a loop. The jay, reappearing to the left, decided him to cross the beech grove. He did so, and took a narrow ride up through a dark bit of mixed timber with heavy undergrowth. The ride, after favoring the left for a little, bent away to the right; Sir Arthur followed it hurriedly, conscious that twilight was gathering fast. It must bend again to the left in a minute! It did, and then to the right, and, the undergrowth remaining thick, he could only follow on, or else retrace his steps. He followed on, beginning to get hot in spite of a sleet shower falling through the dusk. He was not framed by Nature for swift traveling — his knees turning in and his toes turning out — but he went at a good bat, uncomfortably aware that the ride was still taking him away from home, and expecting it at any minute to turn left again. It did not, and hot, out of breath, a little bewildered, he stood still in three-quarter darkness, to listen. Not a sound save that of wind in the tops of the trees, and a faint creaking of timber, where two stems had grown athwart and were touching.

The path was a regular will-o'-the-wisp. He must make a beeline of it through the undergrowth into another ride! He had never before been amongst his timber in the dusk, and he found the shapes of the confounded trees more weird, and as if menacing, than he had ever dreamed of. He stumbled quickly on in and out of them among the undergrowth, without coming to a ride.

"Here I am stuck in this cursed wood!" he thought. To call these formidably encircling shapes "a wood" gave him relief. After all, it was *his* wood, and nothing very untoward could happen to a man in his own wood, however dark it might get; he could not be more than a mile and a half at the outside from his dining room! He looked at his watch, whose hands he could just see — nearly half past seven! The sleet had become snow, but it hardly fell on him, so thick was the timber just here. But he had no overcoat, and suddenly he felt that first sickening little drop in his chest, which presages alarm. Nobody knew he was in this cursed wood! And in a quarter of an hour it would be black as your hat! He *must* get on and out! The trees amongst which he was stumbling produced quite a sick feeling now in one who hitherto had never taken trees seriously. What monstrous growths they were! The thought that seeds, tiny seeds or saplings, planted by his ancestors, could attain such huge impending and imprisoning bulk — ghostly great growths mounting up to heaven and shutting off this world, exasperated and unnerved him. He began to run, caught his foot in a root and fell flat on his face. The cursed trees seemed to have a down on him! Rubbing elbows and forehead with his snow-wetted hands, he leaned against a trunk to get his breath, and summon the sense of direction to his brain. Once as a young man he had been " bushed " at night in Vancouver Island; quite a scary business! But he had come out all right, though his camp had been the only civilized spot within a radius of twenty miles. And here he was, on his own estate, within a mile or two of home, getting into a funk. It was childish! And he laughed. The wind answered, sighing and threshing in the treetops. There must be a regular blizzard blowing now, and, to judge by the cold, from the north — but whether northeast or northwest was the question. Besides, how keep definite direction without a compass, in the dark? The timber, too, with its thick trunks, diverted the wind into keen, directionless drafts. He looked up, but could make nothing of the two or three stars that he could see. It was a mess! And he lighted a second cigar with some difficulty, for he had begun to shiver. The wind in this blasted wood cut through his Norfolk jacket and crawled about his body, which had become hot from his exertion, and now felt clammy and half-frozen. This would mean pneumonia, if he didn't look out! And, half feeling his way from trunk to trunk, he started on again, but for all he could tell he might be going round in a circle, might even be crossing rides without realizing, and again that sickening drop occurred in his chest. He stood still and shouted. He had the feeling of shouting into walls of timber, dark and heavy, which threw the sound back at him.

" Curse you! " he thought; " I wish I'd sold you six months ago! "

The wind fleered and mowed in the treetops; and he started off again at a run in that dark wilderness; till, hitting his head against a low branch, he fell stunned. He lay several minutes unconscious, came to himself deadly cold, and struggled up on to his feet.

"By Jove!" he thought, with a sort of stammer in his brain; "this is a bad business! I may be out here all night!" For an unimaginative man, it was extraordinary what vivid images he had just then. He saw the face of the Government official who had bought his timber, and the slight grimace with which he had agreed to the price. He saw his butler, after the gong had gone, standing like a stuck pig by the sideboard, waiting for him to come down. What would they do when he didn't come? Would they have the *nous* [1] to imagine that he might have lost his way in the coverts, and take lanterns and search for him? Far more likely they would think he had walked over to "Greenlands" or "Berrymoor," and stayed there to dinner. And, suddenly, he saw himself slowly freezing out here, in the snowy night, among this cursed timber. With a vigorous shake, he butted again into the darkness among the tree trunks. He was angry now — with himself, with the night, with the trees; so angry that he actually let out with his fist at a trunk against which he had stumbled, and scored his knuckles. It was humiliating; and Sir Arthur Hirries was not accustomed to humiliation. In anybody else's wood — yes; but to be lost like this in one's own coverts! Well, if he had to walk all night, he would get out! And he plunged on doggedly in the darkness.

He was fighting with his timber now, as if the thing were alive and each tree an enemy. In the interminable stumbling exertion of that groping progress his angry mood gave place to half-comatose philosophy. Trees! His great-great-grandfather had planted them! His own was the fifth man's life, but the trees were almost as young as ever; they made nothing of a man's life! He sniggered: And a man made nothing of theirs! Did they know they were going to be cut down? All the better if they did, and were sweating in their shoes. He pinched himself — his thoughts were becoming so queer! He remembered that once, when his liver was out of order, trees had seemed to him like solid, tall diseases — bulbous, scarred, cavernous, witch-armed, fungoid emanations of the earth. Well, so they were!

[1] nous: intelligence.

And he was among them, on a snowy pitch-black night, engaged in this death struggle! The occurrence of the word death in his thoughts brought him up all standing. Why couldn't he concentrate his mind on getting out; why was he mooning about the life and nature of trees instead of trying to remember the conformation of his coverts, so as to rekindle in himself some sense of general direction? He struck a number of matches to get a sight of his watch again. Great heaven! He had been walking nearly two hours since he last looked at it; and in what direction? They said a man in a fog went round and round because of some kink in his brain! He began now to feel the trees, searching for a hollow trunk. A hollow would be some protection from the cold—his first conscious confession of exhaustion. He was not in training, and he was sixty-five. The thought: "I can't keep this up much longer," caused a second explosion of sullen anger. Here he was—for all he could tell—standing where he had sat perhaps a dozen times on his spread shooting stick; watching sunlight on bare twigs, or the nose of his spaniel twitching beside him, listening to the tap of the beaters' sticks, and the shrill, drawn-out: "Marrk! Cock over!" Would they let the dogs out, to pick up his tracks? No! ten to one they would assume he was staying the night at the Summertons', or at Lady Mary's, as he had done before now, after dining there. And suddenly his strained heart leaped. He had struck a ride again! His mind slipped back into place like an elastic let-go, relaxed, quivering gratefully. He had only to follow this ride, and somewhere, somehow, he would come out. And be hanged if he would let them know what a fool he had made of himself! Right or left—which way? He turned so that the flying snow came on his back, hurrying forward between the denser darkness on either hand, where the timber stood in walls, moving his arms across and across his body, as if dragging a concertina to full stretch, to make sure that he was keeping in the path. He went what seemed an interminable way like this, till he was brought up all standing by trees, and could find no outlet, no continuation. Turning in his tracks, with the snow in his face now, he retraced his steps till once more he was brought up short by trees. He stood panting. It was ghastly—ghastly! And in a panic he dived this way and that to find the bend, the turning, the way on. The sleet stung his eyes, the wind fleered and whistled, the boughs sloughed and moaned. He struck matches, trying to shade them with his cold, wet hands, but one by one they went out, and still he found no turning. The ride must have a blind alley at either end, the turning be down the side somewhere! Hope revived in him. Never say die! He began a second retracing of his steps, feeling the trunks along one side, to find a gap. His breath came with difficulty. What would old Brodley say if he could see him, soaked, frozen, tired to death, stumbling along in the darkness among this cursed timber — old Brodley who had told him his heart was in poor case! . . . A gap? Ah! No trunks — a ride at last! He turned, felt a sharp pain in his knee and pitched forward. He could not rise — the knee dislocated six years ago was out again. Sir Arthur Hirries clenched his teeth. Nothing more could happen to him! But after a minute — blank and bitter — he began to crawl along the new ride. Oddly he felt less discouraged and alarmed on hands and knee — for he could use but one. It was a relief to have his eyes fixed on the ground, not peering at the tree trunks; or perhaps there was less strain for the moment on his heart. He crawled, stopping every minute or so to renew his strength. He crawled mechanically, waiting for his heart, his knee, his lungs to stop him. The earth was snowed over, and he could feel its cold wetness as he scraped along. Good tracks to follow, if anybody struck them! But in this dark forest ——! In one of his halts, drying his hands as best he could, he struck a match, and sheltering it desperately, fumbled out his watch. Past ten o'clock! He wound the watch, and put it back against his heart. If only he could wind his heart! And squatting there he counted his matches — four! "Well," he thought grimly, "I won't light them to show me my blasted trees. I've got a cigar left; I'll keep them for that." And he crawled on again. He must keep going while he could!

He crawled till his heart and lungs and knee struck work; and, leaning his back against a tree, sat huddled together, so exhausted that he felt nothing save a sort of bitter heartache. He even dropped asleep, waking with a shudder, dragged from a dream armchair at the Club into this cold, wet darkness and the blizzard moaning in the trees. He tried to crawl again, but could not, and for some minutes stayed motionless, hugging his body with his arms. "Well," he thought vaguely, "I *have* done it!" His mind was in such lethargy that he could not even pity himself. His matches: could he make a fire? But he was no woodsman, and, though he groped around, could find no fuel that was not soaking wet. He scraped a hole and with what papers he had in his pockets tried to kindle the wet wood. No good! He had only two matches left now, and he remembered his cigar. He took it out, bit the end off, and began with infinite precautions to prepare for lighting it. The first burned, and the cigar drew. He had one match left, in case he dozed and let the thing go out. Looking up through the blackness he could see a star. He fixed his eyes on it, and leaning against the trunk, drew the smoke down into his lungs. With his arms crossed tightly on his breast he smoked very slowly. When it was finished — what? Cold, and the wind in the trees until the morning! Halfway through the cigar, he dozed off, slept a long time, and woke up so cold that he could barely summon vitality enough to strike his last match. By some miracle it burned, and he got his cigar to draw again. This time he smoked it nearly to its end, without mentality, almost without feeling, except the physical sense of bitter cold. Once with a sudden clearing of the brain, he thought faintly: "Thank God, I sold the —— trees, and they'll all come down!" The thought drifted away in frozen incoherence, drifted out like his cigar smoke into the sleet; and with a faint grin on his lips he dozed off again. . . .

An underkeeper found him at ten o'clock next morning, blue from cold, under a tall elm tree, within a mile of his bed, one leg stretched out, the other hunched up toward his chest, with its foot dug into the undergrowth for warmth, his head huddled into the collar of his coat, his arms crossed on his breast. They said he must have been dead at least five hours. Along one side snow had drifted against him; but the trunk had saved his back and other side. Above him, the spindly top boughs of that tall tree were covered with green-gold clusters of tiny crinkled elm flowers, against a deep blue sky — gay as a song of perfect praise. The wind had dropped, and after the cold of the night the birds were singing their clearest in the sunshine.

They did not cut down the elm tree under which they found his body, with the rest of the sold timber, but put a little iron fence round it. and a little tablet on its trunk.

READING WITH INSIGHT

1. One way to describe the progress of this story is in terms of what the woods meant to Sir Arthur at various times. What did the woods mean to him when he was a boy about to inherit the family estate? What did they mean to him when Royalty hunted in them? When he sold them? After he sold them? When he began to think he might be lost? When he was sure he was lost?

2. Sir Arthur's first mistake was to enter the woods so late. What was his second mistake?

3. How could he have saved himself, once he realized he was lost?

4. Trace the steps in his growing fear. How did fear change his way of thinking?

5. What symbolic meaning, if any, can you see in Sir Arthur smoking a cigar while he was freezing to death in the woods? In the fact that one of the trees he had just sold protected him partly from the snow?

6. How does the author get you excited over this story? Are the stirrings of hope in Sir Arthur's mind more conducive to suspense than his fears?

7. By what different means does Galsworthy tell you what kind of man Sir Arthur is?

8. Do you feel any sympathy for Sir Arthur? If so, why? Can you think of any person who is entirely bad or entirely good? Should any well-drawn character be entirely bad or entirely good?

9. What does the setting contribute to the story? Does the author use it chiefly as a background, or as a way of showing what the main character was thinking, or as an illustration of the story's meaning?

10. In what ways would it be inaccurate or incomplete to say that the meaning of this story is, "Selfishness always gets what it deserves"?

11. Is a part of the meaning the thought that, although man can sell property, still he has no real power over it, for property goes on but man dies? Are there any evidences in the story that this meaning is a part of Galsworthy's intention?

12. What experiences can you recall when you have felt a sense of the lasting quality of nature as compared to the transitory quality

of man? There are some famous poems on the subject. Can you name any of them?

If you like this story, you will be interested in

Galsworthy. *Quality.*
  The Forsyte Saga (novel).
W. Somerset Maugham. *The Lotus-Eater.*
  Lord Mountdrago.
Leo Tolstoy. *God Sees the Truth but Waits.*
Stephen Vincent Benét. *The Devil and Daniel Webster.*

H. G. WELLS

The Man Who Could Work Miracles

GALSWORTHY started as a lawyer, Wells as a teacher of science. Neither stayed very long with those professions. As might be expected, Galsworthy turned to writing social criticism, Wells to writing science fiction. An amazing group of scientific romances came from Wells' pen. A few of the titles will give you some idea of the content: *The Time Machine*, *The Invisible Man*, *The War in the Air*, *The War of the Worlds* (which, when made into a radio drama a few years ago, still possessed enough vitality to scare half of North America into shivers and to start a riot in South America!). He wrote other kinds of books, too — novels like *Mr. Britling Sees It Through*, social philosophy in *New Worlds for Old*, pleasant fiction like *The History of Mr. Polly* and *Tono-Bungay*, and, best known of all, *An Outline of History*. But through all his work runs the strain of scientific interest which he did not give up when he stopped teaching, but only transferred to a bigger classroom.

The story that follows is a fantasy like the scientific novels, and it turns on a scientific fact — that if the earth were suddenly to stop revolving, the people and houses and everything on it would fly out into the air at approximately 1,000 miles an hour. The story does not contain as much criticism of social conditions as the novels, but you can see in it the qualities of imagination which made the scientific romances so popular.

Wells was born in 1866, graduated from the University of London, died in 1946. The rest of his story is mostly what he wrote.

IT is doubtful whether the gift was innate. For my own part, I think it came to him suddenly. Indeed, until he was thirty he was a skeptic, and did not believe in miraculous powers. And here, since it is the most convenient place, I must mention that he was a little man, and had eyes of a hot brown, very erect red hair, a mustache with ends that he twisted up, and freckles. His name was George McWhirter Fotheringay — not the sort of name by any means to lead to any expectation of miracles — and he was clerk at Gomshott's. He was greatly addicted to assertive argument. It was while he was asserting the impossibility of miracles that he had his first intimation of his extraordinary powers. This particular argument was being held in the bar of the Long Dragon, and Toddy Beamish was conducting the opposition by a monotonous but effective "So *you* say," that drove Mr. Fotheringay to the very limit of his patience.

There were present, besides these two, a very dusty cyclist, landlord Cox, and Miss Maybridge, the perfectly respectable and rather portly barmaid of the Dragon. Miss Maybridge was standing with her back to Mr. Fotheringay, washing glasses; the others were watching him, more or less amused by the present ineffectiveness of the assertive method. Goaded by the tactics of Mr. Beamish, Mr. Fotheringay determined to make an unusual rhetorical effort. "Looky here, Mr. Beamish," said Mr. Fotheringay. "Let us clearly understand what a miracle is. It's something contrariwise to the course of nature done by power of Will, something what couldn't happen without being specially willed."

"So *you* say," said Mr. Beamish, repulsing him.

Mr. Fotheringay appealed to the cyclist, who had hitherto been a silent auditor, and received his assent — given with a hesitating cough and a glance at Mr. Beamish. The landlord would express no opinion, and Mr. Fotheringay, returning to Mr. Beamish, received the unexpected concession of a qualified assent to his definition of a miracle.

"For instance," said Mr. Fotheringay, greatly encouraged. "Here would be a miracle. That lamp, in the natural course of nature, couldn't burn like that, upsy-down, could it, Beamish?"

"*You* say it couldn't," said Beamish.

"And you?" said Fotheringay. "You don't mean to say — eh?"

"No," said Beamish reluctantly. "No, it couldn't."

"Very well," said Mr. Fotheringay. "Then here comes someone, as it might be me, along here, and stands as it might be here, and says to that lamp, as I might do, collecting all my will – 'Turn upsy-down without breaking, and go on burning steady,' and – Hullo! "

It was enough to make anyone say "Hullo! " The impossible, the incredible, was visible to them all. The lamp hung inverted in the air, burning quietly with its flame pointing down. It was as solid, as indisputable as ever a lamp was, the prosaic common lamp of the Long Dragon bar.

Mr. Fotheringay stood with an extended forefinger and the knitted brows of one anticipating a catastrophic smash. The cyclist, who was sitting next the lamp, ducked and jumped across the bar. Everybody jumped, more or less. Miss Maybridge turned and screamed. For nearly three seconds the lamp remained still. A faint cry of mental distress came from Mr. Fotheringay. "I can't keep it up," he said, "any longer." He staggered back, and the inverted lamp suddenly flared, fell against the corner of the bar, bounced aside, smashed upon the floor, and went out.

It was lucky it had a metal receiver, or the whole place would have been in a blaze. Mr. Cox was the first to speak, and his remark, shorn of needless excrescences, was to the effect that Fotheringay was a fool. Fotheringay was beyond disputing even so fundamental a proposition as that! He was astonished beyond measure at the thing that had occurred. The subsequent conversation threw absolutely no light on the matter so far as Fotheringay was concerned; the general opinion not only followed Mr. Cox very closely but very vehemently. Everyone accused Fotheringay of a silly trick, and presented him to himself as a foolish destroyer of comfort and security. His mind was in a tornado of perplexity, he was himself inclined to agree with them, and he made a remarkably ineffectual opposition to the proposal of his departure.

He went home flushed and heated, coat collar crumpled, eyes smarting and ears red. He watched each of the ten street lamps nervously as he passed it. It was only when he found himself alone in his little bedroom in Church Row that he was able to grapple seriously with his memories of the occurrence, and ask, "What on earth happened? "

He had removed his coat and boots, and was sitting on the bed with his hands in his pockets repeating the text of his defense for the seventeenth time, "*I* didn't want the confounded thing to upset," when it occurred to him that at the precise moment he had said the commanding words he had inadvertently willed the thing he said, and that when he had seen the lamp in the air he had felt that it depended on him to maintain it there without being clear how this was to be done. He had not a particularly complex mind, or he might have stuck for a time at that "inadvertently willed," embracing, as it does, the abstrusest problems of voluntary action; but as it was, the idea came to him with a quite acceptable haziness. And from that, following, as I must admit, no clear logical path, he came to the test of the experiment.

He pointed resolutely to his candle and collected his mind, though he felt he did a foolish thing. "Be raised up," he said. But in a second that feeling vanished. The candle was raised, hung in the air one giddy moment, and as Mr. Fotheringay gasped, fell with a smash on his toilet table, leaving him in darkness save for the expiring glow of its wick.

For a time Mr. Fotheringay sat in the darkness, perfectly still. "It did happen, after all," he said. "And 'ow I'm to explain it I *don't* know." He sighed heavily, and began feeling in his pockets for a match. He could find none, and he rose and groped about the toilet table. "I wish I had a match," he said. He resorted to his coat, and there were none there, and then it dawned upon him that miracles were possible even with matches. He extended a hand and scowled at it in the dark. "Let there be a match in that hand," he said. He felt some light object fall across his palm, and his fingers closed upon a match.

After several ineffectual attempts to light this, he discovered it was a safety match. He threw it down, and then it occurred to him that he might have willed it lighted. He did, and perceived it burning in the midst of his toilet-table mat. He caught it up hastily, and it went out. His perception of possibilities enlarged, and he felt for and replaced the candle in its candlestick. "Here! *you* be lit," said Mr. Fotheringay, and forthwith the candle was flaring, and he saw a little black hole in the toilet cover, with a wisp of smoke rising from it. For a time he stared from this to the little flame and back, and then looked up and met his own gaze in the looking glass. By this help he communed with himself in silence for a time.

"How about miracles now?" said Mr. Fotheringay at last, addressing his reflection.

The subsequent meditations of Mr. Fotheringay were of a severe but confused description. So far as he could see, it was a case of pure willing with him. The nature of his first experiences disinclined him for any further experiments except of the most cautious type. But he lifted a sheet of paper, and turned a glass of water pink and then green, and he created a snail, which he miraculously annihilated, and got himself a miraculous toothbrush. Somewhen in the small hours he had reached the fact that his will power must be of a particularly rare and pungent quality, a fact of which he had certainly had inklings before, but no certain assurance. The scare and perplexity of his first discovery was now qualified by pride in this evidence of singularity and by vague intimations of advantage. He became aware that the church clock was striking one, and as it did not occur to him that his daily duties at Gomshott's might be miraculously dispensed with, he resumed undressing, in order to get to bed without further delay. As he struggled to get his shirt over his head, he was struck with a brilliant idea. "Let me be in bed," he said, and found himself so. "Undressed," he stipulated; and, finding the sheets cold, added hastily, "and in my nightshirt—no, in a nice soft woolen nightshirt. Ah!" he said with immense enjoyment. "And now let me be comfortably asleep. . . ."

He awoke at his usual hour and was pensive all through breakfast time, wondering whether his overnight experience might not be a particularly vivid dream. At length his mind turned again to cautious experiments. For instance, he had three eggs for breakfast; two his landlady had supplied, good, but shoppy, and one was a delicious fresh goose egg, laid, cooked, and served by his extraordinary will. He hurried off to Gomshott's in a state of profound but carefully concealed excitement, and only remembered the shell of the third egg when his landlady spoke of it that night. All day he could do no work because of this astonishingly new self-knowledge, but this caused him no inconvenience, because he made up for it miraculously in his last ten minutes.

As the day wore on, his state of mind passed from wonder to elation, albeit the circumstances of his dismissal from the Long Dragon were still disagreeable to recall, and a garbled account of the matter that had reached his colleagues led to some badinage. It was evident he must be careful how he lifted frangible articles, but in other ways his gift promised more and more as he turned it over in his mind. He intended among other things to increase his personal property by unostentatious acts of creation. He called into existence a pair of very splendid diamond studs, and hastily annihilated them again as young Gomshott came across the countinghouse to his desk. He was afraid Gomshott might wonder how he had come by them. He saw quite clearly the gift required caution and watchfulness in its exercise, but so far as he could judge the difficulties attending its mastery would be no greater than those he had already faced in the study of cycling. It was that analogy, perhaps, quite as much as the feeling that he would be unwelcome in the Long Dragon, that drove him out after supper into the lane beyond the gasworks, to rehearse a few miracles in private.

There was possibly a certain want of originality in his attempts, for apart from his will power Mr. Fotheringay was not a very exceptional man. The miracle of Moses' rod [1] came to his mind, but the night was dark and unfavorable to the proper control of large miraculous snakes. Then he recollected the story of "Tannhäuser" [2] that he had read on the back of the Philharmonic program. That seemed to him singularly attractive and harmless. He stuck his walking stick into the turf that edged the footpath, and commanded the dry wood to blossom. The air was immediately full of the scent of roses, and by means of a match he saw for himself that this beautiful miracle was indeed accomplished. His satisfaction was ended by advancing footsteps. Afraid of a premature discovery of his powers, he addressed the blossoming stick hastily: "Go back." What he meant was "Change back"; but of course he was confused. The stick receded at a considerable velocity, and incontinently came a cry of anger and a bad word from the approaching person. "Who are you throwing brambles at, you fool?" cried a voice. "That got me on the shin."

[1] **miracle of Moses' rod:** it could turn into a snake.

[2] **Tannhäuser:** Wagner's opera, which deals with miraculous events in the enchanted cavern of the Venusberg.

"I'm sorry, old chap," said Mr. Fotheringay, and then realizing the awkward nature of the explanation, caught nervously at his mustache. He saw Winch, one of the three Immering constables, advancing.

"What d'yer mean by it?" asked the constable. "Hullo! It's you, is it? The gent that broke the lamp at the Long Dragon!"

"I don't mean anything by it," said Mr. Fotheringay. "Nothing at all."

"What d'yer do it for then?"

"Oh, bother!" said Mr. Fotheringay.

"Bother, indeed! D'yer know that stick hurt? What d'yer do it for, eh?"

For the moment Mr. Fotheringay could not think what he had done it for. His silence seemed to irritate Mr. Winch. "You've been assaulting the police, young man, this time. That's what *you* done."

"Look here, Mr. Winch," said Mr. Fotheringay, annoyed and confused, "I'm very sorry. The fact is —"

"Well?"

He could think of no way but the truth. "I was working a miracle He tried to speak in an offhand way, but try as he would he couldn't.

"Working a — ! 'Ere, don't you talk rot. Working a miracle, indeed! Miracle! Well, that's downright funny! Why, you's the chap that don't believe in miracles. . . . Fact is, this is another of your silly conjuring tricks — that's what this is. Now, I tell you —"

But Mr. Fotheringay never heard what Mr. Winch was going to tell him. He realized he had given himself away, flung his valuable secret to all the winds of heaven. A violent gust of irritation swept him to action. He turned on the constable swiftly and fiercely. "Here," he said, "I've had enough of this, I have! I'll show you a silly conjuring trick, I will! Go to Hades! Go, now!"

He was alone!

Mr. Fotheringay performed no more miracles that night, nor did he trouble to see what had become of his flowering stick. He returned to the town, scared and very quiet, and went to his bedroom. "Lord," he said, "it's a powerful gift — an extremely powerful gift. I didn't hardly mean as much as that. Not really. . . . I wonder what Hades is like?"

He sat on the bed taking off his boots. Struck by a happy thought he transferred the constable to San Francisco, and without any more interference with normal causation went soberly to bed. In the night he dreamed of the anger of Winch.

The next day Mr. Fotheringay heard two interesting items of news. Someone had planted a most beautiful climbing rose against the elder Mr. Gomshott's private house in the Lullaborough Road, and the river as far as Rawling's Mill was to be dragged for Constable Winch.

Mr. Fotheringay was abstracted and thoughtful all that day, and performed no miracles except certain provisions for Winch, and the miracle of completing his day's work with punctual perfection in spite of all the bee-swarm of thoughts that hummed through his mind. And the extraordinary abstraction and meekness of his manner was remarked by several people, and made a matter for jesting. For the most part he was thinking of Winch.

On Sunday evening he went to chapel, and oddly enough, Mr. Maydig, who took a certain interest in occult matters, preached about "things that are not lawful." Mr. Fotheringay was not a regular chapelgoer, but the system of assertive skepticism, to which I have already alluded, was now very much shaken. The tenor of the sermon threw an entirely new light on these novel gifts, and he suddenly decided to consult Mr. Maydig immediately after the service. So soon as that was determined, he found himself wondering why he had not done so before.

Mr. Maydig, a lean, excitable man with quite remarkably long wrists and neck, was gratified at a request for a private conversation from a young man whose carelessness in religious matters was a subject for general remark in the town. After a few necessary delays, he conducted him to the study of the Manse, which was contiguous to the chapel, seated him comfortably, and standing in front of a cheerful fire — his legs threw a Rhodian [1] arch of shadow on the opposite wall — requested Mr. Fotheringay to state his business.

At first Mr. Fotheringay was a little abashed, and found some difficulty in opening the matter. "You will scarcely believe me, Mr. Maydig, I am afraid" — and so forth for some time. He tried a question at last, and asked Mr. Maydig his opinion of miracles.

[1] **Rhodian:** the legs of the gigantic Colossus of Rhodes spanned the harbor entrance.

Mr. Maydig was still saying " Well " in an extremely judicial tone, when Mr. Fotheringay interrupted again: " You don't believe, I suppose, that some common sort of person — like myself, for instance — as it might be sitting here now, might have some sort of twist inside him that made him able to do things by his will."

" It's possible," said Mr. Maydig. " Something of the sort, perhaps, is possible."

" If I might make free with something here, I think I might show you by a sort of experiment," said Mr. Fotheringay. " Now, take that tobacco jar on the table, for instance. What I want to know is whether what I am going to do with it is a miracle or not. Just half a minute, Mr. Maydig, please."

He knitted his brows, pointed to the tobacco jar, and said: " Be a bowl of vi'lets."

The tobacco jar did as it was ordered.

Mr. Maydig started violently at the change, and stood looking from the thaumaturgist [1] to the bowl of flowers. He said nothing. Presently he ventured to lean over the table and smell the violets; they were fresh-picked and very fine ones. Then he stared at Mr. Fotheringay again.

" How did you do that? " he asked.

Mr. Fotheringay pulled his mustache. " Just told it — and there you are. Is that a miracle, or is it black art, or what is it? And what do you think's the matter with me? That's what I want to ask."

" It's a most extraordinary occurrence."

" And this day last week I knew no more that I could do things like that than you did. It came quite sudden. It's something odd about my will, I suppose, and that's as far as I can see."

" Is *that* — the only thing? Could you do other things besides that? "

" Lord, yes! " said Mr. Fotheringay. " Just anything." He thought, and suddenly recalled a conjuring entertainment he had seen. " Here! " He pointed. " Change into a bowl of fish — no, not that — change into a glass full of water with goldfish swimming in it. That's better! You see that, Mr. Maydig? "

" It's astonishing. It's incredible. You are either a most extraordinary . . . But no — "

[1] **thaumaturgist** (thô'mȧ-tûr'jĭst): a worker of miracles.

"I could change it into anything," said Mr. Fotheringay. "Just anything. Here! be a pigeon, will you?"

In another moment a blue pigeon was fluttering round the room and making Mr. Maydig duck every time it came near him. "Stop there, will you," said Mr. Fotheringay; and the pigeon hung motionless in the air. "I could change it back to a bowl of flowers," he said, and after replacing the pigeon on the table worked that miracle. "I expect you will want your pipe in a bit," he said, and restored the tobacco jar.

Mr. Maydig had followed all these later changes in a sort of ejaculatory silence. He stared at Mr. Fotheringay and, in a very gingerly manner, picked up the tobacco jar, examined it, replaced it on the table. "*Well!*" was the only expression of his feelings.

"Now, after that it's easier to explain what I came about," said Fotheringay; and proceeded to a lengthy and involved narrative of his strange experiences, beginning with the affair of the lamp in the Long Dragon and complicated by persistent allusions to Winch. As he went on, the transient pride Mr. Maydig's consternation had caused passed away; he became the very ordinary Mr. Fotheringay of everyday intercourse again. Mr. Maydig listened intently, the tobacco jar in his hand, and his bearing changed also with the course of the narrative. Presently, while Mr. Fotheringay was dealing with miracle of the third egg, the minister interrupted with a fluttering extended hand—

"It is possible," he said. "It is credible. It is amazing, of course, but it reconciles a number of difficulties. The power to work miracles is a gift—a peculiar quality like genius or second sight—hitherto it has come very rarely and to exceptional people. But in this case . . . I have always wondered at the miracles of Mahomet,[1] and at Yogi's miracles, and the miracles of Madame Blavatsky. But, of course! Yes, it is simply a gift! It carries out so beautifully the arguments of that great thinker"—Mr. Maydig's voice sank—"his Grace the Duke of Argyll. Here we plumb some profounder law—deeper than the ordinary laws of nature. Yes—yes. Go on. Go on!"

Mr. Fotheringay proceeded to tell of his misadventure with

[1] **Mahomet:** the great Mohammedan prophet. Yogi was the supposed founder of the yoga cult in India. Madame Blavatsky was a Russian theosophist. All of these were supposed to have the power to accomplish supernatural things.

Winch, and Mr. Maydig, no longer overawed or scared, began to jerk his limbs about and interject astonishment. "It's this what troubled me most," proceeded Mr. Fotheringay; "it's this I'm most mijitly in want of advice for; of course he's at San Francisco—wherever San Francisco may be—but of course it's awkward for both of us, as you'll see, Mr. Maydig. I don't see how he can understand what has happened, and I dare say he's scared and exasperated something tremendous, and trying to get at me. I dare say he keeps on starting off to come here. I send him back, by a miracle, every few hours, when I think of it. And of course, that's a thing he won't be able to understand, and it's bound to annoy him; and, of course, if he takes a ticket every time it will cost him a lot of money. I done the best I could for him, but of course it's difficult for him to put himself in my place. I thought afterward that his clothes might have got scorched, you know—if Hades is all it's supposed to be—before I shifted him. In that case I suppose they'd have locked him up in San Francisco. Of course I willed him a new suit of clothes on him directly I thought of it. But, you see, I'm already in a deuce of a tangle—"

Mr. Maydig looked serious. "I see you are in a tangle. Yes, it's a difficult position. How you are to end it . . ." He became diffuse and inconclusive.

"However, we'll leave Winch for a little and discuss the larger question. I don't think this is a case of the black art or anything of the sort. I don't think there is any taint of criminality about it at all, Mr. Fotheringay—none whatever, unless you are suppressing material facts. No, it's miracles—pure miracles—miracles, if I may say so, of the very highest class."

He began to pace the hearthrug and gesticulate, while Mr. Fotheringay sat with his arm on the table and his head on his arm, looking worried. "I don't see how I'm to manage about Winch," he said.

"A gift of working miracles—apparently a very powerful gift," said Mr. Maydig, "will find a way about Winch—never fear. My dear sir, you are a most important man—a man of the most astonishing possibilities. As evidence, for example! And in other ways, the things you may do . . ."

"Yes, *I've* thought of a thing or two," said Mr. Fotheringay. "But some of the things came a bit twisty. You saw that fish at first?

Wrong sort of bowl and wrong sort of fish. And I thought I'd ask someone."

"A proper course," said Mr. Maydig, "a very proper course — altogether the proper course." He stopped and looked at Mr. Fotheringay. "It's practically an unlimited gift. Let us test your powers, for instance. If they really *are* . . . if they really are all they seem to be."

And so, incredible as it may seem, in the study of the little house behind the Congregational Chapel, on the evening of Sunday, November 10, 1896, Mr. Fotheringay, egged on and inspired by Mr. Maydig, began to work miracles. The reader's attention is specially and definitely called to the date. He will object, probably has already objected, that certain points in this story are improbable, that if any things of the sort already described had indeed occurred, they would have been in all the papers a year ago. The details immediately following he will find particularly hard to accept, because among other things they involve the conclusion that he or she, the reader in question, must have been killed in a violent and unprecedented manner more than a year ago. Now a miracle is nothing if not improbable, and as a matter of fact the reader *was* killed in a violent and unprecedented manner a year ago. In the subsequent course of this story that will become perfectly clear and credible, as every right-minded and reasonable reader will admit. But this is not the place for the end of the story, being but little beyond the hither side of the middle. And at first the miracles worked by Mr. Fotheringay were timid little miracles — little things with the cups and parlor fitments, as feeble as the miracles of Theosophists,[1] and, feeble as they were, they were received with awe by his collaborator. He would have preferred to settle the Winch business out of hand, but Mr. Maydig would not let him. But after they had worked a dozen of these domestic trivialities, their sense of power grew, their imagination began to show signs of stimulation, and their ambition enlarged. Their first larger enterprise was due to hunger and the negligence of Mrs. Minchin, Mr. Maydig's housekeeper. The meal to which the minister conducted Mr. Fotheringay was certainly ill-laid and uninviting as refreshment for two industrious miracle-workers; but they were seated, and Mr.

[1] **Theosophists:** a religious sect which believes that human beings can communicate directly with God.

Maydig was descanting in sorrow rather than in anger upon his housekeeper's shortcomings, before it occurred to Mr. Fotheringay that an opportunity lay before him. "Don't you think, Mr. Maydig," he said, "if it isn't a liberty, I — "

"My dear Mr. Fotheringay! Of course! No — I didn't think."

Mr. Fotheringay waved his hand. "What shall we have? " he said, in a large, inclusive spirit, and at Mr. Maydig's order, revised the supper very thoroughly. "As for me," he said, eying Mr. Maydig's selection, "I am always particularly fond of a tankard of stout and a nice Welsh rarebit, and I'll order that. I ain't much given to Burgundy," and forthwith stout and Welsh rarebit promptly appeared at his command. They sat long at their supper, talking like equals, as Mr. Fotheringay presently perceived with a glow of surprise and gratification, of all the miracles they would presently do. "And, by the bye, Mr. Maydig," said Mr. Fotheringay, "I might perhaps be able to help you — in a domestic way."

"Don't quite follow," said Mr. Maydig, pouring out a glass of miraculous old Burgundy.

Mr. Fotheringay helped himself to a second Welsh rarebit out of vacancy, and took a mouthful. "I was thinking," he said, "I might be able (*chum, chum*) to work (*chum, chum*) a miracle with Mrs. Minchin (*chum, chum*) — make her a better woman."

Mr. Maydig put down the glass and looked doubtful. "She's — She strongly objects to interference, you know, Mr. Fotheringay. And — as a matter of fact — it's well past eleven and she's probably in bed and asleep. Do you think, on the whole — "

Mr. Fotheringay considered these objections. "I don't see that it shouldn't be done in her sleep."

For a time Mr. Maydig opposed the idea, and then he yielded. Mr. Fotheringay issued his orders, and a little less at their ease, perhaps, the two gentlemen proceeded with their repast. Mr. Maydig was enlarging on the changes he might expect in his housekeeper next day, with an optimism that seemed even to Mr. Fotheringay's super senses a little forced and hectic, when a series of confused noises from upstairs began. Their eyes exchanged interrogations, and Mr. Maydig left the room hastily. Mr. Fotheringay heard him calling up to his housekeeper and then his footsteps going softly up to her.

In a minute or so the minister returned, his step light, his face radiant. " Wonderful! " he said, " and touching! Most touching! "

He began pacing the hearthrug. " A repentance — a most touching repentance — through the crack of the door. Poor woman! A most wonderful change! She had got up. She must have got up at once. She had got up out of her sleep to smash a private bottle of brandy in her box. And to confess it too! . . . But this gives us — it opens — a most amazing vista of possibilities. If we can work this miraculous change in *her* . . ."

" The thing's unlimited seemingly," said Mr. Fotheringay. " And about Mr. Winch — "

" Altogether unlimited." And from the hearthrug Mr. Maydig, waving the Winch difficulty aside, unfolded a series of wonderful proposals — proposals he invented as he went along.

Now what those proposals were does not concern the essentials of this story. Suffice it that they were designed in a spirit of infinite benevolence, the sort of benevolence that used to be called post-prandial. Suffice it, too, that the problem of Winch remained unsolved. Nor is it necessary to describe how far that series got to its fulfillment. There were astonishing changes. The small hours found Mr. Maydig and Mr. Fotheringay careering across the chilly market square under the still moon, in a sort of ecstasy of thaumaturgy, Mr. Maydig all flap and gesture, Mr. Fotheringay short and bristling, and no longer abashed at his greatness. They had reformed every drunkard in the Parliamentary division, changed all the beer and alcohol to water (Mr. Maydig had overruled Mr. Fotheringay on this point), they had, further, greatly improved the railway communication of the place, drained Flinder's swamp, improved the soil of One Tree Hill, and cured the Vicar's wart. And they were going to see what could be done with the injured pier at South Bridge. " The place," gasped Mr. Maydig, " won't be the same place tomorrow. How surprised and thankful everyone will be! " And just at that moment the church clock struck three.

" I say," said Mr. Fotheringay, " that's three o'clock! I must be getting back. I've got to be at business by eight. And besides, Mrs. Wimms — "

" We're only beginning," said Mr. Maydig, full of the sweetness of unlimited power. " We're only beginning. Think of all the good we're doing. When people awake — "

" But — " said Mr. Fotheringay.

Mr. Maydig gripped his arm suddenly. His eyes were bright and wild. " My dear chap," he said, " there's no hurry. Look " — he pointed to the moon at the zenith — " Joshua! " [1]

" Joshua? " said Mr. Fotheringay.

" Joshua," said Mr. Maydig. " Why not? Stop it."

Mr. Fotheringay looked at the moon.

" That's a bit tall," he said after a pause.

" Why not? " said Mr. Maydig. " Of course it doesn't stop. You stop the rotation of the earth, you know. Time stops. It isn't as if we were doing harm."

" H'm! " said Mr. Fotheringay. " Well." He sighed. " I'll try. Here — "

He buttoned up his jacket and addressed himself to the habitable globe, with as good an assumption of confidence as lay in his power. " Jest stop rotating, will you," said Mr. Fotheringay.

Incontinently he was flying head over heels through the air at the rate of dozens of miles a minute. In spite of the innumerable circles he was describing per second, he thought; for thought is wonderful — sometimes as sluggish as flowing pitch, sometimes as instantaneous as light. He thought in a second, and willed. " Let me come down safe and sound. Whatever else happens, let me down safe and sound."

He willed it only just in time, for his clothes, heated by his rapid flight through the air, were already beginning to singe. He came down with a forcible, but by no means injurious, bump in what appeared to be a mound of fresh-turned earth. A large mass of metal and masonry, extraordinarily like the clock tower in the middle of the market square, hit the earth near him, ricocheted over him, and flew into stonework, bricks, and masonry, like a bursting bomb. A hurtling cow hit one of the large blocks and smashed like an egg. There was a crash that made all the most violent crashes of his past life seem like the sound of falling dust, and this was followed by a descending series of lesser crashes. A vast wind roared throughout

1 **Joshua**: The story of Joshua says that the sun stopped in the heavens so that the Hebrew army could complete the rout of its enemies by daylight.

earth and heaven, so that he could scarcely lift his head to look. For a while he was too breathless and astonished even to see where he was or what had happened. And his first movement was to feel his head and reassure himself that his streaming hair was still his own.

"Lord!" gasped Mr. Fotheringay, scarce able to speak for the gale, "I've had a squeak! What's gone wrong? Storms and thunder. And only a minute ago a fine night. It's Maydig set me on to this sort of thing. *What* a wind! If I go on fooling in this way I'm bound to have a thundering accident! Where's Maydig?"

"What a confounded mess everything's in!"

He looked about him so far as his flapping jacket would permit. The appearance of things was really extremely strange. "The sky's all right anyhow," said Mr. Fotheringay. "And that's about all that is all right. And even there it looks like a terrific gale coming up. But there's the moon overhead. Just as it was just now. Bright as midday. But as for the rest — Where's the village? Where's — where's anything? And what on earth set this wind a-blowing? *I* didn't order no wind."

Mr. Fotheringay struggled to get to his feet in vain, and after one failure, remained on all fours, holding on. He surveyed the moonlit world to leeward, with the tails of his jacket streaming over his head. "There's something seriously wrong," said Mr. Fotheringay. "And what it is — goodness knows."

Far and wide nothing was visible in the white glare through the haze of dust that drove before a screaming gale but tumbled masses of earth and heaps of inchoate ruins, no trees, no houses, no familiar shapes, only a wilderness of disorder vanishing at last into the darkness beneath the whirling columns and streamers, the lightnings and thunderings of a swiftly rising storm. Near him in the livid glare was something that might once have been an elm tree, a smashed mass of splinters, shivered from boughs to base, and further a twisted mass of iron girders — only too evidently the viaduct — rose out of the piled confusion.

You see, when Mr. Fotheringay had arrested the rotation of the solid globe, he had made no stipulation concerning the trifling movables upon its surface. And the earth spins so fast that the surface at its equator is traveling at rather more than a thousand miles an hour, and in these latitudes at more than half the pace. So that the village, and Mr. Maydig, and Mr. Fotheringay, and everybody and everything had been jerked violently forward at about nine miles per second — that is to say, much more violently than if they had been fired out of a cannon. And every human being, every living creature, every house, and every tree — all the world as we know it — had been so jerked and smashed and utterly destroyed. That was all.

These things Mr. Fotheringay did not, of course, fully appreciate. But he perceived that his miracle had miscarried, and with that a great disgust of miracles came upon him. He was in darkness now, for the clouds had swept away together and blotted out his momentary glimpse of the moon, and the air was full of fitful struggling tortured wraiths of hail. A great roaring of wind and waters filled earth and sky, and peering under his hand through the dust and sleet to windward, he saw by the play of the lightnings a vast wall of water pouring toward him.

"Maydig!" screamed Mr. Fotheringay's feeble voice amid the elemental uproar. "Here! — Maydig!"

"Stop!" cried Mr. Fotheringay to the advancing water. "Oh, for goodness' sake, stop!"

"Just a moment," said Mr. Fotheringay to the lightnings and thunder. "Stop jest a moment while I collect my thoughts. . . . And now what shall I do?" he said. "What *shall* I do? Lord! I wish Maydig was about."

"I know," said Mr. Fotheringay. "And for goodness' sake let's have it right *this* time."

He remained on all fours, leaning against the wind, very intent to have everything right.

"Ah!" he said. "Let nothing what I'm going to order happen until I say 'Off.' . . . Lord! I wish I'd thought of that before!"

He lifted his little voice against the whirlwind, shouting louder and louder in the vain desire to hear himself speak. "Now then! — here goes! Mind about that what I said just now. In the first place, when all I've got to say is done, let me lose my miraculous power, let my will become just like anybody else's will, and all these dangerous miracles be stopped. I don't like them. I'd rather I didn't work 'em. Ever so much. That's the first thing. And the second is — let me be back just before the miracles begin; let everything be just as it was before the blessed lamp turned up. It's a big job, but it's the last.

Have you got it? No more miracles, everything as it was — me back in the Long Dragon just before I drank my half-pint. That's it! Yes."

He dug his fingers into the mold, closed his eyes, and said, " Off! "

Everything became perfectly still. He perceived that he was standing erect.

" So *you* say," said a voice.

He opened his eyes. He was in the bar of the Long Dragon, arguing about miracles with Toddy Beamish. He had a vague sense of some great thing forgotten that instantaneously passed. You see, except for the loss of his miraculous powers, everything was back as it had been; his mind and memory therefore were now just as they had been at the time when this story began. So that he knew absolutely nothing of all that is told here, knows nothing of all that is told here to this day. And among other things, of course, he still did not believe in miracles.

" I tell you that miracles, properly speaking, can't possibly happen," he said, " whatever you like to hold. And I'm prepared to prove it up to the hilt."

" That's what *you* think," said Toddy Beamish, and " Prove it if you can."

" Looky here, Mr. Beamish," said Mr. Fotheringay. " Let us clearly understand what a miracle is. It's something contrariwise to the course of nature done by power of Will. . . ."

READING WITH INSIGHT

1. Wells calls this story " A Pantoum in Prose." If you do not know what a pantoum is, look it up in the dictionary and try to see why Wells feels that this story resembles a pantoum.

2. How does Wells give you hints of the excitement to come? Do these build up your interest?

3. This is the Aladdin's lamp plot. The test of this kind of story is whether the author's imagination is exciting enough. Does he do only the obvious things with the supernatural power, or does he do the unexpected, challenging things? You might begin this line of thought by asking yourself what you would do if you had the mysterious power suddenly given Fotheringay.

4. Of course, what is done with the mysterious power is limited by the kind of person Fotheringay is. Why didn't he realize the full force of his powers? Why didn't he use them for more important ends?

5. The basic question, then, is whether Wells did enough with the story. Is it funny enough? Is it imaginative enough? Has the fantasy an exciting quality? How would you compare the quality of imagination with Stephen Benét's "By the Waters of Babylon"?

6. Why do you suppose Wells chose a name like George McWhirter Fotheringay for his main character? Does such a name help to characterize him? What other stories can you think of in which the names themselves have helped to characterize?

7. How else could the story have ended? Would another ending have been satisfying to you?

8. What explanation is there in the story of why all this happened? Should there be such an explanation?

9. Do you think this really happened to Fotheringay, or was it a dream or a daydream? What evidence can you find to back up your answer?

10. What is Beamish's contribution to the story? Is he just a bit of decoration, or really important?

11. Is this story just an entertaining romp, or has it some general meaning?

12. What is the difference between Fotheringay's attitude toward his miraculous powers, and the feeling of modern scientists who have seen their science develop the atomic bomb?

If you like this story, you will be interested in

Wells. *The Stolen Bacillus.*
The War of the Worlds (novel).
The Time Machine (novel).
Stephen Vincent Benét. *By the Waters of Babylon.*
Eric Knight. *The Flying Yorkshireman.*

KATHERINE MANSFIELD

The Dill Pickle

KATHERINE MANSFIELD was born Kathleen Beauchamp, in Wellington, New Zealand, in 1888. She came to England to attend Queen's College, lived on in London to study music and write, married the English critic John Middleton Murry, and died in 1923 of tuberculosis. Katherine Mansfield was the name she signed to her stories.

"A small but exquisite talent" is one great critic's judgment of Miss Mansfield. It was small in the sense that she never wrote a novel, never tried to wrestle with great social and political issues; rather she took her subjects from the most ordinary events and the most ordinary people, and seemed to turn a bright light into them to illuminate the meaning behind everything they said and did. In this and many other respects, she was a follower of Chekov. To her, as to him, plot was secondary; surface events were secondary; everything of importance lay below the surface. Thus in reading one of Miss Mansfield's stories, you must not approach it as though it were an adventure story, because all the adventures in it are likely to be mental or psychological adventures. What the characters do is important only as it tells why they do it, and what it means. Therefore, you have to look below the surface for meanings and relationships and symbols.

But in Chekov you will never find such an exquisite polish and finish as shines on all Miss Mansfield's work. There is never a word wasted, never a word without meaning and importance. She wrote her stories by keeping them in her mind, working them over and over until they were ready to put down on paper with hardly a changed word.

AND then, after six years, she saw him again. He was seated at one of those little bamboo tables decorated with a Japanese vase of paper daffodils. There was a tall plate of fruit in front of him, and very carefully, in a way she recognized immediately as his "special" way, he was peeling an orange.

He must have felt that shock of recognition in her for he looked up and met her eyes. Incredible! He didn't know her! She smiled; he frowned. She came toward him. He closed his eyes an instant, but opening them his face lit up as though he had struck a match in a dark room. He laid down the orange and pushed back his chair, and she took her little warm hand out of her muff and gave it to him.

"Vera!" he exclaimed. "How strange. Really, for a moment I didn't know you. Won't you sit down? You've had lunch? Won't you have some coffee?"

She hesitated, but of course she meant to.

"Yes, I'd like some coffee." And she sat down opposite him.

"You've changed. You've changed very much," he said, staring at her with that eager, lighted look. "You look so well. I've never seen you look so well before."

"Really?" She raised her veil and unbuttoned her high fur collar. "I don't feel very well. I can't bear this weather, you know."

"Ah, no. You hate the cold — "

"Loathe it." She shuddered. "And the worst of it is that the older one grows — "

He interrupted her. "Excuse me," and tapped on the table for the waitress. "Please bring some coffee and cream." To her: "You are sure you won't eat anything? Some fruit, perhaps. The fruit here is very good."

"No, thanks. Nothing."

"Then that's settled." And smiling just a hint too broadly he took up the orange again. "You were saying — the older one grows — "

"The colder," she laughed. But she was thinking how well she remembered that trick of his — the trick of interrupting her — and of how it used to exasperate her six years ago. She used to feel then as though he, quite suddenly, in the middle of what she was saying, put his hand over her lips, turned from her, attended to something different, and then took his hand away, and with just the same slightly too broad smile, gave her his attention again — Now we are ready, That is settled.

"The colder!" He echoed her words, laughing too. "Ah, ah. You still say the same things. And there is another thing about you that is not changed at all — your beautiful voice — your beautiful way of speaking." Now he was very grave; he leaned toward her, and she smelled the warm, stinging scent of the orange peel. "You have only to say one word and I would know your voice among all other voices. I don't know what it is — I've often wondered — that makes your voice such a — haunting memory. . . . Do you remember that first afternoon we spent together at Kew Gardens? You were so surprised because I did not know the names of any flowers. I am still just as ignorant for all your telling me. But whenever it is very fine and warm, and I see some bright colors — It's awfully strange — I hear your voice saying: 'Geranium, marigold and verbena.' And I feel those three words are all I recall of some forgotten, heavenly language — You remember that afternoon?"

"Oh, yes, very well." She drew a long, soft breath, as though the paper daffodils between them were almost too sweet to bear. Yet, what had remained in her mind of that particular afternoon was an absurd scene over the tea table. A great many people taking tea in a Chinese pagoda, and he behaving like a maniac about the wasps — waving them away, flapping at them with his straw hat, serious and infuriated out of all proportions to the occasion. How delighted the sniggering tea drinkers had been. And how she had suffered.

But now, as he spoke, that memory faded. His was the truer. Yes, it had been a wonderful afternoon, full of geranium and marigold and verbena — and warm sunshine. Her thoughts lingered over the last two words as though she sang them.

In the warmth, as it were, another memory unfolded. She saw herself sitting on a lawn. He lay beside her, and suddenly, after a long silence, he rolled over and put his head in her lap.

"I wish," he said, in a low, troubled voice, "I wish that I had taken poison and were about to die — here now!"

At that moment, a little girl in a white dress, holding a long, dripping water lily, dodged from behind a bush, stared at them, and dodged back again. But he did not see. She leaned over him.

"Ah, why do you say that? I could not say that."

But he gave a kind of soft moan, and taking her hand he held it to his cheek.

"Because I know I am going to love you too much—far too much. And I shall suffer so terribly, Vera, because you never, never will love me."

He was certainly far better looking now than he had been then. He had lost that dreamy vagueness and indecision. Now he had the air of a man who has found his place in life and fills it with a confidence and an assurance which was, to say the least, impressive. He must have made money, too. His clothes were admirable, and at that moment he pulled a Russian cigarette case out of his pocket.

"Won't you smoke?"

"Yes, I will." She hovered over them. "They look very good."

"I think they are. I get them made for me by a little man in St. James's Street.[1] I don't smoke very much. I'm not like you—but when I do, they must be delicious, very fresh cigarettes. Smoking isn't a habit with me; it's a luxury—like perfume. Are you still so fond of perfumes? Ah, when I was in Russia—"

She broke in: "You've really been to Russia?"

"Oh, yes. I was there for over a year. Have you forgotten how we used to talk of going there?"

"No, I've not forgotten."

He gave a strange half laugh and leaned back in his chair. "Isn't it curious? I have really carried out all those journeys that we planned. Yes, I have been to all those places that we talked of, and stayed in them long enough to—as you used to say, 'air oneself' in them. In fact I have spent the last three years of my life traveling all the time. Spain, Corsica, Siberia, Russia, Egypt. The only country left is China, and I mean to go there, too, when the war is over."

As he spoke, so lightly, tapping the end of his cigarette against the ash tray, she felt the strange beast that had slumbered so long within her bosom stir, stretch itself, yawn, prick up its ears, and suddenly bound to its feet, and fix its longing, hungry stare upon those faraway places. But all she said was, smiling gently: "How I envy you."

He accepted that. "It has been," he said, "very wonderful—especially Russia. Russia was all that we had imagined, and far, far more.

[1] St. James's Street: a street in London.

I even spent some days on a river boat on the Volga. Do you remember that boatman's song you used to play? "

" Yes." It began to play in her mind as she spoke.

" Do you ever play it now? "

" No, I've no piano."

He was amazed at that. " But what has become of your beautiful piano? "

She made a little grimace. " Sold. Ages ago."

" But you were so fond of music," he wondered.

" I've no time for it now," said she.

He let it go at that. " That river life," he went on, " is something quite special. After a day or two you cannot realize that you have ever known another. And it is not necessary to know the language – the life of the boat creates a bond between you and the people that's more than sufficient. You eat with them, pass the day with them, and in the evening there is that endless singing."

She shivered, hearing the boatman's song break out again loud and tragic, and seeing the boat floating on the darkening river with melancholy trees on either side – " Yes, I should like that," she said, stroking her muff.

" You'd like almost everything about Russian life," he said warmly. " It's so informal, so impulsive, so free without question. And then the peasants are so splendid. They are such human beings – yes, that is it. Even the man who drives your carriage has – has some real part in what is happening. I remember the evening a party of us, two friends of mine and the wife of one of them, went for a picnic by the Black Sea. We took supper and champagne and ate and drank on the grass. And while we were eating the coachman came up. 'Have a dill pickle,' he said. He wanted to share with us. That seemed to me so right, so – you know what I mean? "

And she seemed at that moment to be sitting on the grass beside the mysteriously Black Sea, black as velvet, and rippling against the banks in silent, velvet waves. She saw the carriage drawn up to one side of the road, and the little group on the grass, their faces and hands white in the moonlight. She saw the pale dress of the woman outspread and her folded parasol, lying on the grass like a huge pearl crochet hook. Apart from them, with his supper in a cloth on his knees, sat the coachman. " Have a dill pickle," said he, and although she was not certain what a dill pickle was, she saw the greenish glass jar with a red chili like a parrot's beak glimmering through. She sucked in her cheeks; the dill pickle was terribly sour –

"Yes, I know perfectly what you mean," she said.

In the pause that followed they looked at each other. In the past when they had looked at each other like that they had felt such a boundless understanding between them that their souls had, as it were, put their arms around each other and dropped into the same sea, content to be drowned, like mournful lovers. But now, the surprising thing was that it was he who held back. He who said:

"What a marvelous listener you are. When you look at me with those wild eyes I feel that I could tell you things that I would never breathe to another human being."

Was there just a hint of mockery in his voice or was it her fancy? She could not be sure.

"Before I met you," he said, "I had never spoken of myself to anybody. How well I remember one night, the night that I brought you the little Christmas tree, telling you all about my childhood. And of how I was so miserable that I ran away and lived under a cart in our yard for two days without being discovered. And you listened, and your eyes shone, and I felt that you had even made the little Christmas tree listen too, as in a fairy story."

But of that evening she had remembered a little pot of caviar. It had cost seven and sixpence.[1] He could not get over it. Think of it – a tiny jar like that costing seven and sixpence. While she ate it he watched her, delighted and shocked.

"No, really, that is eating money. You could not get seven shillings into a little pot that size. Only think of the profit they must make – " And he had begun some immensely complicated calculations – But now good-by to the caviar. The Christmas tree was on the table, and the little boy lay under the cart with his head pillowed on the yard dog.

"The dog was called Bosun," she cried delightedly.

But he did not follow. "Which dog? Had you a dog? I don't remember a dog at all."

"No, no. I mean the yard dog when you were a little boy." He laughed and snapped the cigarette case to.

[1] **seven and sixpence: at that time, about $1.80.**

"Was he? Do you know I had forgotten that. It seems such ages ago. I cannot believe that it is only six years. After I had recognized you today — I had to take such a leap — I had to take a leap over my whole life to get back to that time. I was such a kid then." He drummed on the table. "I've often thought how I must have bored you. And now I understand so perfectly why you wrote to me as you did — although at the time that letter nearly finished my life. I found it again the other day, and I couldn't help laughing as I read it. It was so clever — such a true picture of me." He glanced up. "You're not going?"

She had buttoned her collar again and drawn down her veil.

"Yes, I am afraid I must," she said, and managed a smile. Now she knew that he had been mocking.

"Ah, no, please," he pleaded. "Don't go just for a moment," and he caught up one of her gloves from the table and clutched at it as if that would hold her. "I see so few people to talk to nowadays, that I have turned into a sort of barbarian," he said. "Have I said something to hurt you?"

"Not a bit," she lied. But as she watched him draw her glove through his fingers, gently, gently, her anger really did die down, and besides, at the moment he looked more like himself of six years ago —

"What I really wanted then," he said softly, "was to be a sort of carpet — to make myself into a sort of carpet for you to walk on so that you need not be hurt by the sharp stones and the mud that you hated so. It was nothing more positive than that — nothing more selfish. Only I did desire, eventually, to turn into a magic carpet and carry you away to all those lands you longed to see."

As he spoke she lifted her head as though she drank something; the strange beast in her bosom began to purr —

"I felt that you were more lonely than anybody else in the world," he went on, "and yet, perhaps, that you were the only person in the world who was really, truly alive. Born out of your time," he murmured, stroking the glove, "fated."

Ah, God! What had she done! How had she dared to throw away her happiness like this. This was the only man who had ever understood her. Was it too late? Could it be too late? *She* was that glove that he held in his fingers —

"And then the fact that you had no friends and never had made friends with people. How I understood that, for neither had I. Is it just the same now?"

"Yes," she breathed. "Just the same. I am as alone as ever."

"So am I," he laughed gently, "just the same."

Suddenly with a quick gesture he handed her back the glove and scraped his chair on the floor. "But what seemed to me so mysterious then is perfectly plain to me now. And to you, too, of course – It simply was that we were such egoists, so self-engrossed, so wrapped up in ourselves that we hadn't a corner in our hearts for anybody else. Do you know," he cried, naïve and hearty, and dreadfully like another side of that old self again, "I began studying a Mind System when I was in Russia, and I found that we were not peculiar at all. It's quite a well-known form of – "

She had gone. He sat there, thunderstruck, astounded beyond words – And then he asked the waitress for his bill.

"But the cream has not been touched," he said. "Please do not charge me for it."

READING WITH INSIGHT

1. This story gives much in little. Almost every word counts. Recall exactly what happens in the story. How many characters are there? What do they do? How much of the setting is described? Can you recall another story in this book which has as little action?

2. The story, of course, is only one scene in a much longer story which we are left to imagine. How much that has previously happened between and to these characters can you reconstruct? In what sense is this story really the climax of the longer untold story? Outline this longer story as it might have been written.

3. What do you learn about the two characters by hearing what different things they remember?

4. What does his habit of interrupting her tell you about him?

5. What evidence of his stinginess is there in the story? Of her need of money? Recall the last paragraph of the story. How is that example of his stinginess related to the meaning of the story?

6. What does Miss Mansfield tell you *directly* about the charac-

ters? How much of what you know about them do you have to infer from their actions, speech, and appearance?

7. Was the man mocking the lady? Trying to hurt her? Or simply not understanding what he was doing to her?

8. Why does Miss Mansfield start the story, "And then . . ."? Is she trying to give it a conversational tone? Trying to give the impression that what is about to happen in the story was connected with previous events?

9. What is meant by the several references to "the strange beast in her bosom"?

10. What evidence is there in the story that the characters have changed or not changed since their last meeting?

11. What evidence is there that they are both self-centered? Was that why they could never be happy together? Try to describe the meaning of the story in terms of self-centeredness.

12. Does the dill pickle symbolize anything in particular? For a clue, reread the paragraph immediately following the first mention of the dill pickle.

If you like this story, you will be interested in

Mansfield. *A Cup of Tea.*
The Doll's House.
Marriage à la Mode.
Anton Chekov. *The Lament.*
Katherine Anne Porter. *The Jilting of Granny Weatherall.*
Manuel Komroff. *Napoleon's Hat Under Glass.*

W. SOMERSET MAUGHAM

The Lotus-Eater

GOOD writing," W. Somerset Maugham once said, "should be like the conversation of a well-bred man." You will see that the following story fits his definition of good writing admirably. Clifton Fadiman once said of Maugham that "to read his stories is like listening to the reminiscent talk of a man who has been everywhere and seen everything, but prefers not to absorb too much, not to take anything too seriously or too frivolously."

Maugham was born in Paris in 1874. His father was a British lawyer, and Maugham went to school in England and at Heidelberg, and studied medicine in London. He never practiced medicine, but his experiences as a medical student helped give him material for his best-known novel, *Of Human Bondage*. He has traveled all over the world, and has lived for many of his later years in France and recently in the United States. His stories, novels, and plays have all been popular, and he has written a good deal of trenchant criticism.

In the introduction to his fine anthology of stories, *Tellers of Tales,* Maugham has explained what kind of story he tries to write. At the base of it, he says, is an anecdote. "You could tell it over the dinner table or in a ship's smoking room and hold the attention of your listeners. . . . But of course it is much more than an anecdote. . . . The scene is set before you with brevity, as the medium requires, but with clearness; and the persons concerned, the life they lead and their deterioration, are shown to you with just the amount of detail that is needed to make the circumstances of the case plain. You are told everything that you should know about them. From this appears the second excellence of this sort of story: when you have read it to find out what happens you can read it again for the cleverness of the telling. . . . This brings me to the third characteristic of this kind of story. The author does not copy life;

he arranges it in order the better to interest, excite, and surprise. This has caused the sort of narrative with which I am now dealing to fall of late years into some discredit. People say that in real life things do not happen with this neatness; real life is an affair of broken threads and loose ends: to arrange them into a pattern falsifies. [The author of this kind of story] does not mind; he is not aiming at a transcription of life, but at a dramatization of it."

The story that follows is an admirable example of Maugham's own literary theory.

MOST people, the vast majority in fact, lead the lives that circumstances have thrust upon them, and though some repine, looking upon themselves as round pegs in square holes, and think that if things had been different they might have made a much better showing, the greater part accept their lot, if not with serenity, at all events with resignation. They are like tramcars [1] traveling forever on the selfsame rails. They go backward and forward, backward and forward, inevitably, till they can go no longer and then are sold as scrap iron. It is not often that you find a man who has boldly taken the course of his life into his own hands. When you do, it is worth while having a good look at him.

That was why I was curious to meet Thomas Wilson. It was an interesting and a bold thing he had done. Of course the end was not yet, and until the experiment was concluded it was impossible to call it successful. But from what I had heard it seemed he must be an odd sort of fellow, and I thought I should like to know him. I had been told he was reserved, but I had a notion that with patience and tact I could persuade him to confide in me. I wanted to hear the facts from his own lips. People exaggerate, they love to romanticize, and I was quite prepared to discover that his story was not nearly so singular as I had been led to believe.

And this impression was confirmed when at last I made his acquaintance. It was on the Piazza in Capri,[2] where I was spending the

[1] **tramcars**: trolley cars.

[2] **Capri**: you will find the Island of Capri off the coast of Italy near Naples. Most of the scenery mentioned in this story is on Capri or visible from it. This is a region of great beauty. The isle itself is a famous beauty spot, and it is al-

month of August at a friend's villa, and a little before sunset, when most of the inhabitants, native and foreign, gather together to chat with their friends in the cool of the evening. There is a terrace that overlooks the Bay of Naples, and when the sun sinks slowly into the sea the island of Ischia is silhouetted against a blaze of splendor. It is one of the most lovely sights in the world. I was standing there with my friend and host watching it, when suddenly he said:

"Look, there's Wilson."

"Where?"

"The man sitting on the parapet, with his back to us. He's got a blue shirt on."

I saw an undistinguished back and a small head of gray hair short and rather thin.

"I wish he'd turn round," I said.

"He will presently."

"Ask him to come and have a drink with us at Morgano's."

"All right."

The instant of overwhelming beauty had passed and the sun, like the top of an orange, was dipping into a wine-red sea. We turned round and, leaning our backs against the parapet, looked at the people who were sauntering to and fro. They were all talking their heads off, and the cheerful noise was exhilarating. Then the church bell, rather cracked, but with a fine resonant note, began to ring. The Piazza at Capri, with its clock tower over the footpath that leads up from the harbor, with the church up a flight of steps, is a perfect setting for an opera by Donizetti,[1] and you felt that the voluble crowd might at any moment break out into a rattling chorus. It was charming and unreal.

I was so intent on the scene that I had not noticed Wilson get off the parapet and come toward us. As he passed us, my friend stopped him.

"Hulloa, Wilson, I haven't seen you bathing the last few days."

"I've been bathing on the other side for a change."

---

most directly opposite the Bay of Naples, which has sometimes been called the world's most beautiful harbor. Vesuvius overlooks this harbor, still smokes and rumbles. The ruins of Pompeii are at the foot of Vesuvius.

[1] Donizetti: composer of Italian opera. Perhaps his most famous is "Lucia di Lammermoor."

My friend then introduced me. Wilson shook hands with me politely, but with indifference; a great many strangers come to Capri for a few days, or a few weeks, and I had no doubt he was constantly meeting people who came and went; and then my friend asked him to come along and have a drink with us.

"I was just going back to supper," he said.

"Can't it wait?" I asked.

"I suppose it can," he smiled.

Though his teeth were not very good, his smile was attractive. It was gentle and kindly. He was dressed in a blue cotton shirt and a pair of gray trousers, much creased and none too clean, of a thin canvas, and on his feet he wore a pair of very old espadrilles. The getup was picturesque, and very suitable to the place and the weather, but it did not at all go with his face. It was a lined, long face, deeply sunburned, thin-lipped, with small gray eyes rather close together and tight, neat features. The gray hair was carefully brushed. It was not a plain face — indeed in his youth Wilson might have been good-looking — but a prim one. He wore the blue shirt open at the neck, and the gray canvas trousers, not as though they belonged to him, but as though, shipwrecked in his pajamas, he had been fitted out with odd garments by compassionate strangers. Notwithstanding this careless attire he looked like the manager of a branch office in an insurance company, who should by rights be wearing a black coat with pepper and salt trousers, a white collar and an unobjectionable tie. I could very well see myself going to him to claim the insurance money when I had lost a watch, and being rather disconcerted, while I answered the questions he put to me, by his obvious impression, for all his politeness, that people who made such claims were either fools or knaves.

Moving off, we strolled across the Piazza and down the street till we came to Morgano's. We sat in the garden. Around us people were talking in Russian, German, Italian, and English. We ordered drinks. Donna [1] Lucia, the host's wife, waddled up and in her low, sweet voice passed the time of day with us. Though middle-aged now and portly, she had still traces of the wonderful beauty that, thirty years before, had driven artists to paint so many bad portraits of her. Her eyes, large and liquid, were the eyes of Hera, and her

[1] **Donna:** lady; not a title of nobility; used more like "Mrs."

smile was affectionate and gracious. We three gossiped for a while, for there is always a scandal of one sort or another in Capri to make a topic of conversation, but nothing was said of particular interest, and in a little while Wilson got up and left us. Soon afterward we strolled up to my friend's villa to dine. On the way he asked me what I had thought of Wilson.

"Nothing," I said. "I don't believe there's a word of truth in your story."

"Why not?"

"He isn't the sort of man to do that sort of thing."

"How does anyone know what anyone is capable of?"

"I should put him down as an absolutely normal man of business who's retired on a comfortable income from gilt-edged securities. I think your story's just the ordinary Capri tittle-tattle."

"Have it your own way," said my friend.

We were in the habit of bathing at a beach called the Baths of Tiberius.[1] We took a fly down the road to a certain point and then wandered through lemon groves and vineyards, noisy with cicadas and heavy with the hot smell of the sun, till we came to the top of the cliff down which a steep winding path led to the sea. A day or two later, just before we got down, my friend said:

"Oh, there's Wilson back again."

We scrunched over the beach, the only drawback to the bathing place being that it was shingle and not sand, and as we came along Wilson saw us and waved. He was standing up, a pipe in his mouth, and he wore nothing but a pair of trunks. His body was dark brown, thin but not emaciated, and, considering his wrinkled face and gray hair, youthful. Hot from our walk, we undressed quickly and plunged at once into the water. Six feet from the shore it was thirty feet deep, but so clear that you could see the bottom. It was warm, yet invigorating.

When I got out, Wilson was lying on his belly, with a towel under him, reading a book. I lit a cigarette and sat down beside him.

"Had a nice swim?" he asked.

He put his pipe inside his book to mark the place and, closing it, put it down on the pebbles beside him. He was evidently willing to talk.

[1] **Tiberius:** Roman emperor.

" Lovely," I said. " It's the best bathing in the world."

" Of course people think those were the Baths of Tiberius." He waved his hand toward a shapeless mass of masonry that stood half in the water and half out. " But that's all rot. It was just one of his villas, you know."

I did. But it is just as well to let people tell you things when they want to. It disposes them kindly toward you if you suffer them to impart information. Wilson gave a chuckle.

" Funny old fellow, Tiberius. Pity they're saying now there's not a word of truth in all those stories about him."

He began to tell me all about Tiberius. Well, I had read my Suetonius [1] too, and I had read histories of the Early Roman Empire, so there was nothing very new to me in what he said. But I observed that he was not ill-read. I remarked on it.

" Oh, well, when I settled down here I was naturally interested, and I have plenty of time for reading. When you live in a place like this, with all its associations, it seems to make history so actual. You might almost be living in historical times yourself."

I should remark here that this was in 1913. The world was an easy, comfortable place, and no one could have imagined that anything might happen seriously to disturb the serenity of existence.

" How long have you been here? " I asked.

" Fifteen years." He gave the blue and placid sea a glance, and a strangely tender smile hovered on his thin lips. " I fell in love with the place at first sight. You've heard, I daresay, of the mythical German who came here on the Naples boat just for lunch and a look at the Blue Grotto and stayed forty years; well, I can't say I exactly did that, but it's come to the same thing in the end. Only it won't be forty years in my case. Twenty-five. Still, that's better than a poke in the eye with a sharp stick."

I waited for him to go on. For what he had just said looked indeed as though there might be something after all in the singular story I had heard. But at that moment my friend came dripping out of the water very proud of himself because he had swum a mile, and the conversation turned to other things.

After that I met Wilson several times, either in the Piazza or on the beach. He was amiable and polite. He was always pleased to have

[1] **Suetonius:** Roman historian, who wrote the lives of the Caesars.

a talk and I found out that he knew not only every inch of the island but also the adjacent mainland. He had read a great deal on all sorts of subjects, but his specialty was the history of Rome, and on this he was very well informed. He seemed to have little imagination and to be of no more than average intelligence. He laughed a good deal, but with restraint, and his sense of humor was tickled by simple jokes. A commonplace man. I did not forget the odd remark he had made during the first short chat we had had by ourselves, but he never so much as approached the topic again. One day on our return from the beach, dismissing the cab at the Piazza, my friend and I told the driver to be ready to take us up to Anacapri at five. We were going to climb Monte Solaro, dine at a tavern we favored, and walk down in the moonlight. For it was full moon, and the views by night were lovely. Wilson was standing by while we gave the cabman instructions, for we had given him a lift to save him the hot dusty walk, and more from politeness than for any other reason I asked him if he would care to join us.

"It's my party," I said.

"I'll come with pleasure," he answered.

But when the time came to set out, my friend was not feeling well, he thought he had stayed too long in the water, and would not face the long and tiring walk. So I went alone with Wilson. We climbed the mountain, admired the spacious view, and got back to the inn as night was falling, hot, hungry, and thirsty. We had ordered our dinner beforehand. The food was good, for Antonio was an excellent cook, and the wine came from his own vineyard. It was so light that you felt you could drink it like water, and we finished the first bottle with our macaroni. By the time we had finished the second we felt that there was nothing much wrong with life. We sat in a little garden under a great vine laden with grapes. The air was exquisitely soft. The night was still, and we were alone. The maid brought us *bel paese*[1] cheese and a plate of figs. I ordered coffee and strega, which is the best liqueur they make in Italy. Wilson would not have a cigar, but lit his pipe.

"We've got plenty of time before we need start," he said. "The moon won't be over the hill for another hour."

"Moon or no moon," I said briskly, "of course we've got plenty

[1] **bel paese: the native or local cheese.**

of time. That's one of the delights of Capri, that there's never any hurry."

"Leisure," he said. "If people only knew! It's the most priceless thing a man can have and they're such fools they don't even know it's something to aim at. Work? They work for work's sake. They haven't got the brains to realize that the only object of work is to obtain leisure."

Wine has the effect on some people of making them indulge in general reflections. These remarks were true, but no one could have claimed that they were original. I did not say anything, but struck a match to light my cigar.

"It was full moon the first time I came to Capri," he went on reflectively. "It might be the same moon as tonight."

"It was, you know," I smiled.

He grinned. The only light in the garden was what came from an oil lamp that hung over our heads. It had been scanty to eat by, but it was good now for confidences.

"I didn't mean that. I mean, it might be yesterday. Fifteen years it is, and when I look back it seems like a month. I'd never been to Italy before. I came for my summer holiday. I went to Naples by boat from Marseilles, and I had a look round – Pompeii, you know, and Paestum and one or two places like that; then I came here for a week. I liked the look of the place right away, from the sea, I mean, as I watched it come closer and closer; and then when we got into the little boats from the steamer and landed at the quay, with all that crowd of jabbering people who wanted to take your luggage, and the hotel touts, and the tumble-down houses on the Marina and the walk up to the hotel, and dining on the terrace – well, it just got me. That's the truth. I didn't know if I was standing on my head or my heels. I'd never drunk Capri wine before, but I'd heard of it; I think I must have got a bit tight. I sat on that terrace after they'd all gone to bed and watched the moon over the sea, and there was Vesuvius with a great red plume of smoke rising up from it. Of course I know now that wine I drank was ink, Capri wine my eye, but I thought it all right then. But it wasn't the wine that made me drunk, it was the shape of the island and those jabbering people, the moon and the sea and the oleander in the hotel garden. I'd never seen an oleander before."

It was a long speech, and it had made him thirsty. He took up his glass, but it was empty. I asked him if he would have another strega.

"It's sickly stuff. Let's have a bottle of wine. That's sound, that is, pure juice of the grape and can't hurt anyone."

I ordered more wine, and when it came filled the glasses. He took a long drink and after a sigh of pleasure went on.

"Next day I found my way to the bathing place we go to. Not bad bathing, I thought. Then I wandered about the island. As luck would have it, there was a *festa* up at the Punta di Timberio, and I ran straight into the middle of it. An image of the Virgin and priests, acolytes swinging censers, and a whole crowd of jolly, laughing, excited people, a lot of them all dressed up. After that I went down one night to have a look at the Faraglioni [1] by moonlight. If the fates had wanted me to go on being a bank manager they oughtn't to have let me take that walk."

"You were a bank manager, were you?" I asked.

I had been wrong about him, but not far wrong.

"Yes. I was manager of the Crawford Street branch of the York and City.[2] It was convenient for me because I lived up Hendon way. I could get from door to door in thirty-seven minutes."

He puffed at his pipe and relit it.

"That was my last night, that was. I'd got to be back at the bank on Monday morning. When I looked at those two great rocks sticking out of the water, with the moon above them, and all the little lights of the fishermen in their boats catching cuttlefish, all so peaceful and beautiful, I said to myself, well, after all, why should I go back? It wasn't as if I had anyone dependent on me. My wife had died of bronchial pneumonia four years before, and the kid went to live with her grandmother, my wife's mother. She was an old fool, she didn't look after the kid properly and she got blood poisoning, they amputated her leg, but they couldn't save her and she died, poor little thing."

"How terrible," I said.

"Yes, I was cut up at the time, though of course not so much as if the kid had been living with me, but I daresay it was a mercy. Not

[1] **Faraglioni:** two great rocks in the ocean near Capri.

[2] **The York and City:** a bank in London.

much chance for a girl with only one leg. I was sorry about my wife, too. We got on very well together. Though I don't know if it would have continued. She was the sort of woman who was always bothering about what other people'd think. She didn't like traveling. Eastbourne [1] was her idea of a holiday. D'you know, I'd never crossed the channel till after her death."

"But I suppose you've got other relations, haven't you?"

"None. I was an only child. My father had a brother, but he went to Australia before I was born. I don't think anyone could easily be more alone in the world than I am. There wasn't any reason I could see why I shouldn't do exactly what I wanted. I was thirty-four at that time."

He had told me he had been on the island for fifteen years. That would make him forty-nine. Just about the age I should have given him.

"I'd been working since I was seventeen. All I had to look forward to was doing the same old thing day after day till I retired on my pension. I said to myself, 'Is it worth it? What's wrong with chucking it all up and spending the rest of my life down here?' It was the most beautiful place I'd ever seen. But I'd had a business training, I was cautious by nature. 'No,' I said, 'I won't be carried away like this, I'll go tomorrow like I said I would and think it over. Perhaps when I get back to London I'll think quite differently.' Damned fool, wasn't I? I lost a whole year that way."

"You didn't change your mind, then?"

"You bet I didn't. All the time I was working I kept thinking of the bathing here and the vineyards and the walks over the hills and the moon and the sea, and the Piazza in the evening when everyone walks about for a bit of a chat after the day's work is over. There was only one thing that bothered me; I wasn't sure if I was justified in not working like everybody else did. Then I read a sort of history book, by a man called Marion Crawford [2] it was, and there was a story about Sybaris and Crotona. There were two cities; and in Sybaris they just enjoyed life and had a good time, and in Crotona they were hardy and industrious and all that. And one day

[1] **Eastbourne:** a seaside town not far from London.

[2] **Marion Crawford:** American nineteenth-century novelist who was born in Italy.

the men of Crotona came over and wiped Sybaris out, and then after a while a lot of other fellows came over from somewhere else and wiped Crotona out. Nothing remains of Sybaris, not a stone, and all that's left of Crotona is just one column. That settled the matter for me."

"Oh?"

"It came to the same in the end, didn't it? And when you look back now, who were the mugs?"

I did not reply, and he went on.

"The money was rather a bother. The bank didn't pension one off till after thirty years' service, but if you retired before that they gave you a gratuity. With that and what I'd got for the sale of my house and the little I'd managed to save, I just hadn't enough to buy an annuity to last the rest of my life. It would have been silly to sacrifice everything so as to lead a pleasant life and not have a sufficient income to make it pleasant. I wanted to have a little place of my own, a servant to look after me, enough to buy tobacco, decent food, books now and then, and something over for emergencies. I knew pretty well how much I needed. I found I had just enough to buy an annuity for twenty-five years."

"You were thirty-five at the time?"

"Yes. It would carry me on till I was sixty. After all, no one can be certain of living longer than that; a lot of men die in their fifties, and by the time a man's sixty he's had the best of life."

"On the other hand no one can be sure of dying at sixty," I said.

"Well, I don't know. It depends on himself, doesn't it?"

"In your place I should have stayed on at the bank till I was entitled to my pension."

"I should have been forty-seven then. I shouldn't have been too old to enjoy my life here, I'm older than that now and I enjoy it as much as I ever did, but I should have been too old to experience the particular pleasure of a young man. You know, you can have just as good a time at fifty as you can at thirty, but it's not the same sort of good time. I wanted to live the perfect life while I still had the energy and the spirit to make the most of it. Twenty-five years seemed a long time to me, and twenty-five years of happiness seemed worth paying something pretty substantial for. I'd made up my mind to wait a year, and I waited a year. Then I sent in my resignation, and as soon as they paid me my gratuity I bought the annuity and came on here."

"An annuity for twenty-five years?"

"That's right."

"Have you never regretted?"

"Never. I've had my money's worth already. And I've got ten years more. Don't you think after twenty-five years of perfect happiness one ought to be satisfied to call it a day?"

"Perhaps."

He did not say in so many words what he would do then, but his intention was clear. It was pretty much the story my friend had told me, but it sounded different when I heard it from his own lips. I stole a glance at him. There was nothing about him that was not ordinary. No one, looking at that neat, prim face, could have thought him capable of an unconventional action. I did not blame him. It was his own life that he had arranged in this strange manner, and I did not see why he should not do what he liked with it. Still, I could not prevent the little shiver that ran down my spine.

"Getting chilly?" he smiled. "We might as well start walking down. The moon'll be up by now."

Before we parted, Wilson asked me if I would like to go and see his house one day; and two or three days later, finding out where he lived, I strolled up to see him. It was a peasant's cottage, well away from the town, in a vineyard, with a view of the sea. By the side of the door grew a great oleander in full flower. There were only two small rooms, a tiny kitchen and a lean-to in which firewood could be kept. The bedroom was furnished like a monk's cell, but the sitting room, smelling agreeably of tobacco, was comfortable enough, with two large armchairs that he had brought from England, a large roll-top desk, a cottage piano and crowded bookshelves. On the walls were framed engravings of pictures by G. F. Watts and Lord Leighton.[1] Wilson told me that the house belonged to the owner of the vineyard who lived in another cottage higher up the hill, and his wife came in every day to do the rooms and the cooking. He had found the place on his first visit to Capri, and taking it on his return for good had been there ever since. Seeing the piano and music open on it, I asked him if he would play.

[1] **G. F. Watts and Lord Leighton:** English painters.

"I'm no good, you know, but I've always been fond of music, and I get a lot of fun out of strumming."

He sat down at the piano and placed one of the movements from a Beethoven sonata. He did not play very well. I looked at his music, Schumann and Schubert, Beethoven, Bach and Chopin.[1] On the table on which he had his meals was a greasy pack of cards. I asked him if he played patience.[2]

"A lot."

From what I saw of him then and from what I heard from other people I made for myself what I think must have been a fairly accurate picture of the life he had led for the last fifteen years. It was certainly a very harmless one. He bathed; he walked a great deal, and he seemed never to lose his sense of the beauty of the island which he knew so intimately; he played the piano and he played patience; he read. When he was asked to a party he went and, though a trifle dull, was agreeable. He was not affronted if he was neglected. He liked people, but with an aloofness that prevented intimacy. He lived thriftily, but with sufficient comfort. He never owed a penny. I imagine he had never been a man whom sex had greatly troubled, and if in his younger days he had had now and then a passing affair with a visitor to the island whose head was turned by the atmosphere, his emotion, while it lasted, remained, I am pretty sure, well under his control. I think he was determined that nothing should interfere with his independence of spirit. His only passion was for the beauty of nature, and he sought felicity in the simple and natural things that life offers to everyone. You may say that it was a grossly selfish existence. It was. He was of no use to anybody, but on the other hand he did nobody any harm. His only object was his own happiness, and it looked as though he had attained it. Very few people know where to look for happiness; fewer still find it. I don't know whether he was a fool or a wise man. He was certainly a man who knew his own mind. The odd thing about him to me was that he was so immensely commonplace. I should never have given him a second thought but for what I knew, that on a certain day, ten years from then, unless a chance illness cut the

1 **Schumann, etc.:** Wilson's taste was for eighteenth- and early nineteenth-century music, mostly German.

2 **patience:** a game of solitaire.

thread before, he must deliberately take leave of the world he loved so well. I wondered whether it was the thought of this, never quite absent from his mind, that gave him the peculiar zest with which he enjoyed every moment of the day.

I should do him an injustice if I omitted to state that he was not at all in the habit of talking about himself. I think the friend I was staying with was the only person in whom he had confided. I believe he told me the story only because he suspected I already knew it, and on the evening on which he told it me he had drunk a good deal of wine.

My visit drew to a close, and I left the island. The year after, war broke out. A number of things happened to me, so that the course of my life was greatly altered, and it was thirteen years before I went to Capri again. My friend had been back some time, but he was no longer so well off, and had moved into a house that had no room for me; so I was putting up at the hotel. He came to meet the boat, and we dined together. During dinner I asked him where exactly his house was.

"You know it," he answered. "It's the little place Wilson had. I've built on a room and made it quite nice."

With so many other things to occupy my mind, I had not given Wilson a thought for years; but now, with a little shock, I remembered. The ten years he had before him when I made his acquaintance must have elapsed long ago.

"Did he commit suicide as he said he would?"

"It's rather a grim story."

Wilson's plan was all right. There was only one flaw in it, and this, I suppose, he could not have foreseen. It had never occurred to him that after twenty-five years of complete happiness, in this quiet backwater, with nothing in the world to disturb his serenity, his character would gradually lose its strength. The will needs obstacles in order to exercise its power; when it is never thwarted, when no effort is needed to achieve one's desires, because one has placed one's desires only in the things that can be obtained by stretching out one's hand, the will grows impotent. If you walk on a level all the time, the muscles you need to climb a mountain will atrophy. These observations are trite, but there they are. When Wilson's annuity expired he had no longer the resolution to make the end which was the price he had agreed to pay for that long period of happy tranquillity. I do not think, as far as I could gather, both from what my friend told me and afterward from others, that he wanted courage. It was just that he couldn't make up his mind. He put it off from day to day.

He had lived on the island for so long and had always settled his accounts so punctually, that it was easy for him to get credit; never having borrowed money before, he found a number of people who were willing to lend him small sums when now he asked for them. He had paid his rent regularly for so many years that his landlord, whose wife Assunta still acted as his servant, was content to let things slide for several months. Everyone believed him when he said that a relative had died and that he was temporarily embarrassed because, owing to legal formalities, he could not for some time get the money that was due to him. He managed to hang on after this fashion for something over a year. Then he could get no more credit from the local tradesmen, and there was no one to lend him any more money. His landlord gave him notice to leave the house unless he paid up the arrears of rent before a certain date.

The day before this he went into his tiny bedroom, closed the door and the window, drew the curtain and lit a brazier of charcoal. Next morning when Assunta came to make his breakfast she found him insensible but still alive. The room was drafty, and though he had done this and that to keep out the fresh air he had not done it very thoroughly. It almost looked as though at the last moment, and desperate though his situation was, he had suffered from a certain infirmity of purpose. Wilson was taken to the hospital, and though very ill for some time he at last recovered. But as a result either of the charcoal poisoning or of the shock, he was no longer in complete possession of his faculties. He was not insane, at all events not insane enough to be put in an asylum, but he was quite obviously no longer in his right mind.

"I went to see him," said my friend. "I tried to get him to talk, but he kept looking at me in a funny sort of way, as though he couldn't quite make out where he'd seen me before. He looked rather awful lying there in bed, with a week's growth of gray beard on his chin; but except for that funny look in his eyes he seemed quite normal."

"What funny look in his eyes?"

"I don't know exactly how to describe it. Puzzled. It's an absurd comparison, but suppose you threw a stone up into the air and it didn't come down but just stayed there . . ."

"It would be rather bewildering," I smiled.

"Well, that's the sort of look he had."

It was difficult to know what to do with him. He had no money and no means of getting any. His effects were sold, but for too little to pay what he owed. He was English, and the Italian authorities did not wish to make themselves responsible for him. The British consul in Naples had no funds to deal with the case. He could of course be sent back to England, but no one seemed to know what could be done with him when he got there. Then Assunta, the servant, said that he had been a good master and a good tenant, and as long as he had the money had paid his way; he could sleep in the woodshed in the cottage in which she and her husband lived, and he could share their meals. This was suggested to him. It was difficult to know whether he understood or not. When Assunta came to take him from the hospital, he went with her without remark. He seemed to have no longer a will of his own.

She had been keeping him now for two years.

"It's not very comfortable, you know," said my friend. "They've rigged him up a ramshackle bed and given him a couple of blankets, but there's no window, and it's icy cold in winter and like an oven in summer. And the food's pretty rough. You know how these peasants eat: macaroni on Sundays and meat once in a blue moon."

"What does he do with himself all the time?"

"He wanders about the hills. I've tried to see him two or three times, but it's no good; when he sees you coming he runs like a hare. Assunta comes down to have a chat with me now and then, and I give her a bit of money so that she can buy him tobacco, but God knows if he ever gets it."

"Do they treat him all right?" I asked.

"I'm sure Assunta's kind enough. She treats him like a child. I'm afraid her husband's not very nice to him. He grudges the cost of his keep. I don't believe he's cruel or anything like that, but I think he's a bit sharp with him. He makes him fetch water and clean the cowshed and that sort of thing."

"It sounds pretty rotten," I said.

"He brought it on himself. After all, he's only got what he deserved."

"I think on the whole we all get what we deserve," I said. "But that doesn't prevent its being rather horrible."

Two or three days later my friend and I were taking a walk. We were strolling along a narrow path through an olive grove.

"There's Wilson," said my friend suddenly. "Don't look, you'll only frighten him. Go straight on."

I walked with my eyes on the path, but out of the corners of them I saw a man hiding behind an olive tree. He did not move as we approached, but I felt that he was watching us. As soon as we had passed I heard a scamper. Wilson, like a hunted animal, had made for safety. That was the last I ever saw of him.

He died last year. He had endured that life for six years. He was found one morning on the mountainside lying quite peacefully as though he had died in his sleep. From where he lay he had been able to see those two great rocks called the Faraglioni which stand out of the sea. It was full moon, and he must have gone to see them by moonlight. Perhaps he died of the beauty of that sight.

READING WITH INSIGHT

1. The story begins conversationally, philosophically. Does it win your interest? Does it obey Poe's rule about the first sentence? In what way does the beginning set the tone for what is to come?

2. How, in this conversational manner, does Maugham retain suspense and interest? One device for this purpose is his talking about his curiosity concerning Wilson. What are others?

3. Who tells the story? What are the advantages of having it told from the viewpoint of a minor character? How would it have been a different story if told by the main character? If told in the third person so that we could watch Wilson all the time?

4. How does the setting contribute to the story? With what does it contrast?

5. The story draws a comparison between two kinds of men. One

would have stayed with his job until pensioned and secure; the other broke away and took a chance. In which class do you fit?

6. What kind of man is the main character? Lazy? Fearful? Clever? Trying to run away from something? A realist? An idealist? How would you describe him?

7. Did Wilson enjoy his years at Capri? Would you enjoy them if you were there in his situation? What, in the midst of all this beauty and privacy, didn't he have? What does Maugham imply was wrong with what Wilson did? Was it a good plan, except for the man's own weakness?

8. The narrator says, "I think on the whole we all get what we deserve." Do you agree?

9. What is the effect of this conversational manner of telling a story? Recall some of the other first-person stories in this book – "The Secret Sharer" and "The Summer of the Beautiful White Horse," for instance. These are rather different kinds of stories. Does there seem to be any common reason why the authors of all these stories chose the first-person form? If so, what?

10. Why is the title an appropriate one for this story? If you are unfamiliar with the story of the lotus-eaters, read the story in a collection of classical mythology, or read Tennyson's poem "The Lotus-Eaters."

If you like this story, you will be interested in

Maugham. *Lord Mountdrago.*
 Taipan.
Washington Irving. *The Stout Gentleman.*
Anton Chekov. *The Kiss.*
Luigi Pirandello. *War.*
John Galsworthy. *Quality.*

The Short Story in Other Countries

ALPHONSE DAUDET

The Death of the Dauphin

THIS story of the little Dauphin is an example of what might be called the " stripped-down " story. It is so little furnished, so bare of details, that it is almost a parable. And yet you will notice that the story is remarkably rich in meaning, and extremely suggestive and stimulating to the imagination. You will be interested in comparing this to another very brief story, Miss Mansfield's " The Dill Pickle," and also to some of the great Biblical parables, like the story of the prodigal son. These parables, old and new, raise the question of what are the essentials of a story. How much is needed in a story? How much can a writer depend on a reader's imagination to fill in details? Read this story first just for enjoyment. Then see if you can figure out why the great story-tellers since Daudet's time have admired this story so much.

Alphonse Daudet was born at Nîmes, France, in 1840. He went to Paris when he was a young man, and found that city so much to his liking that he stayed until he died, in 1897. Like many other young Frenchmen of his generation, he began his artistic career as a poet. He made his reputation as a novelist and as a writer of such skillful short stories as the one in this book, but many critics have observed that he remained a poet in fiction, and that such short stories as " The Death of the Dauphin " have the compression, the suggestiveness, and the beauty of poetry.

THE little Dauphin [1] is sick; the little Dauphin is going to die. In all the churches of the realm the Blessed Sacrament is exposed night and day, and tall candles are burning for the recovery of the royal child. The streets in the old residence are sad and silent, the bells no longer ring, and carriages go at a footpace. About the palace the curious citizens watch, through the iron grilles, the porters with gilt paunches talking in the courtyards with an air of importance.

The whole château is in commotion. Chamberlains, major-domos, run hastily up and down the marble staircases. The galleries are full of pages and of courtiers in silk garments, who go from group to group asking news in undertones. On the broad steps weeping maids of honor greet one another with low courtesies, wiping their eyes with pretty embroidered handkerchiefs.

In the orangery [2] there is a great assemblage of long-robed doctors. Through the windows they can be seen flourishing their long black sleeves and bending majestically their hammerlike wigs. The little Dauphin's governor and equerry [3] walk back and forth before the door, awaiting the decision of the faculty. Scullions pass them by without saluting them. The equerry swears like a heathen, the governor recites lines from Horace. And meanwhile, in the direction of the stables one hears a long, plaintive neigh. It is the little Dauphin's horse, calling sadly from his empty manger.

And the king? Where is *monseigneur* [4] the king? The king is all alone in a room at the end of the château. Majesties do not like to be seen weeping. As for the queen, that is a different matter. Seated at the little Dauphin's pillow, her lovely face is bathed in tears, and she sobs aloud before them all, as a linen draper's wife might do.

In his lace-bedecked crib the little Dauphin, whiter than the cushions upon which he lies, is resting now with closed eyes. They think

[1] **Dauphin** (dô′fĭn): eldest son of the King of France.

[2] **orangery**: a sort of greenhouse used to raise tropical fruits in cool climates.

[3] **equerry**: the man in charge of the Dauphin's horses. A number of the palace staff are mentioned in this story. The Dauphin's governor is his tutor. The major-domo is the chief of the palace staff, and the chamberlain is the head steward. Scullions are kitchen helpers. Maids of honor attend the queen, and courtiers are noblemen in attendance at the king's court.

[4] **monseigneur**: my lord.

that he sleeps; but no. The little Dauphin is not asleep. He turns to his mother, and seeing that she is weeping, he says to her:

"Madame queen, why do you weep? Is it because you really believe that I am going to die?"

The queen tries to reply. Sobs prevent her from speaking.

"Pray do not weep, madame queen; you forget that I am the Dauphin, and that dauphins cannot die like this."

The queen sobs more bitterly than ever, and the little Dauphin begins to be alarmed.

"I say," he says, "I don't want Death to come and take me and I will find a way to prevent his coming here. Let them send at once forty very strong troopers to stand guard around our bed! Let a hundred big guns watch night and day with matches lighted, under our windows! And woe to Death if it dares approach us!"

To please the royal child the queen makes a sign. In a moment they hear the big guns rumbling through the courtyard; and forty tall troopers, halberds in hand, take their places about the room. They are all old soldiers with gray mustaches. The little Dauphin claps his hands when he sees them. He recognizes one of them and calls him:

"Lorrain! Lorrain!"

The soldier steps forward toward the bed.

"I love you dearly, my old Lorrain. Let me see your big sword. If Death tries to take me you must kill him, won't you?"

"Yes, *monseigneur*," Lorrain replies. And two great tears roll down his bronzed cheeks.

At that moment the chaplain approaches the little Dauphin and talks with him for a long time in a low voice, showing him a crucifix. The little Dauphin listens with an expression of great surprise, then, abruptly interrupting him, he says:

"I understand what you say, *monsieur l'abbé;* but tell me, couldn't my little friend Beppo die in my place, if I gave him a lot of money?"

The chaplain continues to speak in a low voice, and the little Dauphin's expression becomes more and more astonished.

When the chaplain has finished, the little Dauphin replies with a deep sigh:

"All this that you tell me is very sad, *monsieur l'abbé;* but one thing consoles me, and that is that up yonder, in the paradise of the stars, I shall still be the Dauphin. I know that the good Lord is my cousin, and that He cannot fail to treat me according to my rank."

Then he adds, turning to his mother:

"Let them bring me my richest clothes, my doublet of white ermine, and my velvet slippers! I wish to make myself handsome for the angels, and to enter paradise in the costume of a Dauphin."

A third time the chaplain leans toward the little Dauphin and talks to him for a long time in a low voice. In the midst of his harangue, the royal child angrily interrupts:

"Why, then, to be Dauphin is to be nothing at all!"

And, refusing to listen to anything more, the little Dauphin turns toward the wall and weeps bitterly.

READING WITH INSIGHT

1. Does one of the following statements seem to you to state the conflict in this story? If so, explain why. If not, say what you think is the conflict.

   The power of the Dauphin, versus Death.
   The Dauphin's idea of his own power, versus Death.
   The idea of royalty, versus Death.
   The idea of royalty, versus the idea that all men are equal.
   Human power, versus Death.
   Immortality, versus mortality.

2. Trace the steps in the Dauphin's disillusionment — the defenses he throws up and what happens in each case to his defense.

3. This story is a kind of parable — like many of the stories in the Bible. What are the signs of a parable in this story?

4. This story is very short. What has the author left out (which many authors would have included) in order to make it so short?

5. How might an author like Hawthorne have written this story? Or how might it have been written by one of the other authors who have stories about children in this book?

6. What would have been the effect of having the little Dauphin himself tell this story? What advantages can you see in telling the story thus from the third-person viewpoint?

7. How much attention is paid to activities in the palace? Why are these certain things described, and all the other details omitted?

8. The story ends with the child weeping bitterly, petulantly. What is the apparent reason for that kind of ending? What is its effect? For instance, what if the story had ended with the child's death, or with his calm acceptance of the situation, or with a stormy refusal to accept it? Why do you suppose Daudet selected the ending he did out of all the possible endings?

9. Is the story merely pathetic — that is, merely a sad story of a child's disillusionment and approaching death? If not, what more is there to the story?

10. What is the irony in this story?

If you like this story, you will be interested in

Daudet. *The Last Class.*
Lord Edward Dunsany. *The Sword and the Idol.*
Paul Morand. *Monsieur U.*
Guy de Maupassant. *The Two Little Soldiers.*
Katherine Mansfield. *The Doll's House.*

GUY DE MAUPASSANT

The Inn

It is ironic that Maupassant, who wrote so powerfully in this story of a young man going mad, should himself die insane at the age of 43. He was born in Normandy in 1850, lived for a time in Paris, and died in 1893. In his 20 productive years he wrote four novels and more than 200 stories.

Like O. Henry he wrote many of the stories for newspapers and learned how to tell a story briefly. Like Chekov he preferred to write about ordinary people and their problems. He was much more plot-conscious than Chekov, and perfectly capable of writing surprise endings like O. Henry. At his best he was able to write a richer and a deeper story than O. Henry, and to take advantage of all the interest-making qualities of plot which Chekov ignored. He was never able to illuminate the inner life of his characters as Chekov could, and for that reason later writers have more often tended to follow Chekov than Maupassant. But in his own time Maupassant was without dispute the master of the short story in France and probably the best-known short story writer in the world.

The story that follows is one of the psychological studies that foreshadowed Maupassant's own fate. It is interesting because it shows the writer's mastery of form, and his ability to build exciting and ironic plot out of ordinary people and very lifelike surroundings.

LIKE all the little wooden inns in the higher Alps, tiny auberges [1] situated in the bare and rocky gorges which intersect the white summits of the mountains, the inn of Schwarenbach is a refuge for travelers who are crossing the Gemmi.[2]

It is open six months in the year, and is inhabited by the family of

[1] **auberges**: inns.

[2] **Gemmi**: Gemmi Pass. You will find this setting in the Bernese Alps south of Interlaken, in Switzerland. Look for the Gemmi pass and the Wildstrubel, a famous mountain.

Jean Hauser. As soon as the snow begins to fall, and fills the valley so as to make the road down to Loëche impassable, the father, with mother, daughter, and the three sons depart, leaving the house in charge of the old guide, Gaspard Hari, with the young guide, Ulrich Kunsi, and Sam, the great mountain dog.

The two men and the dog remain till spring in their snowy prison, with nothing before their eyes except immense, white slopes of the Balmhorn, surrounded by light, glistening summits, and shut up, blocked up, and buried by the snow which rises around them, enveloping and almost burying the little house up to the eaves.

It was the day on which the Hauser family were going to return to Loëche, as winter was approaching, and the descent was becoming dangerous. Three mules started first, laden with baggage and led by the three sons. Then the mother, Jeanne Hauser, and her daughter Louise mounted a fourth mule, and set off in their turn. The father followed them, accompanied by the two men in charge, who were to escort the family as far as the brow of the descent. First of all they skirted the small lake, now frozen over, at the foot of the mass of rocks which stretched in front of the inn; then they followed the valley, which was dominated on all sides by snow-covered peaks.

A ray of sunlight glinted into that little white, glistening, frozen desert, illuminating it with a cold and dazzling flame. No living thing appeared among this ocean of hills; there was no stir in that immeasurable solitude, no noise disturbed the profound silence.

By degrees the young guide, Ulrich Kunsi, a tall, long-legged Swiss, left daddy Hauser and old Gaspard behind, in order to catch up with the mule which carried the two women. The younger one looked at him as he approached, as if she would call him with her sad eyes. She was a young, light-haired peasant girl, whose milk-white cheeks and pale hair seemed to have lost their color by long dwelling amid the ice. When Ulrich had caught up with the animal which carried the women, he put his hand on the crupper, and relaxed his speed. Mother Hauser began to talk to him, and enumerated with minutest detail all that he would have to attend to during the winter. It was the first winter he would spend up there, while old Hari had already spent fourteen winters amid the snow, at the inn of Schwarenbach.

Ulrich Kunsi listened, without appearing to understand, and looked incessantly at the girl. From time to time he replied: "Yes, Madame Hauser"; but his thoughts seemed far away, and his calm features remained unmoved.

They reached Lake Daube, whose broad, frozen surface reached to the bottom of the valley. On the right, the Daubenhorn showed its black mass, rising up in a peak above the enormous moraines of the Lömmeon glacier, which soared above the Wildstrubel. As they approached the neck of the Gemmi, where the descent to Loëche begins, the immense horizon of the Alps of the Valais, from which the broad, deep valley of the Rhône separted them, came in view.

In the distance, there was a group of white, unequal, flat or pointed mountain summits, which glistened in the sun; the Mischabel with its twin peaks, the huge group of the Weisshorn, the heavy Brunegghorn, the lofty and formidable pyramid of Mont Cervin, slayer of men, and the Dent Blanche, that terrible coquette.

Then beneath them, as at the bottom of a terrible abyss, they saw Loëche, its houses looking like grains of sand which had been thrown into that enormous crevice which finishes and closes the Gemmi, and which opens, down below, on to the Rhône.

The mule stopped at the edge of the path, which turns and twists continually, zigzagging fantastically and strangely along the steep side of the mountain, as far as the almost invisible little village at its feet. The women jumped into the snow, and the two old men joined them.

"Well," father Hauser said, "good-by, and keep up your spirits till next year, my friends," and old Hari replied: "Till next year."

They embraced each other, and then Madame Hauser in her turn, offered her cheek, and the girl did the same. When Ulrich Kunsi's turn came, he whispered in Louise's ear:

"Do not forget those up yonder," and she replied: "No," in such a low voice, that he guessed what she had said, without hearing it.

"Well, adieu," Jean Hauser repeated, "and don't fall ill." Then, going before the two women, he commenced the descent, and soon all three disappeared at the first turn in the road, while the two men returned to the inn at Schwarenbach.

They walked slowly side by side, without speaking. The parting was over, and they would be alone together for four or five months.

Then Gaspard Hari began to relate his life last winter. He had remained with Michael Canol, who was too old now to stand it; for an accident might happen during that long solitude. They had not been dull, however; the only thing was to be resigned to it from the first, and in the end one would find plenty of distraction, games and other means of whiling away the time.

Ulrich Kunsi listened to him with his eyes on the ground, for in thought he was with those who were descending to the village. They soon came in sight of the inn, which was scarcely visible, so small did it look, a mere black speck at the foot of that enormous billow of snow. When they opened the door, Sam, the great curly dog, began to romp round them.

"Come, my boy," old Gaspard said, "we have no women now, so we must get our own dinner ready. Go and peel the potatoes." And they both sat down on wooden stools, and began to put the bread into the soup.

The next morning seemed very long to Kunsi. Old Hari smoked and smoked beside the hearth, while the young man looked out of the window at the snow-covered mountain opposite the house. In the afternoon he went out, and going over the previous day's ground again, he looked for the traces of the mule that had carried the two women; then when he had reached the neck of the Gemmi, he laid himself down on his stomach, and looked at Loëche.

The village, in its rocky pit, was not yet buried under the snow, although the white masses came quite close to it, balked, however, of their prey by the pine woods which protected the hamlet. From his vantage point the low houses looked like paving stones in a large meadow. Hauser's little daughter was there now in one of those gray-colored houses. In which? Ulrich Kunsi was too far away to be able to make them out separately. How he would have liked to go down while he was yet able!

But the sun had disappeared behind the lofty crest of the Wildstrubel, and the young man returned to the chalet. Daddy Hari was smoking, and, when he saw his mate come in, proposed a game of cards to him. They sat down opposite each other for a long time and played the simple game called *brisque;* then they had supper and went to bed.

The following days were like the first, bright and cold, without any more snow. Old Gaspard spent his afternoons in watching the eagles and other rare birds which ventured on to those frozen heights, while Ulrich journeyed regularly to the neck of the Gemmi to look at the village. In the evening they played at cards, dice, or dominoes, and lost and won trifling sums, just to create an interest in the game.

One morning Hari, who was up first, called his companion. A moving cloud of white spray, deep and light, was falling on them noiselessly, and burying them by degrees under a dark, thick coverlet of foam. This lasted four days and four nights. It was necessary to free the door and the windows, to dig out a passage, and to cut steps to get over this frozen powder, which a twelve-hours' frost had made as hard as the granite of the moraines.

They lived like prisoners, not venturing outside their abode. They had divided their duties and performed them regularly. Ulrich Kunsi undertook the scouring, washing, and everything that belonged to cleanliness. He also chopped up the wood, while Gaspard Hari did the cooking and attended to the fire. Their regular and monotonous work was relieved by long games at cards or dice, but they never quarreled, and were always calm and placid. They were never even impatient or ill-humored, nor did they ever use hard words, for they had laid in a stock of patience for this wintering on the top of the mountain.

Sometimes old Gaspard took his rifle and went after chamois, and occasionally killed one. Then there was a feast in the inn at Schwarenbach, and they reveled in fresh meat. One morning he went out as usual. The thermometer outside marked eighteen degrees of frost, and as the sun had not yet risen, the hunter hoped to surprise the animals at the approaches to the Wildstrubel. Ulrich, being alone, remained in bed until ten o'clock. He was of a sleepy nature, but would not have dared to give way like that to his inclination in the presence of the old guide, who was ever an early riser. He breakfasted leisurely with Sam, who also spent his days and nights in sleeping in front of the fire; then he felt low-spirited and even frightened at the solitude, and was seized by a longing for his daily game of cards, as one is by the domination of an invincible habit. So he went out to meet his companion, who was to return at four o'clock.

The snow had leveled the whole deep valley, filled up the crevasses, obliterated all signs of the two lakes and covered the rocks, so that between the high summits there was nothing but an immense, white, regular, dazzling, and frozen surface. For three weeks, Ulrich had not been to the edge of the precipice, from which he had looked down on to the village, and he wanted to go there before climbing the slopes which led to the Wildstrubel. Loëche was now covered by the snow, and the houses could scarcely be distinguished, hidden as they were by that white cloak.

Turning to the right, Ulrich reached the Lämmern glacier. He strode along with a mountaineer's long swinging pace, striking the snow, which was as hard as a rock, with his iron-shod stick, and with piercing eyes looking for the little black, moving speck in the distance, on that enormous, white expanse.

When he reached the end of the glacier he stopped, and asked himself whether the old man had taken that road, and then he began to walk along the moraines with rapid and uneasy steps. The day was declining; the snow was assuming a rosy tint, and a dry, frozen wind blew in rough gusts over its crystal surface. Ulrich uttered a long, shrill, vibrating call. His voice sped through the deathlike silence in which the mountains were sleeping; it reached into the distance, over the profound and motionless waves of glacial foam, like the cry of a bird over the waves of the sea; then it died away and nothing answered him.

He started off again. The sun had sunk behind the mountaintops, which still were purpled with the reflection from the heavens; but the depths of the valley were becoming gray, and suddenly the young man felt frightened. It seemed to him as if the silence, the cold, the solitude, the wintry death of these mountains were taking possession of him, were stopping and freezing his blood, making his limbs grow stiff, and turning him into a motionless and frozen object; and he began to run rapidly toward the dwelling. The old man, he thought, would have returned during his absence. He had probably taken another road; and would, no doubt, be sitting before the fire, with a dead chamois at his feet.

He soon came in sight of the inn, but no smoke rose from it. Ulrich ran faster. Opening the door he met Sam who ran up to him to greet him, but Gaspard Hari had not returned. Kunsi, in his alarm, turned round suddenly, as if he had expected to find his comrade hidden in a corner. Then he relighted the fire and made the soup; hoping every moment to see the old man come in. From time to time he went out to see if Gaspard were not in sight. It was night now, that wan night of the mountain, a livid night, with the crescent moon, yellow and dim, just disappearing behind the mountaintops, and shining faintly on the edge of the horizon.

Then the young man went in and sat down to warm his hands and feet, while he pictured to himself every possible sort of accident. Gaspard might have broken a leg, have fallen into a crevasse, have taken a false step and dislocated his ankle. Perhaps he was lying on the snow, overcome and stiff with the cold, in agony of mind, lost and perhaps shouting for help, calling with all his might, in the silence of the night.

But where? The mountain was so vast, so rugged, so dangerous in places, especially at that time of the year, that it would have required ten or twenty guides walking for a week in all directions, to find a man in that immense space. Ulrich Kunsi, however, made up his mind to set out with Sam, if Gaspard did not return by one in the morning; and he made his preparations.

He put provisions for two days into a bag, took his steel climbing irons, tied a long, thin, strong rope round his waist and looked to see that his iron-shod stick and his ax, which served to cut steps in the ice, were in order. Then he waited. The fire was burning on the hearth, the great dog was snoring in front of it, and the clock was ticking in its case of resounding wood, as regularly as a heart beating.

He waited, his ears on the alert for distant sounds, and shivered when the wind blew against the roof and the walls. It struck twelve, and he trembled. Then, as he felt frightened and shivery, he put some water on the fire, so that he might have hot coffee before starting. When the clock struck one he got up, woke Sam, opened the door and went off in the direction of the Wildstrubel. For five hours he ascended, scaling the rocks by means of his climbing-irons, cutting into the ice, advancing continually, and occasionally hauling up the dog, who remained below at the foot of some slope that was too steep for him, by means of the rope. About six o'clock he reached one of the summits to which old Gaspard often came after chamois, and he waited till it should be daylight.

The sky was growing pale overhead, and suddenly a strange light, springing, nobody could tell whence, suddenly illuminated the immense ocean of pale mountain peaks, which stretched for many leagues around him. It seemed as if this vague brightness arose from the snow itself, in order to spread itself into space. By degrees the highest and most distant summits assumed a delicate, fleshlike rose color, and the red sun appeared behind the ponderous giants of the Bernese Alps.

Ulrich Kunsi set off again, walking like a hunter, stooping and looking for any traces, and saying to his dog: "Seek old fellow, seek!"

He was descending the mountain now, scanning the depths closely, and from time to time shouting, uttering a loud, prolonged, familiar cry which soon died away in that silent vastness. Then, he put his ear to the ground, to listen. He thought he could distinguish a voice, and so he began to run and shout again. But he heard nothing more and sat down, worn out and in despair. Toward midday he breakfasted and gave Sam, who was as tired as himself, something to eat also; then he recommenced his search.

When evening came he was still walking, having traveled more than thirty miles over the mountains. As he was too far away to return home, and too tired to drag himself along any further, he dug a hole in the snow and crouched in it with his dog, under a blanket which he had brought with him. The man and the dog lay side by side, warming themselves one against the other, but frozen to the marrow, nevertheless. Ulrich scarcely slept, his mind haunted by visions and his limbs shaking with cold.

Day was breaking when he got up. His legs were as stiff as iron bars, and his spirits so low that he was ready to weep, while his heart was beating so that he almost fell with excitement whenever he thought he heard a noise.

Suddenly he imagined that he *also* was going to die of cold in the midst of this vast solitude. The terror of such a death roused his energies and gave him renewed vigor. He was descending toward the inn, falling down and getting up again, and followed at a distance by Sam, who was limping on three legs. They did not reach Schwarenbach until four o'clock in the afternoon. The house was empty, and the young man made a fire, had something to eat, and went to sleep, so worn out that he did not think of anything more.

He slept for a long time, for a very long time, the unconquerable sleep of exhaustion. But suddenly a voice, a cry, a name: "Ulrich," aroused him from his profound slumber, and made him sit up in bed. Had he been dreaming? Was it one of those strange appeals which cross the dreams of disquieted minds? No, he heard it still, that reverberating cry, – which had entered at his ears and remained in his brain, – thrilling him to the tips of his sinewy fingers. Certainly, somebody had cried out, and called: "Ulrich!" There was somebody there, near the house, there could be no doubt of that, and he opened the door and shouted: "Is it you, Gaspard?" with all the strength of his lungs. But there was no reply, no murmur, no groan, nothing. It was quite dark, and the snow looked wan.

The wind had risen, that icy wind which cracks the rocks, and leaves nothing alive on those deserted heights. It came in sudden gusts, more parching and more deadly than the burning wind of the desert, and again Ulrich shouted: "Gaspard! Gaspard! Gaspard!" Then he waited again. Everything was silent on the mountain! Then he shook with terror, and with a bound he was inside the inn. He shut and bolted the door, and then fell into a chair, trembling all over, for he felt certain that his comrade had called him at the moment of dissolution.

He was certain of that, as certain as one is of conscious life or of taste when eating. Old Gaspard Hari had been dying for two days and three nights somewhere, in some hole, in one of those deep, untrodden ravines whose whiteness is more sinister than subterranean darkness. He had been dying for two days and three nights and he had just then died, thinking of his comrade. His soul, almost before it was released, had taken its flight to the inn where Ulrich was sleeping, and it had called him by that terrible and mysterious power which the spirits of the dead possess. The voiceless soul had cried to the worn-out soul of the sleeper; it had uttered its last farewell, or its reproach, or its curse on the man who had not searched carefully enough.

And Ulrich felt that it was there, quite close to him, behind the wall, behind the door which he had just fastened. It was wandering about, like a night bird which skims a lighted window with his wings, and the terrified young man was ready to scream with horror. He wanted to run away, but did not dare go out; he did not dare, and would never dare in the future, for that phantom would remain there day and night, round the inn, as long as the old man's body was not recovered and deposited in the consecrated earth of a churchyard.

Daylight came, and Kunsi recovered some of his courage with the return of the bright sun. He prepared his meal, gave his dog some food, and then remained motionless on a chair, tortured at heart as he thought of the old man lying on the snow. Then, as soon as night once more covered the mountains, new terrors assailed him. He now walked up and down the dark kitchen, which was scarcely lighted by the flame of one candle. He walked from one end of it to the other with great strides, listening, listening to hear the terrible cry of the preceding night again break the dreary silence outside. He felt himself alone, unhappy man, as no man had ever been alone before! Alone in this immense desert of snow, alone five thousand feet above the inhabited earth, above human habitations, above that stirring, noisy, palpitating life, alone under an icy sky! A mad longing impelled him to run away, no matter where, to get down to Loëche by flinging himself over the precipice; but he did not even dare to open the door, as he felt sure that the other, the *dead,* man would bar his road, so that he might not be obliged to remain up there alone.

Toward midnight, tired with walking, worn out by grief and fear, he fell into a doze in his chair, for he was afraid of his bed, as one is of a haunted spot. But suddenly the strident cry of the preceding evening pierced his ears, so shrill that Ulrich stretched out his arms to repulse the ghost, and he fell on to his back with his chair.

Sam, who was awakened by the noise, began to howl as frightened dogs do, and trotted all about the house trying to find out where the danger came from. When he got to the door, he sniffed beneath it, smelling vigorously, with his coat bristling and his tail stiff while he growled angrily. Kunsi, who was terrified, jumped up, and holding his chair by one leg, cried: "Don't come in, don't come in, or I shall kill you." And the dog, excited by this threat, barked angrily at that invisible enemy who defied his master's voice. By degrees, however, he quieted down, came back and stretched himself in front of the fire. But he was uneasy, and kept his head up, and growled between his teeth.

Ulrich, in turn, recovered his senses, but as he felt faint with terror, he went and got a bottle of brandy out of the sideboard, and drank off several glasses, one after another, at a gulp. His ideas became vague, his courage revived, and a feverish glow ran through his veins.

He ate scarcely anything the next day, and limited himself to alcohol; so he lived for several days, like a drunken brute. As soon as he thought of Gaspard Hari he began to drink again, and went on drinking until he fell on to the floor, overcome by intoxication. And there he remained on his face, dead drunk, his limbs benumbed, and snoring with his face to the ground. But scarcely had he digested the maddening and burning liquor, than the same cry, "Ulrich," woke him like a bullet piercing his brain, and he got up, still staggering, stretching out his hands to save himself from falling, and calling to Sam to help him. And the dog, who appeared to be going mad like his master, rushed to the door, scratched it with his claws, and gnawed it with his long white teeth, while the young man, his neck thrown back, and his head in the air, drank the brandy in gulps, as if it were cold water, so that it might by-and-by send his thoughts, his frantic terror, and his memory, to sleep again.

In three weeks he had consumed all his stock of ardent spirits. But his continual drunkenness only lulled his terror, which awoke more furiously than ever, as soon as it was impossible for him to calm it by drinking. His fixed idea, which had been intensified by a month of drunkenness, and which was continually increasing in his absolute solitude, penetrated him like a gimlet. He now walked about his house like a wild beast in its cage, putting his ear to the door to listen if the other were there, and defying him through the wall. Then as soon as he dozed, overcome by fatigue, he heard the voice which made him leap to his feet.

At last one night, as cowards do when driven to extremity, he sprang to the door and opened it, to see who was calling him, and to force him to keep quiet. But such a gust of cold wind blew into his face that it chilled him to the bone. He closed and bolted the door again immediately, without noticing that Sam had rushed out. Then, as he was shivering with cold, he threw some wood on the fire, and sat down in front of it to warm himself. But suddenly he started, for somebody was scratching at the wall, and crying. In desperation he called out: " Go away! " but was answered by another long, sorrowful wail.

Then all his remaining senses forsook him, from sheer fright. He repeated: " Go away! " and turned round to find some corner in which to hide, while the other person went round the house still crying, and rubbing against the wall. Ulrich went to the oak sideboard, which was full of plates and dishes and of provisions, and lifting it up with superhuman strength, he dragged it to the door, so as to form a barricade. Then piling up all the rest of the furniture, the mattresses, paillasses, and chairs, he stopped up the windows as men do when assailed by an enemy.

But the person outside now uttered long, plaintive, mournful groans, to which the young man replied by similar groans, and thus days and nights passed without their ceasing to howl at each other. The one was continually walking round the house and scraped the walls with his nails so vigorously that it seemed as if he wished to destroy them, while the other, inside, followed all his movements, stooping down, and holding his ear to the walls, and replying to all his appeals with terrible cries. One evening, however, Ulrich heard nothing more, and he sat down, so overcome by fatigue that he went to sleep immediately, and awoke in the morning without a thought, without any recollection of what had happened, just as if his head had been emptied during his heavy sleep. But he felt hungry, and he ate.

The winter was over, and the Gemmi pass was practicable again, so the Hauser family started off to return to their inn. As soon as they had reached the top of the ascent, the women mounted their mule, and spoke about the two men who they would meet again shortly. They were, indeed, rather surprised that neither of them had come down a few days before, as soon as the road became passable, in order to tell them all about their long winter sojourn. At last, however, they saw the inn, still covered with snow, like a quilt. The door and the windows were closed, but a little smoke was coming out of the chimney, which reassured old Hauser; on going up to the door, however, he saw the skeleton of an animal which had been torn to pieces by the eagles, a large skeleton lying on its side.

They all looked closely at it, and the mother said: "That must be Sam." Then she shouted: "Hi! Gaspard!" A cry from the interior of the house answered her, so sharp a cry that one might have thought some animal uttered it. Old Hauser repeated: "Hi! Gaspard!" and they heard another cry, similar to the first.

Then the three men, the father and the two sons, tried to open the door, but it resisted their efforts. From the empty cow stall they took a beam to serve as a battering-ram, and hurled it against the door with all their might. The wood gave way, and the boards flew into splinters; then the house was shaken by a loud voice, and inside, behind the sideboard which was overturned, they saw a man standing upright, his hair falling on to his shoulders and a beard descending to his breast, with shining eyes and nothing but rags to cover him. They did not recognize him, but Louise Hauser exclaimed: "It is Ulrich, Mother." And her mother declared that it was Ulrich, although his hair was white.

He allowed them to go up to him, and to touch him, but he did not reply to any of their questions, and they were obliged to take him to Loëche, where the doctors found that he was mad. Nobody ever knew what had become of his companion.

Little Louise Hauser nearly died that summer of decline, which the medical men attributed to the cold air of the mountains.

READING WITH INSIGHT

1. This is a story of the effect of nature on man. Nature is therefore almost like a character in the story. What details does Maupassant put into the story to make you feel the power of nature? What details to make you feel the loneliness and monotony of life in the high mountains?

2. Why is the mountaineer's daughter in the story? To make the end sadder? To dramatize Ulrich's loneliness and his wish to go back to civilization? If not for one of those reasons, why?

3. Did Ulrich really hear a cry from Gaspard, or was it his imagination? What evidence can you cite for your answer?

4. You might compare this story of horror and madness with Poe's "The Tell-Tale Heart." What differences are there in the way the two authors develop the mood of terror in their characters?

5. Do Ulrich's actions seem credible to you? That is, does he behave as you would expect him to, on the basis of what the author tells you about Ulrich's character, his surroundings, and his problem?

6. Have you ever been lonely and frightened? If so, did you feel any of the emotions Ulrich felt?

7. Would you say that the events in this story are logical and believable, and that there is a reason for all of them — or that the story is merely accident and coincidence? For example, the dog's being shut out and not allowed to come back in — is that a logical thing to happen, or is the author stacking the cards to make his effect more powerful?

8. Do the last paragraphs seem sentimental or are they genuinely moving? Why do you think Maupassant at that point turned our attention away from Ulrich to Louise Hauser?

9. A critic has said that "Maupassant does not analyze his characters. He takes little interest in the reason why. They act but wherefor we do not know." Find evidence in this story to support or disprove this criticism.

10. What meaning if any does this story have beyond the fact that loneliness sometimes brings on madness?

If you like this story, you will be interested in

Maupassant. *The Necklace.*
The Two Little Soldiers.
The Piece of String.
The Crowd.
Fright.
Pedro Prado. *The Laugh in the Desert.*
Edgar Allan Poe. *The Tell-Tale Heart.*
O. Henry. *The Furnished Room.*

ANTON CHEKOV

The Beggar

Anton Chekov was born in southern Russia in 1860 and died in 1904 at the height of his success and powers, only 44 years old. He was one of Russia's greatest playwrights and one of the most influential of all the world's short story writers.

His stories were very different from those of the great masters who had preceded him – Poe, Hawthorne, among them. He wrote about the most ordinary people and the most ordinary situations. "Why write about a man getting into a submarine and going to the North Pole to reconcile himself to the world, while his beloved at that moment throws herself with a hysterical shriek from the balcony?" Chekov asked. "All this is untrue and does not happen in real life. One must write about simple things: how Peter Semionovitch married Maria Ivanovna. That is all." "Take two or three persons, describe their mutual relations, and leave it at that," he advised young writers.

Therefore, his characters are not very exciting and his stories hardly have a plot. But he had the ability to make these everyday people and scenes almost luminous with reality. As someone said, the subconscious almost seems to come to the surface in Chekov's fiction. The important events he writes about are not on the surface; the important conflicts are not between armies or even between muscles – they are in the minds and emotions of his characters. As much as any story writer who ever lived, Chekov had this ability to illuminate what was happening beneath the surface of ordinary life, and thus his stories are exciting in a different way from Poe's or Conrad's or Kipling's. This combination of surface formlessness and inner reality is what the many writers who have followed his method have tried to learn from him.

KIND sir, have pity; turn your attention to a poor, hungry man! For three days I have had nothing to eat; I haven't five kopecks [1] for a lodging. I swear it before God. For eight years I was a village schoolteacher and then I lost my place through intrigues. I fell a victim to calumny. It is a year now since I have had anything to do ——"

The advocate Skvortsoff looked at the ragged, fawn-colored overcoat of the applicant, at his dull, drunken eyes, at the red spot on either cheek, and it seemed to him as if he had seen this man somewhere before.

"I have now had an offer of a position in the province of Kaluga," [2] the mendicant went on, "but I haven't the money to get there. Help me kindly; I am ashamed to ask, but — I am obliged to by circumstances."

Skvortsoff's eyes fell on the man's overshoes, one of which was high and the other low, and he suddenly remembered something.

"Look here, it seems to me I met you day before yesterday in Sadovaya Street," he said, "but you told me then that you were a student who had been expelled, and not a village schoolteacher. Do you remember?"

"No-no, that can't be so," mumbled the beggar, taken aback. "I am a village schoolteacher, and if you like I can show you my papers."

"Have done with lying! You called yourself a student and even told me what you had been expelled for. Don't you remember?"

Skvortsoff flushed and turned from the ragged creature with an expression of disgust.

"This is dishonesty, my dear sir!" he cried angrily. "This is swindling! I shall send the police for you, damn you! Even if you are poor and hungry, that does not give you any right to lie brazenly and shamelessly!"

The waif caught hold of the door handle and looked furtively round the antechamber, like a detected thief.

"I — I am not lying — " he muttered. "I can show you my papers."

"Who would believe you?" Skvortsoff continued indignantly.

[1] **kopeck**: worth about one-half cent.

[2] **Kaluga**: south of Moscow in Russia.

" Don't you know that it's a low, dirty trick to exploit the sympathy which society feels for village schoolteachers and students? It's revolting."

Skvortsoff lost his temper and began to berate the mendicant unmercifully. The impudent lying of the ragamuffin offended what he, Skvortsoff, most prized in himself: his kindness, his tender heart, his compassion for all unhappy things. That lie, an attempt to take advantage of the pity of its " subject," seemed to him to profane the charity which he liked to extend to the poor out of the purity of his heart. At first the waif continued to protest innocence, but soon he grew silent and hung his head in confusion.

" Sir! " he said, laying his hand on his heart, " the fact is I — was lying! I am neither a student nor a schoolteacher. All that was a fiction. Formerly I sang in a Russian choir and was sent away for drunkenness. But what else can I do? I can't get along without lying. No one will give me anything when I tell the truth. With truth a man would starve to death or die of cold for lack of a lodging. You reason justly, I understand you, but — what can I do? "

" What can you do? You ask what you can do? " cried Skvortsoff, coming close to him. " Work! That's what you can do! You must work! "

" Work — yes, I know that myself; but where can I find work? "

" Rot! You're young and healthy and strong; you could always find work if you only wanted to, but you're lazy and spoiled and drunken! There's a smell about you like a taproom. You're rotten and false to the core, and all you can do is to lie. When you consent to lower yourself to work, you want a job in an office or in a choir or as a marker at billiards — any employment for which you can get money without doing anything! How would you like to try your hand at manual labor? No, you'd never be a porter or a factory hand; you're a man of pretentions, you are! "

" You judge harshly," cried the beggar with a bitter laugh. " Where can I find manual labor? It's too late for me to be a clerk because in trade one has to begin as a boy; no one would ever take me for a porter because they couldn't order me about; no factory would have me because for that one has to know a trade, and I know none."

"Nonsense! You always find some excuse! How would you like to chop wood for me? "

"I wouldn't refuse to do that, but in these days even skilled woodcutters find themselves sitting without bread."

"Huh! You loafers all talk that way. As soon as an offer is made you, you refuse it! Will you come and chop wood for me? "

"Yes, sir; I will."

"Very well; we'll soon find out. Splendid – we'll see – "

Skvortsoff hastened along, rubbing his hands, not without a feeling of malice, and called his cook out of the kitchen.

"Here, Olga," he said, "take this gentleman into the woodshed and let him chop wood."

The tatterdemalion scarecrow shrugged his shoulders as if in perplexity, and went irresolutely after the cook. It was obvious from his gait that he had not consented to go and chop wood because he was hungry and wanted work, but simply from pride and shame, because he had been trapped by his own words. It was obvious, too, that his strength had been undermined by vodka and that he was unhealthy and did not feel the slightest inclination for toil.

Skvortsoff hurried into the dining room. From its windows one could see the woodshed and everything that went on in the yard. Standing at the window, Skvortsoff saw the cook and the beggar come out into the yard by the back door and make their way across the dirty snow to the shed. Olga glared wrathfully at her companion, shoved him aside with her elbow, unlocked the shed, and angrily banged the door.

"We probably interrupted the woman over her coffee," thought Skvortsoff. "What an ill-tempered creature! "

Next he saw the pseudo teacher, pseudo student seat himself on a log and become lost in thought with his red cheeks resting on his fists. The woman flung down an ax at his feet, spat angrily, and judging from the expression of her lips, began to scold him. The beggar irresolutely pulled a billet of wood toward him, set it up between his feet, and tapped it feebly with the ax. The billet wavered and fell down. The beggar again pulled it to him, blew on his freezing hands, and tapped it with his ax cautiously, as if afraid of hitting his overshoe or of cutting off his finger. The stick of wood again fell to the ground.

Skvortsoff's anger had vanished and he now began to feel a little sorry and ashamed of himself for having set a spoiled, drunken, perchance sick man to work at menial labor in the cold.

"Well, never mind," he thought, going into his study from the dining room. "I did it for his own good."

An hour later Olga came in and announced that the wood had all been chopped.

"Good! Give him half a ruble,"[1] said Skvortsoff. "If he wants to he can come back and cut wood on the first day of each month. We can always find work for him."

On the first of the month the waif made his appearance again and earned half a ruble, although he could barely stand on his legs. From that day on he often appeared in the yard and every time work was found for him. Now he would shovel snow, now put the woodshed in order, now beat the dust out of rugs and mattresses. Every time he received from twenty to forty kopecks, and once, even a pair of old trousers were sent out to him.

When Skvortsoff moved into another house he hired him to help in the packing and hauling of the furniture. This time the waif was sober, gloomy, and silent. He hardly touched the furniture, and walked behind the wagons hanging his head, not even making a pretense of appearing busy. He only shivered in the cold and became embarrassed when the carters jeered at him for his idleness, his feebleness, and his tattered, fancy overcoat. After the moving was over Skvortsoff sent for him.

"Well, I see that my words have taken effect," he said, handing him a ruble. "Here's for your pains. I see you are sober and have no objection to work. What is your name?"

"Lushkoff."

"Well, Lushkoff, I can now offer you some other, cleaner employment. Can you write?"

"I can."

"Then take this letter to a friend of mine tomorrow and you will be given some copying to do. Work hard, don't drink, and remember what I have said to you. Good-by!"

Pleased at having put a man on the right path, Skvortsoff tapped Lushkoff kindly on the shoulder and even gave him his hand at part-

[1] ruble: worth a little over 50 cents.

ing. Lushkoff took the letter, and from that day forth came no more to the yard for work.

Two years went by. Then one evening, as Skvortsoff was standing by the ticket window of a theater paying for his seat, he noticed a little man beside him with a coat collar of curly fur and a worn sealskin cap. This little individual timidly asked the ticket seller for a seat in the gallery and paid for it in copper coins.

"Lushkoff, is that you?" cried Skvortsoff, recognizing in the little man his former woodchopper. "How are you? What are you doing? How is everything with you?"

"All right. I am a notary now and get thirty-five rubles a month."

"Thank Heaven! That's fine! I am delighted for your sake. I am very, very glad, Lushkoff. You see, you are my godson, in a sense. I gave you a push along the right path, you know. Do you remember what a roasting I gave you, eh? I nearly had you sinking into the ground at my feet that day. Thank you, old man, for not forgetting my words."

"Thank you, too," said Lushkoff. "If I hadn't come to you then I might still have been calling myself a teacher or a student to this day. Yes, by flying to your protection I dragged myself out of a pit."

"I am very glad, indeed."

"Thank you for your kind words and deeds. You talked splendidly to me then. I am very grateful to you and to your cook. God bless that good and noble woman! You spoke finely then, and I shall be indebted to you to my dying day; but, strictly speaking, it was your cook, Olga, who saved me."

"How is that?"

"Like this. When I used to come to your house to chop wood she used to begin: 'Oh, you sot, you! Oh, you miserable creature! There's nothing for you but ruin.' And then she would sit down opposite me and grow sad, look into my face and weep. 'Oh, you unlucky man! There is no pleasure for you in this world and there will be none in the world to come. You drunkard! You will burn in hell. Oh, you unhappy one!' And so she would carry on, you know, in that strain. I can't tell you how much misery she suffered, how many tears she shed for my sake. But the chief thing was—she used to chop the wood for me. Do you know, sir, that I did not chop one single stick of wood for you? She did it all. Why this saved me, why I changed, why I stopped drinking at the sight of her I cannot explain. I only know that, owing to her words and noble deeds a change took place in my heart; she set me right and I shall never forget it. However, it is time to go now; there goes the bell."

Lushkoff bowed and departed to the gallery.

READING WITH INSIGHT

1. Can you describe this story in terms of rising action, climax, and falling action? If that pattern does not fit well, how would you describe the story movement?

2. Would this story be interesting if told in brief form as an anecdote? Name the stories you have read so far in this volume which would not make good ancedotes. What kind of story is it that seems to require reading in full, rather than anecdotal telling? Is this a characteristic of recent stories?

3. For sake of comparison, try to imagine how Poe might have written this story.

4. What is the difference between the kind of subject matter Chekov used in this story and the kind of subject matter that went into the stories of such writers as Harte, Crane, Kipling, and Conrad in this book?

5. Do you ever see a story in the ordinary everyday events around you? Try yourself: What stories and what hidden explanations might lie behind some of the people and events you know well?

6. How much setting is there in this story? Why does Chekov need less setting than some other writers in this book?

7. Chekov had a great power to characterize briefly. Test this by asking yourself how you found out what sort of person the beggar is? Skvortsoff? Olga?

8. This would be called a character story, in distinction to a plot story, a theme story, or a mood story. By this we mean simply that the author seems to have been chiefly interested in his characters, rather than in the working out of the plot, or in the illustrating of a theme, or in developing an emotional quality by means of the story. Therefore, the focus of the story is on the characters. What other

stories can you recall in this volume which you would call character stories?

9. What is the irony in this story? What turned out differently from the results the characters had intended?

10. Express in general terms what seems to you to be the meaning of the story.

11. Maugham has written this about Chekov:

"For Chekov life is like a game of billiards in which you never pot the red, bring off a losing hazard, or make a carrom, and should you by a miraculous chance get a fluke you will almost certainly cut the cloth. He sighs sadly because the futile do not succeed, the idle do not work, liars do not speak the truth, drunkards are not sober, and the ignorant have no culture. . . . His men are shadowy creatures, with vague impulses to good, but without will power, shiftless, untruthful, fond of fine words, often with great ideals, but with no power of action. His women are lachrymose, slatternly, and feeble-minded."

Would you say Maugham's criticisms apply to this story? What do they leave unsaid about Chekov's view of life and his characters?

12. Two of the greatest influences on the development of the short story were Poe and Chekov. Most writers followed the general pattern of Poe, until Chekov's time. Still the two traditions exist, and some writers follow one, some the other. In general, writers like Miss Mansfield, Anderson, Hemingway are in the tradition of Chekov; writers like Maugham, Maupassant, Doyle, and Conrad have followed the tradition of Poe. Try to state the differences between the Poe kind of story and the Chekov kind of story, or — more simply — between Maugham's and Chekov's stories in this volume.

If you like this story, you will be interested in

Chekov. *The Bet.*
The Kiss.
The Lament.
Luigi Pirandello. *War.*
Katherine Mansfield. *A Cup of Tea.*
Leo Tolstoy. *What Men Live By.*
Sherwood Anderson. *Sophistication.*

STEFAN ZWEIG

The Invisible Collection

Stefan Zweig came to the end of the road in Brazil in 1942. Born in Austria in 1881, he reacted as a kindly and sensitive man sometimes does to war, and as many men of Jewish parentage did to the rise of Hitler and the Nazis. He fled the German countries and lived for a while in London. When World War II broke out, he went to Rio de Janeiro. Even here, he could not shut out the sight of Europe destroying itself. He wrote a letter thanking the people of Brazil for their hospitality, and explaining why he was going to do what he was about to do. He had seen his own country fall and his spiritual land destroying itself, he said. He wrote a long letter. Then he drank poison.

Zweig was a playwright, a novelist, and a story writer. The story in this volume shows the kindness and sensitivity of his nature, his interest in human psychology, and the analytical manner with which he looked at the ironies of life.

TWO stations beyond Dresden an elderly gentleman entered our compartment, greeted us courteously and then, looking at me, nodded again to me especially as to an acquaintance. At first I could not remember him, but as soon as he gave me his name, with a little smile, I knew at once who he was – one of the best-known art dealers and antiquarians of Berlin, at whose shop before the war I had frequently examined and bought old books and autographs. At first we talked of indifferent things. Suddenly, without any transition, he said:

"I must tell you where I have just been. For the experience I have had is about the queerest one that I, an old art peddler, have met with in my thirty-seven years of business. You yourself probably know how the art trade is going nowadays, since the value of money has evaporated like gas. The newly rich have suddenly discovered their interest in Gothic Madonnas and incunabula,[1] in old engravings and pictures. One cannot find enough for them. One must even take care that they do not empty your house and room entirely. If they could, they would like to buy the cuff links from your shirt sleeves and the lamp from your desk. Consequently it becomes more and more difficult to replenish the merchandise. Pardon me for thoughtlessly calling these things which used to be revered by our class 'merchandise' — but these terrible people have made one used to considering a wonderful Venetian fifteenth-century book merely as the equivalent of so and so many dollars and a drawing by Guercino[2] as a reincarnation of a few one thousand franc bills. Against the importunate urging of these suddenly eager buyers no resistance avails. As a result I was entirely sold out from one day to another and should have liked to have closed up the shop. I was so ashamed of seeing in our old business, which my father had inherited from my grandfather, nothing but miserable stuff which in former times no peddler in Northern Germany would have put in his cart.

"In this difficult situation it occurred to me to look over our old ledgers, to hunt up old customers from whom I might perhaps get back a few of their duplicates. Such an old customers' list is always a kind of morgue, especially in these times, and it really didn't tell me much that was new. Most of our former clients had long since had to dispose of their possessions at auction, or had died, and from the few steadfast ones nothing was to be hoped. But then I suddenly found a whole bundle of letters from perhaps our oldest customer, whom I had only forgotten to think of because since the beginning of the World War, since 1915, he had never addressed any order or inquiry to us. Strange to say, the correspondence extended back over almost sixty years. He had bought even from my father and grandfather, and yet I did not remember that he had ever entered our shop in the thirty-seven years of my own connection with the business. And everything pointed to the fact that he must be a strange,

[1] **incunabula** (literally "cradle books"): books published before 1500, in the first 50 years of printing. Gothic Madonnas are medieval religious pictures.

[2] **Guercino**: a famous Italian painter who lived 1591–1666.

old-fashioned, eccentric person, one of those forgotten Menzel or Spitzweg Germans who as rare specimens have survived down to the present day in small provincial towns. His longhand letters were like copperplate,[1] beautifully written, the amounts underlined with ruler and red ink. Besides, he always repeated the figures, so as to be sure of avoiding errors. This, as well as the exclusive use of detached blank pages and economical envelopes, pointed to the pettiness and fanatical economy of a hopeless provincial. Moreover, the strange documents were always signed both with his name, and with the clumsy title: *Retired Councillor of Forestry and Agriculture, retired Lieutenant, decorated with the Iron Cross of the first class.* As a veteran of the war of 1870, he must be at least eighty years old, if he were still living. But this eccentric, ridiculous cheeseparing [2] miser showed as a collector of the old graphic arts a quite unusual prudence, knowledge, and excellent taste. As I was putting his orders together, one by one, covering almost sixty years, the first of which was still billed in *Silbergroschen*,[3] I became aware that, at the time when it was still possible to buy a great number of the most beautiful wood engravings for a few marks, this little provincial had quietly brought together a collection of engravings which could probably take a very honorable stand beside the much-advertised ones of the newly rich. For even what he had bought from us alone in little amounts, in marks and pfennigs,[4] in the course of half a century would represent today an astounding value, and besides it was likely that he must have bought no less advantageously at auction sales and from other dealers. Since 1914 no new order had arrived from him; but, on the other hand, I was so familiar with all events in the art trade that the auction or the sale of the whole collection of such a size could not have escaped my attention. Therefore, it was probable that this strange man was still alive or else that the collection was in the hands of his heirs.

"I was so interested in the affair that I took the train immediately the next day, that is to say last night, straightway into one of the

[1] **copperplate**: engraving.

[2] **cheeseparing**: economizes by paring the last cheese from the rind.

[3] **Silbergroschen**: a German silver coin, long out of use.

[4] **marks and pfennigs**: small coins. Marks were worth about 25 cents, pfennigs about ¼ cent.

most impossibly Saxon provincial towns that there are in Saxony.[1] As I was strolling from the little depot through the main street, it appeared to me almost incredible that there, in the midst of these trivial, nondescript houses, with their middle-class junk, that in any one of these rooms there should live a man who could own the finest of Rembrandt's [2] etchings, besides remarkably complete series of engravings by Dürer [3] and others. I was astonished when I was told in the post office, in answer to my question whether a Councillor of Forestry and Agriculture was living here, that the old gentleman was indeed still alive — I went to see him that very morning — not without considerable nervousness, I must admit.

"There was no difficulty in finding his apartment. It was on the second floor of one of those economical, provincial houses which some speculative mason-architect had hastily put up in the eighteen sixties. The first floor was inhabited by an honest merchant tailor; on the second floor left was the shining name plate of the postmaster; on the right was a white porcelain plate with the name of the Councillor of Forestry and Agriculture. I rang the bell with some hesitation. Immediately the door was opened by a very old, white-haired lady, with a neat black cap on her head. I handed her my card and asked whether the Councillor of Forestry was at home. Astonished, and with a certain mistrust, she looked first at me and then at the card. In this out-of-the-way town, in this old-fashioned house, a visitor from the outside world seemed to be something of an event. But she told me kindly to wait, took the card and went into the room. First, I heard a low whispering and then suddenly a loud, boisterous masculine voice: 'Oh, Mr. R——, from Berlin, the great antiquarian! Let him come in! Let him come in! I am very glad to meet him!' And then the dear old lady came tripping back and invited me into the parlor.

"I took off my wraps and entered. In the middle of the modest room there stood, very erect, an old but still sturdy man with a bushy mustache, in a braided half-military lounging robe, who cordially held out both hands to me. But in spite of this friendly gesture of obviously joyful and spontaneous greeting there was a strange rigid-

1 **Saxony**: southeast Germany, on Czech border.
2 **Rembrandt**: famous Dutch painter, 1606–1669.
3 **Dürer**: famous German painter and engraver, 1471–1528.

ity in the way he was standing there. He didn't take a single step to meet me and I had to go straight up to him, a little puzzled, in order to grasp his hands. And as I was going to grasp them, I noticed from the immovable horizontal position of these hands that they were not looking for mine, but were expecting them. And in the next moment I understood it all. The old gentleman was blind!

"From my early childhood I had always been uncomfortable in the presence of blind people. I could never quite help feeling ashamed and somewhat embarrassed at realizing that a man was entirely alive and yet knowing at the same time that he did not sense me the same way as I did him. And then, too, I had first to overcome a shock when I saw those dead eyes under the bristling, white, bushy brows, rigidly staring into empty space. But the blind man did not leave me much time for such embarrassment, for as soon as my hand touched his, he shook it very heartily and renewed the greeting in an impetuous, comfortably boisterous way. 'A rare visit!' he said, laughing heartily. 'Indeed, a miracle, that for once one of those great Berlin men finds his way into our little town! But we have to be cautious when one of you dealers takes the train to come here. In my home they used to say, "Close your gates and your pockets when the gypsies come." Yes, I can imagine what you are coming for. Business is going badly now in our poor impoverished Germany. There are no buyers and, therefore, the gentlemen think again of their old customers and look for the lost sheep. But I am afraid you will not have any too much luck with me. We poor old pensioners are glad if we have our crust of bread at the table. We cannot run in the race any more, with the crazy prices that you ask nowadays. People of our class are sidetracked forever.'

"I immediately put him right, and told him that he had misunderstood me, that I had not come to sell him something, but that I had just been in the neighborhood and did not want to miss the opportunity to pay my respects to him as an old customer of our firm and one of the greatest collectors of Germany. Scarcely had I said the words 'one of the greatest collectors of Germany' when a strange change took place in the face of the old man. He was still standing upright and rigid in the middle of the room, but now an expression of sudden brightness and innermost pride came into his attitude and he turned in the direction where he supposed his wife was, as if to say: 'Do you hear that?' And his voice full of joy, without a trace of that harsh military tone in which it had pleased him to speak a moment before, but softly, almost tenderly, he turned toward me: 'That is indeed very kind of you, but you shall not have come in vain either. You shall see something that you do not see every day, not even in your smart Berlin—some items more beautiful than any that can be found in the Albertina or in Paris, curse her! [1] Well, when one collects for sixty years he gets all kinds of things which are not just to be found in the streets! Louise, please get me the key to the cupboard.'

"And now something unexpected happened. The dear old lady, who was standing beside him and had taken part politely in our conversation, with a smiling, gently listening kindness, suddenly lifted both hands toward me imploringly, and at the same time made a decided negative movement of the head, a sign that I did not immediately understand. Then she approached her husband and put her two hands gently on his shoulders. 'But Herwarth,' she said warningly, 'you do not ask the gentleman whether he has time to look at the collection now. It is almost noon, you know, and after dinner you must rest for an hour. The doctor has expressly insisted on that. Would it not be better for you to show the gentleman all those things after dinner? We can then have coffee together. Then, too, Anna Marie will be here. She understands everything so much better and can help you.' And again scarcely had she finished these words when she repeated, as it were in front of the unsuspecting man, that imploring and urging gesture which I now understood. I realized that she wanted me to decline an immediate inspection and I improvised an appointment for dinner. I said that it would be a pleasure and an honor for me to be allowed to see his collection, but it would hardly be possible before three o'clock, but that then I should come very gladly.

"Peeved, like a child whose best toy has been taken away from him, the old man turned around. 'Of course,' he grumbled, 'these gentlemen from Berlin never have time, but on this occasion you will have to take time, for this is not merely three or five pieces. This is a collection of twenty-seven portfolios, one for each artist,

[1] **curse her!**: he says this because the memory of Germany's wars with France is fresh in his mind.

and none of them half empty. Well, at three o'clock then, but be on time; otherwise we won't get through.'

" Again he extended his hand to me into empty space. 'Look here,' said he, ' you may be glad or vexed, and the more vexed you are the gladder I shall be. That is the way we collectors are. Everything for ourselves and nothing for the others.' And again he shook my hand vigorously.

" The little old lady accompanied me to the door. I had noticed in her all the time a sort of uneasiness and an expression of embarrassed timidity. Suddenly, close to the entrance, she stuttered with a quite depressed voice: ' Might — might — my daughter Anna Marie call for you before you come to our house? It is better for several reasons. I suppose you dine at the hotel? '

" ' Certainly, I shall be glad, and it will be a pleasure for me,' said I.

" And, indeed, an hour later, when I had just finished my dinner in the little dining room of the hotel on the market place, an elderly spinster, very plainly dressed, entered the room and looked around. I approached her, introduced myself and said that I was ready to go with her at once to see the collection; but she suddenly blushed and asked me, with the same embarrassed confusion which her mother had shown, whether she could not say a few words to me first. And I saw immediately that it was hard for her. Whenever she wanted to pull herself together and tried to speak, an embarrassed red flush covered her whole face, and her hand played nervously with her dress. At last she began hesitatingly, and she stammered again and again:

" ' Mother has sent me to you — she has sent me to you — she has told me everything and — we want to ask you a great favor — that is, we should like to inform you before you come to see Father — of course, Father will want to show you the collection — and the collection — the collection — is not quite complete any more — a number of pieces are missing — indeed, quite a lot — '

" Again she had to stop for breath. Then she suddenly looked at me and said hastily: ' I must talk to you quite openly. You know these hard times. You will understand everything. After the beginning of the war, Father became completely blind. Even before that time his eyesight was somewhat impaired and the excitement has robbed him of it entirely. You know that, in spite of his seventy-six years, he still wanted to join the army in France and when the army did not make headway immediately, as it did in 1870, he became terribly excited and from then on his eyesight failed very rapidly. Otherwise he is still quite hearty. Until a short time ago he was able to walk about for hours, even to follow his favorite sport, hunting. But now his walks are all over, and his collection is his only joy. He looks at it every day. Of course, he does not actually see it. You know he does not see anything any more. But every afternoon he gets out all of his portfolios so as to at least handle the prints, one after another, always in the same order as he has known them by heart for decades. He is no longer interested in anything else and I must read to him from the paper about all the auction sales, and the higher the prices he hears of the happier he is — for that really is the most terrible thing, that Father does not understand the prices and our times any more. He does not know that we have lost everything and that it is impossible to live on his pension for more than two days in the month. Then too, the husband of my sister was killed in the war and she was left behind with four little children. But Father does not know anything at all of our financial difficulties. At first we economized, economized even more than before, but that did not answer. Then we began to sell — of course, we did not touch his beloved collection. We sold the little jewelry that we had, but that certainly was not much, for during sixty years Father had spent on nothing but his prints every cent that we could save. And one day there was nothing left. We did not know what to do. And then — then — Mother and I sold one print. Father would never have allowed it. He does not know how badly off we are. He does not know how hard it is to get a little food through illicit trade. Nor does he know that we have lost the war and that Alsace-Lorraine has been ceded to France. We do not read such things to him any more from the paper, so that he will not get excited.'

" 'The first piece which we sold was a very valuable specimen, a Rembrandt etching. The dealer offered us many thousand marks for it and with that we hoped to be free from worry for years. But you know how the money melts away! We had put the balance in the bank, but after two months it was all gone. So we had to sell another specimen, and then another one, and the dealer always sent the money so late that it had depreciated by the time it arrived. Then we tried auction sales and there too we were cheated, in spite of the millions they paid us. Before the millions reached us they were always nothing but worthless pieces of paper.[1] In this way gradually the best part of his collection dwindled away, except for a few good pieces, just enough to pay for the barest necessities, and Father has no idea of it. That is why my Mother was so frightened when you came today. For if he opens his portfolios to you everything will be betrayed. In the old portfolios, each of which he knows by the touch, we have put facsimiles of other specimens in place of the ones sold, so that he does not notice it when he handles them. And if he can only touch them and count them(he remembers the order exactly) he has precisely the same pleasure as before when he saw them with his open eyes. There is nobody in this little town whom Father would have considered worthy of showing his treasures to. And he loves every single copy with such a fanatical love that I believe his heart would break if he knew that all that has long since disappeared from under his hand. Since the former curator of the Dresden Print Department died, you are the first one in all these years to whom he has offered to show his portfolios. Therefore, let me ask you — '

" And suddenly the aging spinster lifted her hands, and tears came into her eyes.

" ' — Let me beg of you, don't make him unhappy! Don't make us unhappy! Don't destroy his last illusion! Help us to make him believe that all these specimens, which he will describe to you, are still there! He would not live through it if he even suspected it! Perhaps we have done him a wrong, but we could not do otherwise. Didn't we have to live? And human lives, four orphan children such as those of my sister's, are after all more important than printed sheets. And then, up to this day we have not robbed him of any pleasure. He is happy that he can go over his portfolios every afternoon for three hours, and speak to every specimen as if he were talking to a human being. And today might be his happiest day, for he has been waiting for years to have an opportunity to show his favorite prints

[1] **worthless pieces of paper**: this was a period of great inflation when prices climbed to fantastic heights and money was worth little.

to a connoisseur. Please, I implore you with uplifted hands, do not take this joy from him! '

" All this had been said in such a pathetic way that my story cannot of course do justice to it. Goodness knows we dealers have seen many of these people who have been cruelly robbed, relentlessly cheated by the inflation, whose most precious family property, centuries old, has been pilfered away from them for a song. But here destiny willed a special situation which touched me deeply. Of course, I promised her to be silent and to do what I could.

" We went to the house together. On the way I learned, full of resentment, with what ridiculous amounts they had cheated these poor ignorant women; but that only strengthened my resolution to help them in their extremity. We went upstairs and as soon as we opened the door, we heard from inside the room the joyfully boisterous voice of the old man: ' Come in! Come in! ' With the acute hearing of a blind man he must have recognized our steps on the stairs.

" ' Herwarth has not been able to sleep today; he is so impatient to show you his treasures,' said the little old mother smilingly. A single glance from her daughter had already reassured her about my agreement. All the piles of portfolios were spread out waiting on the table and, as soon as the blind man felt my hand, he took hold of my arm without further formality and pushed me down into the armchair.

" ' All right, let us begin at once. There is much to be seen and the gentlemen from Berlin never have time. The first portfolio here is Master Dürer and, as you will see, rather complete, — and, at that, one copy more beautiful than the other! Well, you will see for yourself. Look here! ' He opened to the first sheet of the portfolio. ' The big horse! '

" And now he took from the portfolio, with that same tender care which people use to touch fragile things, with extremely cautious, highly considerate finger tips, a passe-partout [1] in which there was framed an entirely blank yellow sheet of paper, and he held the worthless scrap before himself, full of enthusiasm. He looked at it for minutes, without really seeing, but he held the blank sheet with

[1] passe-partout: a way of framing in which picture, mat, and frame are held together by strips pasted over the edges.

his hand spread out ecstatically at eye level. His whole face expressed magically the strange attitude of the keen observer. And in his eyes, staring with their dead pupils, I suddenly saw—was it a reflection of the paper or a gleam from within?—a mirrored brightness, a knowing light.

"'Well,' he said proudly, 'have you ever seen a more beautiful copy? How sharply, how clearly every detail stands out in relief there! I have compared this copy with the one in Dresden, but that has a flat and dull look in comparison. In addition, the pedigree! Look there!'—and he turned the sheet around and pointed with his fingernail to a place on the back of the blank sheet, so that I had to look involuntarily to see whether the signs were not actually there. —'There you have the stamp of the Nagler collection. Here are the ones of Rémy and Esdaille.[1] They would never have thought, those illustrious former owners, that their copy would ever get here into this little room.'

"A chill went up my spine when the unsuspecting man praised so enthusiastically an entirely blank sheet. And it was ghastly to see how he pointed with his fingernail, with minute exactness to the invisible collectors' signs which no longer existed except in his imagination. I felt choked with horror. I did not know what to answer. But as I looked up confused to the two women I saw again the hands of the trembling and excited old lady lifted up imploringly. Then I regained my self-possession and began to play my part.

"'Incredible!' I finally managed to stammer. 'A wonderful copy!' And immediately his whole face began to glow with pride. 'But that is nothing,' he said triumphantly, 'you should see the "Melancholia" or the "Passion,"[2] a colored specimen which is hardly to be found elsewhere in the same state. Look here!'—and again his fingers moved tenderly over an imaginary picture.—'This freshness, this rough, warm tone! Berlin, with all its art dealers and museum professors, would go wild over this!'

"And in this fashion the rushing talking triumph continued for fully two hours. No, I cannot describe to you how ghastly it was, to look with him at these one or two hundred blank scraps of paper or poor reproductions which were so incredibly real to the memory

[1] **Rémy, Esdaille:** well-known collectors.

[2] **"Melancholia," "Passion":** prints by Dürer.

of this tragically unsuspecting man that he praised and described every one of them with the most precise details, without mistake, in perfect order. The invisible collection, which long since must have been dispersed all over the world, still existed unimpaired for this blind man, so pathetically cheated, and the passion of his vision was so overpowering that I almost began to believe in it too. Only once the somnambulist assurance of his examining enthusiasm was terribly interrupted by the danger of an awakening. Looking at an 'Antiope'[1] (a proof copy which indeed must have had an immeasurable value) he had again praised the distinctness of the print and at the same time his nervously sensitive finger had followed affectionately the lines of the impression, but without the refined tactile nerves finding that familiar depression on the entirely different sheet. Then, suddenly, a shadow seemed to glide over his forehead; his voice became confused. 'Isn't that — the "Antiope"?' he murmured, a little embarrassed. Whereupon I started up at once, hastily took the mounted sheet out of his hands, and enthusiastically described the etching, with which I too was familiar, in all possible details. Then the face of the blind man lost its tension and its expression of embarrassment, and the more I praised the more a jovial cordiality, a jolly warmth began to blossom forth in this sturdy, old-fashioned man. 'Here at last is somebody who knows something about it,' he said joyfully, turning triumphantly to his family. 'At last, somebody from whom you hear also how much these prints are worth. You, always full of distrust, have scolded me because I have invested all my money in my collection. It is true that for sixty years there has been no beer, no wine, no tobacco, no travel, no theater, no books for me, nothing but saving and saving for these prints. But some day you will see, when I am no longer here. Then you will be rich, richer than anybody in town, and as rich as the richest people in Dresden. Then at last you will be glad of my folly. But as long as I live, not a single print shall leave the house! They must carry me out first, and then my collection.'

"And with that he stroked the long-since rifled portfolios tenderly, like something living. It was ghastly and yet at the same time pathetic for me, for in all those years of the war I had not seen such a perfect, such a pure expression of happiness on any German face.

1 Antiope: a character in Greek mythology.

And beside him stood the women mysteriously resembling the female characters in that etching of the German master depicting the women who had come to visit the tomb of their Savior and stood before the empty tomb with an expression of terrified fright and at the same time of ecstatic belief and joy at the miracle. Just as in that picture the faces of the disciples glow with an unearthly realization that Christ had risen from the dead, so these two aging, worn-out, miserable, middle-class women were affected by the childlike joyful happiness of the old man, half laughing, half in tears. I have never seen a sight so pathetic as this one. But the old man could not get enough of my praise. Again and again he piled up the portfolios, and turned them over, thirstily imbibing every word. So it was a relief for me when at last the deceitful portfolios were put aside and he had reluctantly cleared the table for the coffee. But what was my guilty breath of relief in comparison with the exalted, tumultuous joyfulness, with the high spirits of the old man who seemed to be thirty years younger!

" He told many a story about his quests and purchases. He got up awkwardly, again and again refusing help in order to bring out another and still another print. He was elated and intoxicated as if with wine. But when, at last, I said that I had to leave, he was actually scared, acted glum, like a stubborn child, and stamped his feet spitefully and said that it was impossible, because I had scarcely seen half of the collection. And the women had a hard time to make him understand that he must not be stubborn and delay me any longer because I would miss my train. When at last, after desperate resistance, he gave in and we began to say good-by, his voice became quite soft. He took my hands and his fingers stroked them caressingly, even up to the wrists, with all the feeling of a blind man — as if they wanted to know more about me and to express to me more love than words were able to do. 'You have given me a great, great joy with your visit,' he began with heartfelt emotion, which I shall never forget. 'It was a real blessing for me to have at last an opportunity to look over my beloved pictures with a connoisseur, and you will see that you have not come in vain to this blind old man. I promise you here, before my wife as a witness, that I will add a clause to my will, entrusting your old and reputed firm with the auction sale of my collection. You shall have the honor to administer this unknown treasure — and with that he laid his hand affectionately on the rifled portfolios — 'until the day that it will be dispersed over the world. Only promise me that you will make a beautiful catalogue. It shall be my monument! I do not want a better one.'

"I looked at his wife and daughter. They stood close together and sometimes a tremor ran from one to the other, as if they were a single body trembling with their common emotion. And I myself was in a somewhat solemn mood when the pathetically unsuspecting man charged me with the administration of his invisible, long-since dispersed collection, as if it were a great treasure. Deeply stirred, I promised him what I could never fulfill. Again his dead eyes began to glow. I realized how his longing from within tried to sense me bodily. I noticed it from the tenderness, from the loving pressure of his fingers, which were holding mine in thankfulness and as a pledge.

"The women accompanied me to the door. They did not dare to speak because he would have caught every word with a sensitive ear, but with what warm tears, with what overflowing thankfulness did they look at me, radiantly! Quite stunned, I found my way down the stairs. In reality I felt ashamed. Like the angel in the fairy tale, I had entered the room of poor people, had made a blind man see for an hour by just lending my help to a pious fraud and by lying outrageously. I had really come as a shabby jobber in order to get a few precious specimens out of somebody through a ruse; but what I got out of it was worth much more. I had for once had a chance to feel pure enthusiasm alive in a dull joyless time, a kind of intellectually transparent ecstasy, entirely devoted to art, which our people seemed to have lost long ago. And I somehow felt — I cannot express it in any other way — full of awe, though I was still ashamed and did not really know why.

"I was already down in the street when I heard a window opening above me and my name called. Indeed, the old man had insisted upon looking after me with his blind eyes in the direction in which he supposed I was going. He leaned out so far that the two women had to protect him carefully, and waving his handkerchief he called out 'Safe journey' with the merry refreshing voice of a boy. That sight was unforgettable to me. That happy face of the white-haired old man up there in the window, soaring high above all the morose, hurrying, bustling people in the street, was softly lined out of our real and repulsive world by the white cloud of a bountiful imagination. And again I was reminded, as so often before, of the true old saying — I think it is Gothe's — 'Collectors are happy people.'"

READING WITH INSIGHT

1. This story, like "Windwagon Smith," might have started from a picture in the author's mind – in this case, the picture of a blind man glorying in a collection of prints which he could not see and which, in fact, did not exist. What did Zweig do to that picture to make it a story?

2. Is there any great tension or excitement in the story? Where is the high point of interest? Does the interest end when the collector decides he will keep the secret? If not, how is the interest kept up?

3. What is gained by having a minor character tell this story?

4. Observe how the atmosphere of the blind collector's house is carefully built up. What methods are chiefly used to give you a feeling of the life and appearance of that house?

5. Does this story have a climax, and if so where? It is possible for a story to have more than one climax, but of different kinds and related to different levels of the story? Does this story fit that group?

6. This story is analytical, rather than adventurous or exciting or moody. What stories in the book most resemble it in this respect? One might be Maugham's. What are others?

7. Did the narrator make the right decision? Should he have told the blind man the truth? Why or why not? Should his family have told him the truth? Do you anticipate trouble in that household someday because the man does not know the truth?

8. Recall the rather tense and unpleasant scene when the characters all look at the blank pages and the visiting collector praises the collection. Is this sentimental? Ironic? Does it make you sorry or make you understand, or both?

9. What experiences have you had when you could honestly say it was better not to tell someone the truth?

10. Where are your sympathies in this story? More with the blind man, or with his family? Are they chiefly victims of their own do-

ing, or of a situation they could not help? Does the narrator pity the blind man? Why or why not?

11. Is this story merely a little sentimental tale, or has it some general meaning? If the latter, how would you express the meaning? What is the lesson which the art collector learns, a lesson which he said his countrymen had forgotten?

12. Is there any suggestion in this story that many people live by values or distinctions which they cannot see or only imagine? What evidence, if any, can you find in the story for believing that the author intended or did not intend this for part of the meaning?

If you like this story, you will be interested in

Thomas Mann. *A Railway Accident.*
Arthur Schnitzler. *The Fate of Baron von Leisenbohg.*
Arnold Zweig. *Kong at the Seaside.*
W. Somerset Maugham. *Lord Mountdrago.*
Björnstjerne Björnson. *The Father.*

PEDRO PRADO

The Laugh in the Desert

It is fitting that the last story in this collection should come from a part of the Americas whose fiction is all too little known to readers in the United States. The story is by Pedro Prado, a journalist and architect, who was born in 1894 and now lives in Santiago, Chile.

The story itself is remarkable for its high imaginative quality, for the same sharp, almost grotesque pictorial quality that we have come to expect in some of the best Mexican and South American art, and for a general skill and competence in handling the story form. Prado doesn't spell out the lesson; he merely shows us a sharp picture and lets us deduce the meaning. In this case, he weaves his story around the theme of loneliness which is characteristic of all frontiers and all new countries. He lets us see how several different persons behave in the face of loneliness. The story is no more plotted than Chekov's stories, which it in some ways resembles. And like Chekov, Prado leads us into the minds and inner lives of the characters.

THE manager of Manto Verde mines was a fat man starving for company and conversation. At first Otamendi avoided him; the man inspired him with a feeling of vague discomfort. But after spending the whole day with his theodolite [1] out on the parched ridges under the blazing sun, and interminable hours afterward in his dark hut making calculations, where else was he to go?

The manager was conscious of Otamendi's secret aversion, but he felt sure of his victim. During their second breakfasts, before the

THE LAUGH IN THE DESERT By Pedro Prado, published in *The Living Age*, July 3, 1926. Reprinted by permission of the author and Mr. Irvine Harvey Williams.

[1] **theodolite:** an instrument used by surveyors for measuring angles.

lethargy of repletion and the scorching heat of midday drove them to their siestas, he would talk a steady stream between one course and another, and between one mouthful and another, with a sort of insatiable loquacity that left him scarcely time to bolt his food. And after listening to these long monologues Otamendi found a siesta more indispensable than ever.

If the young engineer had not been homesick and depressed by his isolation and loneliness he might not have conceived so strong an antipathy for his fat and garrulous host, since the man was, after all, both intelligent and original. But in his present mood the fellow's pock-marked face, decayed teeth, bristly brows, and bloodshot eyes filled Otamendi with morbid loathing.

The manager's name was Menares; his given name may have been Pedro, or Juan or Diego or something else – Otamendi, in his dislike of the fellow, always forgot it. Nevertheless, the engineer's attention was caught now and then by an original remark that seemed to betray considerable delicacy of sentiment in his rough and vulgar host. On such occasions he would try to learn something about the man's life, but Menares skillfully evaded his inquiries. For in the same way that we wrap up fragile articles in cotton batting until they make big parcels, so Menares seemed to have wrapped up a subtle and sensitive spirit in his gross and enormous body.

One noontime when the heat weighed like lead on the galvanized-iron roof, when the shadow of the boulders outside shrank and shrank and finally vanished, when the sun's shafts were so intense that they seemed almost to collide in a sort of dazzling darkness, the two men sat silent, stewing in their perspiration. Otamendi stared through the dusty reddish windows across the glare of the parched, tawny desert. Suddenly Menares broke the silence, and without other preface said: "I'm used to feeling the mood of the people around me. Don't try to hide your dislike."

"What's that?" asked Otamendi, stammering with surprise.

"Nothing. Don't be disturbed. I don't care how you feel as long as you listen. But you must do that. I've got to talk. I understand and I pardon anything except a refusal to hear what I say."

"But, Mr. Menares –"

"No buts. Your obvious aversion has made you my debtor, and it's only fair that you should pay what you owe. I shall make you pay it by telling you a story to the point, about us men who live in the desert. Have another glass of wine? One more? No? Or do you prefer the *pajarete?*[1] Ah, very well. To your health, then, Friend Otamendi. Now listen. Do you know, that's not bad wine! " And the fat man clicked his tongue. " Well, now, I'm going to tell you of a case just like our own."

" Why do you talk that way? I never — "

" That's all right, Señor Otamendi. Can't you see that this is just a little stratagem of mine to compel you to pay better attention? Have you offended me? When? Quite the contrary. I'm extremely grateful for your company. You seem like an old friend. I was merely joking. Did you think I was serious? Come on now, I don't want you to get that idea. Why, you haven't drunk all your wine! We can't have that. I'll join you."

And fat Menares, after drinking another glass, broke out into a roar of laughter. " See how I bluffed you. Don't tell me I'm no psychologist. There is no better way to get the attention of a true gentleman than to make him think he has offended you. Now listen, listen as a favor. Why have you got up? Cigarettes? Here, I have them."

" Thanks, I've stopped smoking, but my legs were asleep," explained Otamendi, stretching himself lazily.

Fat Menares also rose, a little disturbed, and carefully making his way around the table placed himself directly in the doorway. Once there his eyes sparkled. His victim was trapped. A sigh of satisfaction escaped him, and he took several heavy pulls at his cigarette, so that for a minute or two afterward his words were enveloped in smoke.

" Listen, and draw your own conclusions, my young friend. When I was doing my military service in Arica Regiment, stationed at La Serena — I am talking of twenty years ago — my lieutenant, Casares, and I, and a corporal named Padilla were ordered to reconnoiter on horseback the country between that point and Copiapó, with a view to marching the whole regiment with its artillery and baggage train overland to the latter point. Do you know the mountain country one must cross to get from La Serena to the Huasco Valley?[2] Have you

[1] **pajarete**: a Chilean wine.

[2] **Huasco Valley**: you will find this and the other places mentioned in the

ever passed that great desert vestibule that stretches from Vallenar to Copiapó? No? Well, you're lucky. You can't imagine, then, the job they had laid out for us. It was a trip of I don't know how many kilometers — six hundred, or perhaps seven hundred. But you must have covered every foot of it on horseback to appreciate what real thirst, real hunger, real longing for shade and verdure, are. In those days we had no railway up the coast. Our orders were, moreover, to take a short cut instead of detouring along the sea, to find watering places, and to select sites for supply camps."

Otamendi sat down again with a look of resignation on his face.

"We left La Serena on a foggy morning. I was in high spirits, as was natural for an eighteen-year-old youngster starting on a long trip that promised all sorts of adventures. I felt very grateful to the major for selecting me — so grateful, indeed, that I forgot to think of Lieutenant Casares's reputation in the army. He was famous for his rudeness and brutality, and had already passed forty without receiving a promotion, because of that reputation. He was stubborn as a mule, strong as an ox, and savage as — I don't know of an animal with which to compare him.

"Nevertheless, I saw that fellow really moved by emotion once on this trip. When I got back and told about it none of my fellow officers would believe me. I think you will, though, Friend Otamendi, because you're having a somewhat similar experience."

Otamendi lifted his eyes with interest. Menares's last words had been spoken in a high falsetto, as if his voice were breaking with emotion. Yes, his bloodshot eyes were actually moist. To tell the truth, he had been drinking liberally of the Huasco wine they called pajarete. Seeing himself detected, Menares burst into raucous laughter and hurriedly resumed: —

"The only time when we saw even the ghost of a cloud was on leaving La Cerena. After that the sun scorched as if its rays were focused by a burning glass. The first day out, after consulting our military map, we gave up the idea of following a trail and headed first for Alta Gracia Gulch, and later in the day followed up another deep valley with a dry boulder-strewn bed. On the colossal

story in Chile north of Santiago and Valparaíso. La Serena is on the coast; Vallenar and Copiapo are in the desert country between the coast and the Andes mountains.

ridges that hemmed us in on either side we saw no trees or vegetation except at rare intervals a solitary cactus or a withered thorn bush. Everywhere else the steep ascents were strewn with broken stone, as if the brown ridges were enormous leather or sacks that had burst and disgorged their contents. We did not catch a glimpse of a living creature, even a bird, except now and then a vulture flying so high that it made a mere speck in the sky. I rode on listlessly, scorched even through my light clothing by the sun, and half blinded by the glare. When we halted at night and stretched out on the parched ground, we avoided touching the heated stones; and long after sunset the cliffs still radiated heat like an oven. Our poor horses, half starved and half dying of thirst — what little they had to drink was more sand than water — made no effort to graze, because the search for herbage was obviously so futile, but stood stupidly motionless when unsaddled, hanging their heads with fatigue.

"In a couple of days, through the Lieutenant's oversight, miscalculation, or obstinacy, we found ourselves without a crumb of food or a drop of wine. Late that night we came to Los Choros River. It makes a fine show on the map, but it proved to be nothing but a broad, stone-strewn valley, virtually waterless. Fortunately, however, we found a little trickle half hidden among the huge boulders, and this probably saved the lives of both ourselves and our horses."

Otamendi's face had assumed a good-natured grin, with which he tried to hide the fact that he was half asleep. But his corpulent companion tolerated no such pretense. He lifted his voice, and, emphasizing his words to arouse his drowsy companion, continued: "Just imagine it, Friend Otamendi. Three days, our horses worn out, our brains frying under our heavy military caps! At two o'clock, faint from lack of food, wild thoughts of murder crept into my brain — for Lieutenant Casares had been heaping insults on me all day long: 'Aspirante [1] Menares, haven't you any eyes to guide your horse? *Can you hear me?*' "

The fat manager roared the last few words at the top of his voice in imitation of the Lieutenant.

"What's the matter?" exclaimed Otamendi with a start.

"Don't be stupid. When will you get some sense?"

[1] **Aspirante:** Cadet.

Otamendi blushed with embarrassment, not knowing whether the last remark was intended for him or whether it was a part of the story. But he smiled placatingly. Menares gloated.

"'If you're going to stray like that you'd better get out and be done with it,' Lieutenant Casares roared. I fingered my revolver. The unconscious fool rode ahead of me and Corporal Padilla behind. But I was so crazed with heat, hunger, and anger that I didn't care a continental whether the Corporal saw what I did or not. I pulled my gun desperately. Then I recalled that it was not loaded. I was just sticking cartridges in the chamber, as many as it would hold, when Corporal Padilla shouted, 'A house up there! Up there on top! I see a house and smoke!'

"I looked up without returning my pistol to the holster. Yes, in the remote distance, half hidden in a fold of the ridge that rose as abruptly as a wall from the valley bottom, were some white structures looking like the buildings around a mine head.

"'There *is* a little smoke,' observed the Lieutenant in a more human tone of voice. We had previously passed one or two ruined cabins and bits of wall around deserted mines, but they had all been long since abandoned, and had only added to the loneliness of the solitude.

"I have always remembered the climb up to this house as the most perilous ride of my life. What a trail! I had to lean forward till my chin touched the horse's mane to keep from slipping off behind. I could feel the panting sides of the poor beast throb between my thighs, and it seemed as if we should never reach the top. It tired me more than if we had gone on foot. The higher we got the farther off the house seemed to be. Finally, however, we saw that we were coming near. A man came running down to meet us. He was quite young, and thin as a rail. I have never been welcomed so joyously elsewhere in my life. He helped us to dismount. Seeing that we were stiff with riding, he offered us his arm. He circled around us like a fawning dog. We discovered that he was here all alone, guarding the provisional improvements of the mine. Work had been stopped because the company had run out of funds. You may remember that big mining boom on the Santiago Stock Exchange—in 1906, if my memory doesn't deceive me . . ."

"Yes, in 1906," assented Otamendi, in order to say something.

"The young fellow brought chairs and boxes for us to sit on, and inquired eagerly whether we preferred beer or wine. Beer or wine! Imagine our astonishment. Yes, yes, we should be delighted. Beer first. We were dying of thirst. And did he have anything to eat?

"What! Hadn't we had breakfast? He'd have something ready in a jiffy. His storehouse was well supplied — *pâté de foie gras*, salmon, goat cheese, ham. If we would wait a little while he'd have some roast kid. There were wild goats back in the mountains, which he hunted now and then for fresh meat. We had come at a lucky moment, for he had shot a young kid the day before. So we dined like kings. Nothing was lacking, not even canned milk for our coffee — except bread; he had no bread, but to make up for that he served ten different kinds of biscuits. But he rattled on so incessantly while he was serving us that the testy Lieutenant finally burst out: 'Good, good. You'll drive us crazy with so much stuff. Just calm down and don't talk so much.' The thin young fellow took Casares's rude admonition as a joke, and bustled about with a high treble laugh.

"'What about the horses?' Corporal Padilla whispered to me.

"The mine guard divined what he was saying, and made more than ten trips with a pail, which he filled from a tiny stream at the back of the house, before our mounts had quenched their thirst. Between trips, laughing constantly, he asked us what was happening in the world.

"We were busy eating, half starved and dead tired. How were we to answer? Our brief replies disappointed him. He looked cast down for a moment, but he was a man of resource. He commenced to make up his own answers from our gestures of negation or assent, and kept talking constantly while we waved our hands like somnambulists. Soon he had recovered his high spirits again, and his interminable laughing and chattering became fearfully wearisome. Lieutenant Casares grew more and more irritated. When the young fellow, in his excitement, began to slap us on the shoulders to emphasize his words, the Lieutenant seized him and roughly thrust him away.

"I watched curiously to see what would happen during the moment's silence that followed, but the fellow, who had stopped in front of a bottle, grabbed it and began to fill our glasses as if he took

Casares's brusqueness for a joke or a direction. Then, without interrupting his hysterical giggling, he brought out cigarettes.

"Casares was at a complete loss; I didn't know what to do; and Padilla was completely absorbed eating his cheese.

"Finally, disconcerted by our stolid silence, the young fellow changed his tone and began to talk in a studied way, as if to entertain us. Imagining from the Lieutenant's rough manner that he might have said something foolish, he started to tell us stories — ancient anecdotes that he garbled horribly.

"'If you don't know something newer than that, you'd better shut up,' the Lieutenant finally roared in exasperation.

"'Something new? New stories? I'll show you!' And the young fellow darted out into the neighboring room, returning with a fat leather-bound notebook, which he thumbed over rapidly, as if trying to make up his mind what to select. I could see that it contained a collection of anecdotes written out with a pen. 'This one about Saldaña, the country greenhorn, is awfully funny. No, no, the German stories are better. Yah, yah, yah! This one about Don Otto — you'll find it bully.'

"Lieutenant Casares gazed around the room the personification of futile wrath. Finally, fixing his eyes on me, he shouted, 'Aspirante Menares, what are you staring at me for?' and began to call me down savagely for nothing at all.

"But our would-be entertainer paid no attention. He evidently considered our wrangling none of his business. Good Lord, Otamendi, if you could have heard the fellow! His horrible imitation German dialect; that young shrimp playing off a Dutchman. First of all, he read that moth-eaten tale about selling the sofa. Then the one about Don Otto trying to buy a dog. And he laughed uproariously at every one of them. Then he turned over some pages and began to read to us — what do you imagine? — conundrums! 'Why is a pipe like a crazy Dutchman?'

"At last Casares could contain himself no longer. Drawing his revolver with a gesture of exasperation, he yelled, 'Shut up, or I'll kill you!'

"The young fellow stammered, and then, laughing like a madman, began to look for more anecdotes as aged as the others. He hadn't read two words when the Lieutenant fired in the air. Instantly the book fell from the poor fellow's hands, and I witnessed a scene that I shall never forget. Doubling up in his chair and bending over the table, he buried his face in his arms and began to sob like a child.

"Lieutenant Casares, considerably agitated, and imagining that the fellow must be hurt, rose quickly, and without abandoning his brusque manner shook him and made him lift his head. 'Haven't you sense enough to let us rest a minute? Can't you see what a fool you're making of yourself, when we've come here more dead than alive? And now you're crying. Have you been hurt? '

"'Pardon me, Señor Lieutenant,' said the young fellow, his face wet with tears. 'No, no, Lieutenant, I'm not hurt. It was silly, very silly, but I've been here alone so long. I've been so starved for a chance to talk and laugh . . .' And when he said this he burst out into a long, shrieking laugh so violent that the tears ran down his cheeks and he fell twitching to the ground. There he lay writhing on the floor, frothing at the mouth like an epileptic.

"Casares paced up and down the room like a bear in a cage. Corporal Padilla jumped to the boy's assistance and lifted his head. His forehead was bleeding where it had hit a table leg when he fell. Padilla bathed it with water and fanned him with the copybook. When he began to breathe more regularly and opened his eyes we heard him mutter: 'Juan! Juan! ' Whom was he calling, if he lived alone? When he recognized us he blushed scarlet.

"'What did you say? ' I asked him.

"He made no answer, and did not utter another word; but rising up, indifferent to the blood that was still flowing from his forehead, he walked slowly out of the cabin and seated himself on a box outside the door. There he sat bowed over in silence.

"Lieutenant Casares suddenly stopped pacing up and down and shouted in his loud, hoarse, parade-ground voice: 'To horse. Let's get out of this.' I heard him ask the poor fellow how much we owed him for the breakfast, but the latter never as much as lifted his head. I wanted at least to bid him good-by, but a certain feeling of delicacy prevented me. He watched us mount our horses without making a move. We descended the steep trail in gloomy silence. As we turned a bend in the trail I thought I heard a shout, and looked back, but I could not see the house or the young fellow. As I slowed up my horse Lieutenant Casares passed me. I saw his eyes were filled with tears, and he said: 'Aspirante, don't you think I'm a brute?'

"Yes, those were his very words."

When he had finished his story, Menares sat silent for a moment. The young engineer hardly knew what to say. After a moment his host added: "Have another glass of pajarete before your siesta, Friend Otamendi. It will make you sleep better."

READING WITH INSIGHT

1. This is another story, like Maupassant's "The Inn," of the effect of loneliness. The setting, you will notice, is heat instead of the cold of "The Inn," desert instead of mountains. Compare the effects of physical surroundings on the characters in the two stories. What differences are there in the atmospheres created by the two stories?
2. This is a story within a story (like the famous play within a play, in *Hamlet*). Do you like the story told this way? How else might Prado have designed his story to give the same effect?
3. Menares is presented at first as a rather unlovable person. Does your impression of him change during the story? If so, how? Do you understand him better? Like him better? If your impression changes, can you tell why?
4. What were the effects of loneliness on the Lieutenant, on the young man at the oasis, on Menares? Why were the effects different in each case?
5. Why did Menares choose this particular story to tell Otamendi? What is the situation existing between him and Otamendi? What is the connection of his story to that situation?
6. Notice the tactics employed by Menares in forcing Otamendi to pay attention. What do these tell you about Menares?
7. What was Menares trying to do? Teach Otamendi a lesson? Help him? Punish him? Or was he merely being cruel or satisfying his own need to talk?
8. The meaning of the story is related to the characters of the lonely men. Why does Menares feel he has to talk, whereas Otamendi does not? What are the apparent reasons why Otamendi dis-

likes Menares? Why does Otamendi not feel the need of human companionship as does Menares?

9. Obviously the meaning of the story is not completely expressed by saying that loneliness affects different people differently. How would you express the meaning?

10. How would you describe the author's attitude toward these characters? Is he merely trying to describe human nature as he thinks it is? Is he sympathetic? Is he trying to paint the unpleasant sides of these people? What kind of picture is he making?

If you like this story, you will be interested in

Anton Chekov. *The Lament.*
Guy de Maupassant. *The Inn.*
Pedro Alarcon. *The Tall Woman.*
Selma Lagerlof. *The Outlaws.*
Honore de Balzac. *A Passion in the Desert.*

Other Stories That May Interest You

American Stories

Albee, George. *Fame Takes the J Car.*
Aldrich, Thomas Bailey. *Marjorie Daw.*
Anderson, Sherwood. *Death in the Woods.*
I'm a Fool.
Mother.
Queer.
Benét, Stephen Vincent. *Daniel Webster and the Sea-Serpent.*
The Devil and Daniel Webster.
Doc Melhorn and the Pearly Gates.
Freedom's a Hard-Bought Thing.
The Sobbin' Women.
The Treasure of Vasco Gomez.
Benson, Sally. *The Overcoat.*
Bercovici, Conrad. *Ghitza.*
Bierce, Ambrose. *The Boarded Window.*
A Horseman in the Sky.
The Man and the Snake.
Occurrence at Owl Creek Bridge.
The Stranger.
Watcher of the Dead.
Buck, Pearl. *The Enemy.*
The Frill.
Bunner, Henry Cuyler. *The Love Letters of Smith.*
Nice People.
The Tenor.
Zenobia's Infidelity.

Burnett, Whit. *Sherrel.*
Burt, Struthers. *The Water-Hole.*
Cable, George W. *Posson Jone.*
Caldwell, Erskine. *Daughter.*
Callaghan, Morley. *A Wedding-Dress.*
Capote, Truman. *Miriam.*
Cather, Willa. *Double Birthday.*
Paul's Case.
The Sculptor's Funeral.
Cobb, Irvin. *The Belled Buzzard.*
Boys Will Be Boys.
Connolly, J. B. *The Truth About the Oliver Cromwell.*
Crawford, F. Marion. *The Upper Berth.*
Curwood, James Oliver. *Kazan.*
Daly, Maureen. *Sixteen.*
Danielson, Richard Ely. *Corporal Hardy.*
Derleth, August. *Geese Flying South.*
Edmonds, Walter D. *Adam Helmer's Run.*
Blind Eve
The Death of Red Peril.
Escape from the Mine.
Farrell, James. *Helen, I Love You.*
Ferber, Edna. *The Gay Old Dog.*
Meadow Lark.
Shore Leave.
Fisher, Dorothy Canfield. *The Heydey of the Blood.*
Portrait of a Philosopher.
The Thread Without a Knot.
Foley, Martha. *One with Shakespeare.*
Freeman, Mary Wilkins. *The Copy Cat.*
The New England Nun.
Garland, Hamlin. *The Return of a Private.*
Under the Lion's Paw.
Up the Cooly.
Gordon, Caroline. *The Last Day in the Field.*
Hale, Edward Everett. *The Man Without a Country.*
My Double and How He Undid Me.
Harris, Joel Chandler. Any of the stories from *Uncle Remus.*

Harte, Bret. *The Luck of Roaring Camp.*
The Postmistress of Laurel Run.
Tennessee's Partner.
Hawthorne, Nathaniel, *The Ambitious Guest.*
The Birthmark.
Ethan Brand.
The Gray Champion.
The Great Stone Face.
Dr. Heidegger's Experiment.
Mr. Higginbotham's Catastrophe.
The Minister's Black Veil.
The White Old Maid.
Hemingway, Ernest. *After the Storm.*
The Doctor and the Doctor's Wife.
In Another Country.
The Killers.
The Undefeated.
Henry, O. *The Gift of the Magi.*
A Municipal Report.
The Third Ingredient.
The Whirligig of Life.
Hergesheimer, Joseph. *The Token.*
Tol'able David.
Heyward, Dubose. *The Half-Pint Flask.*
Hurst, Fannie. *Humoresque.*
Ice Water, Pl——.
Irving, Washington. *The Devil and Tom Walker.*
The Legend of Sleepy Hollow.
Rip Van Winkle.
The Spectre Bridegroom.
The Stout Gentleman.
Jewett, Sarah Orne. *The Dulham Ladies.*
Johnson, Josephine. *Arcadia Recalled.*
Johnson, Owen. *The Great Pancake Record.*
Kantor, MacKinlay. *The Voice of Bugle Ann.*
Komroff, Manuel. *Napoleon's Hat Under Glass.*
Lafarge, Oliver. *North Is Black.*

Lardner, Ring. *Alibi Ike.*
Dinner.
The Golden Honeymoon.
Haircut.
Harmony.
Horseshoes.
Hurry Kane.
The Ides of June.
My Roomy.
One Hit, One Error, One Left.
There Are Smiles.
Lewis, Sinclair. *Ring around a Rosy.*
Willow Walk.
Young Man Axelbrod.
London, Jack. *The Call of the Wild.*
To Build a Fire.
Maltz, Albert. *Man on a Road.*
March, William. *The Little Wife.*
Marquand, J. P. *Good Morning, Major.*
Marshall, Edison. *The Elephant Remembers.*
Milburn, George. *A Pretty Cute Little Stunt.*
A Student in Economics.
Morris, I. V. *The Sampler.*
Mott, Frank Luther. *The Man with the Good Face.*
Page, Thomas Nelson. *Marse Chan.*
Poe, Edgar Allan. *A Cask of Amontillado.*
A Descent into the Maelstrom.
The Fall of the House of Usher.
The Gold Bug.
Manuscript Found in a Bottle.
The Masque of the Red Death.
Murders in the Rue Morgue.
The Pit and the Pendulum.
The Purloined Letter.
Ross, Leonard Q. (Rosten, Leo). Any of the stories in *The Education of H*Y*M*A*N K*A*P*L*A*N.*
Saroyan, William. *Inhale, Exhale.*
Locomotive 38, The Ojibway.

A Nice Old-Fashioned Romance.
Resurrection of a Life.
Schramm, Wilbur. Any of the stories in *Windwagon Smith and Other Yarns.*
Shumway, Naomi. *Ike and Us Moons.*
Steele, Wilbur Daniel. *Blue Murder.*
Ching, Ching Chinaman.
Footfalls.
The Woman at Seven Brothers.
The Yellow Cat.
Stegner, Wallace. *Bugle Song.*
Steinbeck, John. *Flight.*
The Red Pony.
Stockton, F. R. *The Lady or the Tiger.*
Street, James, *The Biscuit Eater.*
Stuart, Jesse. *Split Cherry Tree.*
Suckow, Ruth. *Four Generations.*
Golden Wedding.
The Man of the Family.
Uprooted.
Tarkington, Booth. *Henry the Great.*
Monsieur Beaucaire.
Penrod's Busy Day.
Thurber, James. *The Night the Ghost Got In.*
The Secret Life of Walter Mitty.
Twain, Mark. *The Celebrated Jumping Frog of Calaveras County.*
The Man that Corrupted Hadleyburg.
Van Dyke, Henry. *The Story of the Other Wise Man.*
Wharton, Edith. *The Other Two.*
Xingu.
White, William Allen. *The King of Boyville.*
Williams, Ben Ames. *Sheener.*
They Grind Exceeding Small.
Wister, Owen. *Philosophy 4.*
Wolfe, Thomas. *Only the Dead Know Brooklyn.*
Wood, Francis Gilchrist. *Turkey Red*
Yezierska, Anna. *Hunger.*

Stories from Great Britain and Ireland

Barrie, James M. *How Gavin Birse Put It to Mag Lownie.*
Two of Them.
Bennett, Arnold. *The Idiot.*
A Letter Home.
Mary with the High Hand.
Conrad, Joseph. *Gaspar Ruiz.*
The Heart of Darkness.
The Inn of the Two Witches.
The Lagoon.
Typhoon.
Youth.
Coppard, A. E. *The Black Dog.*
Dickens, Charles. *The Boots of the Holly Tree Inn.*
The Poor Relation's Story.
The Signal Man.
Doyle, A. Conan. Any of the stories in *The Adventures of Sherlock Holmes.*
The Adventures of the Bruce-Partington Plans.
The Speckled Band.
Dunsany, Lord Edward. *The Sword and the Idol.*
Galsworthy, John. *The Purist.*
Quality.
Hardy, Thomas. *The Three Strangers.*
The Withered Arm.
Jacobs, W. W. *The Monkey's Paw.*
Joyce, James. *Araby.*
Counterparts.
Eveline.
Kipling, Rudyard. *The Arrest of Lieutenant Golightly.*
The Drums of the Fore and Aft.
Germ Destroyer.
His Wedded Wife.
In Flood Time
In the Matter of a Private
The Man Who Would Be King.
The Sending of Dana Da.

Knight, Eric. *The Flying Yorkshireman.*
Leacock, Stephen. *A Hero in Homespun.*
Mansfield, Katherine. *A Cup of Tea.*
The Doll's House.
Marriage à la Mode.
Maugham, W. Somerset. *Lord Mountdrago.*
The Taipan.
Morrison, Arthur. *That Brute Simmons.*
Munro, H. H. (Saki). *The Lumber Room.*
Mrs. Packletide's Tiger.
The Open Door.
The Reticence of Lady Anne.
Tobermory.
Pickthall, Marjorie L. C. *The Stove.*
Scott, Sir Walter. *The Two Drovers.*
Wandering Willie's Tale.
Stevenson, Robert Louis. *The Cream Tarts.*
A Lodging for the Night.
Markheim.
The Sire de Maletroit's Door.
The Suicide.
Will o' the Mill.
Wells, H. G. *The Stolen Bacillus.*
Wilde, Oscar. *The Happy Prince.*

Stories from Other Countries

Alarcon, Pedro. *The Tall Woman.*
Arabian Nights. Aladdin and His Wonderful Lamp.
Ali Baba.
Sinbad the Sailor.
Balzac, Honore de. *Christ in Flanders.*
An Episode of the Terror.
A Passion in the Desert.
Becquer, Gustavo. *The Organist.*
The Devil's Cross.
Björnson, Björnstjerne. *The Father.*
Fidelity.
The Fisher Maiden.

Capek, Karel. *The Imprint.*
Chekov, Anton. *The Bet.*
The Kiss.
The Lament.
Daudet, Alphonse. *The Last Class.*
Dumas, Alexandre. *Zodomirsky's Duel.*
France, Anatole. *The Procurator of Judea.*
Heyse, Paul. *L'Arrabiata.*
Hoffman, E. T. W. *A Cremona Violin.*
Lagerlöf, Selma. *A Christmas Guest.*
The Girl from the Marsh Croft.
The Outlaws.
The Silver Mine.
Mann, Thomas. *A Railway Accident.*
Maupassant, Guy de. *The Crowd.*
Fright.
The Hand.
Happiness.
The Journey.
The Necklace.
The Piece of String.
The Two Little Soldiers.
The Wreck.
Mérimée, Prosper. *Mateo Falcone.*
Morand, Paul. *Monsieur U.*
Pirandello, Luigi. *War.*
Pushkin, Alexander. *The Queen of Spades.*
The Snowstorm.
Schnitzler, Arthur. *The Fate of Baron von Leisenborg.*
Tolstoy, Leo. *God Sees the Truth but Waits.*
Master and Man.
The Prisoner of the Caucasus.
What Men Live By.
Turgenev, Ivan. *Biryuk.*
The District Doctor.
A Lear of the Steppes.
Mumu.
Zweig, Arnold. *Kong at the Seaside.*

Collections of Stories

Many of the authors in the foregoing list have collected their short stories and published them as one or more volumes. For example, there are the stories of Stephen Benét in two volumes, and 49 of Ernest Hemingway's stories in a volume called *The Fifth Column and the First Forty-Nine.* Poe, Harte, Lardner, O. Henry, Conrad, Doyle, Kipling, Maupassant, Chekov, and others can be read in collected editions, and you will find this a good introduction to each author — a way in which you can choose your own favorite stories from him without relying on some editor to do it for you. The following list, however, does not include these collected stories of individual authors. It is a list of collections each of which includes a number of writers and a number of stories.

Best American Short Stories (published as *Best Short Stories,* annually from 1915 through 1941; as *Best American Short Stories,* annually from 1942 to the present. Until 1943 it was edited by Edward J. O'Brien; from 1943 to the present, by Martha Foley)

O. *Henry Memorial Award Prize Stories* (published annually since 1919; edited by Blanche Colton Williams until 1933; by Harry Hansen, from 1933)

Aymar, Gordon C. *A Treasury of Sea Stories*

Bates, Sylvia Chatfield. *Twentieth Century Short Stories*

Brooks, Cleanth, and Warren, Robert Penn. *Understanding Fiction* (with textual materials on a college level)

Brown, Leonard. *Modern Short Stories*

Burnett, Whit. *Time to Be Young; Stories of the Growing Years*

Canby, Henry Seidel, and Bailey, Robeson. *The Book of the Short Story*

Cerf, Bennett. *The Fireside Book of Famous American Stories*

Dashiell, Alfred. *Editor's Choice*

Fischer, Marjorie, and Humphries, Rolfe, *Strange to Tell* (mystery and ghost stories)

Frederick, John T. *Thirty-four Present Day Short Stories*

French, Joseph Lewis. *The Ghost Story Omnibus*

Great Pirate Stories

Great Sea Stories

Goodman, Jack. *The Fireside Book of Dog Stories*
Haydn, Hiram, and Cournos, John. *A World of Great Stories*
Jessup, Alexander, and Canby, Henry Seidel. *The Book of the Short Story*
Kesten, Herman, *The Blue Flower* (romantic stories)
Knickerbocker, Edwin. *Notable Short Stories of Today*
Laing, Alexander. *Great Ghost Stories of the World*
Maugham, W. Somerset. *Tellers of Tales*
Sayers, Dorothy L. *Great Short Stories of Detection, Mystery, and Horror* (three series)
Scarborough, Dorothy. *Selected Short Stories of Today*
Schweikert, H. C. *Short Stories*
Stern, Philip Van Doren. *Travelers in Time* (stories of journeys into the past and the future)
Tomlinson, H. M. *Great Sea Stories of All Nations*
Wagenknecht, Edward. *A Fireside Book of Yuletide Tales*